In honor of 75 Years with Nuclear Fission

Preface

Donald R. Hoffman
ANS President

The discovery of nuclear fission in December 1938 was an event that, in time, changed the world. With the conclusion of World War II, the world began to learn details about fission and began attempts to incorporate fission into society. An important pivotal point was created in December 1953 when President Dwight D. Eisenhower delivered his now famous "Atoms for Peace" speech before the United Nations. In response to Eisenhower's speech, concerned American scientists and engineers began meeting at the National Academy of Sciences (NAS) in Washington DC to discuss the need for a nuclear society within which information about the possible uses of fission would be openly discussed and information could be widely disseminated. During its December 1954 meeting at NAS, this planning and organizing group created the American Nuclear Society (ANS).

December 1988 marked the 50th anniversary of the discovery of nuclear fission. To mark this golden anniversary, ANS and NAS collaborated with numerous other individuals, organizations, and agencies to produce the 1989 ANS topical conference, "50 Years with Nuclear Fission." About 20 pioneers of the nuclear enterprise together with more than 400 participants from more than 15 countries attended this conference. Full papers were solicited from the pioneers and the other participants, and a conference proceedings was assembled and published by ANS.

Twenty five years have now passed and we have once again reached an important milestone anniversary, the diamond anniversary of fission. Sadly, many of the pioneers who were present at the golden anniversary have passed away. Their written words, however, and their spoken words still exist. It seemed most appropriate to share the 50th anniversary conference proceedings at the 75th anniversary. With this in mind, the ANS Scientific Publications and Standards Department has run a second printing of the 50th anniversary proceedings in time for the 75th anniversary.

ANS will acknowledge the 75th anniversary within its 2013 ANS Winter Meeting, in Washington DC, from November 10–14, 2013. The theme for this ANS Winter Meeting is "The 75th Anniversary of the Discovery of Nuclear Fission." Beginning at the 2011 ANS Annual Meeting in Hollywood, Florida, and at each national meeting following that, ANS divisions were contacted and encouraged to include this anniversary theme in their technical program planning efforts. You will see their efforts celebrating the 75th anniversary in the *Transactions* of the 2013 ANS Winter Meeting.

Perhaps the organizers of the 100th anniversary (The Centennial of Fission) will ensure a special publication outlining the 100 year history of fission, and hopefully the proceedings from the 50th anniversary will, once again, be printed and available. Thank you for picking up this 50th anniversary proceedings in 2013 to add to your library of knowledge on nuclear science and engineering. Please treasure these words contained herein from some of the pioneers of the nuclear enterprise.

Donald R. Hoffman
ANS President
Fall 2013

In honor of 75 Years with Nuclear Fission

Foreword

James W. Behrens
USN - retired

The discovery of nuclear fission took place in Germany in December 1938. It followed the equally important discoveries of radioactivity in France by Henri Becquerel in 1896 and the neutron in England by James Chadwick in 1932. From the very beginning, the story of nuclear fission has been international, involving such countries as France, England, Italy, and Germany. Between 1932 and 1938, numerous scientists were bombarding the heavy elements with neutrons, and their excitement levels of discovery were great. However, the early work of Irene Joliot-Curie and Pavle Savić in France and of Enrico Fermi, Emilio Segre, and Edoardo Amaldi in Italy misinterpreted what was really happening. It was the German team of Otto Hahn and Fritz Strassman that concluded (though hesitatingly) in December 1938 that the atoms they were bombarding were not becoming transuranic elements, as others had thought, but instead were actually splitting apart. Nuclear fission had been discovered. News of fission was delivered to the United States by Niels Bohr in January 1939—the first American to learn about fission was John A. Wheeler—and news of the discovery was given by them to a broader audience at a theoretical physics conference held in Washington DC that same year. Fifty years later, in April 1989, the American Nuclear Society held a conference titled "50 Years with Nuclear Fission," and I had the privilege and honor of organizing it, which started with opening plenary sessions at the National Academy of Sciences (NAS) in Washington DC and concluded with two additional days at the National Institute of Standards & Technology in nearby Gaithersburg, Maryland. Twenty five years have now passed since this highly successful and well-attended conference, and ANS is now acknowledging "The 75th Anniversary of the Discovery of Nuclear Fission" within its 2013 ANS Winter Meeting in Washington DC, from November 10–14, 2013. Once again, I have the privilege and honor of helping to organize this anniversary, which is the meeting's theme.

Many of the pioneers of the nuclear enterprise who were part of the 1989 Washington conference have now passed away. They are with us, however, in spirit, through their written and spoken words. Fortunately, the presentations given by these pioneers at NAS in 1989 were recorded, and film clips from this 12-hour collection of recordings will be shown at the 2013 ANS Winter Meeting. Also, these pioneers are still with us through their words written for the conference proceedings. For the 75th anniversary, the original two-volume set (1,000 page), "50 Years with Nuclear Fission" (ANS, 1989) has gone through a second printing, thereby bringing back the written words of these truly great pioneers—Edoardo Amaldi, Georgy Flerov, Siegfried Fluegge, Bertrand Goldschmidt, Rudolf Peirels, Pavle Savić, Glenn Seaborg, Emilio Segre, Edward Teller, John Wheeler, and Walter Zinn—and many others who played an active and important role during the early years and throughout the 50-year history following fission's discovery.

Where did the efforts develop within ANS for the 50th anniversary of fission, and now the 75th anniversary? How did I become involved? Why did I choose to become an experimental nuclear physicist and devote most of my professional career to studying the fission process and to working on various applied physics efforts that utilize fission's enormous power? It would seem appropriate at this, the 75th anniversary of fission, to mention my own 50th anniversary of my connection to fission (1963–2013). Yes, I started down this path the same year that fission was having its 25th anniversary in 1963. As all stories should do, let's start at the beginning, which takes us back to Germany during the 1800s. Ironically, my family comes from the very country where fission was discovered and I am descended from German families who came to America during the mid-1800s and eventually settled in south central Illinois. My childhood was spent in the small farming community of Bunker Hill (formerly Wolf Ridge), Illinois, located just northeast of St. Louis, Missouri, within former coal mining areas of Illinois. I owe a great deal to two of my teachers who taught within the Bunker Hill school system. My sixth grade teacher, Mrs. Ola Nitz, recognized that I had potential, but that I was not motivated to use it. With her help, I applied myself more to my learning and schoolwork and my grades slowly improved. The other instructor who influenced me was a high school science teacher, Mrs. Helen Myers, who became

a most valuable ally and my first mentor, encouraging me to become an active participant in annual high school science fairs. As a freshman in Mrs. Myers' general science class, I recall wondering what I would do for my first science fair. In reading from my science book, I came upon how radioactivity was discovered by Becquerel, the French physicist, back in 1896. Radioactivity was discovered quite by accident when a sample of uranium was stored in a drawer next to undeveloped photographic plates. Once developed, the plates were fogged and, upon further examination, Becquerel determined that the uranium was emitting something (invisible radiation) that affected the plates. Radioactivity was discovered. For my first science fair project, I would repeat Becquerel's experiment, using the radium dials from the hands on my bedroom clock and some undeveloped dental x-ray film packages provided by Carl Behrens, DDS, from Bunker Hill. My science project, titled "Autoradiographs," won first prize awards at the local and district science fairs and went to state competition at the University of Illinois (U of I) where it got a second place award. From this early beginning in science and with the continuing strong encouragement of my teacher Mrs. Myers, my future with science was becoming focused and set. Another school year and another science fair needed to be planned. During my sophomore year, I was in Mrs. Myers' biology class and I continued my previous science fair effort by building a project titled "Radioisotopes as Tracers," wherein a radioactive isotope, phosphorus-32, was traced through a frog's digestive system. This project won first place awards at the local, district, and state levels and placed highest at the South Central Illinois regional competition held at Greenville College. As a result of winning the regional competition, I was sent as a finalist to the 1963 National Science Fair in Albuquerque, New Mexico, where four prominent gentlemen came to encourage us participants to enter careers in science. These four men were Glenn Seaborg, Edward Teller, Hyman Rickover, and Werner Von Braun. Because of this national science fair and these four men, I decided in May 1963 to become a scientist.

From my high school experiences with science fairs, including state science fair competitions held at the U of I, it was easy for me to decide where to go to college. I entered the U of I's College of Engineering in the fall of 1965. During my undergraduate years, I was hired by Peter Axel to do part-time work at the U of I's 25 MeV Betatron Laboratory as an assistant to several of his graduate students doing research. I also served as president of the U of I's Physics Club during my senior year and interacted with numerous physics professors, including John Bardeen. I graduated in February 1970 with a B.S. in engineering physics and went on to the University of California where I entered a work-study program at Lawrence Livermore National Laboratory (LLNL) while attending graduate school at the nearby Department of Applied Science, Davis-Livermore campus. Using a painting technique developed at Los Alamos in the 1940s, I began producing targets (fission foils for ionization fission chambers) for use in a wide variety of neutron-induced fission measurements being conducted at the newly completed LLNL 100-MeV Electron Linear Accelerator. My career had rather humble beginnings as a painter, doing neutron physics experiments, with more than 300 fission foils produced by using high purity isotopes of thorium, protactinium, uranium, neptunium, plutonium, americium, and curium made by and available from the Oak Ridge calutrons and prepared as fission foils using facilities at Livermore. In 1978, I joined the National Bureau of Standards, Center for Radiation Research, Gaithersburg, Maryland. In that same year, I joined ANS (encouraged by John Hubbell) and started to attend meetings and contribute papers at ANS topical conferences and national meetings. My research efforts continued to involve fission and my publications continued to grow in number from the numerous measurements of neutron-induced fission cross sections in the MeV range that had been completed while I was a graduate student at Livermore. These measurements were all published in the ANS technical journal Nuclear Science & Engineering between 1977 and 1983. My involvements with ANS continued to multiply and grow, leading to the 50th anniversary with fission in 1989 and now the 75th anniversary in 2013.

In the fall of 2009, I retired from federal service and the following year I started to promote and help organize the 75th anniversary with fission. At the 2011 ANS Annual Meeting in Hollywood, Florida, I met Eric Loewen, who was about to become ANS president, and we agreed to work together on organizing the 75th anniversary. During the 2011 ANS Winter Meeting in Washington DC, Eric and I presented a resolution to the ANS Board of Directors in which the 2013 ANS Winter Meeting would acknowledge the 75th anniversary with fission. The resolution passed unanimously and included the board's desire that we reach out once again to NAS, and also include the National Academy of Engineering, to assist ANS in preparing a valuable program to acknowledge the 75th anniversary. We also reached out to James E. Rogers of Duke Energy, who agreed to serve as general chairman for the 2013 Winter Meeting. Steve Nesbit of Duke Energy and I were appointed assistant general co-chairs by Rogers. During the 2012 ANS Annual Meeting in Chicago, the 2012 ANS Winter Meeting in San Diego, and the 2013 ANS Annual Meeting in Atlanta, planning and organizing meetings for the 75th anniversary were held and most of the necessary preparations were completed by July 2013.

In this foreword I have blended discussion about the 50th and 75th anniversaries with information about ANS and my personal career in nuclear science and technology. I have long realized the important building blocks that helped me along the way toward a career in science, such as the influence of teachers. It has been one of my goals—and I hope it is one of yours—to always emphasize how valuable our teachers can be in helping to guide and direct their students and to promote activities such as annual science fairs, which can direct

the young to pursue careers in science and technology. It is also important to recognize the importance of mentors who influence and help guide us to become interested in science and to get involved with societies such as ANS, thereby giving scientists and engineers a forum through which to share research, stimulate minds, and organize meaningful events such as topical conferences and national meetings. And, we must remember special events, such as the 75th anniversary with fission, which cause us to pause and look back over past accomplishments as we then turn our focus to the future.

I've also been lucky enough to contribute in other ways, such as through the Behrens-Nitz Fund, which was created in 2011 within the Bunker Hill Educational Foundation. This fund helps young students by providing financial support to the Wolf Ridge elementary and junior high schools and to their science and math teachers to help stimulate young minds in math and the sciences and to encourage participation in annual science fairs within the junior high school levels. In addition, another fund—the Behrens-Myers Fund—has been established to provide financial support to the Bunker Hill high school to help promote the teaching of science. Also, the Behrens-Myers Science & Engineering Scholarship is awarded each year to graduating seniors who show an interest in pursuing careers in science and engineering. It is my hope that these funds will help stimulate young minds and provide the encouragement to pursue careers in science and engineering and to experience the adventure of discovery within the fascinating world in which we all live.

In closing, let me share a story from the 50th anniversary celebration. Pavle Savić (1909–1994), the Serbian chemist and physicist, joined The Radium Institute in Paris from 1937–1938 on a scholarship granted to him by the French government. At the age of 28, he had the privilege to work closely with Irene Joliot-Curie (daughter of Marie Curie, founder of The Radium Institute). The team of Curie and Savić came very close to discovering fission. Savić, commenting at the banquet for the 50th anniversary, stated that he greatly appreciated being treated like a human being at the celebration and not like "an old fossil from the past." He praised the other pioneers joining him at the head table, together with the over 400 international participants at the conference, for their ability to share feelings of warmth and friendship. He was very optimistic about the prospects for our future, citing as an example the international cooperation being generated by conferences such as the 50th anniversary. He acknowledged that in all the many years that he had been attending conferences, he had never been made to feel such welcome. In appreciation, Savić presented me with his set of 35mm presentation slides used during his talk at NAS in the long ago. To this day I greatly treasure these slides, knowing that he wanted me to have a personal gift expressing his thanks and appreciation for an excellent conference and a job well done. I became very close to many of the pioneers through the 50th anniversary planning and preparation, and I continued to correspond and interact with a number of them for many years after the conference was over. They have all passed away now, but they still live in my thoughts and memories. By having available this second printing of the 50th anniversary proceedings, I feel that they are still with us, in spirit, and that they will be with us for many years to come. The 75th anniversary provides us an opportunity to reflect back over the past "75 Years with Nuclear Fission" as we now turn our attention to looking forward to the next 25 years and "The First Centennial of Nuclear Fission," which will occur in 2038. To acknowledge the 100th anniversary of the discovery of nuclear fission, in 2038, we will assuredly gather again.

I sincerely hope that you find these proceedings informative and useful and that you will place this two-volume set with other books of importance in your personal library on nuclear science and technology.

James W. Behrens, USN - retired
Assistant General Co-Chairman
2013 ANS Winter Meeting in Washington, DC

Annapolis, MD
Fall 2013

50 YEARS WITH NUCLEAR FISSION

National Academy of Sciences
Washington, D.C.
and
National Institute of Standards and Technology
Gaithersburg, Maryland

April 25–28, 1989

Edited by
James W. Behrens
Allan D. Carlson

Sponsored by

American
Nuclear
Society

United States
Department of Commerce
National Institute of Standards and Technology

Published by the
American Nuclear Society, Inc.
La Grange Park, Illinois 60525 USA

Cosponsored by
- American Chemical Society
- American Physical Society

In Cooperation with
- Accademia Nazionale dei Lincei
- Carnegie Institution of Washington
- George Washington University–
    Institute for Technology and Strategic Research
- U.S. Department of Energy
- Electric Power Research Institute
- International Atomic Energy Agency
- National Academy of Sciences
- National Science Foundation
- U.S. Nuclear Regulatory Commission
- OECD Nuclear Energy Agency
- Princeton University
- University of California–Berkeley

ISBN 0-89448-144-4
ANS Order No. 700136

MEETING OFFICIALS

Honorary Co-Chairmen

John A. Wheeler   Edoardo Amaldi

General Co-Chairmen

Glenn T. Seaborg   Emilio Segrè

Assistant to Chairman Seaborg

Sherrill Whyte

Executive Chairman

Oren A. Wasson

Finance Chairman

Clyde P. Jupiter

Publications Chairman

James W. Behrens

PROGRAM COMMITTEE

Co-Chairmen

James W. Behrens (NIST)
Allan D. Carlson (NIST)

Robert E. Chrien (BNL)
Albert Ghiorso (LBL)
Evans Hayward (NIST)
Neil M. Howard (Bechtel-Gaithersburg)
W. Michael Howard (LLNL)
John Huizenga (Univ of Rocheser)
Glenn F. Knoll (Univ of Michigan)

James W. Meadows (ANL)
Michael S. Moore (LANL)
Robert W. Peelle (ORNL)
Stanley L. Whetstone (DOE)
Roger White (LLNL)
Ned Wogman (Battelle, PNL)

PRESENTATION REVIEW COMMITTEE

James W. Behrens (NIST)
Allan D. Carlson (NIST)
Robert E. Chrien (BNL)
Neil M. Howard (Bechtel-Gaithersburg)
Michael S. Moore (LANL)

Robert W. Peelle (ORNL)
Roald A. Schrack (NIST)
Oren A. Wasson (NIST)
Stanley L. Whetstone (DOE)
Ned Wogman (Battelle, PNL)

INTERNATIONAL ADVISORY COMMITTEE

S. Bjornholm (Niels Bohr Inst–Denmark)
J. Boldeman (AAEC–Australia)
H. Britt (LLNL)
N. Cindro (Inst Rudjer Boskovic–Yugoslavia)
H. Condé (Gustaf Werner Inst–Sweden)
A. Deruytter (CBNM–Belgium)
T. Fuketa (JAERI–Japan)
F. Gönnenwein (Univ of Tübingen–FRG)
W. Greiner (Univ of Frankfurt–FRG)
James J. Griffin (Univ of Maryland)
Darleane C. Hoffman (LBL)
S. S. Kapoor (BARC–India)
V. Konshin (IAEA–Austria)
J. Eric Lynn (AERE Harwell–England)
André Michaudon (Inst Laue-Langevin–France)

L. G. Moretto (LBL)
J. Rayford Nix (LANL)
David Okrent (UCLA)
Norman Rasmussen (MIT)
M. Salvatores (CEA/CEN Cadarache–France)
J. Schmidt (IAEA–Austria)
D. Seeliger (Tech Univ of Dresden–DDR)
V. Strutinsky (INR–USSR)
John J. Taylor (EPRI)
Edward Teller (LLNL)
J. P. Theobold (Inst für Kernphysik–FRG)
Robert Vandenbosch (Univ of Washington)
C. Wagemans (SCK-CEN–Belgium)
Alvin M. Weinberg (IEA)

ORGANIZING COMMITTEE

J. D. T. Arruda-Neto (Univ of Sao Paulo–Brazil)
James W. Behrens (NIST)
George I. Coulbourn (Boeing)
Octave J. Du Temple (ANS)
V. Gay Easly (ANS)
Mary Beth Gardner (ANS)
Robert J. Howerton (LLNL)
Mary J. Keenan (ANS)
John Knabenschuh (Westinghouse WVNS)

Ma Hongchang (IAE-PRC)
Theresa de Mazancourt (EdF–France)
K. K. S. Pillay (LANL)
Gianni Reffo (ENEA-Italy)
Thomas H. Row (ORNL)
Gerard de Saussure (ORNL)
Alan B. Smith (ANL)
Charles Thomas (LANL–retired)
P. G. Young (LANL)

EXECUTIVE COMMITTEE

Chairman

Oren A. Wasson (NIST)

Joyce Antokol (NIST)
James W. Behrens (NIST)
Allan D. Carlson (NIST)
B. Stephen Carpenter (NIST)
Wayne Cassatt (NIST)

Jan Hauber (NIST)
Evans Hayward (NIST)
Clyde P. Jupiter (Jupiter Assoc)
Roald A. Schrack (NIST)
Sara Torrence (NIST)

LOCAL ARRANGEMENTS COMMITTEE

Joyce Antokol (NIST)
James W. Behrens (NIST)
Allan D. Carlson (NIST)
B. Stephen Carpenter (NIST)
Wayne Cassatt (NIST)
Randall S. Caswell (NIST)
Kenneth R. Fulton (NAS)
Jan Hauber (NIST)
Evans Hayward (NIST)

Clyde P. Jupiter (Jupiter Assoc)
Julia Marks (NIST)
Jean P. Marterre (NAS)
Robert Martin (NIST)
Peter H. Raven (NAS)
Roald A. Schrack (NIST)
Kathy Stang (NIST)
Sara Torrence (NIST)
Oren A. Wasson (NIST)
Eva Wood (NIST)

ACKNOWLEDGMENTS

The meeting sponsors greatly appreciate the major financial contributions received from the U.S. Department of Energy, Office of Nuclear Energy, and the U.S. Nuclear Regulatory Commission to help offset publication costs.

In addition, contributions were received from the following:

American Nuclear Insurers
Atomic Energy of Canada Limited
Babcock & Wilcox Company
Combustion Engineering
Duke Power Company
Electric Power Research Institute
Excek Services Corporation
Fluor Daniel
NV Gemeenschappelijke-Kern
A. Giambusso
H & R Technical Associates, Incorporated
Israel Electric Corporation
Korea Atomic Industrial Forum
Walter Loewenstein
Maurice McIntosh
National Academy of Sciences
Pacific Gas & Electric Company
Philadelphia Electric Company
Promon Engenharia SA
Promotion Marches Exterieurs
Public Service Company of New Mexico
Rowe & Associates
Societé Génerale pour les Techniques Nouvelles
Siemens AG
Studsvik Energiteknik AB
Total Minerals Corporation
Westinghouse Electric Corporation
Fusion Technology Institute/University of Wisconsin

DEDICATION

"Ah, but a man's reach should exceed his grasp, or what's a heaven for."
— Robert Browning

"In an enterprise such as the building of the atomic bomb the difference between ideas, hopes, suggestions and theoretical calculations, and solid numbers based on measurement, is paramount. All the committees, the politicking and the plans would have come to naught if a few unpredictable nuclear cross sections had been different from what they are by a factor of two."
— Emilio Segrè

The discovery of nuclear fission placed a vast and mysterious energy source within the reach of man during a time when the world was preparing for war. These proceedings, and the anniversary conference that they represent, are dedicated to the pioneers who grasped and directed the course that began with fission's discovery and led mankind into the Atomic Age. Theirs was a most formidable task, one filled with an entire spectrum of human achievement and human emotion.

James W. Behrens
Joint Staff
The Pentagon
Washington, D.C.

TABLE OF CONTENTS

NATIONAL INSTITUTE OF STANDARDS AND TECHNOLOGY PLENARY: NUCLEAR REACTORS, SECURE ENERGY FOR THE FUTURE

Chairmen: *John A. Wheeler (Princeton Univ/ Univ of Texas-Austin) Bertrand Goldschmidt (CEA Paris- France)*

FISSION DATA

Chairmen: *Michael S. Moore (LANL) Lee Stewart (LANL-retired)*

VOLUME II

FISSION SCIENCE II

Chairman: *John Huizenga (Univ of Rochester)*

MEDICAL AND INDUSTRIAL APPLICATIONS OF BY-PRODUCTS

Chairman: *Randall S. Caswell (NIST)*

POSTER SESSION: REACTORS AND SAFEGUARDS

POSTER SESSION: GENERAL RESEARCH, INSTRUMENTATION AND BY-PRODUCTS

POSTER SESSION: FISSION DATA, ASTROPHYSICS, AND SPACE APPLICATIONS

FISSION SCIENCE II

Chairman
John Huizenga (Univ of Rochester)

FISSION THROUGHOUT THE PERIODIC TABLE

LUCIANO G. MORETTO and GORDON J. WOZNIAK

Nuclear Science Division, Lawrence Berkeley Laboratory,

1 Cyclotron Rd., Berkeley, California, 94720, USA

ABSTRACT

The dualistic view of fission and evaporation as two distinct compound nucleus processes is substituted with a unified view in which fission, complex fragment emission, and light particle evaporation are seen as different aspects of a single process.

I. INTRODUCTION

A. Early history and traditional views

The answer to the simple question "What is fission?" is not unique but depends upon the space and time cross section of the scientists to whom the question is addressed. Before 1939, fission was still in imaginary space. It soon emerged into an altogether too real world by virtue of two chemists who dared thinking the unthinkable. Even today many of our physics colleagues think of fission as a peculiar reaction occurring around uranium, a somewhat embarassing process that gave and still gives us a bad reputation; then with nuclear bombs, now with nuclear energy.

Even among "experts," fission is typically associated with heavy elements. If its presence is acknowledged, as far down as the Lead region and even lower, its existence becomes progressively more evanescent as one moves farther down the periodic table and its cross section becomes lost in the abyss of nanobarns. Most emphatically, fission is believed to be a unique kind of compound nucleus reaction when compared with the more commonplace decays, like those involving the emission of protons, alphas and other "particles." Fission appeared so different from the other modes of compound nucleus decay that a separate theory was devised to calculate its decay width. As a result, we now have one theory for "evaporation" and another for fission.

Yet, a typical mass distribution of fission fragments while peaked, at times sharply, at masses near the symmetric splitting, is nonetheless a continuous distribution for which there are no firm boundaries other than those set by the total mass of the system. In all fairness, the search for ever lighter (and heavier) fission products was actively pursued by radiochemists, who were eventually stopped only by the abysmally small cross sections. So the belief was consolidated that fission fragments were confined to a rather narrow range of masses, despite the occasional disturbing detection of intermediate mass or complex fragments like Na, Si, etc. in higher energy reactions.[1-4] With a curious twist of insight, these lighter fragments were at times attributed to ternary fission, rather than to a more obvious, highly asymmetric binary fission. But, why should the fission mass distribution not extend all the way to alpha particles and protons?

B. The turbulent history of complex fragments

The advent of low energy heavy ions familiarized the nuclear community with products of deep inelastic reactions ranging throughout the periodic table.[5-7] While, in many ways, deep inelastic reactions do remind us of fission, the obvious genetic relationship of these products with either target or projectile keeps these processes more or less within the categorical boundaries of "direct reactions."

Complex fragments made their grand entrance with intermediate-energy heavy ion reactions. In these processes, the elegant simplicity of quasi and deep inelastic processes is substituted by a glorious mess of products that seem to bear no relationship to either of the entrance channel partners. Their glaringly abundant production, together with the turbid experimental environment prevailing in early studies, prompted a tumultuous development of theories, claims and counterclaims about their origin and manner of production.

The broad mass range and abundance of these fragments suggested mechanisms like the shattering of glass-like nuclei[8] or the condensation of droplets out of a saturated nuclear vapor.[9-14]

Fortunately, in spite of the confusion, it did not escape some perceptive members of our community that most, if not all of the complex fragments were associated with essentially binary processes. Furthermore, after an allowance was made for target and projectile-like fragments, the remaining fragments appeared to originate from the binary decay of an isotropic source. Finally, the excitation functions of these fragments appeared to behave in accordance with compound nucleus branching ratios. The inescapable conclusion was that compound nucleus decay was responsible for the production of these fragments by a mechanism able to feed all the possible asymmetries. Such a mechanism without undue strain of the imagination could be well identified with a generalized fission process.

C. Fission, fission everywhere.....

This evidence, which continues to grow by the day, demonstrates the very pervasive presence of statistical complex fragment emission throughout the periodic table, at low and high excitation energies, covering the entire range of asymmetries, though not with equal intensity. In fact, the observed modulation of the mass distribution is a most revealing signature of the underlying potential energy as a function of mass asymmetry and underscores the essential unity of these processes.

Here one has the key for the unification of all compound nucleus decays into a single process. The natural connection between all these modes of decay is the mass asymmetry coordinate. Typical light particle evaporation (n, p, alpha, etc.) corresponds to very *asymmetric* decays, while "fission" of heavy systems corresponds to a very *symmetric* decay. The lack of emission at intermediate asymmetries is only apparent. Such an emission does in fact occur, albeit very rarely at low energies. The rarity of this occurrence is due to the important but accidental fact of the high potential barriers associated with the emission. A suitable increase of the excitation energy, or the lowering of the barriers by an increase in the angular momentum, readily increases the cross section of these intermediate mass fragments to an easy level of detection.

Similarly the apparent lack of "fission" in lighter systems, suggested by the absence of a symmetric fission peak in the mass distribution, is another manifestation of the underlying potential energy that forces the mass distribution to assume a characteristic U shape. Consequently, in spite of the variety of mass distributions brought about by the different dependence of the potential energy on the mass asymmetry, we are confronted with a single process responsible for the production of the whole range of masses from the decay of compound nuclei throughout the periodic table (with the notable exception of gamma ray and meson emission). This process, with a minimal generalization of the term might well be called "fission."

In this way we have reached a very remarkable conclusion. Fission, rather than being a peculiar process relegated to the upper reaches of the periodic table and to a remote area of nuclear physics cultivated by oddball scientists, surprisingly turns out to be the most general, all-pervasive reaction in compound-nucleus physics. If anything, it is the standard evaporation that should be regarded as a peculiar limiting case of very asymmetric fission... Like the ghost of Hamlet's father, fission is "*hic et ubique* ," here, there and everywhere.

II. GENERALIZED FISSION THEORY

Particle evaporation traditionally includes neutron, proton and alpha particle emission. In its simplest form, the decay width is typically written down in terms of the inverse cross section and of the phase space of the system with the particle at infinity as:

$$\Gamma(\varepsilon)d\varepsilon = \frac{8\pi g m}{2\pi\rho(E)h^2} \varepsilon\sigma(\varepsilon) \rho(E-B-\varepsilon)d\varepsilon \qquad (1)$$

where $\rho(\varepsilon)$ and $\rho(E-B-\varepsilon)$ are the level densities of the compound nucleus and residual nucleus, respectively; m, ε, g are mass, kinetic energy and spin degeneracy of the emitted particle; and $\sigma(\varepsilon)$ is the inverse cross section.[15-18]

The fission decay width is commonly evaluated by following the Bohr-Wheeler formalism which makes use of the transition-state method. In this approach, the reaction (fission) coordinate is determined at a suitable point in coordinate space, (typically at the saddle point) and the decay rate is identified with the phase space flux across a hyperplane in phase space passing through the saddle point and perpendicular to the fission direction. The decay width is written[19] as:

$$\Gamma_f = \frac{1}{2\pi\rho(E)} \int \rho^*(E-B_f-\varepsilon)d\varepsilon, \qquad (2)$$

where $\rho(E)$ and $\rho^*(E-B_f-\varepsilon)$ are the level densities of the compound nucleus and of the saddle point; ε is the kinetic energy along the fission mode; and B_f is the fission barrier. So, the dichotomy between fission and evaporation is emphasized even in the expressions for the corresponding decay rates.

It was observed some time ago that this dichotomy is deceptive.[20,21] The separation between evaporation and fission, is an optical illusion due to the very low cross section of products with masses intermediate between ^{4}He and fission fragments. There is no need to consider the two extremes of this distribution as two independent processes. **Rather, fission and evaporation are the two, particularly (but accidentally) obvious extremes of a single statistical decay process, the connection being provided in a very natural way by the mass asymmetry coordinate.**

A. Potential energy, absolute and conditional saddle points, and ridge line

The potential-energy surface $V(\tilde{q})$ as a function of a set of deformation coordinates $\tilde{q}$ has been studied in detail first within the framework of the liquid-drop model,[22-24] and, more recently of the finite-range model.[25,26]

In general, only the stationary points of the potential-energy surface corresponding to the solutions of the above equation are of intrinsic physical significance. However, saddle-point shapes for fissility parameter values of x < 0.7 are strongly constricted at the neck, so that the nascent fission fragments are already well defined in mass, and a physical significance to the mass asymmetry parameter $A_1/(A_1 + A_2)$ can be assigned. Then it is possible to consider a cut in the potential energy along the mass-asymmetry coordinate passing through the fission saddle point, with the property that at any point the potential energy is stationary with respect to all the other degrees of freedom. Each point is then a "conditional saddle point" with the constraint of a fixed mass asymmetry. This line has been called[20,21] the "ridge line" in analogy with the term "saddle point". The general shape of the ridge line depends on whether the fissility parameter lies above or below the Businaro-Gallone point.[27] The properties of the ridge line above and below the Businaro-Gallone point are illustrated in Fig. 1.

Below the Businaro-Gallone point, the ridge line shows a single maximum at symmetry. This is a saddle point of degree of instability two (the system is unstable both along the fission mode and the mass asymmetry mode). As the fissility parameter x increases above x_{BG}, this saddle point splits into three saddle points. The symmetric saddle point is stable with respect to the mass-asymmetry mode (degree of instability one) and is the ordinary fission saddle point. The other two saddles, of degree of instability two, are called Businaro-Gallone mountains, and flank symmetrically the fission saddle point.

The incorporation of angular momentum maintains essentially the same topology. Its main effect is to decrease the overall heights of the barriers and to displace the Businaro-Gallone point towards lower values of the fissility parameter.

B. Complex fragment radioactivity as a very asymmetric spontaneous fission decay.

The explicit introduction of the mass-asymmetry coordinate in the problem of complex fragment emission, resulting in the ridge line as a generalization of the fission saddle point, leads, as a first application, to the theory of complex fragment radioactivity. Let us consider the qualitative picture in Fig. 2 where the potential energy is shown as a function of the mass asymmetry coordinate as well as of the fission coordinate (decay coordinate). The ridge line divides the compound nucleus domain from the fission-fragment domain. A continuum of trajectories is available for the decay, from the easy path through the saddle point, to the very arduous path reaching up to the Businaro-Gallone mountains, and down to the progressively easier paths of more and more asymmetric decays, eventually leading to α-particle and nucleon decay.

For spontaneous decay we can associate each path with the action integral:

$$S(Z) = \int |p(x)|dx = \int_a^b [2\mu(Z) V(Z,x)]^{1/2}dx \quad (3)$$

where $|p(x)|$ is the modulus of the momentum along the fission coordinate x; $\mu(Z)$ and $V(Z,x)$ are the inertia and the potential energy for each asymmetry Z; and **a** and **b** are the classical turning points of the trajectory. The decay rate P(Z) can be written, semiclassically, as:

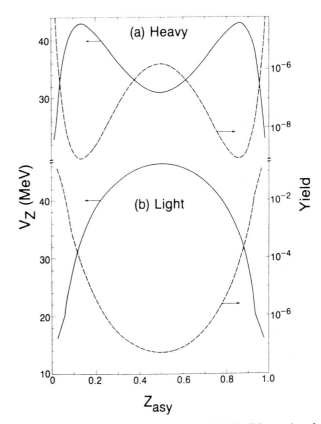

Fig. 1   Schematic ridge-line potentials (solid curve) and expected yields (dashed curve) for: a) a heavy CN above the Businaro-Gallone point; and b) a light CN below the Businaro-Gallone point as a function of the mass asymmetry coordinate (Z_{asy}). See Eq. 6 in the text.

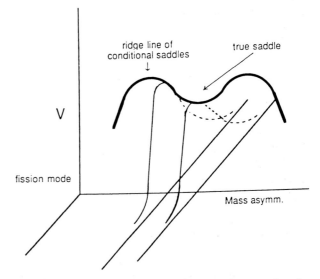

Fig. 2   Schematic potential energy surface as a function of the reaction coordinate and of the mass-asymmetry coordinate.

$$P(Z) = w(Z) \exp\left[\frac{-2S(Z)}{\hbar}\right] \qquad (4)$$

where $w(Z)$ is the frequency of assault of the barrier for the asymmetry Z.

This simple expression accomodates the radioactive emission of any fragment, provided that the process is energetically possible. Of course the strong dependence of the decay rate on the barrier height tends to favor the emission of very light particles on the one hand, and, for very heavy elements, spontaneous fission decay. For light particle emission, shell effects play a dominant role. The strong magicity of ^{4}He accounts for the very pervasive α radioactive decay. The recently observed[28-31] radioactive emission of ^{14}C and ^{24}Ne can be accounted for in a very similar way by the very strong shell corrections associated with the residual nuclei in the ^{208}Pb region. Extensive discussions of this problem can be found in Refs 32, 33 &34.

C.   Complex fragment decay width

The role of the ridge line on the emission of complex fragments can be appreciated by observing that for $x < 0.7$ at all asymmetries and for $x > 0.7$ over a progressively reduced range of asymmetries, the nuclear shapes at the ridge line are so profoundly necked-in that ridge and scission lines approximately coincide. This means that, as the system reaches a given point on the ridge line, it is, to a large extent, committed to decay with the corresponding saddle asymmetry. On the basis of the transition-state theory one can write, for the partial decay width:[21]

$$\Gamma(Z) = \frac{1}{2\pi\rho(E)} \int \rho^{**}[E - B(Z) - \epsilon]d\epsilon \qquad (5)$$

where $\rho(E)$ is the compound nucleus level density, and $\rho**[E - B(Z) - \epsilon]$ is the level density at the conditional saddle of energy $B(Z)$, which the system is transiting with kinetic energy ϵ.

Equation 5 can be further simplified as follows:

$$\Gamma_Z \propto \frac{\rho^{**}[E - B(Z)]}{\rho(E)} \propto e^{-B(Z)/T_Z} \qquad (6)$$

where T_Z represents the nuclear temperature calculated from the excitation energy above the barrier.
This means that the mass or charge yield mirrors the ridge line, being characterized by high emission probabilities in the regions of low potential energy and vice-versa. This is illustrated in Fig. 1 for two systems, one below the Businaro-Gallone point and the second above it. In the former case the yield has a characteristic U shape; in the latter case, one observes also a peak at symmetry which becomes more and more prominent with increasing fissility parameter x and which can be identified as the fission peak.

D.   A transition state formalism for thermal spectra

In the case of neutron emission, the kinetic energy spectra can be easily calculated, since the velocity of the system at the conditional saddle corresponds closely to the velocity of the neutron at infinity. This is not quite the case for the emission of a charged complex fragment for which the kinetic energy at infinity comes also from the potential and kinetic energies associated with other modes.

We can write down the complex fragment decay rate in terms of the normal modes about a "saddle point" in a suitable deformation space.[20-21] It is helpful to consider a sphere-spheroid model where the smaller spherical fragment is in contact with a larger spheroidal fragment of variable eccentricity. The relevant collective degrees of freedom can be catalogued as shown in Fig. 3 in the framework of the sphere-spheroid model.

i) decay mode:

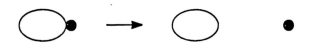

ii) non-amplifying mode:

iii) amplifying mode:

Fig. 3   Schematic representation of the three kinds of normal modes at the conditional saddle point, which control the kinetic energy at infinity.

The first class corresponds to the decay mode, which is unbound and analogous to the fission mode.

The second class includes the non-amplifying modes whose excitation energy is directly translated into kinetic energy at infinity without amplification. Two such modes could be, for instance, the two orthogonal oscillations of the particle about the tip of the "spheroidal" residual nucleus.

The third class corresponds to the amplifying modes. In these modes the total potential energy remains rather flat about the minimum, while complementary substantial changes occur in the Coulomb and surface energies. As shown in Fig. 4, an oscillation about this mode involving an amount of energy on the order of the temperature corresponds to a variation in the monopole - monopole term of the Coulomb energy

$$\Delta E_C = 2\sqrt{\frac{c^2 T}{k}} = 2\sqrt{pT} \qquad (7)$$

where the coefficients c and k are defined by the quadratic expansion of the total potential energy and by the linearization of the Coulomb energy along the deformation mode Z:

$$V(z) = B_0 + kz^2; \qquad E_{Coul} = E^0_{Coul} - cz. \qquad (8)$$

Because of its effect, illustrated in Fig. 4, p is called the "amplification parameter". An input thermal noise of the order of the temperature T is magnified in accordance to Eq. 7 and Fig. 4 giving an output kinetic energy fluctuation much greater than the temperature. This effect is probably responsible also for the great widths of the kinetic energy distributions in ordinary fission.

We are now going to consider two specific cases. The first and simplest deals in detail with only one decay mode and one amplifying mode. For this case the final kinetic energy distribution is:

$$P(E) = 1/2 \, (\pi pT)^{1/2} \, e^{\frac{p}{4T}} \, e^{-\frac{x}{T}}$$

$$\left\{ erf\left[\frac{2E^0_{Coul} + p}{2(pT)^{1/2}}\right] - erf\left[\frac{p - 2x}{2(pT)^{1/2}}\right] \right\} \qquad (9)$$

where $x = E - E^0_{Coul}$.

The addition of <u>two</u> harmonic non-amplifying modes (potential energy only) like those illustrated in Fig. 3 or of <u>one</u> non-amplifying mode (potential + kinetic energy) leads to a more general expression:

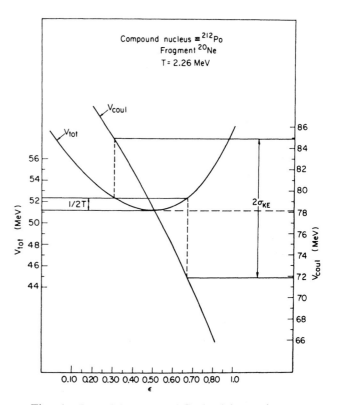

Fig. 4   Potential energy and Coulomb interaction energy as a function of the deformation of the large fragment (sphere-spheroid model). The thermal fluctuations about the ridge point result in larger amplified fluctuations in the Coulomb repulsion energy.[21]

$$P(E) = \frac{(\pi pT)^{1/2}}{2} e^{\frac{p}{4T}} e^{-\frac{x}{T}} \left[\frac{2x - p}{2} \left\{ erf\left[\frac{2E^0 + p}{2(pT)^{1/2}}\right] - erf\left[\frac{p - 2x}{2(pT)^{1/2}}\right] \right\} - \left(\frac{pT}{\pi}\right)^{1/2} \left\{ exp-\left[\frac{(2E^0 + p)^2}{4pT}\right] - exp-\left[\frac{(p - 2x)^2}{4pT}\right] \right\} \right] . (10)$$

This formula not only portrays the same features as that derived previously, but also allows for emission of the particle from any point of the surface (if the Coulomb potential is assumed to vary quadratically as the particle moves away from the pole toward the equator of the residual nucleus).

The general shapes predicted by these equations depend on the parameter p. At small values of p corresponding to the emission of small particles, the distributions are skewed and Maxwellian-like, while at larger values of p, corresponding to the emission of sizeable fragments, the distributions become Gaussians. This is illustrated in Figs. 5a & b, where the kinetic energy distributions assuming 0,1,2 non amplifying modes are calculated at various temperatures for the emission of an α particle (small p) and a carbon ion (large p) from a ^{212}Po compound nucleus.

In the limit of large p, these equations become of the form $p(x) \cong \exp[-x^2/pT]$, which reminds us of the Gaussian kinetic energy distributions observed in ordinary fission. Another pleasing feature of these equations is the limit to which they tend for p=0:

$$P(E) \propto e^{-E/T} \quad \text{and} \quad P(E) \propto E\, e^{-E/T}. \quad (11)$$

The latter form is the standard "evaporation" expression for the neutron spectra. Therefore the evolution of the kinetic energy spectra from Maxwellian-like to Gaussian-like as one goes from "evaporation" to "fission" is naturally predicted in this model.

E.   Angular distributions

Continuing the generalization of the fission process, the angular distributions for the emitted particles can also be derived. The ridge-point configuration, for the great majority of cases, can be identified with the scission configuration. Furthermore, the disintegration axis and the symmetry axis of the system at the ridge point should approximately coincide. As a consequence, the projection K of the total angular momentum I on the symmetry/disintegration axis should remain constant from the ridge point to infinity. In the present case, the closeness of the ridge and the scission points should make the theory work even better than in fission.

Then the angular distribution becomes:[21]

$$W(\theta) \propto \exp(-s_{max})\left[I_0(s_{max}) + I_1(s_{max})\right] +$$

$$\frac{\beta I^2_{max}}{2}\exp(-s_{max})\left[I_0(s_{max}) + \frac{2I_1(s_{max})}{3} - \frac{I_2(s_{max})}{3}\right]. (12)$$

where $s_{max} = I^2_{max}\sin^2\theta/4K^2_o$, and I_o, I_1, I_2 are the modified Bessel functions of order 0, 1, 2. This expression has two interesting limits. As $g = I^2_{max}/4K^2_o$ tends to infinity (either because K^2_o tends to zero or because I_{max}

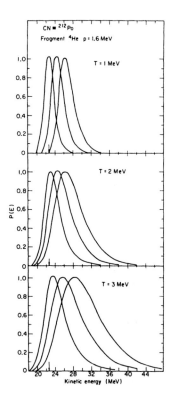

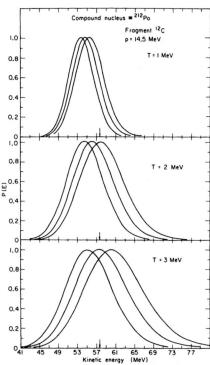

Fig. 5   Calculated kinetic energy distributions at three temperatures for small [(a) α particles] and large [(b)^{12}C fragments] values of the amplification parameter p for the decay of a ^{212}Po nucleus. The curves corresponding to 0,1,2 non amplifying modes can be identified by their progressive shift towards higher kinetic energies. The arrows indicate the energies corresponding to the ridge line Coulomb energies.[21]

becomes very large), one obtains:

$$\lim_{g \to \infty} W(\theta) \propto \frac{1}{\sin \theta} \,. \qquad (13)$$

On the other hand, as $g \to 0$ (either because $I_{max} \approx 0$ or $K^2_o \to \infty$) one obtains:

$$\lim_{g \to 0} W(\theta) = \text{constant} \,. \qquad (14)$$

These limits represent the two extreme cases for the coupling between total and orbital angular momentum. The coupling parameter g depends upon the principal moments of inertial of the ridge configuration. This allows one to make a very simple prediction. At constant I_{max}, g becomes larger the bigger the difference between $\Im_\parallel$ and $\Im_\perp$, or in other words, the more elongated the ridge configuration is. Thus the anisotropy $W(0^0)/W(90^0)$ progressively increases as one considers the emission of a neutron, an α-particle, a lithium particle, a beryllium particle, etc. (see Fig. 6).

III. EXPERIMENTAL EVIDENCE FOR STATISTICAL BINARY DECAY

A. Compound nucleus emission at low energies

In the midst of a confusing experimental situation at intermediate energies, a descent to lower energies helped to clarify the compound nucleus emission of complex fragments. The reaction chosen for this purpose,[35] was ^{3}He + Ag. The excitation energy of the compound nucleus ranged from 50 MeV to 130 MeV, the lower limit being barely 10 MeV above the highest barriers. Complex fragments were detected with cross sections dropping precipitously with decreasing energy. Their kinetic energy spectra resembled closely the shapes predicted by the theory illustrated above. In particular, the shapes evolved from Maxwellian-like for the lowest Z values to Gaussian-like for the highest Z values.

However, the crucial proof is given by the measurement of excitation functions extending down almost to the threshold. These excitation functions, are shown in Fig. 7. They demonstrate with their rapid rise with increasing energy, that these fragments originate from compound nucleus decay and compete, in their emission, with the major decay channel, namely neutron emission.

The compound nucleus fits shown in the same figure, on the one hand demonstrate quantitatively the agreement with the compound nucleus hypothesis, and on the other allow one to extract the conditional barriers. The extracted barriers are presented in Fig. 8 together with two calculations.[25] The standard liquid-drop model fails dramatically in reproducing the barriers, while the finite-range model, accounting for the surface-surface interaction (so important for these highly indented conditional saddle shapes) reproduces the experimental values almost exactly.

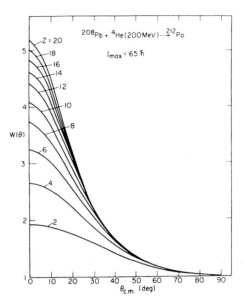

Fig. 6 Calculated angular distributions of various fragments emitted by the compound nucleus formed in the reaction ^{208}Pb + 200 MeV ^{4}He $\to [^{212}$Po$^*] \to$ Z + (84 - Z). Note the progressive approach to a $1/\sin \theta$ distribution with increasing atomic number of the fragments.[21]

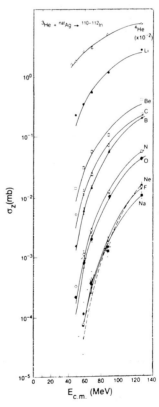

Fig. 7 Dependence of the total integrated cross sections (symbols) for emission of complex fragments on the center-of-mass energy, $E_{c.m.}$, in the reaction ^{3}He + ^{nat}Ag. The curves are compound nucleus fits to the data.[44]

Additional studies at low energies have demonstrated the role of the potential energy along the ridge line.[36] As was shown previously, the charge distribution is U shaped or has an additional maximum at symmetry depending on whether the system is below or above the Businaro-Gallone point. The three reactions $^{74}Ge + ^9Be$, $^{93}Nb + ^9Be$ and $^{139}La + ^9Be$, studied at 8.5 MeV/u, produce compound nuclei well below, near, and well above the Businaro-Gallone point, respectively. The observed fragments were emitted from a source with compound nucleus velocity and were characterized by center-of-mass Coulomb-like energies. Their charge distributions are shown in Fig. 9 together with the corresponding compound nucleus calculations. As expected, the U-shaped distributions prevailing at or below the Businaro-Gallone point as exemplified by the $^{74}Ge + ^9Be$ and $^{93}Nb + ^9Be$ reactions, develop in the case of $^{139}La + ^9Be$ a central peak, characteristic of systems above the Businaro-Gallone point. The solid curves in the same figure represent calculations based on the compound nucleus hypothesis.

B.   Compound nucleus emission at higher energies

Compound nucleus emission of complex fragments at low energy implies an even more abundant emission at higher energies, provided that compound nuclei are indeed formed. Part of the initial confusion about complex fragment emission at intermediate energies may have been due to the broad range of compound and non compound nucleus sources associated with the onset and establishment of incomplete fusion. This problem can be minimized to some extent by the choice of rather asymmetric systems. In such systems, the range of impact parameters is geometrically limited by the nuclear sizes of the reaction partners. Furthermore, the projectile-like spectator, if any, is confined to very small masses, and does not obscure other sources of complex fragments.

Incomplete fusion or massive transfer appears to begin at approximately 18 MeV/N bombarding energy and extends probably higher than 100 MeV/u. At even higher bombarding energies, it may be replaced by a participant-spectator mechanism in which the interacting nucleons form a fireball physically separated from the rather cool spectators.

Many reactions have been studied in reverse kinematics to facilitate the detection of most of the fragments over a large center-of-mass angular range.

Representative examples[37] of the invariant cross sections in the $v_{\parallel}$ - $v_{\perp}$ plane for a range of atomic numbers are shown in Fig. 10. For all the reactions studied so far, one observes beautifully developed Coulomb rings whose isotropy indicate that, up to 50 MeV/u, the fragments do in fact arise from binary compound nucleus decay.[37-39] Only the fragments in the neighborhood of the target atomic number show the presence of an additional component at backward angles (big foot), that can be attributed to quasi-elastic and deep-inelastic processes, and/or to the spectator target-like fragment in the incomplete-fusion reactions prevailing at higher bombarding energies.

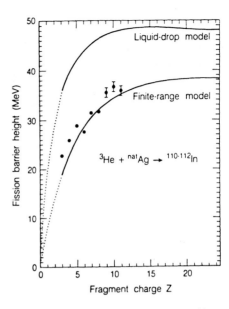

Fig. 8   Calculated[25] and experimental[44] conditional fission barriers as a function of the lighter fragment charge for the fission of ^{111}In. The experimental values are obtained from the fits in Fig. 7. The calculated curves for the liquid drop and finite-range models are shown. The dotted portions of the curves are extrapolations.

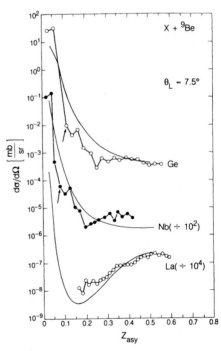

Fig. 9   Center-of mass cross sections[36] for products from the 8.5 MeV/u ^{74}Ge, ^{93}Nb, $^{139}La + ^9Be$ systems detected at $\theta_{lab} = 7.5^o$. The solid line is a compound nucleus calculation of the fragment yield at $\theta_{c.m.} = 30^o$. The arrows indicate the entrance-channel asymmetry.

The center of each ring provides the source velocity for each Z value. For all bombarding energies the extracted source velocities are independent of the fragments' Z value. Up to ~18 MeV/u, one can conclude that a single source with compound nucleus velocity is responsible for the emission of all the fragments. As the bombarding energy increases, it appears that incomplete fusion sets in. The observed source velocities are intermediate between the projectile and compound nucleus velocities. In the case of 50 MeV/u ^{139}La + ^{12}C, the source velocity is halfway between the two limits, indicating that ~1/2 of the ^{12}C target fuses with the ^{139}La projectile.[39] It is truly remarkable that even when incomplete fusion sets in, the source velocity is independent of Z value and quite sharp.

The radii of the Coulomb rings give the emission velocities in the center of mass. The almost linear dependence of these velocities upon fragment Z value is a clear indication of their Coulomb origin. This is also supported by their independence of bombarding energy.[38] The Coulomb calculations reproduce the data, further illustrating the degree of relaxation of the c.m. kinetic energy. The variances of the velocities arise from a variety of causes, among which the inherent Coulomb energy fluctuation due to the shape fluctuations of the "scission point", and the fragment recoil due to sequential evaporation of light particles.

C. Cross sections

All of the evidence presented so far for the intermediate energy complex fragment emission points rather convincingly towards a compound nucleus process. However, the most compelling evidence for this compound mechanism lies in the statistical competition between complex fragment emission and the major decay channels, like n, p, and ^{4}He emission. The simplest and most direct quantity testing this hypothesis is the absolute cross section.

Absolute cross sections as a function of Z value are shown in Figs. 11-15. At first glance one can observe a qualitative difference between the charge distributions from the ^{93}Nb-induced and the ^{139}La-induced reactions. The former distributions portray a broad minimum at symmetry whereas the latter show a broad central fission-like peak that is absent in the former distributions. This difference can be traced to the fact that the former systems are below or near the Businaro-Gallone point while the latter systems are well above.

In general, for a given system, the cross sections associated with the charge distributions increase in magnitude rapidly at low energies, and very slowly at high energy, in a manner consistent with Eq. 6.

The most important information associated with these cross sections is their absolute value and energy dependence. Through them, the competition of complex fragment emission with the major decay channels, like n, p, and a decay is manifested. This is why we attribute a great deal of significance to the ability to fit such data. Examples of these fits are shown in Figs. 11-15. The calculations are performed with an evaporation code GEMINI[38] extended to

$E/A = 18$ MeV ^{139}La + ^{12}C

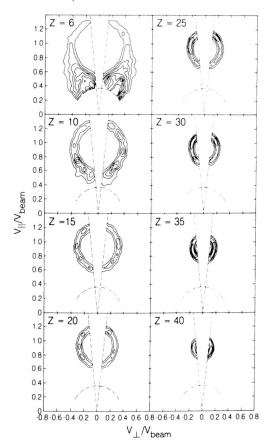

Fig. 10 Contours of the experimental cross section $\partial^2\sigma/\partial V_{||}\partial V_\perp$ in the $V_{||}$-$V_\perp$ plane for representative fragments detected in the reaction $E/A = 18$ MeV ^{139}La + ^{12}C. The beam direction is vertical towards the top of the figure. The dashed lines show the maximum and minimum angular thresholds and the low velocity threshold of the detectors. The magnitudes of the contour levels indicated are relative.[37]

incorporate complex fragment emission. Angular momentum dependent finite-range barriers are used.[25] All the fragments produced are allowed to decay in turn both by light particle emission or by complex fragment emission. In this way higher chance emission, as well as sequential binary emission, are accounted for.

The cross section is integrated over ℓ waves up to a maximum value that provides the best fit to the experimental charge distributions. In the case of the ^{93}Nb + ^{9}Be & ^{12}C, as well ^{139}La + ^{12}C for bombarding energies up to 18 MeV/u, the quality of the fits is exceptionally good and the fitted values of ℓ_{max} correspond very closely to those predicted by the Bass model[40] or by the extra push model,[41] as shown in Fig. 16.

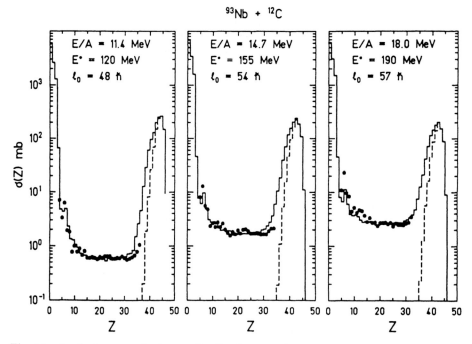

Fig. 11 Angle-integrated charge distributions (solid circles) of complex fragments associated with fusion-like reactions of ^{93}Nb and ^{12}C at three bombarding energies.[38] The histograms represent calculations with the statistical code GEMINI.[45]

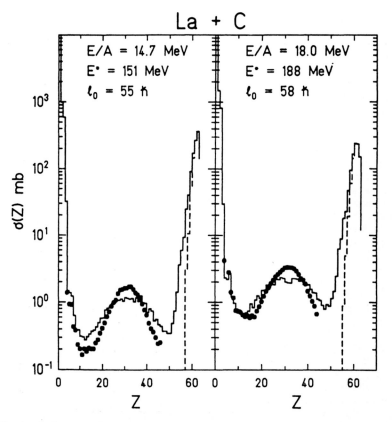

Fig. 12 Angle-integrated cross sections (solid circles) plotted as a function of the fragment Z-value for the 14 & 18 MeV/u ^{139}La + ^{12}C reactions.[37] The histograms represent calculations with the statistical code GEMINI.[38]

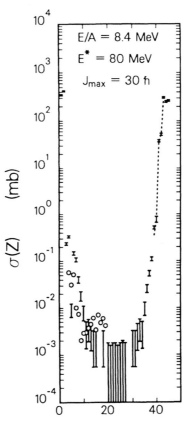

Fig. 13 Comparison of experimental and calculated charge distributions for the ^{93}Nb + ^{9}Be reaction at 8.5 MeV/u. The experimental data are indicated by the hollow circles and the values calculated with the code GEMINI are shown by the error bars.[38] The dashed curve indicates the cross sections associated with classical evaporation residues which decay only by the emission of light particles (Z ≤ 2). Note the value of the excitation energy (E*) corresponding to complete fusion and the value of J_{max} assumed to fit the data.

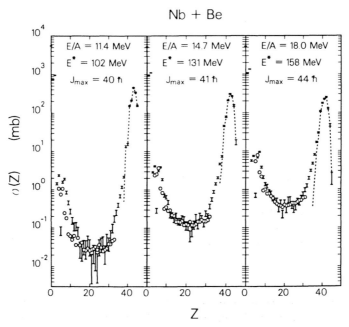

Fig. 14 Comparison of experimental and calculated charge distributions for the ^{93}Nb + ^{9}Be reaction at E/A = 11.4, 14.7, and 18.0. See Fig. 13.

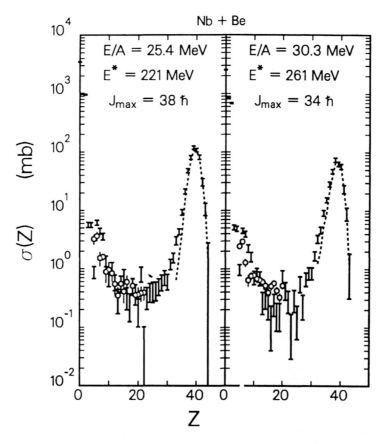

Fig. 15 Same as in Fig. 14, for the ^{93}Nb + ^{9}Be reaction[46] at E/A =25.4 and 30.3.

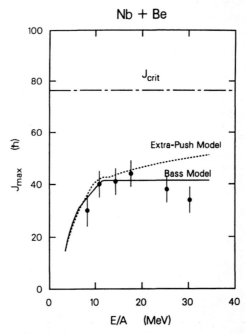

Fig. 16 Plot showing the maximum angular momentum for fusion (J_{max}) obtained by fitting the experimental charge distributions as a function of bombarding energy for the ^{93}Nb + ^{9}Be reactions. The dashed and solid curve show the predictions of the extra-push and Bass models, respectively. The chain dashed lines indicate the angular momentum (J_{crit}) where the barrier for symmetric division vanishes.[38]

492

D. Coincidence data

If any doubt still remains concerning the binary nature of the decay involved in complex fragment production, it can be removed by the detection of binary coincidences. Several examples of Z_1 - Z_2 correlations are shown in Figs. 17 & 18. Some examples of the sum ($Z_1 + Z_2$) spectra are also shown in Figs. 19 & 20. One can observe the binary band in the Z_1 - Z_2 correlation as a general feature persisting up to the highest bombarding energies (100 MeV/u for ^{139}La + ^{12}C)! The binary nature is proven by the correlation angles as well as by the sum of the fragments' atomic numbers which accounts for most of the target + projectile charge. The missing charge can be accounted for by the extent of incomplete fusion and by the sequential evaporation of light charged particles ($A \leq 4$). A particularly interesting example of this verification is shown in Fig. 21 for the reactions ^{93}Nb + ^{9}Be, ^{27}Al. In this figure, the average charge sum $Z_1 + Z_2$ is shown as a function of Z_2. The dashed lines indicate the charge of the compound nucleus obtained in an incomplete fusion process as calculated from the measured source velocities. The solid lines show the reduction in charge brought about by evaporation from the hot primary fragments formed in the binary decay. The excitation energy of the fragments was evaluated on the basis of the source velocity, which tells about the extent of incomplete fusion. The remarkable agreement of these calculations with the data, which is retained over a large range of excitation energies speaks for the internal consistency of such an analysis.

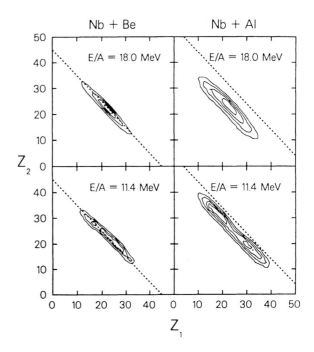

Fig. 17   Representative Z_1-Z_2 contour plots for coincidence events from the reactions ^{93}Nb + ^{9}Be & ^{27}Al at 11.4 and 18.0 MeV/u. Z_1 and Z_2 refer to the Z-values of fragments detected in two detectors at equal angles on opposite sides of the beam.[38]

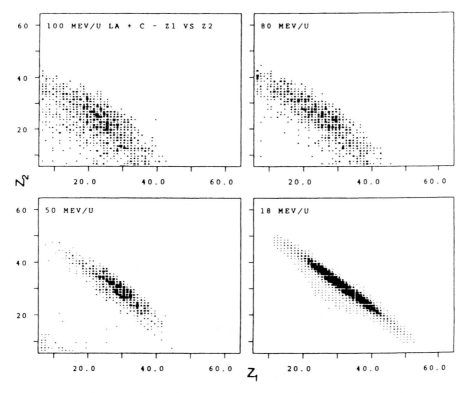

Fig. 18   Scatter plots of the experimental Z_1 - Z_2 correlation for coincident fragments detected at symmetric angles on opposite sides of the beam in the ^{139}La + ^{12}C reactions at 18, 50, 80, and 100 MeV/u.[37,39,47]

This same consistency holds over a very wide range of bombarding energies (8.5 - 30.3 MeV/u). In Fig. 22 the average sum of the symmetric products' final atomic numbers for the reaction ^{93}Nb + ^{27}Al is plotted vs bombarding energy. The five experimental points correspond to bombarding energies of 11.4, 14.7, 18, 25.4 and 30.3 MeV/u. The solid line represents the sum of the target and projectile atomic numbers. The long dashed line corresponds to the compound nucleus atomic number calculated on the basis of the momentum transfer systematics[42] in incomplete fusion. The short dashed line corresponds to the sum of the charges of the final fragments after evaporation as calculated with the code PACE.[43] The agreement between calculation and experiment is very satisfactory and supports our basic understanding of incomplete fusion, mass and energy transfer, as well as of sequential evaporation.

Finally, it is possible to verify that the coincidence rate and the single rate are consistent with each other under the assumption that all the fragments arise from binary decay. This can be done by evaluating the experimental coincidences/singles ratio on one hand, and on the other by computing the same ratio from the singles rate and from the knowledge of the efficiencies of the detectors involved in the coincidence measurement. The good agreement which is observed indicates that all of the coincidences can be accounted for by the singles data. In other words, all the singles data are associated with binary processes.

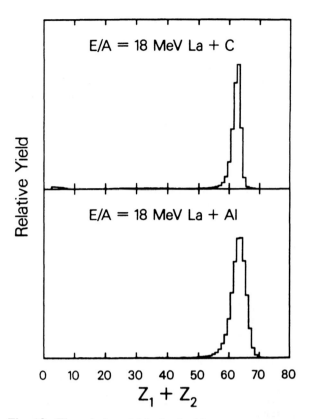

Fig. 19 The relative yield of coincidence events plotted as a function of the sum of the atomic charges of the two coincident fragments for the ^{139}La + ^{12}C & ^{27}Al reactions at 18 MeV/u.[37]

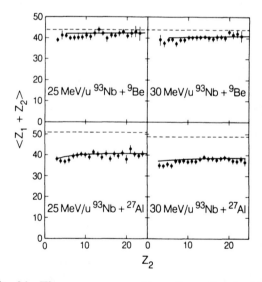

Fig. 21 The mean sum, $<Z_1 + Z_2>$ of coincidence events plotted as a function of Z_2 for the ^{93}Nb + ^{9}Be & ^{27}Al reactions at 25.4 and 30.3 MeV/u. The dashed lines indicate the average charge of the source system estimated from the mass transfer. The charge loss for binary events due to sequential evaporation was estimated using the evaporation code PACE, and the residual $Z_1 + Z_2$ values are indicated by the solid curves.[46]

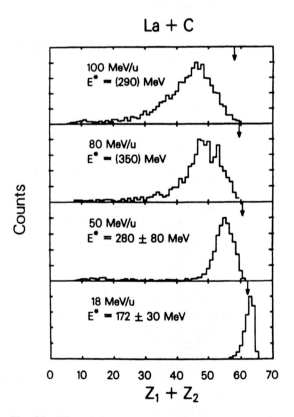

Fig. 20 The relative yield of coincidence events plotted as a function of the sum of the atomic charges of the two coincident fragments for the ^{139}La + ^{12}C reactions at 18, 50, 80 and 100 MeV/u.

IV. OUTLOOK AND CONCLUSIONS

The explicit treatment of the mass asymmetry degree of freedom has allowed us to extend the concept of fission to statistical processes involving the emission of fragments of any size. This generalization makes fission a process that extends throughout the periodic chart and that incorporates as special cases both traditional fission and light particle evaporation.

The experimental evidence allows us to conclude that the statistical emission of complex fragments as a generalized fission process is well established, and its role has been proven important from the lowest excitation energies up to the limits of compound nucleus stability.

Despite the extensive research covered in this presentation, a lot if not most of the work remains yet to be done. The experimental determination of the conditional barriers is so far limited to one isotope, and even that is incomplete. A systematic study of the conditional barriers is clearly necessary to test the validity (or to define the parameters) of the macroscopic models like the finite range model. As it has been done for the symmetric barriers in heavy systems, it should be possible to isolate the shell effects from the macroscopic part of the conditional barriers. Furthermore, the knowledge of the conditional barriers is essential for the predictions of cross sections and reaction rates.

A natural development of these studies should lead to the evaluation of the dependence of the barriers upon angular momentum on one hand and upon temperature on the other. It may well be that complex fragment emission will be the most powerful if not the only tool for the characterization of extremely hot nuclei, their free energy and the temperature dependence of the coefficients of its liquid drop-like expansion. As we are writing, the role and scope of intermediate energy nuclear physics is being debated and defined in the experimental and theoretical arenas. If intermediate energy nuclear physics is the physics of hot nuclei near the limit of their (thermal) stability, it is clear already that fission in its generalized aspect of complex fragment emission will be a shining beacon in the golden twilight of nuclei.

ACKNOWLEDGEMENTS

This work was supported by the Director, Office of Energy Research, Office of High Energy and Nuclear Physics, Division of Nuclear Physics of the U. S. Department of Energy under Contract DE-AC03-76SF00098.

REFERENCES

1. J. M. ALEXANDER, C. BALTZINGER, and M. F. GAZDIK, Phys.Rev., 129, 1826 (1963).

2. A. A. CARETTO, J. HUDIS, and G. FRIEDLANDER, Phys. Rev., 110, 1130 (1958).

3. G. FRIEDLANDER, J. M. MILLER, R.

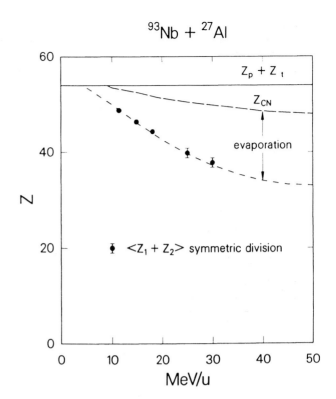

$^{93}Nb + ^{27}Al$

Fig. 22 Comparision of the experimentally determined sum of the charges for symmetric products with calculations performed on the basis of incomplete fusion and sequential evaporation from the primary binary fragments. Data points are shown for five bombarding energies for the $^{93}Nb + ^{27}Al$ reaction.

WOLFGANG, J. HUDIS, and E. BAKER, Phys. Rev., 94, 727 (1954).

4. G. FRIEDLANDER, L. FRIEDMAN, B. GORDON, and YAFFE, Phys. Rev., 129, 1809 (1963).

5. W. U. SCHRÖDER, and J. R. HUIZENGA, Ann. Rev. Nucl. Part. Sci., 27, 465 (1977).

6. L. G. MORETTO and R. P. SCHMITT, J. Phys., 37C5 109 (1976).

7. L. G. MORETTO and G. J. WOZNIAK, Ann. Rev. Nucl. Part. Sci., 34, 189 (1984).

8. J. AICHELIN and J. HÜFNER, Phys. Lett., 138B, 15 (1984).

9. M. E. FISCHER, Phys., 3, 255 (1967).

10. M. E. FISCHER, Rep. Prog. Phys., 67, Vol. 30 615 (1967).

11. G. SAUER, H. CHANDRA, and U. MOSEL, Nucl. Phys., A264, 221 (1976).

12. J. E. FINN, S. AGARWAL, A. BUJAK, J. CHUANG, L. J. GUTAY, A. S. HIRSCH, R. W.

MINICH, N. T. PORILE, R. P. SCHARENBERG, B. C. STRINGFELLOW, and F. TURKOT, Phys. Rev. Lett., 49, 1321 (1982).

13. G. BERTSCH and P. J. SIEMENS, Phys. Lett., 126, 9 (1983).

14. P. J. SIEMENS, Nature, 395, 410 (1983).

15. V. F. WEISSKOPF, Phys. Rev., 52, 295 (1937).

16. V. F. WEISSKOPF and D. H. EWING, Phys. Rev., 57 472 (1940).

17. V. F. WEISSKOPF, Phys. Acta, 23, 187 (1950).

18. V. F. WEISSKOPF, Arts Sci., 82, 360 (1953).

19. J. A. WHEELER, Fast neutron physics part II, Interscience, New York, pp. 2051 (1963).

20. L. G. MORETTO, Phys. Lett., 40B, 185 (1972).

21. L. G. MORETTO, Nucl. Phys., A247, 211 (1975).

22. S. COHEN, F. PLASIL, and W. J. SWIATECKI, Proc. Third Conf. on Reactions Between Complex Nuclei, ed. A. Ghiorso, R. M. Diamond and H. E. Conzett (University of California Press) pp. 325 UCRL-10775 (1963).

23. S. COHEN, F. PLASIL, and W. J. SWIATECKI, Ann. Phys., 82, 557 (1974).

24. J. R. NIX and W. J. SWIATECKI, Nucl. Phys., 71, 1 (1965).

25. A. J. SIERK, Phys. Rev. Lett., 55, 582 (1985).

26. A. J. SIERK, Phys. Rev., C33, 2039 (1986).

27. U. L. BUSINARO and S. GALLONE, Nuovo Cimento, 1, 1277 (1955).

28. S. W. BARWICK, P. B. PRICE, H. L. RAVN, E. HOURANI, and H. HUSSONNOIS, Phys. Rev., C34, 362 (1986).

29. S. GALES, E. HOURANI, M. HUSSONNOIS, J. P. SCHAPIRA, L. STAB, and M. VERGNES, Phys. Rev. Lett., 53, 759 (1984).

30. P. B. PRICE, J. D. STEVENSON, S. W. BARWICK, and H. L. RARN, Phys. Rev. Lett., 54, 297 (1985).

31. H. J. ROSE and G. A. JONES, Nature, 307, 245 (1984).

32. D. N. POENARU, M. IVASCU, A. SANDULESCU, and W. GREINER, Phys. Rev., C32, 572 (1985).

33. Y. J. SHI and W. J. SWIATECKI, Phys. Rev. Lett., 54, 300 (1985).

34. Y. J. SHI and W. J. SWIATECKI, Nucl. Phys., A438, 450 (1985).

35. L. G. SOBOTKA, M. L. PADGETT, G. J. WOZNIAK, G. GUARINO, A. J. PACHECO, L. G. MORETTO, Y. CHAN, R. G. STOKSTAD, I. TSERRUYA, and S. WALD, Phys. Rev., Lett. 51, 2187 (1983).

36. L. G. SOBOTKA, M. A. McMAHAN, R. J. McDONALD, C. SIGNARBIEUX, G. J. WOZNIAK, M. L. PADGETT, J. H. GU, Z. H. LIU, Z. Q. YAO, and L. G. MORETTO, Phys. Rev. Lett., 53, 2004 (1984).

37. R. J. CHARITY, N. COLONNA, M. A. McMAHAN, G. J. WOZNIAK, R. J. McDONALD, L. G. MORETTO, G. GUARINO, A. PANTALEO, L. FIORE, A. GOBBI, and K. D. HILDENBRAND, Lawrence Berkeley Laboratory preprint, LBL-26859 (1989).

38. R. J. CHARITY, M. A. McMAHAN, G. J. WOZNIAK, R. J. McDONALD, L. G. MORETTO, D. G. SARANTITES, L. G. SOBOTKA, G. GUARINO, A. PANTALEO, L. FIORE, A. GOBBI, and K. D. HILDENBRAND, Nucl. Phys., A483, 371 (1988).

39. D. R. BOWMAN, W. L. KEHOE, R. J. CHARITY, M. A. McMAHAN, A. MORONI, A. BRACCO, S. BRADLEY, I. IORI, R. J. McDONALD, A. C. MIGNEREY, L. G. MORETTO, M. N. NAMBOODIRI, and G. J. WOZNIAK, Phys. Lett., B189, 282 (1987).

40. R. BASS, Nucl. Phys., A231, 45 (1974).

41. W. J. SWIATECKI, Nucl. Phys., A376, 275 (1982).

42. V. E. VIOLA, B. B. BACK, K. L. WOLF, T. C. AWES, C. K. GELBKE, and H. BREUER, Phys. Rev., C26, 178 (1982).

43. A. GAVRON, Phys. Rev., C21, 230 (1980).

44. M. A. McMAHAN, L. G. MORETTO, M. L. PADGETT, G. J. WOZNIAK, L. G. SOBOTKA, and M. G. MUSTAFA, Phys. Rev., Lett. 54, 1995 (1985).

45. R. J. CHARITY, private communication.

46. R. J. CHARITY, D. R. BOWMAN, Z. H. LIU, R. J. McMDONALD, M. A. McMAHAN, G. J. WOZNIAK, L. G. MORETTO, S. BRADLEY, W. L. KEHOE, and A. C. MIGNEREY, Nucl. Phys., A476, 516 (1988).

47. D. R. BOWMAN, G. F. PEASLEE, N. COLONNA, M.A. McMAHAN, H. HAN, K. JING, D. DELIS, G. J. WOZNIAK, L. G. MORETTO, W. L. KEHOE, B. LIBBY, A. MARCHETTI, A. C. MIGNEREY, A. MORONI, S. ANGIUS, A. PANTALEO, AND G. GUARINO, LBL-2688, (1989).

FISSION AS A PROBE FOR INVESTIGATION
OF NUCLEAR REACTION MECHANISMS

V.E. VIOLA
Department of Chemistry and IUCF
Indiana University, Bloomington, IN 47405

ABSTRACT

Nuclear fission has been extensively employed as a probe for the investigation of projectile-target interaction mechanisms in nucleus-nucleus collisions at low-to-intermediate bombarding energies. Basic features of the fission reaction that prove useful for such applications will first be reviewed, e.g., fission probablities, kinetic energy distributions and angular distributions. This will be followed by discussion of specific examples where fission has served as a reaction mechanism tag in the study of total reaction cross sections, energy and linear momentum deposition, angular momentum and excitation energy sharing in damped reactions, precompound nucleon emission, and intermediate-mass fragment formation.

INTRODUCTION

The discovery of fission[1-3] has provided not only a phenomenon of great intrinsic interest, but a valuable tool for the study of nuclear reaction mechanisms. In this presentation the use of fission as a reaction filter, or tag, for tracing the evolution of nuclear reaction mechanisms from soft, near-barrier collisions to violent events at intermediate bombarding energies will be reviewed. In addition, the application of the techniques developed for the study of fission has also proven useful in the study of the inverse fission process, i.e., damped collisions. These studies will also be discussed here.

Several properties of the fission reaction[4] contribute to its usefulness as a reaction filter:

(1) The large Coulomb field between the fragments at scission produces highly energetic fragments ($\sim$80-100 MeV/

fragment) that can be easily differentiated from other reaction products. For liquid drop fission (i.e. fission at excitation energies $E^* \geq 20$ MeV), the average total kinetic energy release in fission is given by a simple Coulomb expression:[5]

$$\langle E_K \rangle = 0.119 Z^2/A^{1/3} + 7.3 \text{ MeV}, \qquad (1)$$

where Z and A refer to the fissioning nucleus.

(2) The mass division is binary and approximately symmetric. The binary character of fission insures that the fragments must separate axially, with equal momenta in the center-of-mass system. Any deviation of the average fragment separation angle (θ_{AB}) from 180° must therefore be associated with the dynamics of the formation process.

(3) Fission is an intrinsically slow process. Thus, the fissioning nucleus retains an integrated memory of the prior history of the system, thereby shedding light on the reaction time scale.

(4) For heavy nuclei ($Z \geq 90$) the total reaction cross section eventually undergoes fission at bombarding energies below $E/A \approx 50$ MeV, i.e.

$$\sigma_R \approx \sigma_f \; .$$

Thus, all major reaction channels can be surveyed simultaneously using a heavy-element target to provide a fission tag.

LINEAR MOMENTUM TRANSFER: A REACTION MECHANISM OVERVIEW

The basic concept behind the fission fragment angular correlation technique[6,7] is that any deviation from co-linearity exhibited by the separating fragments must, on the average, result from the linear momentum carried by the fissioning

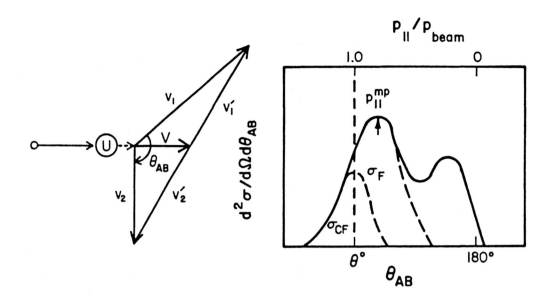

FIGURE 1

Left: Vector diagram of the fission-fragment folding-angle technique. The symbols V, v_i, v'_i represent the velocities of the fissioning system, fragment i in the laboratory system and fragment i in the center-of-mass system, respectively; θ_{AB} is the fragment folding angle. Right: Representative distribution of θ_{AB} at energies well-above the barrier. Angle $\theta°$ represents expected angle for complete fusion followed by symmetric fission; $p_{||}/p_{beam}$ scale is translation of θ_{AB} into longitudinal momentum transfer. Other symbols are defined in text.

nucleus. Thus, measurement of the fragment-fragment folding angle, θ_{AB}, translates into a determination of the linear momentum transferred (LMT) from the projectile to the struck nucleus in the collision. For highly fissile targets, nearly all interactions lead to fission and thus the distribution of folding angles represents an integrated overview of all mechanisms that contribute to the total cross section, at least for low-to-intermediate energy projectiles.

In Fig. 1 a schematic diagram of a representative fission-fragment folding-angle distribution for heavy-ion-induced reactions is shown. In this plot the fission fragment folding angle θ_{AB} can be translated directly into the ratio of the longitudinal linear momentum of the fissioning nucleus to that of the beam, $p_{||}/p_{beam}$. Imposed upon the primary LMT distribution is the dispersion created largely by neutron evaporation from the fission fragments.

The fission fragment angular correlation technique was first employed by Nicholson and Halpern[6] in the study of deuteron-induced fission of ^{238}U. Shortly thereafter, Sikkeland and co-workers[7,8]

applied this method to the study of heavy-ion-induced reactions below projectile energies of E/A = 10 MeV; some of these data are shown in Fig. 2. These measurements showed the first clear definition of the complete fusion and peripheral processes which characterize such reactions. Subsequently, similar measurements have been extended to projectiles ranging from protons to Kr ions and to energies from the barrier to well into the GeV range. References 9-12 contain reviews of this work.

Figure 2 shows a representative set of LMT data for the ^{14}N + ^{238}U system which demonstrates the evolution of the folding-angle distribution over the energy range from E/A = 7-800 MeV.[7,13-15]

At incident energies near the Coulomb barrier,[7] the concordance between the most probable LMT, $p_{||}^{mp}$, and the calculated value for complete LMT indicates that these collisions are dominated by complete fusion processes. Small contributions from low momentum transfer events are due to peripheral collisions such as inelastic scattering or transfer reactions. At higher beam energies two distinct components are observed in the folding angle distributions, one associated with large momentum transfers (or central collisions) and the other with small momentum transfers (or peripheral processes). For energies above E/A ≥ 20 MeV, the most probable folding angle of the central collision peak remains essentially constant near θ_{AB} ≈ 149 deg for ^{14}N, significantly larger than that expected for complete fusion. This observed value of $p_{\parallel}^{mp}$ corresponds to $p_{\parallel}^{mp}$ ≈ 2800 MeV/c, or 200 MeV/c per projectile nucleon. At higher energies the folding-angle distributions become structureless over the entire range of θ_{AB}, corresponding to a broad continuum of linear momentum transfers and deposition energies in the residual system. At relativistic energies the fusion-like component eventually disappears,[16] signalling the onset of more complex mechanisms.[16,17]

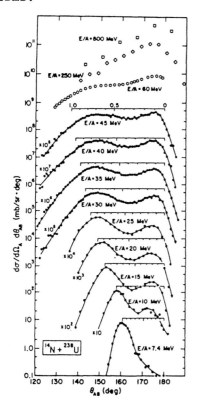

FIGURE 2
Fission-fragment folding angle distributions for the ^{14}N + ^{238}U reaction. For lower-energy measurements a linear momentum transfer scale, $p_{\parallel}/p_{beam}$, is shown immediately above the data. Open circles are from Ref. 13; closed circles from Refs. 7, 14 and 15.

The peak angle of the low momentum transfer (peripheral) component does not exhibit a pronounced energy dependence. However, the relative cross section of these peripheral processes increases

strongly with bombarding energy, and beyond E/A ≈ 40 MeV the fission cross section becomes dominated by peripheral interactions.[16,17]

Linear momentum systematics now exist for a wide variety of projectiles[10-12] ranging from protons[18,19] to ^{40}Ar ions.[20] One observes similar systematic trends of these LMT distributions as a function of bombarding energy for all projectiles. The major projectile dependence appears to be a more rapid disappearance of fusion-like processes as a function of increasing projectile energy for the heavier projectiles. This behavior suggests that the total energy of the system may also be a relevant parameter in limiting the observation of fusion-like processes with the fission LMT technique. Because of the large total energy deposited in collisions initiated by, for example, ^{40}Ar ions relative to lighter ions, high multiplicity precompound decay and/or multifragmentation phenomena may compete successfully with fission.

In Fig. 3 the systematic dependence of linear momentum transfer on projectile mass and energy are summarized for heavy target nuclei in terms of the average linear momentum transfer per projectile nucleon, $\langle p_{\parallel} \rangle / A$. For all projectiles with A ≥ 6 the data lie on a uniform curve. In contrast, the light-ion projectiles deposit increasingly larger momenta per particle with decreasing projectile mass; i.e., the nucleon is the most effective vehicle for momentum transfer in this context. This behavior can be associated with the diminishing influence of the dinuclear mean field on the collision dynamics due to the onset of microscopic collision processes.[21] A second important feature of Fig. 3 is the apparent decrease in $\langle p_{\parallel} \rangle / A$ beyond E/A ≥ 50 MeV for ^{4}He and heavier projectiles. As will be discussed in the following section, this decrease is associated with the opening of competing complex reaction channels for central collisions as relativistic projectile energies are approached.

A third--and most important--feature of Fig. 3 is the deviation between the value for complete linear momentum transfer (heavy solid upper line) and the data beyond E/A ≥ 10 MeV. This difference represents the "missing momentum," $p_m = p_{beam} - p_{\parallel}$, and is observed to become quite large at intermediate energies. The origin of this missing momentum, which contains much of the interesting physics, is discussed in the following section. Finally, the insert

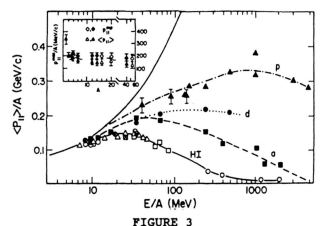

FIGURE 3

Average linear momentum transfer per projectile nucleon, $\langle p_\parallel \rangle /A$, as a function of projectile E/A for reactions with Th and U targets. Symbols for heavy ions are as follows: ^{6}Li (•), ^{12}C (□), ^{14}N (△), ^{16}O (⊗) and ^{20}Ne (○). Insert gives maximum value of the linear momentum transfer per projectile nucleon as a function of projectile mass; diamonds and triangles represent most probable and average value, respectively. Solid points indicate established upper bounds; open points represent the largest values observed over a more restricted range of energies.

in Fig. 3 shows the largest observed values of $p_\parallel^{mp}/A$ and $\langle p_\parallel \rangle /A$ as a function of projectile mass. Other than the previously mentioned large value for light ions, all projectiles exhibit maximum values of $p_\parallel^{mp}/A \approx 190 \pm 10$ MeV/c and $\langle p_\parallel \rangle /A \approx 145 \pm 10$ MeV/c, all observed near $E/A \approx 35$ MeV. Both the maximum momentum transfer per nucleon and the corresponding projectile velocities correspond approximately to the Fermi momentum and velocity. This concordance provides another indication that nucleon-nucleon collisions exert an important influence on limiting momentum and energy transfer.

THE MISSING MOMENTUM: EJECTILE AND SOURCE PROPERTIES

In order to gain a more quantitative understanding of the mechanisms responsible for momentum and energy dissipation at intermediate energies, a more complete characterization of these multibody processes is required. For this purpose, the use of fission reactions as a coincidence tag for the study of associated ejectiles has proven illuminating. One of the first such experiments[2] was performed at the LBL 88-inch cyclotron with E/A = 20 MeV ^{16}O ions incident on ^{238}U. Angle- and energy-

correlated fission fragments were studied in coincidence with both light-charged particles (LCP = H and He isotopes) and projectile fragmentation residues (O, N, C, etc. ejectiles).

The ^{16}O + ^{238}U studies demonstrated that the major source of missing momentum in central (fusion-like) collisions could be nearly quantitatively accounted for by precompound light particle emission. This conclusion was based on the Maxwellian energy spectra, strongly forward-peaked angular distributions and overall linear momentum balance observed for LCP ejectiles. For peripheral reactions, the missing momentum could be attributed to projectile-like fragments possessing the approximate E/A of the beam--consistent with transfer and projectile frag-mentation reaction mechanisms. One unexpected feature of these data was that the proton spectral shapes beyond the grazing angle were nearly identical for both fusion-like and peripheral reactions. This result suggested that fast nucleons are emitted very early in the collision stage, prior to full development of the dinuclear mean field. Hence, these results further emphasized the need for explicit treatment of both the mean field and individual nucleon-nucleon scattering properties in any comprehensive theoretical treatment of collisions above $E/A \gtrsim 20$ MeV. The subsequent theoretical efforts to develop Vlasov-Uehling-Uhlenbeck/Landau-Vlasov approaches for the description of both phenomena have provided an important beginning in this direction.[23-26]

Numerous subsequent experiments of this type at GANIL, Michigan State, VICKSI and IUCF have reinforced these ideas.[11,12]

Studies of this nature demonstrate the relationship between mass transfer and momentum transfer, thus establishing the linear momentum transfer as a reliable impact parameter tag.

In order to quantify the thermal properties of the spectrum of residual nuclei formed in intermediate collisions, it is important to determine the relationship between momentum transfer and excitation energy. This can be done in an ad hoc way by making reasonable assumptions about the correspondence between mass transfer and fission-folding angle in a given reaction.[27] The approximate validity of such assumptions is illustrated definitively via the measurement of neutron multiplicities in

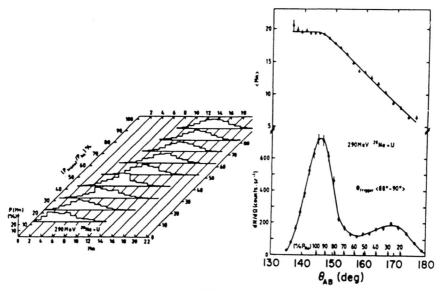

FIGURE 4

(a) Probability distributions of neutron multiplicities as a function of fractional LMT. (b) Lower curve shows inclusive folding-angle distribution; top curve is the absolute average neutron multiplicity at each angle θ_{AB}. From Ref. 28.

coincidence with LMT-tagged fission-fission events. In Fig. 4(a) and (b) are shown data obtained by Galin, Hilscher and co-workers[28] in which a 4π neutron multiplicity meter is used in coincidence with fission fragments from the bombardment of E/A = 14.5 MeV ^{20}Ne + ^{238}U at VICKSI. Fig. 6(a) shows the measured relative neutron multiplicities for incremental momentum-transfer bins ($p_{\parallel}/p_{beam}$). Fig. 6(b) plots the inclusive fission fragment angular correlation distribution along with the absolute multiplicity as a function of θ_{AB} and momentum transfer.

The results show a strong correlation between transferred momentum and excitation energy deposition (as reflected by the number of evaporated neutrons). Complete fusion processes ($p_{\parallel}/p_{beam}$ = 1) exhibit the maximum multiplicities, consistent with values expected on the basis of statistical evaporation from a fusion-like product. With decreasing momentum transfer, the average neutron multiplicity decreases monotonically, approaching values expected for nearly cold fission for θ_{AB} = 180° (i.e. zero LMT). Thus, the link between LMT and excitation energy seems firmly established by these data.[28,29]

For projectile energies up to E/A ≈ 30-40 MeV precompound nucleon emission appears to account for most of the missing momentum in fusion-like reactions between complex nuclei. Similarly, the subsequent cooling of the hot residual nucleus proceeds primarily via sequential light-particle evaporation. Beyond this energy, however, the emission of complex fragments (3 ≤ Z ≤ 20) becomes increasingly probable. Again, the fission angular correlation technique has proven useful in clarifying the complications introduced by this new reaction channel--which can be viewed as a signature of very hot nuclear matter (E* > 100 MeV).

In Figs. 5(a) and (b) the LMT (folding-angle) distributions and corresponding fragment energy spectra are shown for the E/A = 35 MeV ^{14}N + ^{232}Th reaction.[30] Here, the multiplicity of complex fragments from fusion-like reactions can be estimated to be $\langle M_{IMF}\rangle$ ≈ 0.6. Distributions for both forward- and backward-angle IMF emission are shown. Comparison with the inclusive folding-angle distribution demonstrates the strong kinematic shifts imposed by IMF emission. The momentum transfer distributions for θ_{IMF} = 51° emphasize that once forward-angle IMF emission consumes an appreciable fraction of the cross section, the well-defined fusion-like component observed at lower energies must become distinctly perturbed toward larger values of θ_{AB}. Correspondingly, the distortion of the folding-angle distributions created by IMF emission at backward angles serves to complicate attempts to extract complete-fusion cross-section information from inclusive folding-angle data. In this case the

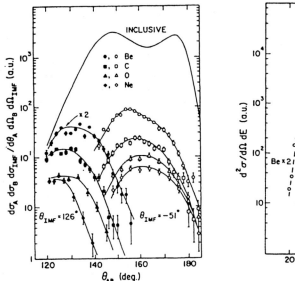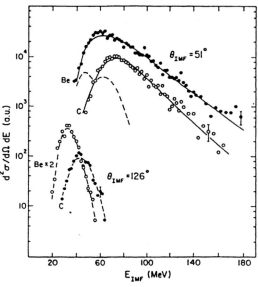

FIGURE 5

Left-hand frame: Fission fragment folding-angle distributions for the E/A = 35 MeV ^{14}N + ^{232}Th reaction in coincidence with Be, C, O and Ne fragments detected at a forward and backward angle. Upper curve is the inclusive θ_{AB} distribution. Right-hand frame: Energy spectra of Be and C fragments in coincidence with angle-correlated fission fragments. Dashed lines represent emission from a fully equilibrated, complete fusion source. Solid lines are based upon a moving two-source fit.

fission-fragment folding angle is pushed forward toward momentum transfer values greater than unity. The basic assumption of the technique to derive complete-fusion cross sections from such data is that all events at the smallest values of θ_{AB} originate from complete fusion followed by binary fission. Obviously, this is not the case once IMF emission is highly probable and values of σ_{CF}/σ_R become increasingly uncertain.

With respect to the source properties of the IMFs, the data of Fig. 8(a) can be analyzed in terms of their missing momentum, p_m. One finds that for forward-emitted fragments, considerable momentum loss is present, corresponding to $p_m/p_0 = 28 \pm 3\%$, nearly independent of fragment Z. In addition, the IMF angular distributions are strongly forward-peaked and their energy spectra exhibit slope temperatures well in excess of those for compound nucleus emission. All of these data are consistent with a non-equilibrium emission mechanism in which considerable precompound nucleon emission occurs prior to or simultaneous with IMF emission.

In contrast, at backward angles the momentum balance is nearly complete, $p_m/p_0 = 95 \pm 5\%$, suggesting equilibrium emission from a complete-fusion source. In addition, the slope temperatures for the backward-angle spectra are consistent

with compound nucleus emission from a source possessing the full beam momentum. Hence, these results demonstrate the presence of both equilibrium and non-equilibrium sources in a single system. Relative to the <u>average</u> excitation energy for this system, however, both sources exhibit significantly <u>higher</u> excitation energies.

As the projectile E/A is increased, it appears that the growth of the non-equilibrium component eventually masks the equilibrium component completely, as seen in similar studies of the E/A = 90 MeV ^{3}He + ^{232}Th system.[31] This suggests that, at least in the threshold region, projectile velocity, rather than total beam energy, is the relevant parameter governing the relative strength of equilibrium and non-equilibrium IMF components. An additional feature of the ^{3}He experiments was that both the missing momentum and its direction were determined. This information yielded information about the time sequence of the various emission processes. Specifically, it was found that precompound light particles were emitted in the beam direction prior to or simultaneously with the intermediate-mass fragments, followed by fission at a later stage.

Finally, a word should be said about

the applicability of the fission LMT tag at energies beyond E/A ≥ 50 MeV. Coincidence studies by Meyer et al.[16] and Warwick et al.[17] with relativistic light- and heavy-ion probes at the LBL Bevalac have demonstrated that at these energies, classical binary fission is observed only for the most peripheral reactions. These measurements show that correlated binary fission events are observed primarily for peripheral interactions ($\theta_{AB} \approx 180°$) and are associated with low multiplicities of light charged particles. For central collisions (high LCP multiplicities), however, correlated fission fragments are not observed. This indicates that at these energies, the violence of the collision is so great and the time scale so rapid, that no residue survives that is capable of undergoing fission. Thus, the complexity of the physics at higher energies is such that the fission-fragment angular correlation technique is limited to the study of peripheral processes.

APPLICATION OF THE TECHNIQUE: INVERSE FISSION REACTIONS

The study of the inverse fission process, or damped (deep-inelastic) collisions, has also benefitted greatly from the use of both fission properties and techniques developed to study fission.[32] Early studies by Wolf et al.[33] used the double-energy, angular-correlation technique to demonstrate that near-barrier damped collisions were indeed binary processes. Vandenbosch and co-workers have also applied our knowledge of low-energy fission very effectively to gain fundamental insights into the properties of damped collisions. For example, by measuring the angular distributions of sequential fission products in Kr-induced reactions on fissionable targets, it was possible to deduce the angular momenta acquired by the target-like fragments from comparison with existing compound-nucleus fission data.[34] This group also took advantage of the evolution of uranium fission mass distributions as a function of excitation energy to gain important information on excitation-energy sharing in damped collisions

As an example of how the techniques developed to study fission-fission correlations can be applied to extract detailed properties of damped collisions, a recent experiment involving the E/A = 8.5 MeV ^{74}Ge + ^{165}Ho reaction will be examined.[36] A major complication encountered in tests of dynamical transport theories of damped reactions[37-39] is the modification of the primary

nuclide distribution due to statistical decay of the excited fragments following scission of the dinuclear complex. Once the binary character of a reaction is confirmed, the reaction kinematics shown in Fig. 1 can be implemented to derive information about the primary masses of the excited fragments from the measured post-evaporation products.[40]

In order to determine primary mass and charge distributions, the ^{74}Ge + ^{165}Ho data were analyzed with the assumption of a two-body primary reaction mechanism followed by isotropic light-particle evaporation from fully equilibrated fragments. The measured fragment angles and PLF time-of-flight for each event completely determine the kinematics of the primary reaction, when averaged over a large number of similar events, thus determining the masses of the primary fragments, A', prior to light-particle evaporation. In addition, the primary (Z') and measured charged distributions are nearly equivalent for this system, as substantiated by statistical decay calculations with the PACE-II Code.[41] Fragment excitation energies can also be derived from the difference between the kinematically reconstructed primary fragment mass and the measured secondary fragment mass, $A_{PLF} = A'_{PLF} - A_{PLF}$, using a statistical decay calculation to reproduce these differences.

In Figure 6 the evolution of the centroids of the nuclide distributions in the N versus Z plane is plotted for successive energy-loss bins up to 180 MeV of energy loss. The squares represent the post-evaporative measured data, open circles are the kinematically-reconstructed primary data, and the solid line is the result of the nucleon exchange transport model[37] for the corresponding energy-loss range.

The experimental primary distributions in Fig. 6 demonstrate that the net transfer of protons from the PLF to the TLF is favored in this reaction; in contrast, the net neutron transfer is small, leading to a weak drift toward mass asymmetry. This behavior is in general agreement with the trends observed in several other inclusive measurements of PLF nuclide distributions for mass-asymmetric projectile target systems.[42,43] Comparison of the centroids of the experimental primary distributions with calculated centroids based on the nucleon exchange transport model reveals a significant disagreement. The model calculations predict very little net proton transfer over nearly the full energy-loss region accompanied by the net pickup of neutrons by the PLF, producing a mass drift toward symmetry. The present results examine the model predictions with experimentally determined primary A' values that do not rely on any assumptions other than that of a binary reaction mechanism and isotropic emission of emitted particles during de-excitation.

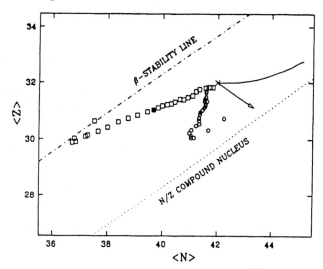

FIGURE 6
Evolution of the centroids of the nuclide distributions in the N-Z plane as a function of energy loss for the E/A = 8.5 MeV ^{74}Ge + ^{165}Ho reaction. Zero energy loss is indicated by the cross (x). Energy damping proceeds sequentially in 4 MeV steps up to 64 MeV (solid points) and in 10 MeV steps from 70 to 180 MeV of energy loss thereafter. Measured distributions are indicated by squares, primary distributions by circles and theoretical predictions by the solid line.

Nonetheless, the results determined here confirm previous conclusions that net nucleon exchange in damped collisions is not adequately accounted for by current transport model calculations.[42,43]

The experiment described above is just one of many examples[32] of how the techniques developed for the study of nuclear fission have been successfully applied to extract detailed information on the properties of damped reactions between heavy nuclei.

SUMMARY

In this review several applications of the fission reaction and fission detection techniques have been described as they relate to the study of low-to-intermediate energy reaction mechanisms. Linear-momentum-transfer studies which employ the fission-fragment angular-correlation technique have yielded a broad overview of the evolution in reaction mechanisms as a function of projectile energy. These range from complete fusion, damped collisions and simple transfer reactions at near-barrier energies through the spectrum of events yielding very hot nuclei, precompound nucleon and complex fragment emission, absorptive breakup, projectile fragmentation, etc. at intermediate energies. Eventually, the disappearance of correlated fission events at relativistic energies signals the onset of highly complex multibody states for which no fissionable residues survive.

More detailed knowledge of the reaction dynamics has been derived from the use of linear momentum transfer as an impact-parameter and excitation-energy gate for coincidence studies with other ejectiles formed in both precompound and statistical decay stages. Coupled with the 4π capabilities of new detector systems, this approach to reaction mechanism studies promises to be highly productive in the next decade.

Similarly, the techniques for the study of fission have been shown to yield second-generation data concerning nucleon and energy exchange in damped collisions. These studies reveal important discrepancies with the predictions of the nucleon exchange model--which has been so successful in accounting for the first-order properties of damped collisions.

ACKNOWLEDGEMENTS

The author wishes to thank the many collaborators who have participated in several of the studies described in this review. In particular, I wish to express my gratitude to Torbjørn Sikkeland, Kris Kwiatkowski, Herbert Breuer, W.G. Meyer, M. Fatyga, C.K. Gelbke and W.G. Lynch for their fundamental contributions at various stages in this research. This work was supported by the US Department of Energy, grant no. DE.FG02-88ER.40404.A000.

REFERENCES

1. O. Hahn and F. Strassman, Naturwissenschaften 27 (1939) 11, 89.

2. L. Meitner and O.R. Frisch, Nature 143 (1939) 239.

3. O.R. Frisch, Nature 143 (1939) 276.

4. R. Vandenbosch and J.R. Huizenga, Nuclear Fission (Academic Press, New York, 1973).

5. V.E. Viola et al., Phys. Rev. C 31 (1985) 155; V.E. Viola, Nucl. and At. Data 1 (1966) 391.

6. W.J. Nicholson and I. Halpern, Phys. Rev. 116 (1959) 175.

7. T. Sikkeland et al., Phys. Rev. C 125 (1962) 1350.

8. T. Sikkeland and V.E. Viola, Proc. 3rd Int. Conf. on Reactions Between Complex Nuclei (UC Press, Asilomar, CA, 1963) p. 232.

9. V.E. Viola et al., Phys. Rev. C 26 (1982) 178.

10. S. Leray, J. de Physique, Colloque C4 47 (1986).

11. V.E. Viola, Nucl. Phys. A471 (1987) 53c.

12. D. Guerreau, Nuclear Matter and Heavy Ion Collisions, in: GANIL Report 89-07 (Les Houches, International School on Nuclear Physics, 1989).

13. H. Oeschler, Workshop on Physics of Intermediate and High-Energy Heavy-Ion Reactions (Krakow, TH Durmstadt Report IKDA-87/37, 1987).

14. M.B. Tsang et al., Phys. Lett. 134B (1984) 169.

15. M. Fatyga et al., Phys. Rev. Lett. 55 (1985) 1376.

16. W.G. Meyer et al., Phys. Rev. C 22, (1980) 179.

17. A.I. Warwick et al., Phys. Rev. C 27 (1983) 1083.

18. F. St. Laurent et al., Nucl. Phys. A422 (1984) 307.

19. M. Fatyga et al., Phys. Rev. C32 (1985) 1496.

20. E.C. Pollacco et al., Nucl. Phys. A488 (1988) 319c.

21. L.W. Woo et al., Phys. Lett. 132B (1983) 283.

22. T.C. Awes et al., Phys. Rev. C24 (1981) 89 and Phys. Rev. Lett. 45 (1980) 513; C.K. Gelbke et al., Phys. Lett. 87B (1979) 43.

23. G.F. Bertsch et al., Phys. Rev. C29 (1984) 673; G.F. Bertsch and S. Das Gupta, Phys. Rep. 160 (1988) 189.

24. J. Aichelin and H. Stöcker, Phys. Lett. B176 (1986) 14.

25. H. Stöcker and W. Greiner, Phys. Rep. 137 (1986) 278.

26. C. Gregoire et al., Nucl. Phys. A471 (1987) 399c.

27. D. Jaquet et al., Nucl. Phys. A445 (1985) 140.

28. J. Galin et al., Zeit. für Physik A331 (1988) 63.

29. U. Janhnke et al., Int. Summer School on Nucl. Phys., Mikołajki, Poland, 1988 (to be published).

30. M. Fatyga et al., Phys. Rev. Lett. 58 (1987) 2529.

31. M. Fatyga et al., Phys. Lett. B185 (1987) 321.

32. W.U. Schröder and J.R. Huizenga, Treatise on Heavy-Ion Science, Vol. 2, Ed. D.A. Bromley (Plenum, New York, 1984) p. 115.

33. K.L. Wolf and C.T. Roche, Proc. Symposium Macroscopic Features of Heavy-Ion Collisions, in: Report ANL/PHY-76, Vol. 1 (Argonne, 1976) p. 115.

34. P. Dyer et al., Phys. Rev. Lett. 39 (1977) 392.

35. R. Vandenbosch et al., Phys. Rev. Lett. 52 (1984) 1964.

36. R. Płaneta et al., Phys. Rev. C39 (1989) 1197.

37. J. Randrup, Nucl. Phys. A307 (1978) 319; A327 (1979) 490; A383 (1982) 468.

38. W. Nörenberg, New Vistas in Nuclear Physics, Ed. P.J. Brussard and J.H. Koch (Plenum, New York, 1986) p. 81.

39. H. Feldmeier, Rep. Prog. Phys. 50 (1987) 1.

40. R. Bock et al., Nucleonika 22 (1977) 529.

41. A. Gavron, Phys. Rev. C21 (1980) 230.

42. R. DeSouza et al., Phys. Rev. C37 (1988) 1783.

43. R. Płaneta et al., Phys. Rev. C⁻ (1988) 195.

A CONTEMPORARY VIEW OF TUNNELING
IN QUANTUM MANY–FERMION SYSTEMS *

J. W. NEGELE

Center for Theoretical Physics
Laboratory for Nuclear Science and Department of Physics
Massachusetts Institute of Technology
Cambridge, Massachusetts 02139 U.S.A.

ABSTRACT

A quantum mean field theory based on the Feynman path integral is applied to nuclear fission. A generalization of the instanton arising in Boson field theory to many Fermions yields a self-consistent determination of the collective path. The role of nodal surfaces and symmetry breaking is discussed and the theory is applied to a pedagogical model and the fission of a nucleus in three dimensions.

I. INTRODUCTION

One of the many challenges posed by nuclear fission is understanding the collective dynamics of the many-Fermion tunneling problem. Developments in the use of path integrals in field theory and many-body theory provide a useful tool for understanding this quantum collective motion. In turn, the rich phenomenology and detailed microscopic studies of nuclear fission have stimulated the generalization of these path integral techniques from the familiar case of instantons in Boson field theory to the case of many-Fermi systems.

The fundamental problem in formulating a microscopic theory of collective motion is to establish a general framework in which the Hamiltonian and the process specify the collective path. Physically, we expect some form of mean-field theory in which the optimal collective path through the classically forbidden region is determined self-consistently. From our experience with the Nilsson model and constrained Hartree-Fock calculations, we know that the arrangement of the nodal structure of single-particle wave functions, and the associated symmetry breaking, will play a crucial role in the dynamics. This physical mean-field picture emerges simply and naturally from path integrals, which provide a powerful and convenient framework for a consistent quantum formulation of the problem. I will briefly re-

view the general theory, details of which may be found in the literature[1-3] and then address an illuminating pedagogical model and the fission of a nucleus in three dimensions.

II MEAN FIELD THEORY

The physical foundation of mean-field theory is the idea that the behavior of each particle is governed by the mean field generated by interactions with all the other particles. This mean field, or equivalently, the one-body density matrix, is the obvious candidate to communicate collective information and we seek a formulation of the quantum many-body problem in which it emerges naturally. A path integral may be expressed in terms of evolution in any convenient complete or overcomplete set of states, and when evaluated in the stationary-phase approximation, yields a path in this space. In this way, a many-body path integral in the space of Boson coherent states yields a self-consistent time-dependent Hartree theory, and a many-Fermion path integral in the space of Slater Determinants yields a time-dependent Hartree-Fock theory. To show the basic idea, I will first review the case of a path integral with a single degree of freedom, and then generalize to the many-body problem.

Path Integral with a Single Degree of Freedom

A path integral deals with the non-commutativity of operators in quantum mechanics by expressing the evolution operator as a product of infinitesimal evolution operators for which non-commutativity may be ignored. Thus, one writes

$$\langle q_f | e^{-iHT} | q_i \rangle$$
$$= \langle q_f | e^{-i\epsilon H} \int dq_n | q_n \rangle \langle q_n | e^{-i\epsilon H} \int dq_{n-1} | q_n - 1 \rangle$$
$$\times \langle q_{n-1} | e^{-i\epsilon H} \cdots \int dq_1 | q_1 \rangle \langle q_1 | e^{-i\epsilon H} | q_i \rangle$$

and

$$(2.1)$$

* This work is supported in part by funds provided by the U. S. Department of Energy (D.O.E.) under contract #DE-AC02-76ER03069.

$$e^{-i\epsilon(T+V)} = e^{-i\epsilon T}\, e^{-i\epsilon V} + \mathcal{O}(\epsilon^2)$$

with the result

$$e^{-iHT} = \int D(q_1\cdots q_n)\, e^{i\epsilon\sum_k\left[\frac{m}{2}\left(\frac{q_{k+1}-q_k}{\epsilon}\right)^2 - V(q_k)\right]}$$

$$\rightarrow \int D\left[q(t)\right] e^{i\int S(q(t))}$$

$$(2.2)$$

where

$$S\left(q(t)\right) = \int_0^T dt\left[\frac{m}{2}\dot{q}(t)^2 - V\left(q(t)\right)\right]$$

is the classical action.

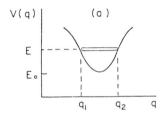

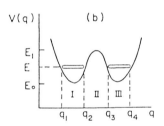

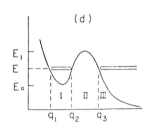

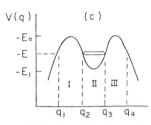

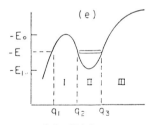

Fig. 1: Sketches of the potentials $V(q)$, periodic trajectories, and turning points as described in the text.

The eigenvalues of the one-dimensional potential sketched in (a) of Fig. 1 are obtained by calculating the poles of the resolvent

$$\mathrm{Tr}\,\frac{1}{E - H + i\eta} = -i\int_0^\infty dT\, e^{iET}\int dq\langle q|e^{-iHT}|q\rangle$$

$$= -i\int_0^\infty dT\, e^{iET}\int dq\int D\left[q(t)\right] e^{iS(q(t))}$$

$$(2.3)$$

where it is understood that each trajectory $q(t)$ is periodic with end point q. The stationary-phase approximation is now applied in turn to each of the three integrals in (2.3). Variation of the trajectory $q(t)$ yields the Euler–Lagrange equations for the stationary solution

$$m\frac{d^2}{dt^2}q_0 = -\nabla(q_1)$$

$$(2.4)$$

and variation of the endpoint yields conservation of p and thus $\dot{q}$ at the endpoint. Finally, stationarity with respect to T yields

$$E = -\frac{\partial S(q_0, T)}{\partial T} = E(T)$$

$$(2.5)$$

where $E(T)$ is the energy of a classical periodic orbit of period T

$$T(E) = \int_{q_1}^{q_2}\sqrt{\frac{m}{2\left(E - V(q)\right)}}\, dq \ .$$

$$(2.6)$$

Summing over all multiples T_n of the fundamental period, we obtain

$$\mathrm{Tr}\,\frac{1}{E - H + i\eta} = A\sum_N f_n\, e^{iW(T_n)}$$

$$(2.7)$$

where

$$W(T_n) = ET_n + \int_0^{T_n}(p\dot{q} - H)\, dt = n\oint p\dot{q}$$

and A and f_n are factors arising from integrating quadratic fluctuations around the stationary points. Ignoring the factor f_n, the geometric series (2.7) yields poles for energies satisfying the quantization condition

$$\oint p\dot{q}\, dt = 2n\pi$$

$$(2.8)$$

for any integer n. Inclusion in f_n of the $\frac{\pi}{2}$ phase at each turning point replaces $2n\pi$ by the Bohr-Sommerfeld condition $(2n + 1)\pi$.

An interesting new feature arises in the analogous treatment of the double well in (b) of Fig. (1). In addition to periodic solutions of the form just discussed in regions I and III, there are stationary points in the complex T plane corresponding to periodic solutions in region II. A picturesque way to think of these solutions is to continue the classical equation of motion (2.4) to imaginary time by replacing (it) by τ, with the result

$$m\frac{d^2}{d\tau^2}q_0 = -\nabla\left(-V(q_0)\right)$$

$$(2.9)$$

507

That is, the trajectory which dominates the action in the stationary-phase sense corresponds to the classical solution in the inverted well. Such solutions were first introduced by Langer[6] in the context of bubble formation and correspond to the so-called instantons,[7,8] or bounces[9] in field theory. These trajectories give rise to the period

$$T_{II}(E) = 2i \int_{q_2}^{q_3} \sqrt{\frac{m}{2\left(V(q)-E\right)}} \, dq \qquad (2.10)$$

and a contribution to the trace of $e^{-W_{II}}$, where

$$W_{II} = 2 \int_{q_2}^{q_3} \sqrt{2m\left(V(q)-E\right)} \, dq \qquad (2.11)$$

A general periodic trajectory in the double well, Fig. 1b, is composed of all possible combinations of periodic orbits in each of the three regions, giving rise to the multiple geometric series.

$$\begin{aligned}
&\mathrm{Tr} \, \frac{1}{E-H+i\eta} \\
&= A \sum_{k\ell m} f_{k\ell m} \, e^{ikW_I(E)-\ell W_{II}(E)+im W_{III}(E)} \\
&= \frac{-2e^{i(W_I+W_{III})} - e^{iW_I} - e^{-W_{II}} - e^{iW_{III}}}{(1+e^{iW_I})(1+e^{iW_{III}}) + e^{-W_{II}}}
\end{aligned} \qquad (2.12)$$

Expansion of the denominator and the relations $\frac{\partial W}{\partial E} = T(E) = \frac{1}{\omega}$ yield the familiar WKB energy splitting

$$E_n = E_n^0 \pm \frac{\omega}{2\pi} e^{-\frac{1}{2}W_{II}} \qquad (2.13)$$

The lifetime of a metastable state is obtained by distorting the right-hand well to extend to the edge of an arbitrarily large normalization box, yielding the potential sketched in Fig. 1d. The lifetime is obtained by evaluating the smoothed level density, defined as the imaginary part of Eq. (2.3) with the infinitesimal η replaced by a finite width γ, such that γ is smaller than any physical width but larger than the level spacing in the normalization box. In this case, we obtain periodic stationary solutions in region I as before, and in lowest approximation these yield the result Eq. (2.8) for the energies of the quasi-stable states. In addition, periodic imaginary-time trajectories are obtained in region II, corresponding to solution of the classical equations of motion in the inverted potential sketched in Fig. 1e. The role of periodic solutions in region III is quite different than for the double well, and one may show that $e^{iW_{III}}$ yields negligibly small contributions.

Thus, the smoothed density of states has poles at complex energies $E_n^0 + \Delta E_n$ satisfying $1+$ $e^{iW_I(E_n^0+\Delta E_n)} = e^{-W_{II}(E_n^0+\Delta E_n)}$ and expansion to first order in ΔE_n yields

$$\Delta E_n = -\frac{i\Gamma_n}{2} \qquad (2.14)$$

where

$$\Gamma_n = 2\frac{\omega(E_n)}{2\pi} \, e^{-W_2(E_n)} \qquad (2.14)$$

Near E_n, the level density is therefore proportional to $\left[(E-E_n)^2 + \left(\frac{\Gamma_n}{2}\right)^2\right]^{-1}$ so that Γ_n is the inverse lifetime of the metastable state. To within the factor of 2 which is presumably corrected by a careful evaluation of all corrections to the stationary-phase approximation, Eq. (2.14) is recognized as the familiar WKB formula for tunneling decay of a metastable state.

This simple example from one-dimensional quantum mechanics turns out to embody all the essential features of our subsequent treatment of the eigenstates of large-amplitude collective motion and tunneling decay of quantum many-body systems.

Many Particles

There are many alternative functional integrals for many-particle systems, each with its own advantages and limitations. The present objective is to obtain mean-field physics in the stationary-phase approximation. Hence, the many-particle Feynman path integral is inappropriate, since it leads yields the classical equations of motion. Rather, we will use overcomplete sets of coherent states and Slater determinants, respectively, for Bosons and Fermions.

The essential idea is most simply displayed for Bosons. Using coherent states $|\phi\rangle = e^{\int d\vec{x}\phi(\vec{x})\hat{\psi}^\dagger(\vec{x})}|0\rangle$ and inserting the completeness relation

$$\int \mathcal{D}[\phi^*(\vec{x}),\phi(\vec{x})] \, e^{-\int dx \, \phi^*(\vec{x})\phi(\vec{x})} |\phi\rangle\langle\phi| = 1 \qquad (2.15)$$

between each factor $e^{-\epsilon H}$ in the evolution operator, we obtain[1]

$$\langle \phi_f|e^{-iHT}|\phi_i\rangle = \int \mathcal{D}\left[\phi^*(\vec{x},t),\phi(\vec{x},t)\right] e^{iS(\phi^*,\phi)} \qquad (2.16)$$

where

$$\begin{aligned}
S(\phi^*,\phi) = \int_0^T dt \int d\vec{x}\, \phi^*(\vec{x},t) \\
\times \left[-\frac{d}{dt} + \frac{\nabla^2}{2m} - \frac{1}{2}\int d\vec{x}\, \phi^*(\vec{x},t)\phi(\vec{x},t)v(\vec{x}-\vec{x})\right]\phi(\vec{x},t)
\end{aligned} \qquad (2.17)$$

plus a boundary term which is not relevant to the present discussion. The action, (2.17), is of the Hartree form and $\phi(x,t)$ has the physical interpretation of the condensate wave function. If we make the stationary-phase approximation and represent the evolution operator by a single optimal stationary trajectory, we obtain the time-dependent Hartree equation for the condensate wave function

$$i\frac{\partial}{\partial t}\phi(\vec{x},t)$$
$$= \left[-\frac{\nabla^2}{2m} + \int d\vec{x}' \, \phi^*(\vec{x}',t)\phi(\vec{x}',t)v(\vec{x}-\vec{x}')\right]\phi(\vec{x},t)$$
$$(2.18)$$

This equation describes the evolution of a drop of liquid ^{4}He in terms of a simple classical, function $\phi(\vec{x},t)$, which for low energy phenomena is nodeless. Although we have not stressed it, all the physics associated with short-range correlations, including the "hole" the repulsive core of the Helium-Helium potential punches in the relative wave function, is subsumed in an effective interaction v. If one could attach repulsive charges of arbitrary strength to each Helium atom, one could generate a fission problem free of any of the Fermion nodal physics familiar in the nuclear case, and the bounce solution would smoothly evolve from a single Helium drop to two separated fragments.

The analogous result for Fermions is obtained economically using the completeness relation in the space of Slater determinants

$$\prod_{k,j}\int \mathcal{D}[\phi_k^*(\vec{x})\phi_j(\vec{x})]\,\delta\left(\int d\vec{x}\phi_k^*(\vec{x})\phi_j(\vec{x}) - \delta_{kj}\right)$$
$$\times \mathcal{N}|\phi_1\phi_2\cdots\phi_N\rangle\langle\phi_1\phi_2\cdots\phi_N| = 1$$
$$(2.19)$$

where $|\phi_1\phi_2\cdots\phi_N\rangle$ denotes a Slater determinant composed of single-particle functions $\phi_1\cdots\phi_N$ and $\mathcal{N}$ is an irrelevant normalization factor.[1,10] The evolution operator becomes

$$\langle\Phi_f|e^{-iHT}|\Phi_i\rangle = \int \mathcal{D}[\phi_1^*\cdots\phi_N^*\phi_1\cdots\phi_N]\prod_{kj}$$
$$\times \delta\left(\int dx\,\phi_k^*(\vec{x},t)\phi_j(\vec{x},t) - \delta_{kj}\right)e^{iS(\phi^*\phi)}$$
$$(2.20)$$

where the action is

$$S(\phi^*\phi) = \int_0^T dt\left[\int dx\sum_k \phi_k^*(\vec{x},t)i\frac{d}{dt}\phi(\vec{x},t) - \mathcal{H}(\phi^*,\phi)\right]$$
$$(2.21)$$

and the Hartree Fock energy functional is defined

$$\mathcal{H}(\phi^*,\phi) = \sum_k\int d\vec{x}\phi_k^*(x)\frac{-\nabla^2}{2m}\phi_k(x)$$
$$+ \frac{1}{2}\sum_{k,j}\int d\vec{x}\,d\vec{x}'\left[\phi_k^*(\vec{x},t)\phi_j^*(\vec{x}',t)v(\vec{x}-\vec{x}')\right.$$
$$\left.\times\left\{\phi_k(\vec{x},t)\phi_j(\vec{x}',t) - \phi_k(\vec{x}',t)\phi_j(\vec{x},t)\right\}\right].$$
$$(2.22)$$

Note that the action (2.21) has the form of a classical field theory[11] with conjugate variables $i\phi_k^*$ and ϕ_k

$$\frac{\partial}{\partial t}\phi_k = \frac{\partial\mathcal{H}}{\partial(i\phi_k^*)} \qquad \frac{\partial}{\partial t}(i\phi_k^*) = -\frac{\partial\mathcal{H}}{\partial\phi_k} \qquad (2.23)$$

so that we might naively expect the results for one degree of freedom to be generalized with $q \to \phi_k$, $p \to i\phi_k^*$.

Application of the stationary-phase approximation to $S(\phi^*\phi)$ with the orthonormality constraint in (2.20) enforced by Lagrange multipliers yields the following four-dimensional generalization of the usual three-dimensional Hartree-Fock problem

$$\left[i\frac{\partial}{\partial t} + \frac{\nabla^2}{2m} - \int d\vec{x}'\sum_k \phi_k^*(\vec{x}',t)\phi_k(\vec{x}',t)v(\vec{x},\vec{x}') + \text{exch}\right]$$
$$\times \phi_j(\vec{x},t) = \lambda_j\phi_j(\vec{x},t)$$
$$(2.24)$$

with the boundary conditions that the $\phi_k(\vec{x},t)$ vanish on the spatial boundary and are periodic with period T. Evaluating Eq. (2.20) using the periodic solutions to Eq. (2.24) yields the stationary phase result

$$Tr\frac{1}{E-H+i\zeta} \propto \int_0^\infty dT\,e^{i[ET+S(T)]} \equiv \int_0^\infty dT\,e^{iW(T)}$$
$$(2.25)$$

where $S(T)$ is the action $S[\phi*,\phi]$, Eq. (2.21), evaluated with the periodic solutions of period T. The stationary-phase approximation to the T integral in Eq. (2.25) is performed precisely as in Eq. (2.17) for the one-dimensional problem, with the result that

$$Tr\frac{1}{E-H+i\zeta} \approx \frac{e^{iW(T_0)}}{1-e^{iW(T_0)}} \qquad (2.26)$$

yielding the quantization condition

$$W(T_0) = \sum_k i\int dx\int_0^T dt\phi_k^*(x,t)\frac{\partial}{\partial t}\phi_k(x,t) = n2\pi$$
$$(2.27)$$

As expected, this quantization condition has the structure of (2.8), with q,p replaced by $i\phi_k^*$ and ϕ_k.

The problem of barrier penetration can also be treated analogously to the one-dimensional example in section 3.1. The first step is to continue from real time to imaginary time. As before, we let $it \to \tau$ and it is convenient to use a symmetric time interval $(T/2, -T/2)$. One then finds[3] that the single-particle wave function $\phi_k(\vec{x}, t) \to \tilde{\phi}_k(\vec{x}, \tau) \equiv \phi_k(\vec{x}, t = \frac{\tau}{i})$ which is purely real. The proper identification of the adjoint wave functions for analytic continuation is $\phi_k(\vec{x}, t^*)^* \to \tilde{\phi}_k(\vec{x}, -\tau)$. Note that the replacement $\phi^*(t)\phi(t)$ by $\tilde{\phi}(-\tau)\phi(\tau)$ systematically incorporates necessary physical properties, such as maintaining normalization of the density, and cancelling time-dependent factors of the form $\tilde{\phi}_k(\vec{x}, \tau) = e^{\lambda \tau} \phi_k(x)$.

The action, Eq. (2.21), thus becomes

$$
\tilde{S}[\tilde{\phi}(-\tau), \tilde{\phi}(\tau)]
$$

$$
= \int d\tau \left[\int d\vec{x} \sum_k \tilde{\phi}_k(\vec{x}, -\tau) [-\frac{\partial}{\partial \tau} + \frac{\nabla^2}{2m}] \tilde{\phi}_k(\vec{x}, \tau) \right.
$$

$$
- \frac{1}{2} \int \int d\vec{x} d\vec{x}' \tilde{\phi}_k(\vec{x}, -\tau) \tilde{\phi}_j(\vec{x}', -\tau) v(\vec{x} - \vec{x}')
$$

$$
\left. \times \{ \tilde{\phi}_k(\vec{x}, \tau) \tilde{\phi}_j(\vec{x}', \tau) - \tilde{\phi}_k(\vec{x}', \tau) \tilde{\phi}_j(\vec{x}, \tau) \} \right]
$$

$$(2.28)$$

To see the analog to the inverted potential (2.9) it is useful to transform from the conjugate variables ϕ^* and ϕ to time-even and time-odd variables which correspond to coordinates and moments. We will seek to express the problem in the general form of a Lagrangian with a position-dependent mass[12]:

$$
L = \frac{1}{2} M(Q) \dot{Q}^2 - V(Q) \tag{2.29a}
$$

so that

$$
P = \frac{\partial L}{\partial \dot{Q}} = M(Q) \dot{Q} \tag{2.29b}
$$

$$
H = P\dot{Q} - L = \frac{P^2}{2M(Q)} + V(Q) \tag{2.29c}
$$

and thus

$$
L = P\dot{Q} - P \frac{1}{2M(Q)} P - V(Q) \tag{2.29d}
$$

Now, consider the real time action (2.21), neglecting exchange terms for convenience, and change variables[3] such that

$$
\phi_k(\vec{x}, t) = \sqrt{\rho_k(\vec{x}, t)} e^{i\chi_k(\vec{x}, t)} \tag{2.30}
$$

where $\rho(\vec{x}, t) = \rho(\vec{x}, -t)$ and $\chi(\vec{x}, t) = -\chi(\vec{x}, -t)$. Then, the action may be written

$$
S = \int dt \left[i \sum_k \phi_k^* \dot{\phi}_k - \mathcal{H}(\phi_k^*, \phi_k) \right]
$$

$$
= \int dt \int d\vec{x} \sum_k \left[\chi_k \frac{\partial}{\partial t} \rho_k - \frac{1}{2m} \rho_k (\nabla \chi_k)^2 \right] - V(\rho_k)
$$

$$(2.31)$$

where

$$
V(\rho_k) = H\left(\sqrt{\rho_k}, \sqrt{\rho_k} \right)
$$

that is, $V(\rho_k)$ is the Hartree-Fock energy functional Eq. (2.5) with a time-even determinant composed of real wave functions $\sqrt{\rho_k}$. The form of Eq. (2.31) is completely analogous to Eq. (2.29) where χ_k corresponds a to momentum, ρ_k corresponds to a coordinate, $\overleftarrow{\nabla} \frac{\rho}{2m} \overrightarrow{\nabla}$ is the inverse coordinate - dependent mass parameter and the potential is given by the HF energy functional.

In the imaginary-time case, the appropriate change of variables is

$$
\tilde{\phi}_k(\vec{x}, \tau) = \sqrt{\tilde{\rho}_k(\vec{x}, \tau)} \, e^{-\tilde{\chi}_k(\vec{x}, \tau)} \tag{2.32}
$$

where

$$
\tilde{\rho}_k(\vec{x}, \tau) \equiv \rho_k \left(\vec{x}, t = \frac{\tau}{i} \right) = \tilde{\rho}_k(\vec{x}, -\tau)
$$

and

$$
\tilde{\chi}_k(\vec{x}, \tau) = -i\chi_k \left(\vec{x}, t = \frac{\tau}{i} \right) = \tilde{\chi}_k(\vec{x}, -\tau)
$$

In this case, the action is

$$
\tilde{S} = - \int d\tau \int d\vec{x} \sum_k \left[\tilde{\chi}_k \frac{\partial}{\partial \tau} \tilde{\rho}_k - \frac{1}{2m} \tilde{\rho}_k \left(\nabla \tilde{\chi}_k^2 \right) + V(\rho_k) \right]
$$

$$(2.33)$$

Comparing Eqs. (2.31) and (2.33) we see that relative to the terms involving χ, $V(\rho)$ undergoes a relative sign change, so that the stationary solutions simply correspond to solution in the inverted potential $V(\rho)$. Note that $V(\rho)$ is the multidimensional HF energy surface, the properties of which are known essentially only through constrained HF calculations.

In one respect, the problem of spontaneous decay in many dimension differs essentially from that in one dimension. Whereas in Fig. 1 parts d and e there was no problem in joining the solutions in the classically allowed and forbidden regions at the classical turning point, to obtain the geometric series, Eq. (2.12), in the multidimensional case the complete wave function composed of single-particle functions $\phi_\kappa(r, t)$ and $\tilde{\phi}_\kappa(r, t)$ must be joined at the classical turning point. Whereas this joining can in fact be demonstrated at the HF minimum, it does not occur in general and one must, therefore, use the alternative dilute instanton gas approximation[1,4,13] to evaluate the premultiplying factor corresponding to $\frac{\omega}{2\pi}$ in Eq. (2.14). With this one deficiency, repetition of the steps leading to Eq. (2.14) yields the following result for the lifetime of a metastable state

$$
\Gamma = \sum_c \lim_{T \to \infty} \Gamma^c(T) \tag{2.34a}
$$

as a sum of particle widths

$$\Gamma^c(T) = \mathcal{K} \, e^{-\int_{-T/2}^{T/2} d\tau \int d\vec{x} \sum_k \tilde{\phi}_k^c(\vec{x},-\tau)\frac{\partial}{\partial\tau}\tilde{\phi}_k^c(\vec{x},\tau)} \quad (2.34b)$$

where $\tilde{\phi}_k^c$ represents a periodic solution to the equation

$$\left[\frac{\partial}{\partial\tau} - \frac{\nabla^2}{2m} + \int d\vec{x}' \sum_k \tilde{\phi}_k(x',\tau)\tilde{\phi}_k(x',\tau)v(\vec{x}-\vec{x}')\right]$$
$$\times \tilde{\phi}_j(\vec{x},\tau) = \lambda_j \tilde{\phi}_j(\vec{x},\tau)$$

$$(2.34c)$$

for a specific fission channel c.

Symmetry Breaking

The truly novel feature of the many-Fermion tunneling problem which sets it apart from familiar problems in field theory is the physics associated with the nodal structure of the wave functions. The bounce solutions entering into vacuum decay and instantons in gauge theory are bosonic and smoothly evolve between classically allowed domains. In contrast, the nodal structure of Fermionic wave functions must rearrange substantially, and accounts for much of the richness of the physics.

The simplest case is in one spatial dimension. The bounce solution to a simple model with four orbitals is shown in Ref. [2]. Whereas the density evolves smoothly through the barrier, the nodes of each of the individual single-particle wave functions are substantially rearranged. At the initial time, the wave functions are simply the zero-, one-, two-, and three-node eigenfunctions of the static HF potential. The elongation to form a neck at the origin at $\tau = 0$ changes the structure, so that the first two wave functions resemble even and odd combinations of nodeless wave functions localized on separate sides of the origin and the last two correspond to even and odd combinations of wave functions located on each side of the origin containing a single node. Hence, a more illuminating representation would be states corresponding to sums and differences of the first two and last two wave functions, in which the total wave function would approximately factorize into two nearly separated subsystems.

In higher dimensions, as the shape of the mean field changes, the relative energies of wave functions with different numbers of nodes in the wide and narrow directions change, and the theory must address the corresponding level crossings.

To be specific, consider a deformed harmonic oscillator potential with the s and p orbital filled to produce a ^{16}O core. As the potential is elongated in the z-direction, an unoccupied state ϕ_{002} with two nodes in the z-direction decreases in energy while the occupied state ϕ_{100} with one node in the x-direction increases in energy, and at some point these levels cross. If the self-consistent field is constrained to be axially and reflection symmetric, these two levels cross without mixing. One possibility is to introduce pairing, in which case the mean field retains its symmetries, the orbitals contribute to the density in the form $a^2|\phi_{100}|^2 + b^2|\phi_{002}|^2$ and the pairing interaction governs the dynamics of tunneling. The other possibility is to allow the mean field to break all symmetries. In this case, near the level crossing the single-particle wave function is some mixture of the two orbitals, the orbitals contribute to the density in the form $|a\phi_{100} + b\phi_{002}|^2$ and the self-consistent broken symmetry mean field governs the dynamics. Before exploring this symmetry breaking in a three-dimensional system, it is illuminating to examine a simple solvable model.

III. A PEDAGOGICAL MODEL

A simple solvable model exhibits the essential features of mean field symmetry breaking.[14] For motivation, we consider a Hartree-like Hamiltonian for a large number of particles which could be in either of two single-particle states of a two-dimensional well: ϕ_x with a node in the x-direction and ϕ_y with a node in the y-direction. Further, we let z_i characterize the deformation of the orbital containing the ith particle. As the single-particle well is elongated in the x-direction, the z_i-increase, the single-particle energy of ϕ_x decreases, and the energy of ϕ_y increases. Since there are only two states in the model, and we are characterizing the deformation of each orbital by the variable z_i, each particle may be represented by the coordinate z_i and a spin. The full Hamiltonian for N distinguishable particles is

$$H = \sum_{i=1}^N \left(-\frac{1}{2}\frac{d^2}{dz^2} + \frac{1}{2}z^2\right)_i + \kappa\left(\sum_{i=1}^N z_i\right)\left(\sum_{i=1}^N \sigma_z(i)\right)$$
$$+ \lambda\left(\sum_{i=1}^N \sigma_x(i)\right)^2 .$$

$$(3.1)$$

The second term represents the dependence of the single-particle energies on the total deformation of the system. The last term is the two-body residual interaction, representing the fact that for either a δ-function interaction or a separable interaction of the form $\sum_i x_i y_i \sum_j x_j y_j$ the following two-body matrix elements are roughly equal $\langle\phi_x\phi_x|v|\phi_z\phi_z\rangle = \langle\phi_x\phi_z|v|\phi_z\phi_x\rangle$. Note that by transforming to collective c.m. variables $z = \sum_{i=1}^N z_i$ and $(N-1)$ relative coordinates, the relative coordinates decouple and one has a single dynamical variable coupled to the total spin. In this sense, the model may be viewed as a generalization of the familiar Lipkin model extended to allow for barrier penetration.[15]

When $\lambda = 0$, the total spin projection $M = \sum_i \sigma_z(i)\rangle$ is a good quantum number, the Hamiltonian is a shifted harmonic oscillator, the wave function is a shifted oscillator state $\phi_i(z, M, \nu) \propto H_\nu\left(\frac{1}{\sqrt{N}}(z - \kappa M N)\right) e^{-\frac{1}{2N}(z-\kappa MN)^2}|M\rangle$, and there are two degenerate ground states: all spin up at $z = \kappa N M$ and all spin down at $z = -\kappa N M$. For non-zero λ, the diagonal matrix elements of the shifted oscillators are supplemented by off-diagonal matrix elements connecting $|M-2, \nu\rangle$ with $|M+2, \nu'\rangle$, the two degenerate ground states are split by tunneling, and the exact solution may be obtained by numerical matrix diagonalization.

The parameters appropriate to nuclear fission have been determined to reproduce a single-particle frequency corresponding to a giant quadrupole frequency of 10 – 15 MeV, a barrier height of 5 MeV and mixing comparable to that obtained in fission with realistic residual interaction matrix elements of the order of 0.2 MeV. Because all N level crossings occur simultaneously, an additional factor of N occurs in the mixing due to coherence, and the strength of the residual interaction has been reduced accordingly. The sign of λ is important in the Hartree solution, and the physical choice is negative λ, corresponding to an attractive residual interaction. The final parameters we use are $N = 40$, $\kappa = 0.00603$ and $\lambda = -0.0005$.

It is instructive to compare two approximations to the exact ground state splitting; the conventional cranking model based on constrained Hartree-Fock solutions and the imaginary time-dependent mean-field approximation derived in the previous section. By the proof of Eq. (6.15) of Ref. [2], one may show that the stationary-phase approximation corresponds to an expansion in $\frac{1}{N}$ for this model and thus should be extremely accurate.

The static mean field solution is obtained in the usual way using a product of single-particle wave functions of the form $\phi_i = \phi(z_i)\binom{\cos\frac{\theta}{2}}{\sin\frac{\theta}{2}}$. Variation yields the single-particle Hamiltonian

$$H_{sp} = -\frac{1}{2}\frac{d^2}{dz^2} + \frac{1}{2}z^2 + \kappa\langle\sigma_z\rangle z + \kappa\langle z\rangle\sigma_z + 2\lambda\langle\sigma_x\rangle\sigma_x + fz \tag{3.2}$$

where f is a constraining field used to constrain $\langle z\rangle$ and $\phi(z)$ is a shifted oscillator. The expectation values of the spin operators in the wave function are $\langle\sigma_z\rangle = N\cos\theta$ and $\langle\sigma_x\rangle = N\sin\theta$, so that $\langle\sigma_x\rangle$ may be expressed in terms of $\langle\sigma_z\rangle$. From the coefficients of σ_x and σ_z in the single-particle Hamiltonian, we conclude that either $\langle\sigma_x\rangle = 0$, in which case all spins are either up or down and there is no symmetry breaking, or else $\langle\sigma_z\rangle = \frac{\kappa\langle z\rangle}{2\lambda}$, corresponding to mixing of the two spin states and symmetry breaking. Using these relations, the energy and $\langle\sigma_x\rangle$ may be expressed as functions of $\langle z\rangle$, with the results shown in Fig. 2. The salient feature is that when the collective variable $\langle z\rangle$ is constrained, the system retains its symmetry for much of the path. Only close to the level crossing is the symmetry broken with a significant expectation value $\langle\sigma_x\rangle \neq 0$. As derived in Ref. [14], the collective energy and cranking inertia in the symmetric regime are

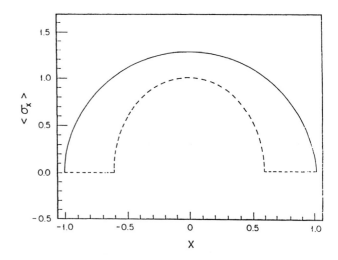

Fig. 2: Collective motion path for the model in constrained mean-field theory (dashed line) and in imaginary-time mean-field theory (solid line).

$$E(\langle z\rangle) = \frac{N}{2} + \frac{\langle z\rangle^2}{2N} - \kappa|\langle z\rangle|N \tag{3.3a}$$
$$I = \kappa^2 N^3$$

and in the broken symmetry regime are

$$E(\langle z\rangle) = \frac{N}{2} + \frac{1}{2}\left(\frac{1}{N} - \frac{\kappa^2}{2|\lambda|}\right)\langle z\rangle^2 + \lambda N^2$$
$$I(\langle z\rangle) = \kappa^2 N^3 - \frac{1}{8\lambda N\left(\frac{4\lambda^2}{\kappa^4 N^2} - \frac{\langle z\rangle^2}{\kappa^2 N^4}\right)} \tag{3.3b}$$

from which the level splitting may be evaluated analytically in the WKB approximation.

The energy splitting in the imaginary-time mean-field theory is given by

$$\Delta E = \frac{\omega}{\pi} e^{-\frac{N}{2}\int_{-T/2}^{T/2} d\tau\langle\phi(-\tau)|\frac{\partial}{\partial\tau}|\phi(\tau)\rangle} \tag{3.4a}$$

where the wave function ϕ is the solution to

$$\left[\frac{\partial}{\partial\tau} - \frac{1}{2}\frac{\partial^2}{\partial z^2} + \frac{1}{2}z^2 + \kappa\langle\sigma_z\rangle_\tau z + \kappa\langle z\rangle_\tau\sigma_z + 2\lambda\langle\sigma_x\rangle_\tau\sigma_x\right]$$
$$\times \phi(z, \tau) = \epsilon\phi(z, \tau) \tag{3.4b}$$

with periodic boundary conditions and $\langle \mathcal{O} \rangle_\tau \equiv \langle \phi(-\tau)|\mathcal{O}|\phi(\tau)\rangle$.

Whereas the penetrability is well-defined and straightforwardly calculable for any energy, the pre-multiplying factor in Eq. 3.4a is more difficult. For the ground state, it is unambiguously defined as the ratio of two determinants in the dilute instanton gas approximation[9] and should be well-approximated by the collective frequency ω in the outer well. We have thus used this oscillator frequency for all energies. As the energy is increased, it is clear physically that other degrees of freedom play increasingly important roles, so this prescription will systematically overestimate the splitting.

The self-consistent path defined by the solution to (3.4b) is shown by the solid line in Fig. 2. Note that in contrast to the constrained case, $\langle \sigma_x \rangle$ is non-zero for the entire trajectory, so that the symmetry is broken for the whole optimal trajectory. In this model, we can improve the static constrained theory appreciably[14] by constraining $\langle \sigma_z \rangle$ instead of $\langle z \rangle$, which generates a path much closer to the optimal path. This constraint effectively grabs hold of the relevant level-crossing degree of freedom from the start. In a realistic fission calculation, however, there is no way to constrain the corresponding single-particle degrees of freedom, so one must necessarily constrain a collective deformation variable analogous to z.

The difference between the optimal path and the static constrained path is dramatically demonstrated by the approximations obtained for level splittings below the barrier. For the ground state splitting, $\Delta E = e^{-12.96}$, the imaginary-time mean field yields $e^{-13.02}$ whereas the constrained mean field yields $e^{-19.5}$. The corresponding results for excited states are equally striking.[14]

IV. FISSION OF ^{32}S IN THREE DIMENSIONS

Finally, I will show the results of a calculation[16] which displays symmetry breaking associated with orbital rearrangement in a nucleus in three dimensions. We calculate the symmetric fission of ^{32}S using a density-dependent interaction with the strength of the Coulomb force increased to produce fission. The collective variable analogous to $\langle z \rangle$ in the previous model is the quadrupole moment. The eighth orbital is the last occupied state and changes from having two nodes in the transverse direction at small deformation to having three nodes in the longitudinal direction at large deformation.

The time-dependent mean field equations are solved as follows.[17] We begin by solving the imaginary-time analog of the RPA equations at the top of the barrier with a constraint on the time average of the quadrupole moment to render the calculation stable.

The period is then successively increased, and for each period the eigenvalue problem (2.33c) is solved iteratively. Since the largest eigenvalue of the evolution operator $e^{-\int_{-T/2}^{T/2} h_{sp}(\tau)d\tau}$ corresponds to the lowest occupied state $\phi_1(-T/2)$, successive application of the evolution operator to an arbitrary state converges to ϕ_1. Higher states are calculated by application of the evolution operator and orthogonalization to all lower states. In this way, the eigenstates $\left\{ \phi_i^{(n+1)} \right\}$ in the potential generated by $\left\{ \phi_i^{(n)} \right\}$ are calculated and iterated to self-consistency. As T is increased, the solution approaches the bounce solution to any desired accuracy.

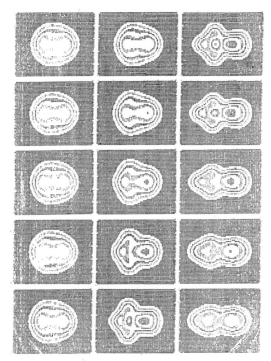

Fig. 3: Contour plots at sequential times of the density integrated over z.

The sequence of shapes through which the nucleus evolves in shown in Fig. 3. The salient feature is the significant symmetry breaking throughout the entire evolution through the barrier, and it is clear that nodal rearrangement is playing a significant role in the dynamics. The similarity between this calculation and the pedagogical model of the last section may be seen by expressing the trajectory by the quadrupole moment Q_2, which characterizes the collective deformation and corresponds to $\langle z^2 \rangle$, and the octupole moment, Q_3, which characterizes the symmetry breaking and corresponds to $\langle \sigma_x \rangle$. The paths for the solution of the imaginary-time mean-field theory and for static mean-field theory with a quadrupole constraint are shown in Fig. 4. The

513

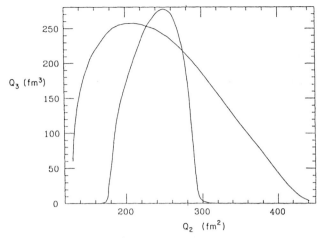

Fig. 4: Collective motion path for the fission of ^{23}S in constrained mean-field theory (dashed line) and in imaginary-time mean-field theory (solid line).

similarity to the paths in Fig. 2 for the spin model is striking. Again the symmetry is broken along the entire optimal path, whereas the symmetry breaking is restricted to a small domain in the immediate vicinity of the level crossing in the constrained theory. Hence, as in the case of the spin model, solving the equations for the optimal path is expected to provide a major quantitative improvement in the theory.

In summary, the quantum mean-field theory which arises naturally from path integrals, self-consistently specifies the optimal collective path, and incorporates the basic physics of nodal rearrangement. It thus provides a microscopic understanding of many key elements of collective dynamics in many-Fermion systems.

ACKNOWLEDGEMENTS

It is a pleasure to acknowledge the essential contributions of George Bertsch, Shimon Levit, Henri Orland, Giovanni Puddu and Rüdiger Wolff to the developments discussed in this talk.

REFERENCES

1. J. W. Negele and H. Orland, *Quantum Many-Particle Systems* (Addison–Wesley, Reading, MA, 1987).

2. J. W. Negele, *Rev. Mod. Phys.* **54** (1982) 947.

3. S. Levit, J. Negele and Z. Paltiel, *Phys. Rev.* **C21** (1980) 1603; **C22** (1980) 1979.

4. H. Reinhardt, *Nucl. Phys.* **A367** (1981) 269.

5. H. Kleinert, *Phys. Lett.* **B69** (1977) 9.

6. J. Langer, *Ann. Phys.* (New York) **54** (1969) 258.

7. A. M. Polyakov, *Nucl. Phys.* **B121** (1977) 429.

8. G. 't Hooft, *Phys. Rev. Lett.* **37** (1976) 8.

9. S. Coleman, *Phys. Rev.* **D15** (1977) 2929.

10. J. P. Blaizot and H. Orland, *Phys. Rev.* **C24** (1981) 1740.

11. A. K. Kerman and S. E. Koonin, *Ann. Phys.* (New York) **100** (1976) 332.

12. H. Tang and J. W. Negele, *Nucl. Phys.* **A406** (1983) 205.

13. J. W. Negele, "Nuclear Structure and Heavy Ion Collisions," Varenna Summer School LXXVII (*Soc. Italiana di Fisica*, Bologna, Italy, 1979).

14. P. Arve, G. F. Bertsch, J. W. Negele and G. Puddu, *Phys. Rev.* **C36** (1987) 2018.

15. H. Lipkin, N. Meshkov and A. Glick, *Nucl. Phys.* **62** (1965) 188.

16. R. Wolff, G. Puddu and J. W. Negele, to be published.

17. G. Puddu and J. Negele, *Phys. Rev.* **C35** (1987) 1007.

COLD FISSION AS A PROBE FOR COMPACT SCISSION CONFIGURATIONS

F. Gönnenwein
Phys. Inst. Univ. Tübingen,
Morgenstelle 14
D-7400 Tübingen, F.R. Germany
7071/296283

B. Börsig
Phys. Inst. Univ. Tübingen,
Morgenstelle 14
D-7400 Tübingen, F.R. Germany
7071/296286

ABSTRACT

Cold Fission is defined to be a process where virtually all of the energy liberated in fission goes into the total kinetic energies of the fragments. The fragments have, therefore, to be formed in their "cold" ground states. Cold Fission may be shown to correspond to compact scission configurations. The process has been studied experimentally for thermal neutron fission of U- and Pu-isotopes, with fragment masses and charges being resolved one-by-one. Cold Fission is indeed observed, but for a limited range of fragment masses only, the heavy mass A_H being centered around $A_H = 132$ u. In a simple model calculation this behaviour is traced back to fragment structure. Surprisingly, even in Cold Fission even and odd mass fragments have comparable yields. This appears to be at variance with the idea of superfluidity being preserved in fission. Charge distributions close to Cold Fission indicate that all of the available phase space is used with constraints, however, being imposed by fragment structure.

INTRODUCTION

Nuclear fission is characterized by a broad distribution of fragment masses and charges. Yet, even for a given mass and/or charge fragmentation, the kinetic and the excitation energies of the fragments are not uniquely fixed. Instead, one again observes distributions, with a typical width (FWHM) for e.g. the total kinetic energy release of 25 MeV. Ever since the discovery of fission it has been a challenge for theory to explain, besides the mean values, the width of mass, charge and energy distributions of fission fragments.

In recent years a series of experiments have been conducted to explore the high energy limit of the distribution of total kinetic fragment energy TKE. Of course, from energy conservation an absolute upper limit for TKE is set by the total energy release in fission, i.e. the Q-value of the reaction under study. However, in the general case, the energy Q will have to be shared by the total kinetic and the excitation energies of the fragments, TKE and TXE, respectively. With Q being settled by the type of reaction and the fragments' masses and charges, a maximum for TKE will correspond to a minimum for TXE. Looking for high TKE events, the question then is how far downwards the minimum of TXE may be pushed close to TXE nil.

An answer may be found from a scission point model illustrated in Fig. 1. The different conceivable scission configurations are parametrized by two almost touching prolate spheroids. Upon deforming the fragment sheroids the Coulomb repulsion potential energy V_C between fragments will decrease, while the energy stored in deforming the fragments V_D will increase. In Fig. 1 the sum of V_C and V_D, the total potential energy of the scission configuration, is called V_P. To conserve energy, V_P has to be smaller than the available energy Q. The difference $(Q - V_P)$ is the energy left to the fissioning system and is displayed in Fig. 1 as the hatched zone "Free Energy". In the simplest case this free energy will just go into the kinetic energy TKE_0 the fragments have upon reaching the scission point, and the internal excitation energy E_0^* of the fragments right at scission. Hence one has

$$Q = V_C + V_D + TKE_0 + E_0^* \ . \qquad (1)$$

Next, one has to realize that the TKE and TXE measured for fragments at infinity is obtained from eq. (1) by rearranging terms:

$$Q = (V_C + TKE_0) + (V_D + E_0^*) = TKE + TXE \ . \ (2)$$

In fact, V_C and V_D will be the main contributions to the observed kinetic and excitation energies of fragments, respectively. The minimum feasible excitation energy as the minimum of the sum $(V_D + E_0^*)$ is read from Fig. 1 to obtain for a scission configuration with vanishing free energy. It corresponds to the most compact scission configuration compatible with energy conservation. This configuration is simple in the sense that one has

515

$$TXE_{min} = V_D \quad \text{and} \quad TKE_{max} = V_C \; , \qquad (3)$$

i.e. both the prescission energy TKE_0 and the internal excitation energy E_0^* vanish, and the experimental quantities TXE and TKE follow directly from the potential energies V_D and V_C at scission, respectively.

The excitation energy TXE being minimal for compact scission shapes, this point in deformation space is denoted as "Cold Fragmentation" in Fig. 1. Evidently, the schematic model having been outlined can neither tell whether the cold fragmentation point is attained at all in fission, nor how large (or better how small) the precise figures for the minimal TXE_{min} as a function of fragment mass and charge might be.

Already in the mid-fifties it has been observed that, for (n,f)-reactions induced by low energy neutrons in ^{233,235}U- and ^{239}Pu-isotopes, fission may proceed with no prompt neutrons being emitted.[1] The probability for no neutron emission is low and does not exceed a few percent for the above actinides. Shortly afterwards it became known that, for the same fissile nuclei, the TKE of fragments from a mass bin centered around the heavy mass 135 u may exhaust nearly all of the available Q-energy.[2] These two experimental findings are obviously complementary to each other, since for TKE approaching Q the fragment nuclei have to be formed close to their ground states at scission and no energy is left for neutron evaporation. This limiting case of fission, viz.

no neutron emission, has been designated "Cold Fission". The above experiments gave a first hint that indeed the cold fragmentation point of the schematic model in Fig. 1 is accessible to a fissioning nucleus and that, moreover, the minimal excitation energy TXE_{min} may fall well behind the neutron binding energy.

The interesting physics that may be learned from studying Cold Fission (CF) was only recognized many years later. Results of a first dedicated CF experiment were published in 1981 by C. Siguarbieux et al.[3] Since then many data pertaining to CF have been taken. The best studied cases so far are thermal neutron fission of ^{233,235}U and ^{239}Pu, and spontaneous fission of ^{252}Cf. It should be stressed that all above fissioning nuclei are of the (e,e) type. The experimental techniques have been pushed to yield besides TKE the masses and, more recently, even the nuclear charges of fragments in CF unambiguously one-by-one. In view of the extremely low yields of CF in the lighter actinides this is considered to be a major technical achievement. More details on the experimental methods may be found in ref.[4]. One should note in passing that CF as studied here in the light actinides U and Pu is closely akin to the high TKE mode in "Bimodal Fission" discovered recently in some heavier actinides centered around ^{258}Fm, ^{260}Md and ^{258,262}No.[5] The relative yields of CF in nuclei showing bimodal fission are rather high. However, the small quantities of nuclei available in the Fm-region and beyond have so far precluded the analysis of finer details of CF aspects in these nuclei.

The present review surveys the experimental results for thermal neutron fission of U- and Pu-isotopes. The experiments have been performed by various groups at the hight flux reactors of the ILL/Grenoble and of Saclay. Some of the more interesting and surprising findings are discussed in terms of simple models.

EXPERIMENTAL RESULTS

The Figs. 2 and 3 show, as a function of fragment mass, experimental TKE data in the high energy limit from two different experiments on ^{233}U(n,f) and ^{235}U(n,f), respectively. For the evaluation of TKE data obtained on the mass separator Lohengrin (ILL)[6] it has been chosen to calculate TKE at a fixed yield level of 10^{-6}/MeV for any given fragment mass ratio A_L/A_H, where the indices L and H stand for the light and heavy fragment, respectively. These TKE values are plotted in Figs. 2 and 3 as squares. It should be noted that very conservatively the uncertainties in the absolute figures for TKE are ± 3 MeV, whereas the relative uncertainties from mass to mass are well below 0.5 MeV. A second set

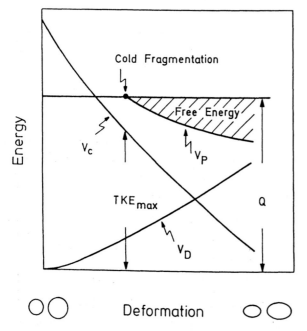

Fig. 1: Schematic Scission Point Model

of TKE data in the figures comes from work with a high resolution back-to-back ionization chamber.[7] The large amount of data having been collected has allowed to trace the high energy tail of the TKE distribution and to find the maximum kinetic energy release TKE_{max} mass by mass. Unfortunately, the pulseheight defects of the energy signals from the ionization chamber are not known very accurately. From auxiliary experiments it appears that for the chamber used the pulseheight defect (PHD) is small. The TKE_{max} values displayed in the Figs. 2 and 3 as thin lines have been obtained without taking a PHD effect into account. Any residual PHD effect would steepen the slope of TKE_{max} versus mass ration A_L/A_H. The TKE data shown are thought to be accurate within about ± 1 MeV. It is noteworthy that from both experiments there are no TKE data close to mass symmetry. This is due to the fact that for symmetric mass splits there are no cold fission events to be observed and, therefore, the symmetric mass region has been excluded from a detailed study.

The full points in the Figs. 2 and 3 indicate the Q-values of the fission reaction as a function of mass fragmentation. For each mass ratio A_L/A_H the charge number ratio Z_L/Z_H maximizing Q has been selected for presentation in the figures. These Q-values are designated as Q_{max} in the figure. Whenever possible the Q-values were calculated from experimental data on nuclide masses.[8] In some cases these data had to be complemented by relying on mass tables based on theory.[8]

The crosses labelled V_{SCI} in Figs. 2 and 3 are the result of a model calculation whose discussion is deferred to the next chapter.

Figure 4 shows the TKE_{max} data obtained for thermal neutron fission of ^{239}Pu. Similar to Figs. 2 and 3 the thin lines display results found with an ionization chamber[7], but in contrast to Figs. 2 and 3 the TKE_{max} values drawn as squares come from a time-of-flight experiment.[3,9] The evaluation scheme being the same, the two experiments differ — apart from the technique and calibration procedure — mainly in the sample size of collected data, with the statistics for the more recent ionization chamber experiments being much superior. The curves identified by Q_{max} and V_{SCI} in Fig. 4 have the same meaning as in Figs. 2 and 3.

Upon comparing in Figs. 2 to 4 the high energy limits of TKE with the respective Q-value as a function of mass, one realizes that, as already pointed out, Cold Fission in the sense of TKE approaching Q, or equivalently TXE approching nil within a few MeV, is not observed for mass divisions close to symmetry. This finding could have been anticipated from earlier work on the kinetic energy dip at mass symmetry. However, one should stress that cold fragmentation understood as a fission process with vanishing small internal excitation energy E_0^* at scission (s. Fig. 1) cannot be outruled on the basis of the present experiments. A new and unexpected feature of nuclear fission showing up in the

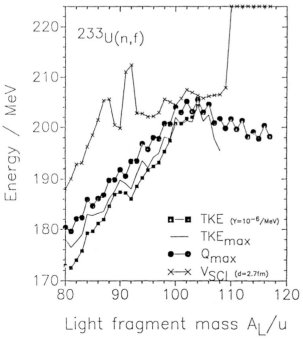

Fig. 2: Cold Fission Energetics for ^{233}U(n,f)

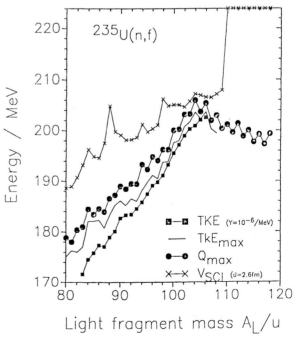

Fig. 3: Cold Fission Energetics for ^{235}U(n,f)

Figs. 2 to 4 is the fact that, for asymmetric fission of the actinides U and Pu studied, Cold Fission is a process being indeed realized for a very broad mass range, with the total excitation energy $TXE = Q - TKE$ left to the fragments being smaller than the neutron binding energy. For a narrow mass interval centered around the heavy fragment mass $A_H = 132u$ one even discovers that, within experimental uncertainty for both TKE_{max} and Q_{max}, the kinetic energy fully exhausts the available energy. In this case TXE virtually vanishes. The process has, therefore, been named "true" Cold Fission.[10] It is this trait which already caught the eye in the early experiments.[2]

The really intriguing feature to be read from the Figs. 2 to 4 is the comparable probability for even and odd fragment masses of being produced in Cold Fission. Starting from an (e,e) compound nucleus and with post-scission neutron emission being excluded, for odd mass fragments at least one proton or neutron pair has to be broken before the fragments separate. For the fission reactions investigated qp-excitations at the saddle point are ruled out, and if superfluidity were to be strictly preserved, only (e,e)-fragments should be present. In fact, the search for a direct manifestation of superfluidity, conjectured to play a role in nuclear fission, had triggered the first studies of Cold Fission.[3] But, even in the case of Cold Fission expected to be most favorable for superfluidity, nucleon pairs are broken.

The next question, then, which may be asked is whether one could differentiate between proton and neutron pairs, and tell from experiment which pairs are broken preferentially. Coming back to the Figs. 2 to 4 it is striking that Q versus fragment mass exhibits a marked odd-even staggering while TKE from the Lohengrin experiments (Figs. 2 and 3) or TKE from the time-of-flight study (Fig. 4) shows a rather smooth dependence on fragment mass. From a closer look at the mass tables, from which the maximal Q-values given in the figures are calculated, it becomes evident that in the large majority of cases even fragment charge numbers Z prevail for the reactions studied Thus, the odd-even staggering of Q is mainly brought about by neutron pairing upon switching between odd and even masses. The smooth dependence of TKE on fragment mass is then readily understood by assuming that at least one neutron pair is always broken. Yet, doubts had been raised whether this ad hoc conjecture is realy compelling.[10] Since then, the high counting statistics reached in the recent ionization chamber measurements has not only had the effect of pushing the high energy limit of TKE still closer to the upper Q-boundary, but also to bring back much of the odd-even structure of Q_{max} into the TKE_{max} values.[7] The hypothesis of preferential neutron pairbreaking is hence put into jeopardy.

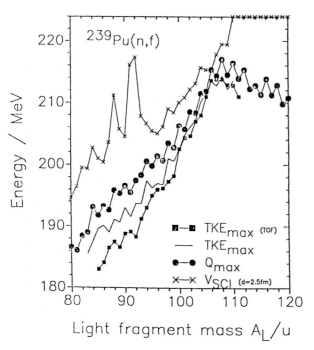

Fig. 4: Cold Fission Energetics for ^{239}Pu(n,f)

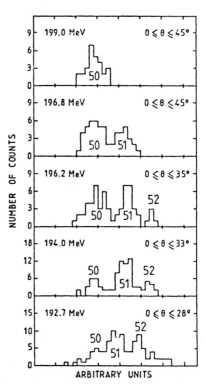

Fig. 5: Charge Distribution for mass ratio $A_L/A_H = 104/132$ in ^{235}U(n,f) at TKE given in insert

Obviously, a clearcut answer to the above question may only come from a full identification of the fragments by mass and by charge. As already indicated, charge measurements on fission fragments are nowadays feasible even for the rare process of Cold Fission. An example is provided in Fig. 5, showing for the reaction ^{235}U(n,f) the charge distribution of the heavy fragment at fixed mass ratio $A_L/A_H = 104/132$ and for narrow bins of TKE close to TKE_{max}.[11] Surprisingly, for this even fragment mass split (o,o)-fragments compete successfully in yield with (e,e)-fragments up to the highest TKE values, until (o,o)-fragments are outruled by their lower Q-value as compared to the charge split $Z_L/Z_H = 42/50$ maximizing Q. This experimental result is a clear indication that, compared to neutron pairs, proton pairs are not favoured concerning their stability against breaking.

More complete data on charge distributions at high TKE have recently been obtained for ^{252}CF(sf)[12], ^{234}U(n,f)[13] and thermal neutron fission of ^{233,235}U and ^{239}Pu[7]. Besides the excellent resolution, it is before all the high counting statistics of the latter experiment having allowed to study in detail the evolution of the charge distribution for given fragment mass upon pushing TKE higher and higher towards the maximum observable TKE_{max}. In the limit TKE_{max} only one charge number for given fragment mass does survive. These charges Z_L of the light fragment are displayed in Fig. 6 as a function of the mass A_L for the reactions studied. Instead of giving Z_L directly, the deviations $\Delta Z = Z_{UCD} - Z_L$ from the unchanged charge $Z_{UCD}/A_L = Z_{CN}/A_{CN}$ (with Z_{CN} and A_{CN} the charge and mass of the compound nucleus, respectively) are plotted as full points. Open circles indicate the charges Z maximizing $Q(Z|A)$ for those masses where the observed Z's are not identical to the Z with maximal Q. As seen from Fig. 6, in the large majority of cases the charges ultimately showing up at TKE_{max} coincide with those predicted for the maximum Q-value Q_{max}. For mass fragmentations where TKE_{max} stays away from Q_{max} by only a few MeV this experimental result is not too astonishing and in case true Cold Fission is indeed attained it merely proves that the charge numbers have been correctly assigned. Nevertheless, the lesson is that in Cold Fission the charge selection is mainly governed by the maximum $Q(Z|A)$ energy release, irrespective of whether proton pairs have to be broken or not. The few exceptions in Fig. 6 to the rule just stated carry interesting information on the fission process. This will become more clear in the next chapter where Cold Fission is discussed in the framework of a scission point model. Finally, in Fig. 6 one should notice that mostly

even charges maximize $Q(Z|A)$. Even charges Z_L of the light fragment are indicated and connected by dashed lines in the figure.

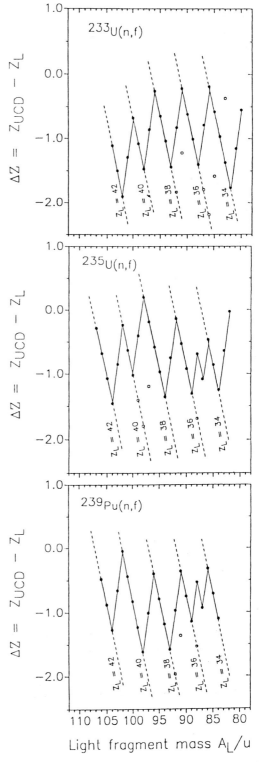

Fig. 6: Ultimate charge at TKE_{max}

DISCUSSION

It was argued in the Introduction that, generally in Cold Fragmentation and particularly in Cold Fission, the potential Coulomb and deformation energies at scission are linked one-to-one to the observable quantities kinetic energy TKE and excitation energy TXE, respectively (s. eq. (3)). We now propose to exploit these simplifying features for discussing the experimental results on Cold Fission having been presented in the preceding chapter.

Referring back to Fig. 1 and recalling that in Cold Fission (CF) virtually all of the available energy Q_{max} is found back as kinetic energy TKE_{max}, it is noted that, if at all, CF will only occur it the deformation energy V_D vanishes at the Cold Fragmentation point shown in the figure. In the limiting case, $TXE_{min} = 0$ and $TKE_{max} = Q_{max}$ obtains. To see how realistic in physical terms the picture underlying Fig. 1 with the particular choice $V_D = 0$ is, one has to set up a more quantitative model. In the spirit of a static scission point model, we imagine the scission configuration to be parametrized by two spheroidal fragments separated by a tip distance d. The tip distance mocks up both, the neck between nascent fragments and the finite surface thickness of nuclei, as taken into account in more sophisticated fission models. It is straightforward to calculate the Coulomb interaction between the two fragment spheroids. While the Coulomb energy is certainly the leading term in the interaction, a nuclear attractive potential should not be neglected for the compact scission shapes considered. Various prescriptions have been given to calculate the nuclear interaction part.[14,15] In a previous report[10] the parametrization of ref.[14] was adopted, while for the present purpose we followed the scheme given in ref.[15]. A very crucial point is to choose the deformations of the fragments corresponding to $V_D = 0$, i.e. the ground state deformations, properly. The deformation data were taken from the tables prepared by Möller and Nix.[16] For the nuclei in question both prolate and oblate ground state deformations are predicted. Though it is questionable whether oblate nuclear shapes come into play in fission, the deformations from the tables[16] were taken at face value. The only free parameter then left is the tip distance d between the two spheroids. From many scission point model studies it emerges that tip distances around $d = 2$ fm are a sensible guess. In fact, one readily realizes that for two touching spheroids with $d = 0$ fm, the sum of the Coulomb and the nuclear energies, which we call the interaction energy V_{SCI} at scission in the following, by far exceeds the available energy Q. These scission configurations are therefore outruled. We then allowed the parameter d to increase, but kept it the same for all mass splits. As soon as for at least one specific mass ratio the interaction energy V_{SCI} became equal to the energy Q, the calculation was stopped.

The results of this model analysis for the interaction energy V_{SCI} at scission are plotted as crosses in the Figs. 2 to 4, with the tip distances found given in the inserts. It is apparent from the figures that most remarkably the general trends of the calculated energies V_{SCI} and the measured kinetic fragment energies TKE_{max} are just mirror images to each other, with the Q_{max}-values as a function of mass serving as the mirror. Indeed, starting from either very asymmetric or symmetric mass ratios both, V_{SCI} and TKE_{max}, converge towards the Q_{max}-value for heavy fragment masses around $A_H = 132u$. For these masses the most compact scission configuration with $V_{SCI} = Q_{max}$ obtains, and with V_{SCI} being fully converted into kinetic energy, true Cold Fission should become observable. For mass combinations outside the above mass bin the fissioning system has to be torn unreasonably far apart in order to bring down V_{SCI} close to Q_{max} and thus avoid violating energy conservation. In reality, in these cases the fragment nuclei will have to be deformed beyond their ground state deformations before reaching the cold fragmentation point (Fig. 1). But since then the deformation energy V_D will not vanish, TKE_{max} will be smaller than Q_{max}. It is thus seen that the simple static model outlined is capable of predicting correctly the mass region of fragments where true Cold Fission might be expected.

A closer inspection of the calculational details shows that it is all-important to include the proper fragment deformations in the model. The correlation between the occurence of CF and prolate deformations in the light fragments was also noted in ref.[17]. For example, it is the pronounced prolate deformation of the light fragment, complementary to the spherical heavy fragment with $A \approx 132u$, which will bring V_{SCI} sufficiently down to make it approach Q_{max} for acceptable values of the parameter d. On the other hand, the strongly oblate deformations predicted for fragments in the vicinity of mass symmetry blow up V_{SCI} and thus inhibit Cold Fission. It may even be ventured to propose the oblate ground state deformations of mass-symmetric fragments to be a suggestive explanation for the kinetic energy dip in this mass region. Therefore, with the above interpretation of Cold Fission studies, the experimental findings may be summarized by stating that, whenever free energy, i.e. phase space, is made available through the interplay of fragment mass (Q-value) and fragment deformation

(V_{SCI}), it is fully made use of in nuclear fission. Incidentally, we may point to a further peculiarity: since in CF one is probing scission configurations pushed as close as possible towards the saddle point in deformation space, the decisive influence of fragment properties on the outcome of CF points to the presence of fragments at an early stage of fission. A similar conclusion may be reached from the analysis of Bimodal Fission.[5]

Coming to the discussion of charge measurements in CF, we have seen in the preceding chapter that, as a rule, the fragment charges at TKE_{max} coincide with those anticipated from the maximal Q-values. However, out of 74 charges determined there are 13 exceptions to this rule, having been marked in Fig. 6 by open circles. Surprisingly, many of these exceptions come for fragments having oblate ground state deformations. In the scission point model outlined an oblate fragment deformation leads to a spike in the interaction energy V_{SCI}. These spikes are to be noticed in the Figs. 2 to 4 not only at mass symmetry, but also for some asymmetric splits where CF could be studied. A good example seems to be provided by ^{239}Pu(n,f): the spikes of V_{SCI} in Fig. 4 for the mass numbers $A_L = 88, 91$ and $92\ u$ correspond exactly to the masses in Fig. 6 marked by open circles. From this observation we may establish the empirical prescription that oblate nuclei are hindered to show up in CF. Obviously, the rule is fully in line with the scission point model inhibiting CF whenever V_{SCI} stays much larger than Q_{max}. Scanning through the U-reactions having been analyzed, one finds spikes in V_{SCI} due to oblate nuclei for $A = 87, 88, 91$ and $92\ u$ in ^{233}U(n,f) and $A = 88$ and $92\ u$ in ^{235}U(n,f). It is only for $A = 88u$ in the former reaction, where Q_{max} overshoots the neighboring Q-values by almost 5 MeV, that the above prescription is violated. Finally, only 5 cases remain unexplained by the stated rules. For all those mass chains there are two different $Q(Z|A)$ differing by less than 1 MeV. There it appears that Z in CF is selected from a balance between deformation properties of the fragment nuclei (strongly prolate deformations are favored) and a Coulomb effect[18] having been advocated to unterstand why mostly the charges tend towards more asymmetric charge splits Z_L/Z_H (s. Fig. 6). The Coulomb effect again invokes the schematic model of Fig. 1. Assuming Q and V_D to remain unchanged when switching for a given mass split from the charge ratio Z_L/Z_H to $(Z_L - 1)/(Z_H + 1)$, the Coulomb energy will be lowered, thereby shifting the Cold Fragmentation point towards more compact fragment shapes. This will have the effect to increase TKE_{max}. Upon searching TKE_{max} events in CF one therefore introduces a bias towards the more asymmetric charge ratio $(Z_L - 1)/(Z_H + 1)$ in comparison to Z_L/Z_H.

In summary, the experiments on fragment charges being ultimately selected in the high energy limit TKE_{max} have disclosed that, besides the predominant influence of the maximum Q-value, the shape structure of the outcoming nuclei and a Coulomb effect come into play. Yet, it should be stressed that, partly also due to experimental difficulties, at the present stage of analysis it is not possible to establish unequivocal rules. For example, from inspecting Fig. 6 one may deduce a rule saying that large charge polarizations with $|\Delta Z| \gtrsim 1.5$ ecu are suppressed in CF. Again, there are also exceptions to this conjecture. The only theory available to be confronted with experiment has considered spontaneous fission of ^{234}U and ^{236}U.[19]. A stepwise increase of Z as a function of fragment mass A with a distinct preference for even Z has been predicted, as observed in the present study. However, apart from these gross features, the detailed comparison is not always satisfactory. This may be due to the difference in excitation energy between the fissioning nuclei from theory and experiment, and to the fact that theory has neglected any fragment deformation.

We would like to point once more to the pronounced odd-even effect in the occurrence of charge numbers at TKE_{max}. Defining the odd-even effect δ_Z as the difference between the number of even Z's counted minus the number of odd Z's, normalized to the sum of these two quantities, one calculates from the data displayed in Fig. 6: $\delta_Z \approx 0.57$ (note that $\delta_Z > 0$ means that even charge splits are favored compared to odd ones, and that for $\delta_Z = 1$ there are only even and no odd charge splits). This figure should be the maximum observable odd-even effect in the U- and Pu-isotopes since, moving away from CF, the chances to break more proton pairs will monotoneously increase and, hence, δ_Z can only decrease. A similar calculation, for the odd-even effect δ_N in the neutron number, yields $\delta_N \approx 0.30$ for the two ^{233}U and ^{235}U(n,f) reactions, while it is $\delta_N = 0.13$ for ^{239}Pu(n,f). Evidently, δ_Z is much larger than δ_N. Odd-even effects as introduced above may also be given for the maximum Q-values. These are $\delta_Z \approx 0.65$ and $\delta_N \approx 0.38$ for the reactions studied. From comparing the figures for δ_Z again the predominant influence of Q_{max} in selecting Z in CF is brought about. Thus it appears justified to correlate the inequality $\delta_Z > \delta_N$ observed from CF data to the similar inequality derived from Q_{max}-values. In the Q_{max}-values, i.e. the fragment ground state masses, favoring even Z more than even N may simply be traced back to the fact that proton pairing energies in medium heavy and heavy nuclei are on the average larger than neutron pairing energies. Thus, the at first sight striking results on fragment charges in Cold Fission are closely connected to facts well known from general nuclear physics.

We now leave the limiting case TKE_{max} discussed so far behind and allow TKE to come down approaching the average fission process. As seen in Fig. 5, in so doing, rather rapidly a charge distribution evolves for any given fragment mass. This is easily understood by once more referring to Fig. 1. Shifting TKE below TKE_{max} is equivalent to increasing the deformation beyond the cold fragmentation point, thereby creating free energy, i.e. prescission kinetic and excitation energy, TKE_0 and E_0^* respectively. Both TKE_0 and E_0^* will increase the phase space available, with the phase space being related to E_0^* depending on nuclear structure through the level density. As soon as TKE has become sufficiently low, the cold deformation point for the charge ratio Z_L/Z_H with the next to maximum Q-value $Q(Z|A)$ may be reached. From here onwards two charges will compete in yield etc. It is interesting to follow this competition. From Fig. 5 one gets the impression that, for the even-mass split shown, the (o,o)-fragments, though definitely unfavored by energy release, keep pace to the (e,e)-fragments. As argued above the higher level density of (o,o)-nuclei as compared to (e,e)-nuclei may offer a qualitative explanation for this observational fact. The same statistical arguments may be applied to understand why in Figs. 2 and 3 the odd-even staggering of Q_{max} as a function of A_L/A_H is not found in the TKE-data at a fixed yield level. In fact, for the (e,e)-compound nuclei studied, Q_{max} is reached for even A fragments by (e,e)-nuclei, while for odd A one has (o,e)- or (e,o)-nuclei. Therefore, to attain the same level density will necessitate a higher excitation energy in even A than in odd A fragments. Assuming that, for a narrow range of masses and energies, the yield of fission fragments is simply governed by the density of final states, equal yields of events should be expected for equal level densities. This then means that at a fixed yield (s. Figs. 2 and 3) even A compared to odd A fragments have to carry a higher excitation energy and, hence, the corresponding TKE will stay farther away from the respective Q_{max}. Stated otherwise, the odd-even staggering of Q_{max} will not show up in TKE-data selected at a fixed yield level.

A final comment should stress that the interpretation of experimental results on CF in terms of a static scission point model cannot explain why CF becomes observable at all. To give quantitative figures for the yields of CF a more sophisticated model is needed. On the other hand, any theory of fission will have to stand the test of CF. For the spontaneous fission of actinides a theory has been worked out by D. Poenaru et al.[21], which besides α- and cluster-emission predicts CF from U- and Pu-isotopes for mass splits with the heavy fragment lying in the mass range $A_H = 130$ to 134 u. Though so far only thermal neutron and not spontaneous CF of these isotopes has been observed, the fragment mass numbers calculated agree well with those found experimentally for true CF. Another model calculation having adressed CF is the microscopic fission theory of J. Berger et al.[22] The potential energy surface of ^{240}Pu as a function of elongation $\langle Q_{20}\rangle$ and necking-in $\langle Q_{40}\rangle$ is displayed in Fig. 7. Two distinct valleys show up, a fission valley V_1 for continuous nuclear shapes and a fusion valley V_2 for separated fragment shapes. The ridge separating the two valleys vanishes for sufficiently elongated shapes. The important point is that the height of the ridge is not prohibitively large and the tunneling probability will hence not be vanishingly small for a fissioning system sloping downwards the fission valley. There will be a finite fission probability all along the ridge. The hatched zone in Fig. 7 indicates the region where, upon leaving the tunnel, scission is thought to take place, i.e. along a scission line. In a dynamical study the relative yield of fission events has been determined along this scission line. The occurence of CF is predicted in fair agreement with experiment for the least feasible elongated scission shapes.

Though the above theory is successful in explaining the yield of high TKE events, the experimental evidence

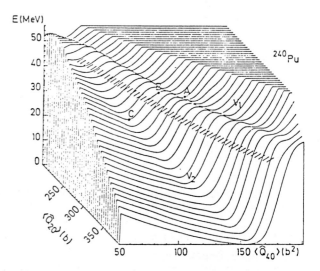

Fig. 7: Potential energy surface of ^{240}Pu (from ref.[22])

522

for pairbreaking in CF is not covered by any theoretical model. But all calculations of the potential energy surface agree that, in the lighter actinides studied here, before reaching a compact scission configuration a barrier has to be overcome for spontaneous or thermal neutron fission. To avoid misunderstandings we underline that this barrier is meant in the sense of Fig. 7 as a ridge separating the fission from the fusion valley. The question then is where pair-breaking does occur: in the fission valley (i.e. before tunnelling) or in the fusion valley (i.e. at the scission line after tunnelling)? Unfortunately, it seems that at least at the moment there is no clearcut answer to this question on the dynamics of the CF process. One may argue in favor of the latter option that all energy has to be concentrated in a collective vibrational mode orthogonal to the fission mode in order to increase the rate of hitting the barrier and hence the tunnelling probability. In this view pairbreaking would have to be suppressed in the fission valley. Nucleon pairs would then have to be broken on the scission line at the exit of the barrier, where the system faces a steep slope towards the bottom of the fusion valley and where, therefore, the adiabaticity condition may be violated. Yet, as already stated, this reasoning should not be construed as a proof. Breaking of proton pairs in the fission valley has been invoked to interpret coherently a large body of nuclear charge data of fission fragments as a function of fissility and fragment kinetic energy.[23] Viewing CF to be just a limiting case of a general phenomenon, it would be more in line with this analysis to assume nucleon pairs to be broken in the fission valley. Anyhow, independent from the details of the dynamics behind pairbreaking, the statistical arguments having been put forward when comparing yields for odd- and even-mass fragments, or (even,even)- and (odd,odd)-nuclei, should remain valid.

CONCLUSION

Cold Fission (CF) from compact scission configurations has been studied with one-by-one mass and charge resolution for thermal neutron fission of ^{233}U, ^{235}U and ^{239}Pu, and for spontaneous fission of ^{252}Cf. In contrast to the heavy Fm, Md and No isotopes, for the above fissioning nuclei there are no CF events for symmetric mass splits. True CF with the kinetic fragment energy exhausting the available energy Q within experimental errors is observed for fragmentations with the heavy fragment mass close to $A_H = 132u$. For more asymmetric splits CF is reached in the somewhat relaxed sense that the excitation energy left to the fragments is not sufficient to evaporate neutrons. These features are interpreted in terms of a static scission point model adapted to the problem at hand. More generally, these distinctive traits may be viewed as the limiting cases of multi-exit channels in fission having been put forward recently.[24] Rather unexpectedly, in CF of (e,e) compound nuclei odd- and even-mass fragmentations compete with each other; similarly, for even mass splits (e,e)- and (o,o)-fragments do show up, i.e. there is no manifestation of superfluidity. The CF studies have revealed that the limit of phase space set by maximum available energy and fragment structure is reached within experimental uncertainty, and that statistical weight factors derived from level densities govern mass and charge yields. The question as to where nucleon pairs are broken in CF cannot be answered unambiguously.

REFERENCES

1. B.C. Diven, H.C. Martin, R.F. Taschek and J. Terrell, Phys. Rev. 101 (1956) 1012

2. J.C.D. Milton and J.S. Fraser, Phys. Rev. Lett. 7 (1961) 67

3. C. Signarbieux, M. Montoya, M. Ribrag, C. Mazur, C. Guet, P. Perrin and M. Maurel, J. Physique Lett. 42 (1981) L 437

4. H.O. Denschlag, Nucl. Sci. and Eng. 94 (1986) 337

5. E.K. Hulet, J.F. Wild, R.J. Dougan, R.W. Lougheed, J. Landrum, A.D. Dougan, M. Schädel, R.L. Hahn, P.A. Baisden, C.M. Henderson, R.J. Dupzyk, K. Sümmerer and G. Bethune, Phys. Rev. Lett. 56 (1986) 313

6. H.-G. Clerc, W. Lang, M. Mutterer, C. Schmitt, J.P. Theobald, U. Quade, K. Rudolph, P. Armbruster, F. Gönnenwein, H. Schrader and D. Engelhardt, Nucl. Phys. A 452 (1986) 277

7. G. Simon, J. Trochon and C. Signarbieux, Proc. "Journées d'Etudes sur la Fission", Arcachon 1986, B. Leroux ed., CENBG 8722, B21

8. A.H. Wapstra, G. Audi and R. Hoekstra, At. Data and Nucl. Data Tables 39 (1988) 281

9. M. Montoya, Z. Phys. A 319 (1984) 219

10. F. Gönnenwein, Proc. "Int. School-Seminar on Heavy Ion Physics", Dubna, USSR, 1986, p 232

11. C. Signarbieux, G. Simon, J. Trochon and F. Brisard, J. Physique Lett. 46 (1985) L 1095

12. C. Budtz-Jørgensen and H.-H. Knitter, Proc. "Seminar on Fission" Pont d'Oye, Belgium 1986, C. Wagemans ed. BLG 586, p 91

13. U. Quade, K. Rudolph, S. Skorka, P. Armbruster, H.-G. Clerc, W. Lang, M. Mutterer, C. Schmitt, J.P. Theobald, F. Gönnenwein, J. Pannicke, H. Schrader, G. Siegert and D. Engelhardt, Nucl. Phys. A 487 (88) 1

14. H.J. Krappe, J.R. Nix and A.J. Sierk, Phys. Rev. C 20 (1979) 992

15. Y.-J. Shi and W.J. Swiatecki, Nucl. Phys. A 464 (1987) 205

16. P. Möller and J.R. Nix, At. Data and Nucl. Data Tables 26 (1981) 165 and Los Alamos Preprint LA-UR-86, 3983, 1986

17. Ch. Straede, C. Budtz-Jørgensen and H.-H. Knitter, Nucl. Phys. A 462 (1987) 85

18. M. Montoya, R.W. Hasse and P. Koczon, Z. Phys. A 325 (1986) 357

19. K. Depta, Hon-ji Wang, J.A. Maruhn, W. Greiner and A. Sandulescu, J. Phys. G.: Nucl. Phys. 14 (1988) 891

20. D.G. Madland and J.R. Nix, Nucl. Phys. A 476 (1988) 1

21. D.N. Poenaru, M.S. Ivascu and W. Greiner, Part. Emission from Nuclei, CRC Press 1989, Vol. III, p 203

22. J.F. Berger, M. Girod and D. Gogny, Nucl. Phys. A 428 (1984) 23 C

23. F. Gönnenwein, XVIIIth Int. Symp. Nucl. Phys. Gaussig/GDR, 1988, to be published

24. U. Brosa, S. Großmann and A. Müller, XVIth Int. Symp. Nucl. Phys. Gaussig/GDR 1986 and Z. Naturf. 41 a (1986) 1341

NUCLEAR-CHARGE AND MASS DISTRIBUTIONS FROM FISSION

Arthur C. Wahl
Department of Chemistry
Washington University
St. Louis, MO 63130
(314)–889–6578

ABSTRACT

Asymmetric division of nuclear charge and mass between the two fission products is much more probable than symmetric division for most fission reactions with excitation energies $<\approx$ 30 MeV. Symmetric mass distributions dominate charged-particle-induced fission of relatively light nuclei and the spontaneous fission of some very heavy nuclei. The average fragment charge to mass-number ratio (Z/A') is greater for light than for heavy fission products, except near symmetry where the reverse is true. The dispersion of independent yields with respect to both Z and A' is approximately Gaussian modulated by nucleon pairing effects. Parameters for empirical models that describe nuclear-charge and mass distributions have been derived for eight fission reactions, and parameters not previously reported for four of these reactions are given in this paper. Model parameters are compared for the eight fission reactions and are found to vary with the mass and atomic numbers of fissioning nuclei and with the average number, $\bar{\nu}$, of prompt neutrons emitted.

INTRODUCTION

This paper reviews the development of knowledge of nuclear-charge and mass distributions from fission and summarizes the current status of the dependence of these distributions on the mass numbers, the atomic numbers, and the excitation energies of the fissioning nuclei and on the average number, $\bar{\nu}$, of prompt neutrons emitted. The probability distributions are usually expressed as yields, and many of the properties of fission-product yields to be discussed are illustrated qualitatively in Fig. 1. The independent yields (IN) of the primary fission products, after prompt neutron emission, are shown as two spiked ridges in the center of the plot, and the dispersion of these yields with respect to both Z and A illustrates the distributions of nuclear charge and mass from fission. The spikes in the distribution result from the probability of formation for even-Z products being greater than that for odd-Z products, an effect associated with proton pairing. The primary products are on the neutron-excess side of beta stability,

Z_A, so they undergo beta decay to form stable end products. The distribution of these stable products, Y(A), shown at the back right of Fig. 1, is the mass-number yield curve. Summation of independent yields over A for each Z gives the atomic-number (charge) yield curve, Y(Z), shown at the back left. The large yields of even-Z elements are apparent as spikes in the distribution.

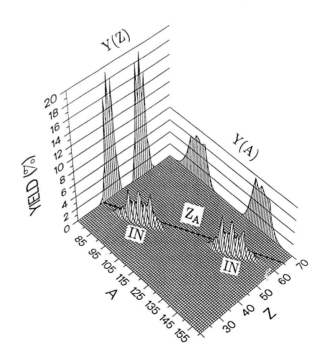

FIG. 1 Independent yields (IN) for thermal-neutron-induced fission of ^{235}U from A'_P model calculations.[1] Sums of IN values over Z for each A give mass-number yields, Y(A), and sums of IN values over A for each Z give atomic-number (charge) yields, Y(Z).

MASS DISTRIBUTION

One of the early observations about low-energy nuclear fission was the asymmetric distribution of fission-product masses, as illustrated by the $Y(A)$ distribution in Fig. 1. Asymmetric mass division is three orders-of-magnitude more probable than symmetric division for many fission reactions. Fission of nuclei with different mass numbers results in changes in position of the light mass peak; the position of the heavy peak remains essentially the same.[2-5]

The principal effect on the mass distribution of varying the excitation energy (E^*) of a fissioning nucleus is to change the probability of symmetric mass division relative to asymmetric division; e.g., excitation of ^{235}U by capture of 14-MeV neutrons, instead of thermal neutrons, increases the relative probability of symmetric mass division by two orders-of-magnitude. For fissioning nuclei with somewhat smaller mass and atomic numbers $(A_F < \approx 230,\ Z_F < \approx 90)$, fission requires considerable excitation energy, and symmetric mass division becomes quite probable resulting in three mass-number yield peaks from fission of ^{227}Ac $(E^* = 16\ MeV)$ and in a single symmetric peak from fission of ^{211}Po $(E^* = 27\ MeV)$.[4] For some nuclei much heavier than ^{235}U $(A_F \geq 258,\ Z_F \geq 100)$ symmetric mass division from spontaneous fission is very probable, possibly because both products can be formed with 50 protons and close to 82 neutrons.[6]

Most of the larger mass-number yields have been measured for a number of fission reactions, and graphical interpolation and extrapolation have been used for estimation of the unmeasured yields.[7] However, there are many fission reactions for which relatively few data exist, and mass-number yields have been estimated for some of these reactions by summation of five Gaussian curves, two complementary pairs for the light and heavy peaks and a single curve for near symmetric fission. Parameters for three curves are derived from the experimental yield data available or are estimated.[8,9]

The empirical A'_P model, to be discussed in the next section, can be considered an extension of the method described above. Mass-number yields are obtained by summation of values from a number of Gaussian curves, which represent the independent-yield distributions for the elements. Both $Y(A)$ and IN values can be estimated by use of the model.[1] Figure 2 shows a plot of results from A'_P model calculations for thermal-neutron-induced fission of ^{241}Pu (symbol P1T). It can be seen that the outer curve of calculated $Y(A)$ values represents well the experimental values shown as squares.

For a single fission reaction, such as thermal-neutron-induced fission of ^{235}U (symbol U5T), there is a broad distribution of fission-product kinetic and excitation energies resulting from varying degrees of deformation of nascent fragments at scission. Fine structure,

associated with shell and pairing effects, appears in the mass distributions from fission events with large fission-product kinetic energies resulting from compact scission configurations with small deformations.[10]

Most low-energy fission reactions give two products plus several neutrons (binary fission). In a small fraction ($\approx 0.2\ \%$) of fission events a light charged particle, most often an alpha particle, is emitted (ternary fission).[11] Ternary fission to give three products of comparable mass does not occur or is extremely rare for low-energy fission.[12,13]

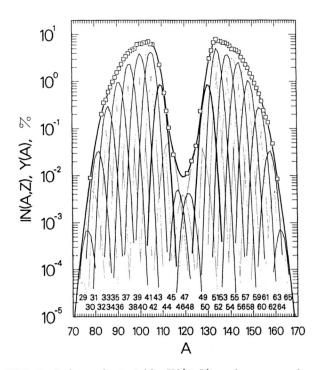

FIG. 2 Independent yields, IN(A,Z), and mass-number yields, $Y(A)$, for thermal-neutron-induced fission of ^{241}Pu. Lines are from A'_P model calculations with parameters given in the Appendix, Table III. Calculated IN values for each Z are connected by lines: dotted for odd Z, continuous for even Z, heavy continuous for $Z = 50$ and 44. Z values are given below the curves inside the border at the bottom. Sums of IN(A,Z) for each A give the calculated $Y(A)$ shown as the heavy outer line, which may be compared to experimental $Y(A)$ shown as □.

NUCLEAR-CHARGE DISTRIBUTION

Independent yields have been measured for only a small fraction of the ≈ 1000 primary fission products, after prompt-neutron emission, for any fission reaction. The small fraction is due both to the very large number of primary products and to the difficulty of yield measurements for the many primary products with very short life-times and small yields.[a] Therefore, knowledge of nuclear-charge distribution has been deduced from systematic trends derived from available data by use of empirical models, which involve simple mathematical functions. The derived functions then allow estimation of unmeasured independent yields.

The earliest models consisted of an assumed universal charge-dispersion curve and various postulates to describe the variation of the maximum in the curve, Z_P, with product mass number.[14] Later it was shown that an empirical Z_P vs. A function could represent data for both light and heavy fission products reasonably well and was about equidistant from Z_A for complementary light and heavy products,[15] and thus approximated predictions of the equal-charge-displacement postulate.[14] Still later, it was shown[16] that Gaussian curves represented data somewhat better than the universal charge-dispersion curve proposed in 1951.[14] As more data became available, the enhancement of yields for even-Z products was deduced,[17] an effect attributed to proton pairing. The abrupt change in magnitude and sign of the charge polarization near $Z = 50$ for U5T has been determined only recently.[18] The change is attributed to the large increase in the yields of fission products with $Z = 50$ compared to those with $Z = 49, 48$, etc.

Most of the early nuclear-charge-distribution data and the comparisons discussed above were for U5T. Methods for the extension of nuclear-charge distribution systematics to other fission reactions have included the estimation of Z_P from values for U5T on the assumptions that the Gaussian width parameter, $\bar{\sigma}_Z$, was the same for all low-energy fission reactions and that the difference between Z_P values for a reaction and that for U5T varied with the differences between Z_F, between A_F, and between $\bar{\nu}$ or E^* values for a fission reaction and the corresponding values for U5T.[19,20]

The current versions of empirical models for nuclear-charge distribution in fission, the Z_P and A'_P models, have been described recently.[1] Gaussian dispersion of yields is assumed for both models, and use is made of the fission-product complementarity relationships: $Z_L + Z_H = Z_F$ and $A'_L + A'_H = A_F$, where

---

[a] Experimental data are obtained by a number of different methods. These include radiochemical and mass-spectrometric measurements, gamma-ray intensity measurements with little or no chemical separation of fission products, measurements with the fission-product-recoil separators LOHENGRIN and HIAWATHA, and measurements with the isotope-separator-on-line systems OSIRIS and SOLIS. The large number (≈ 100) of IN values obtained from measurements with separators gives directly, without use of models, information about nuclear-charge distribution for fission products with the higher yields for several fission reactions. Data from all of the experimental methods have been compiled, evaluated, and averaged for the four most studied fission reactions.[1]

$A' = A + \bar{\nu}_A$, $\bar{\nu}_A$ being the average number of prompt neutrons emitted to form fission products for each mass number. (Subscripts F, H, and L refer, respectively, to a fissioning nucleus and to heavy and light fission products.) Data from thermal-neutron-induced fission of ^{233}U, ^{235}U, and ^{239}Pu (symbols U3T, U5T, and P9T, respectively) and from spontaneous fission of ^{252}Cf (C2S), were used to develop equations and to derive parameters for the models.[1] More independent-yield measurements have been made for these four systems (values for 50 to 230 fission products) than for other fission reactions. Qualitative descriptions of the models follow.

Data for both light and heavy fission products are treated together by the method of least-squares. Gaussian dispersions of yields are modified to include proton- and neutron-pairing effects by multiplication or division of Gaussian yields by $\bar{F}_Z$ and by $\bar{F}_N$, the average even-odd-proton and -neutron factors, respectively.

It is convenient to compare the maxima in dispersion curves, Z_P and A'_P, with values for unchanged-charge division, $Z_{UCD} = A'(Z_F/A_F)$ and $A'_{UCD} = Z(A_F/Z_F)$. The differences, shown in Eqs. 1 and 2, are represented as simple functions.

$$\Delta Z = (Z_P - Z_{UCD})_H = (Z_{UCD} - Z_P)_L \qquad (1)$$

$$\Delta A' = (A'_P - A'_{UCD})_H = (A'_{UCD} - A'_P)_L \qquad (2)$$

The functions consist of connected linear segments, except for $Z_H > 50$, $\Delta A'$ is a function of $ln[Y(Z)]$.[1] (See equation in the notes to Table III in the Appendix.)

Complementary element yields, $Y(Z_L)$ and $Y(Z_H)$, are required to be equal for the A'_P model. $Y(Z_L)$ and $Y(Z_H)$ calculated from the Z_P model are approximately equal, and average values for complementary elements are used. When too few data exist to allow derivation of reliable parameters, e.g., near symmetry, values similar to those derived for U5T are assumed. Uncertainties are large for independent yield estimates from models, varying from $\approx 10\%$ for the largest yields to several orders-of-magnitude for very small yields.[1]

The methods recently described[1] and summarized above are extended to four other fission reactions for which there are relatively few measurements of independent yields (values for 14 to 25 nuclides). These reactions, with symbols given in parentheses, are: thermal-neutron-induced fission of ^{241}Pu (P1T), fast-neutron-induced[b] fission of ^{232}Th (T2F) and of ^{238}U (U8F), and 14-MeV neutron-induced fission of ^{238}U (U8H). The parameters derived for the Z_P and A'_P models are given in the Appendix in Tables II and III, respectively. Because of the paucity of data, some model parameters are

---

[b] The term 'fast neutron' refers to neutrons from fission having approximately the original broad distribution of kinetic energies and an average energy of ≈ 2 MeV.

TABLE I. PARAMETERS DERIVED FOR EQUATION 3

Parameter	α	β	γ	δ	Red. χ^2
Z_P Model[a]					
$\bar{\sigma}_Z$	0.534 ± 0.004	0.016 ± 0.006	-0.007 ± 0.003	0.051 ± 0.015	1.2
ΔZ_{140}	-0.506 ± 0.012	-0.062 ± 0.020	0.019 ± 0.009	0.068 ± 0.038	2.8
$\partial \Delta Z / \partial A'$	-0.011 ± 0.002[b]	(0.0)[c]	(0.0)[c]	(0.0)[c]	2.1
$\overline{F}_Z$	1.269 ± 0.013	-0.016 ± 0.012	(0.0)[c]	-0.143 ± 0.039	1.6
A_P' Model[d]					
$\bar{\sigma}_{A'}$	1.522 ± 0.021	(0.0)[c]	(0.0)[c]	0.156 ± 0.040	2.7
C	1.282 ± 0.018	0.124 ± 0.025	-0.034 ± 0.011	-0.139 ± 0.037	1.4
ZM[e]	55.60 ± 0.10	0.62 ± 0.09	(0.0)[c]	-0.95 ± 0.24	2.7
σ_Y[e]	1.653 ± 0.039	(0.0)[c]	(0.0)[c]	0.476 ± 0.050	2.5

[a] See note *a* for Table II in the Appendix.

[b] Weighted average value.

[c] Assumed value. (Value determined is zero within the calculated uncertainty.)

[d] See note *a* for Table III in the Appendix.

[e] Values dependend on the choice of Z_H for the start of the Gaussian-wing $Y(Z)$ approximation. (See Ref. 1 and the ZM definition in the notes for Table III.)

estimated from values previously determined for other fission reactions,[1] and these estimates are given in the footnotes to Tables II and III. The model parameters are used with and are related to sets of $\bar{\nu}_A(A)$, $Y(A)$, and $Y(Z)$ values that are also derived. These sets for U5T, U3T, P9T, and C2S are given in ref. 1; the sets for P1T, T2F, U8F, and U8H may be obtained from the author on request.[c]

Comparison of the model parameters that could be determined for all eight fission reactions shows that parameter values do vary with the properties of fissioning nuclei. Charge polarization occurs to varying degrees for all eight fission reactions investigated, the average Z/A' ratio being greater for light than for heavy fission

products, except near symmetry where the reverse is true. The width parameters for Gaussian dispersion of yields are not constant, contrary to past assumptions.[7,19-21] Also, the enhancement of yields by nucleon pairing, the even-odd proton and neutron effects, varies considerably for the various fission reactions.

The dependencies of the derived model parameters on the mass and atomic numbers and on the excitation energy of fissioning nuclei are treated by use of an equation similar to those used earlier for estimation of Z_P values.[19,20]

$$P = \alpha + \beta(Z_F - 92) + \gamma(A_F - 236) + \delta(\bar{\nu} - 2.42) \quad (3)$$

P represents the value of the derived model parameter for a fissioning nucleus with atomic and mass numbers Z_F and A_F and emitting $\bar{\nu}$ prompt neutrons. The numbers in Eq. 3 are the corresponding values for U5T. The parameters α, β, γ, and δ, determined from model

[c] Copies of computer files containing the $\bar{\nu}_A(A)$, $Y(A)$, and $Y(Z)$ values may be obtained *via* BITNET or by supplying a small (600 ft) magnetic tape. Printed copies of the files can also be supplied. The author's BITNET address is OGE1715@WUNET.

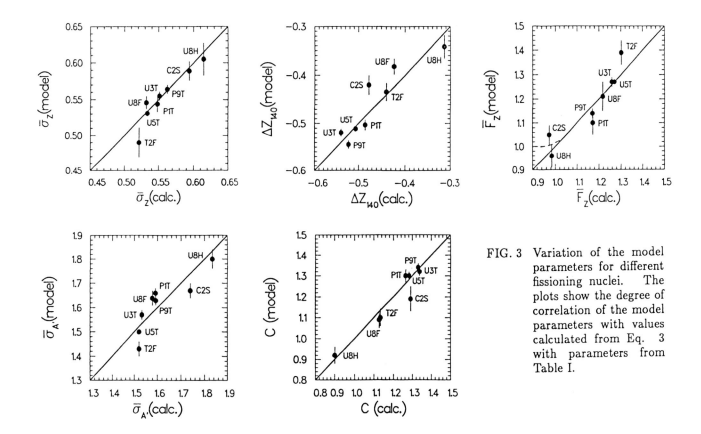

FIG. 3 Variation of the model parameters for different fissioning nuclei. The plots show the degree of correlation of the model parameters with values calculated from Eq. 3 with parameters from Table I.

parameter values for eight fission reactions by least-squares calculations, give the dependence of model parameters on the properties of a fissioning nucleus relative to those for U5T. The parameters derived are listed in Table I. The values of α are similar to the model parameters for U5T.

Figure 3 shows values of model parameters plotted against values calculated from Eq. 3 with parameters from Table I. It can be seen that model parameters do vary for different fission reactions and can be represented approximately by Eq. 3. Table I shows that there is always a dependence (δ) on $\bar{\nu}$ when quantities other than averages can be determined, so $\bar{\nu}$ is an important factor. Also, the β and γ coefficients are of opposite sign, so there is some cancellation of Z_F and A_F effects. Deviations of points from the lines in Fig. 3 show, as do the large reduced χ^2 values listed in Table I, that the dependencies are more complex than the simple representation given by Eq. 3. However, derivation of more complex relationships from the limited information available would be difficult.

CONCLUSIONS

Mass-number distributions are quite well known for a number of fission reactions for which most of the higher yields have been measured, although some estimates are needed especially for the lower yields. Also, there are many fission reactions for which there are relatively few measured yields, and these need to be supplemented by estimated values, such as those obtained from summation of Gaussian curves with parameters derived from the measured yields.

Asymmetric distribution of fission-product masses is much more probable than symmetric division for many fission reactions. Fission of nuclei with different mass numbers results in changes in position of the light mass peak; the position of the heavy peak remains essentially the same. The principal effect on the mass distribution of increasing the excitation energy of a fissioning nucleus is the increase in the probability of symmetric mass division relative to asymmetric division.

Independent yields have been measured for only a small fraction of primary fission products for any fission reaction, so much of the knowledge of nuclear-charge distribution is deduced from systematic trends derived from available data by use of empirical models, which involve simple mathematical functions.

The derived model parameters are different for the various fission reactions investigated. Charge polarization occurs to varying degrees, the average Z/A′ ratio being greater for light than for heavy fission products, except near symmetry where the reverse is true. The width parameters for Gaussian dispersion of yields are not constant, and the enhancement of yields by nucleon pairing, the even-odd proton and neutron effects, varies for different fission reactions. The variation of model parameters depends on the atomic and mass numbers of fissioning nuclei and on $\bar{\nu}$.

Knowledge of nuclear-charge and mass distributions could be improved by additional yield measurements, especially near symmetry and for the many little studied fission reactions. Evaluation of new yield values as well as existing values and derivation of model parameters would increase the understanding of the factors that affect distributions of nuclear charge and mass from fission.

ACKNOWLEDGEMENTS

It is a pleasure for the author to thank A. E. Norris and T. M. Semkow for their helpful comments about this paper.

REFERENCES

1. A. C. WAHL, "Nuclear-Charge Distribution and Delayed Neutron Yields for Thermal-Neutron-Induced Fission of ^{235}U, ^{233}U, ^{239}Pu and for Spontaneous Fission of ^{252}Cf," Atomic Data and Nuclear Data Tables **39**, 1 (1988).

2. C. D. CORYELL and N. SUGARMAN, editors, Radiochemical Studies: The Fission Products, National Nuclear Energy Series, Plutonium Project Record, Div. IV, Vol. 9, McGraw-Hill Book Co. (1951).

3. S. KATCOFF, "Fission-Product Yields from Neutron-Induced Fission," Nucleonics **18**, No. 11, 201 (1960).

4. A. C. WAHL, "Mass and Charge Distribution in Low-Energy Fission," Physics and Chemistry of Fission, International Atomic Energy Agency, Vienna, 1965, p. 317.

5. K. F. FLYNN, E. P. HORWITZ, C. A. A. BLOOMQUIST, R. F. BARNES, R. K. SJOBLOM, P. R. FIELDS, and L. E. GLENDENIN, "Distribution of Mass in the Spontaneous Fission of ^{256}Fm," Phys. Rev. C **5**, 1725 (1972).

6. E. K. HULET, J. F. WILD, R. J. DOUGAN, R. W. LOUGHEED, J. H. LANDRUM, A. D. DOUGAN, M. SCHÄDEL, R. L. HAHN, P. A. BAISDEN, C. M. HENDERSON, R. J. DUPZYK, K. SÜMMERER, and G. R. BETHUNE, "Bimodal Symmetric Fission Observed in the Heaviest Elements," Phys. Rev. Lett. **56**, 313 (1986).

7. B. F. RIDER, "Compilation of Fission Product Yields," NEDO − 12154 − 3(C), Vallecitos Nuclear Center (1981).

8. A. R. deL. MUSGROVE, J. L. COOK, and G. D. TRIMBLE, "Prediction of Unmeasured Fission Product Yields", Proceedings of the Panel on Fission Product Nuclear Data, Bologna, 1973, IAEA-169, Vol. II, International Atomic Energy Agency, Vienna (1974), p. 163.

9. J. K. DICKENS, "Fission Product Yields for Fast-Neutron Fission of ^{243,244,246,248}Cm," Nucl. Sci. Eng. **96**, 8 (1987).

10. W. LANG, H.-G. CLERC, H. WOHLFARTH, H. SCHRADER, and K.-H. SCHMIDT, "Nuclear Charge and Mass Yields for ^{235}U(n_{th},f) as a Function of the Kinetic Energy of the Fission Products," Nucl. Phys. A **345**, 34 (1980).

11. R. VANDENBOSCH and J. R. HUIZENGA, Nuclear Fission, Academic Press, New York, (1973), pp. 377-380.

12. P. SCHALL, P. HEEG, M. MUTTERER, and J. B. THEOBALD, "On Symmetric Tripartition in the Spontaneous Fission of ^{252}Cf," Phys. Lett. B **191**, 339 (1987).

13. R. H. IYER and J. W. COBBLE, "Evidence of Ternary Fission at Lower Energies," Phys. Rev. Lett. **17**, 541 (1966).

14. L. E. GLENDENIN, C. D. CORYELL, and R. R. EDWARDS, "Distribution of Nuclear Charge in Fission", Paper 52, Ref. 2 (1951), p. 489.

15. A. C. WAHL, "Nuclear Charge Distribution in Fission: Cumulative Yields of Short-Lived Krypton and Xenon Isotopes from Thermal-Neutron Fission of ^{235}U," J. Inorg. Nucl. Chem. **6**, 263 (1958).

16. A. C. WAHL, R. L. FERGUSON, D. R. NETHAWAY, D. E. TROUTNER, and K. WOLFSBERG, "Nuclear-Charge Distribution in Low-Energy Fission," Phys. Rev. **126**, 1112 (1962).

17. A. C. WAHL, A. E. NORRIS, R. A. ROUSE, and J. C. WILLIAMS, "Products from Thermal-neutron-induced Fission of ^{235}U: A Correlation of Radiochemical Charge and Mass Distribution Data," Physics and Chemistry of Fission, International Atomic Energy Agency, Vienna, 1969, p. 813.

18. A. C. WAHL, "Nuclear-charge Distribution Near Symmetry for Thermal-neutron-induced Fission of ^{235}U," Phys. Rev. C **32**, 184 (1985).

19. C. D. CORYELL, M. KAPLAN, and R. D. FINK, "Search for Correlations of Most Probable Nuclear Charge Z_P of Primary Fission Fragments with Composition and Excitation Energy," Can. J. Chem. **39**, 646 (1961).

20. D. R. NETHAWAY, "Variation of Z_P in Fission with Changes in Excitation Energy and Compound Nucleus," UCRL-51538, Lawrence Livermore Laboratory (1974).

21. T. R. ENGLAND and B. F. RIDER, "Status of Fission Yield Evaluations," BNL-51778, Brookhaven National Laboratory, 'NEANDC Specialists Meeting on Yields and Decay Data of Fission Product Nuclides', edited by R. E. Chrien and T. W. Burrows (1983), pp. 33-63.

22. A. SRIVASTAVA and H. O. DENSCHLAG, "Nuclear Charge Distribution in the Reactor Neutron Induced Fission of ^{232}Th: Fractional Cumulative Yields of the Isotopes of Krypton and Xenon," Radiochim. Acta **46**, 17 (1989).

APPENDIX

TABLE II. PARAMETER VALUES FOR THE Z_P MODEL

Parameter[a]	P1T	T2F[b]	U8F	U8H
$\overline{\sigma}_Z$	0.544 ± 0.011	0.490 ± 0.021	0.546 ± 0.009	0.605 ± 0.022
ΔZ_{140}	-0.503 ± 0.011	-0.434 ± 0.018	-0.382 ± 0.016	-0.342 ± 0.024
$\partial \Delta Z / \partial A'$	-0.019 ± 0.003	-0.011 ± 0.007	$(-0.011)^c$	-0.019 ± 0.006
$\overline{F}_Z$	$(1.10)^d$	1.39 ± 0.05	1.21 ± 0.06	$(1.00)^c$
No. of FI data	24	14	18	25
Red. χ^2	1.0	0.8	1.1	1.5

[a] $\overline{\sigma}_Z$ is the average Gaussian width parameter.

ΔZ_{140} is the value of the linear ΔZ function at $A' = 140$; $\Delta Z = Z_P - A'(Z_F/A_F)$.

$\partial \Delta Z / \partial A'$ is the slope of the linear ΔZ function.

$\overline{F}_Z$ is the average proton pairing factor.

$\overline{F}_N$ is the average neutron pairing factor. It is assumed to equal $1 + (1 - \overline{F}_Z)/4$, because the average ratio of $(1 - \overline{F}_Z)/(1 - \overline{F}_N)$ for several fission reactions for which there are considerable data is ≈ 4.[1]

Parameter values used near symmetry, $\overline{\sigma}_{50}$, $\Delta A'_Z$, and ΔZ_{max}, are assumed to be similar to the values determined for U5T;[1] values of 0.35, 0.9, and 0.7, respectively, are used, except for U8H it is assumed that $\overline{\sigma}_{50} = \overline{\sigma}_Z$ and that $\Delta Z_{max} = 0.0$.

[b] Recent analyses of similar data give similar parameter values.[22]

[c] Assumed value.

[d] Value derived from element yields determined from A'_P-model calculations.

TABLE III. PARAMETER VALUES FOR THE A'_P MODEL

Parameter[a]	P1T	T2F	U8F	U8H
$\overline{\sigma}_{A'}$	1.66 ± 0.02	1.43 ± 0.03	1.64 ± 0.03	1.80 ± 0.04
C	1.30 ± 0.03	1.10 ± 0.03	1.09 ± 0.04	0.92 ± 0.04
ZM	56.50 ± 0.16	53.17 ± 0.27	54.55 ± 0.23	53.90 ± 0.17
σ_Y	1.82 ± 0.06	1.93 ± 0.08	1.95 ± 0.06	2.62 ± 0.05
$N(Y_Z)$	1.010	1.018	1.017	0.992
No. of IN data	24	14	18	25
No. of Y(A) data	63	53[b]	64[c]	62
Red. χ^2	0.8	1.1	1.3	1.2

[a] $\overline{\sigma}_{A'}$ is the average Gaussian width parameter.[d]

C is the intercept at $Z = 50$ of the $\Delta A'$ function for $Z \geq 51$.[d]

$$\Delta A'_H(Z > 50) = C + (S/2)\{ln[Y(Z_H + 1)] - ln[Y(Z_H - 1)]\}$$

It is assumed that $S = 0.6$, the rounded average value of 0.64 ± 0.05 for the four most studied fission reactions.[1]

ZM is the Z of the maximum of a Gaussian function with a total area of 50 % that is used to approximate small Y(Z) values on the wings of the Y(Z) vs. Z curve. Wings start at $Z_H = 61$ for P1T and U8H, at $Z_H = 60$ for U8F, and at $Z_H = 59$ for T2F.

σ_Y is the width parameter for the Gaussian curve described above.

$N(Y)_Z$ is the normalization factor applied to achieve $\sum_Z[Y(Z)] = 200$ %.

Parameter values that could not be determined because of the small number of IN values are estimated from values derived for the four most studied fission reactions.[1] (U8H parameter values, for which somewhat different estimates were made, are shown in parentheses.)

$\sigma_{A'}$ for $Z = 50, 49$, and $Z_F/2$ to 48: $\quad \overline{\sigma}_{A'}$, 2.1, 1.4 $\quad$ ($\overline{\sigma}_{A'}$ for all)

$\Delta A'$ for $Z = 50, 49$, and 48: $\quad$ 2.0, 0.65, -0.7 $\quad$ (1.3, 0.75, 0.2)

$\overline{F}_N$ values are from the Z_P model; see notes to Table II.

$\overline{F}_Z$ values for the wing Y(Z) estimates are from the Z_P model; see Table II.

[b] Y(A) for $A = 151$ and 153 are not used because experimental data are not in agreement.

[c] $Y(A) < 10^{-4}$ % are not used.

[d] Irregularities in calculated Y(Z) values are smoothed in the valley, where few data exist, and on the wings, where the method of Y(Z) calculation changes near $Z_H = 60$.[1] (See definition of ZM above.) Changes made preserved normalization, $\sum_Z[Y(Z)] = 200$ %, and are usually less than the calculated error. The nuclear-charge-distribution parameters, $\overline{\sigma}_{A'}$ and C, are then redetermined without variation of Y(Z) values; the new parameter values are changed very little from the original ones and are given in the table above.

BIMODAL FISSION

E. K. Hulet

University of California, Lawrence Livermore National Laboratory
Box 808, *Livermore, CA 94551*
(415) 422-6660

ABSTRACT

In recent years, we have measured the mass and kinetic-energy distributions from the spontaneous fission of ^{258}Fm, ^{259}Md, ^{260}Md, ^{258}No, ^{262}No, and ^{260}[104]. All are observed to fission with a symmetrical division of mass, whereas the total-kinetic-energy (TKE) distributions strongly deviated from the Gaussian shape characteristically found in the fission of all other actinides. When the TKE distributions are resolved into two Gaussians, the constituent peaks lie near 200 and near 233 MeV. We conclude two modes or bimodal fission is occurring in five of the six nuclides studied. Both modes are possible in the same nuclide, but one generally predominates. We also conclude the low-energy but mass-symmetrical mode is likely to extend to far heavier nuclei; while the high-energy mode will be restricted to a smaller region, a region of nuclei defined by the proximity of the fragments to the strong neutron and proton shells in ^{132}Sn.

INTRODUCTION

Some years ago we and others had found a sudden transition to sharply symmetrical mass distributions from neutron-induced and spontaneous fission (SF) of the heaviest fermium isotopes.[1,2,3] Furthermore, the spontaneous fission of ^{258}Fm and ^{259}Fm was characterized by total kinetic energies (TKE) approaching 240 MeV or nearly the Q value of the fission reaction. Elsewhere on the nuclide chart, only the isotopes of the elements Tl through Ac fission with symmetrical mass distributions.[4] On-the-other-hand, asymmetrical (two-humped) mass distributions are a common feature in low-energy-induced fission and spontaneous fission of the actinides until ^{258}Fm is reached. The SF properties of ^{258}Fm and ^{259}Fm are remarkable because of the sudden onset of mass symmetry and the high fragment energies. To determine the range of this behavior, to provide critical tests of theory, and to improve our predictions for heavier and more distant nuclei, it was necessary to extend these fission studies to nuclides with greater atomic and neutron numbers.

Using a variety of experimental techniques that are described elsewhere,[5] we have investigated the mass and kinetic-energy distributions from the SF of ^{258}Fm, ^{259}Md, ^{260}Md, ^{258}No, ^{262}No, and ^{260}[104].[5,6,7] The total number of fission events accumulated for each nuclide ranged from 300 to ~2000. It was not possible to obtain larger numbers because of the necessity to produce these nuclides by heavy-ion reactions with actinide targets. For such reactions, the formation cross sections were often as low as 10 to 20 nb. Another unfavorable factor was the extremely short SF half-lives of three of the isotopes, each of these being 20 ms or less. To measure their fragment energies, instruments were developed especially for this purpose, however, their overall detection efficiencies were low, lying near 5 to 6%. Nevertheless, we were able to obtain accurate fragment energies without large interferences from other nuclides coproduced in the nuclear reaction and that also decayed by SF. From the energies of the coincident fragments, we calculated the sum of both fragment energies (TKE) and the provisional fragment masses on the basis of conserving mass and momentum. In this report, we shall be concerned only with the results and conclusions and refer the reader to the references cited above for additional details.

RESULTS

In Figs. 1 and 2, we show the mass and total-kinetic-energy (TKE) distributions for five of the six nuclides studied. We show in Figs. 3 and 4 the same kinds of distributions for 5-ms ^{262}No, which we recently discovered as the electron-capture daughter of ~4-h ^{262}Lr. A small ^{256}Fm contribution, amounting to at most 13%, was subtracted from the distributions for ^{258}Fm, ^{259}Md, ^{258}No, and ^{260}[104]. The nuclides ^{260}Md and ^{262}No were produced free of ^{256}Fm. Because of the pains we had taken to keep the ^{256}Fm contribution small, there was only a slight impact on any distribution from this background subtraction.

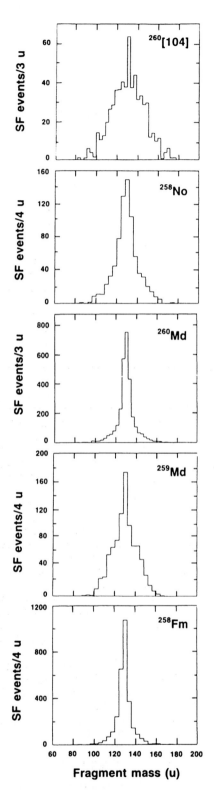

FIG. 1. Provisional mass distributions (no neutron corrections) obtained from correlated fragment energies. The mass bins have been chosen to be slightly different for each nuclide. The distributions are net after subtracting a small ^{256}Fm component.

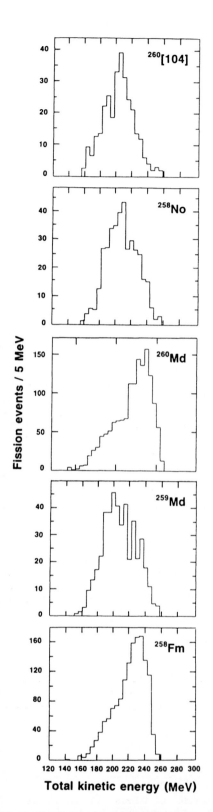

FIG. 2. Provisional total-kinetic-energy (TKE) distributions. A small contribution equivalent to the known amount of ^{256}Fm has been subtracted from all but the the ^{260}Md distribution.

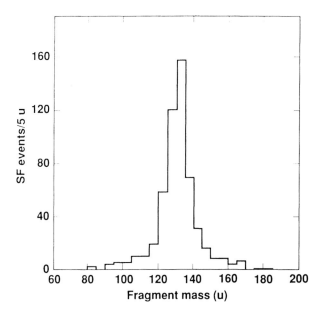

FIG. 3. Provisional mass distribution obtained for 5-ms ^{262}No.

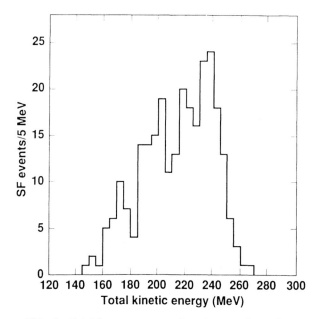

FIG. 4. Total-kinetic-energy distribution from the spontaneous fission of ^{262}No.

Aside from the highly symmetrical mass distributions, we would like to point out a unique feature in the TKE distributions that led us to suggest bimodal fission is occurring in these nuclides. If one is familiar with the TKE distributions measured for other actinide nuclei, it is apparent that five of the six TKE distributions shown here strongly deviate from the Gaussian shape found for lighter actinides. A decided asymmetry is imparted by conspicuous tailing in either energy direction from the central peak. If one inspects these distributions further, it will found that the peak of each distribution is not randomly located along the energy axis, but is positioned very near either 200 or 233 MeV. Although the major peak is at one of these locations in each case, asymmetric tailing from the peaks distributes an appreciable number of events into one or the other these two main energy locations.

When we considered these unusual features, it seemed rather clear that each of the TKE curves, except for ^{260}[104], was a composite of two energy distributions, with each most likely being Gaussian. We then attempted to test this hypothesis by decomposing each of the composite distributions into two Gaussian curves by least-mean-squares fitting. Because the TKE peak for ^{260}[104] appeared to be a single peak and, therefore, a model for the low-energy peak near 200 MeV, we used its full-width-at-half-maximum as a fixed parameter in the Gaussian fitting for the other five nuclides. We resolved each of the gross TKE distributions for ^{258}Fm, ^{258}No, ^{259}Md, ^{260}Md, and ^{262}No into two Gaussian distribution as shown in Figs. 5 and 6. To gauge the accuracy of this procedure, we calculated reduced χ^2 values, which are given in Table I together with the peak centroids and abundances. Because the reduced chi-squares

TABLE I. Parameters obtained from least-mean-squares fitting of two Gaussians to the TKE curves. Reduced χ^2 is a measure of the quality of fit, where values from 0.5 to 1.5 indicate a reasonable probability of a good match.

Nuclide	Low-energy Peak (MeV)	Abundance (%)	High-Energy Peak (MeV)	Abundance (%)	Reduced χ^2
^{258}Fm	205	50	230	50	1.32
^{258}No	204	96	232	4	0.55
^{259}Md	202	88	234	12	0.81
^{260}Md	200	42	235	58	1.10
^{260}[104]	200	100	----	----	0.63
^{262}No	199	53	235	47	0.94

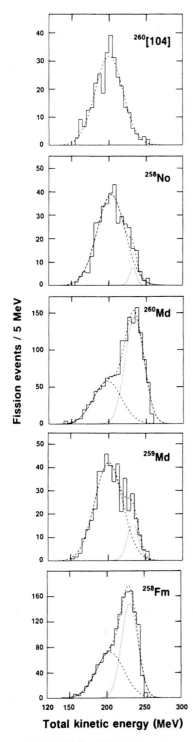

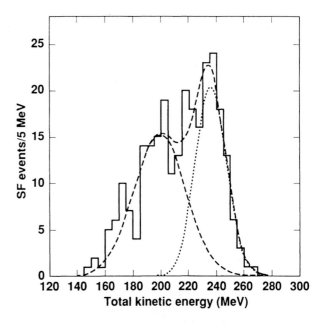

FIG. 5. Unfolding of the asymmetric TKE distributions of Fig. 2 into two Gaussian's by least-mean-squares fitting.

FIG. 6. Same as for Fig. 5 but for ^{262}No.

are near unity, the fitting of two Gaussian functions appears to be a good approximation to the parent distribution. Although the fits to two Gaussians appear to be excellent, this analytical approach should be taken only as suggestive and not as proof.

Returning to the mass distributions for these nuclides, we find that all are symmetrical, unlike those from other actinides. However, the full widths of the mass peaks vary over a range from 7.9 u to 36 u at half-maximum. That for ^{260}[104] is the broadest and is associated with a broad, low-energy TKE distribution. The remainder have a narrow and sharply symmetrical distributions around mass symmetry. The nuclides with the narrowest mass distributions also show a preponderance of high-TKE events. We can demonstrate this obvious feature by sorting events into two bins representing events with TKEs either above or below 220 MeV. This energy was arbitrarily chosen as the dividing line between the low- and high-energy TKE distributions pictured in Figs. 5 and 6. In Fig. 7, we show the mass distributions obtained for five of the nuclides from the events within each of these energy bins. The fission events with high kinetic energies produce fragments lying very close to mass symmetry while the low-energy events produce much broader but still symmetrical distributions. When we choose events with TKEs less than 200 MeV, the mass distributions become even broader and are nearly flat but remain symmetrical, with the exception of ^{258}Fm and ^{259}Md, which revert to asymmetrical distributions. We conclude from these observations that the mass distributions offer an additional feature that is as distinctive as the asymmetrical TKE distributions in pointing to two modes of fission.

CONCLUSIONS

From our observation of distinguishing features in the TKE and mass distributions from five of the six nuclides studied, we suggest there are two different fission processes that produce two modes of fission. In one mode, which we identify as the high-energy mode, the TKE approaches the Q value of the fission reaction and the fragments are closely clustered around mass 129 to 130. Because so much of the available energy has been expended as fragment kinetic energies, this mode has been described as "cold fission" for the lighter actinides for the reason that very little energy is left for internal excitation of the fragments.[8] Our other or low-energy mode is characterized by very broad symmetrical mass and TKE distributions with an average TKE around 200 MeV. The SF properties of ^{260}[104] would appear to typify the low-energy mode, whereas, in the remaining five nuclides, the low-energy mode is a component admixed in varying portions with the high-energy mode. It is these five nuclides that undergo bimodal fission.

From Coulomb repulsion arguments, the configuration for the high-energy mode is required to be compact at the scission point. Additionally, the two fragments must be born with very little deformation energy, again because most of the available energy is removed in the form of the kinetic energy of the fragments. Thus, the fragments are nearly spherical with masses very close to A=130. These properties are the ones known for nuclei near the doubly-closed-shell ^{132}Sn. Indeed, there are theoretical reasons for expecting the mass division to be channeled in the direction of the doubly magic Sn isotopes. There is an emergence of fragment shells between the saddle and scission point that lower the potential-energy path and, thereby, favor the mass division into spherical Sn isotopes near the 82-neutron closed shell.[9,10,11,12] We can then account for the high-energy mode on the basis of the special properties of fragments coming from mass-symmetrical division of nuclei with Z≥100 and N≥156.

An equally plausible explanation for the low-energy mode is not so obvious. We believe it is associated with the dropping of the second fission barrier below the ground state. Both spontaneous fission half-lives and theory indicates the outer fission barrier is disappearing in the region of nuclei we have studied.[13,14,15] Our reason for believing that the disappearance of this outer barrier will cause a reversion to mass symmetry is because theorists have determined that the second or outer fission barrier for mid-actinides is lowered by 0.5 to 2 MeV when shapes from asymmetrical deformations are included in their calculations of potential-energy surfaces (PES).[16] The outer barrier is large and, in some cases, the dominant barrier for many of the lighter actinides. That it favors mass-asymmetrical shapes may well be the

explanation for their asymmetrical mass distributions. When this barrier drops below the ground state, passage through the remaining inner barrier would tend to promote mass-symmetrical division. This is because the PES at the first barrier lies lower for reflection- and mass-symmetrical shapes, being stiff toward any asymmetrical deformations.[15]

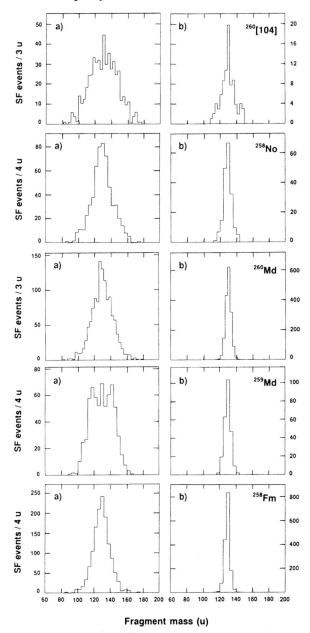

FIG. 7. Mass distributions obtained by sorting fission events according to their total-kinetic energies: (a) for events with TKEs <220 MeV and (b) those with TKEs ≥220 MeV.

If our assumption of the cause of the low-energy mode is correct, we would expect this mass-symmetrical mode to extend to far heavier nuclei, including those still undiscovered. This prediction is based on the fact that all PES calculations show the second barrier not only dropping below the ground state but completely vanishing for all nuclei with $Z \geq 106$. This provides the condition for what we believe is necessary for low-energy, mass-symmetrical fission to prevail. We would expect the fission properties we observe for ^{260}[104] to be typical of nuclides with equal or greater atomic numbers. However, it would not be surprising to find an intrusion of the high-energy mode as the neutron number approaches 164, with the consequent opportunity to divide into fragments with closed 82-neutron shells. We have seen such a propensity in the SF properties of ^{262}No, but it is unknown as to the upward extent in Z that fragment-shell effects will continue to influence the fission process. Nevertheless, we would suggest that the high-energy mode will disappear as rapidly as it appeared, which is when strong fragment shells are no longer available.

The explanations we offer for each mode of bimodal fission are based upon very general features previously established by PES calculations for static deformation. Each mode is derived from the effects of shell structure: one in the parent fissioning nucleus and the other from single-particle couplings in the fragments. For essentially a dynamic process, a surprising aspect is the high degree of qualitative agreement between ours and others experimental findings with the fission properties estimated from static PES. We can only conclude that the dynamic process is adiabatic and that the collective motions are strongly coupled with the intrinsic internal structure of the nucleus during deformation. Without this hypothesis, we would be unable to explain either of the fission modes or the sharp changes in fission properties from the addition of a single nucleon such as from ^{258}Fm to ^{259}Md or ^{259}Md to ^{260}Md. All of these effects appear to approximately track variations in the ground-state Nilsson structure of the individual nuclides, which would, therefore, need to be preserved during dynamic deformation. Static PES derived from the Strutinsky/Nilsson formulation include microscopic shell energies coming from internal structure; hence, the calculated fission barriers reflect much, but not all, of the variations in shell structure from nuclide to nuclide. The ability to include microscopic features in dynamical calculations does not exist yet.

In summary, the fission properties we find for these very heavy isotopes strongly suggest two discrete modes or bimodal nuclear fission. One, the low-energy mode appears to be related to the disappearance of the second fission barrier while the high-energy mode is driven by the opportunity to divide into spherical fragments near doubly-magic ^{132}Sn. Simultaneous occurrence of both modes is likely due to a coincidental alignment of favorable shell structures in the fragments and the fissioning species within the same select group of nuclei.

This research was performed under the auspices of the U.S. Department of Energy by the Lawrence Livermore National Laboratory under Contract No. W-7405-Eng-48.

REFERENCES

1. W. JOHN, E. K. HULET, R. W. LOUGHEED, and J. J. WESOLOWSKI, Phys. Rev. Lett. **27**, 45 (1971).

2. D. C. HOFFMAN, J. B. WILHELMY, J. WEBER, W. R. DANIELS, E. K. HULET, R. W. LOUGHEED, J. H. LANDRUM, J. F. WILD, and R. J. DUPZYK, Phys. Rev. C **21**, 972 (1980).

3. E. K. HULET, R. W. LOUGHEED, J. H. LANDRUM, J. F. WILD, D. C. HOFFMAN, J. WEBER, and J. B. WILHELMY, Phys. Rev. C **21**, 966 (1980).

4. *e.g.* M. G. ITKIS, V. N. OKOLOVICH, A. YA. RUSANOV and G. N. SMIRENKIN, Z. Phys. A **320**, 433 (1985).

5. E. K. HULET, J. F. WILD, R. J. DOUGAN, R. W. LOUGHEED, J. H. LANDRUM. A. D. DOUGAN, P. A. BAISDEN, C. M. HENDERSON, R. J. DUPZYK, R. L. HAHN, M. SCHÄDEL, K SÜMMERER, and G. R. BETHUNE, submitted to Phys. Rev. C (1988).

6. E. K. HULET, J. F. WILD, R. J. DOUGAN, R. W. LOUGHEED, J. H. LANDRUM. A. D. DOUGAN, M. SCHÄDEL, R. L. HAHN, P. A. BAISDEN, C. M. HENDERSON, R. J. DUPZYK, K SÜMMERER, and G. R. BETHUNE, Phys. Rev. Lett. **56**, 313 (1986).

7. R. W. LOUGHEED, E. K. HULET, J. F. WILD, K. J. MOODY, R. J. DOUGAN, C. M. GANNETT, R. A. HENDERSON, D. C. HOFFMAN, and D. M. LEE, Nucl.Chemistry Division Ann. Rept., Lawrence Livermore National Laboratory, Report No. UCAR 10062/88, 1988 (unpublished), p. 135.

8. C. SIGNARBIEUX, M. MONTOYA, M. RIBRAG, C. MAZUR, C. GUET, P. PERRIN, and M. MAUREL, J. Phys. Lettres (Paris) **42**,

L-437 (1981); C. SIGNARBIEUX, G. SIMON, J. TROCHON, and F. BRISARD, J. Phys. Lettres (Paris) **46**, L-1095 (1985).

9. J. R. NIX, Annu. Rev. Nucl. Sci. **22**, 341 (1972).

10. U. MOSEL, J. MARUHN, and W. GREINER, Phys. Lett. **34B**, 587 (1971).

11. U. MOSEL and H. W. SCHMITT, Phys. Rev. C **4**, 2185 (1971).

12. M. G. MUSTAFA, U. MOSEL, and H. W. SCHMITT, Phys. Rev. Lett. **28**, 1536 (1972); M. G. MUSTAFA, U. MOSEL, and H. W. SCHMITT, Phys. Rev. C **7**, 1519 (1973).

13. J. RANDRUP, S. E. LARSSON, P. MÖLLER, S. G. NILSSON, K. POMORSKI, and A. SOBICZEWSKI, Phys. Rev. C **13**, 229 (1976).

14. A. BARAN, K. POMORSKI, A. LUKASIAK, and A. SOBICZEWSKI, Nucl Phys. **A361**, 83 (1981); H. C. PAULI and T. LEDERGERBER, in <u>Proceedings of the Symposium on the Physics and Chemistry of Fission,</u> Rochester, New York, 1973 (International Atomic Energy Agency, Vienna, Austria, 1974), Vol. I, p. 463.

15. M. G. MUSTAFA and R. L. FERGUSON, Phys. Rev. C **18**, 301 (1978).

16. P. MÖLLER and S. G. NILSSON, Phys. Lett. **31B**, 283 (1970); H. C. PAULI, T. LEDERGERBER, and M. BRACK, Phys. Lett. **34B**, 264 (1971); G. GUSTAFSSON, P MÖLLER, and S. G. NILSSON, Phys. Lett. **34B**, 349 (1971).

MEDICAL AND INDUSTRIAL
APPLICATIONS OF
BY-PRODUCTS

Chairman
Randall S. Caswell (NIST)

RADIOIODINE: THE ATOMIC COCKTAIL

Rosalyn S. Yalow, Ph.D.
Veterans Administration Medical Center
130 West Kingsbridge Road
Bronx, New York 10468
(212) 579-1644

ABSTRACT

The use of artificial radionuclides in medicine has continued to increase in importance resulting in the growth of a new medical specialty, Nuclear Medicine. The availability of very low cost radionuclides from Oak Ridge beginning in 1946 initiated a revolution that led to widespread use of ^{131}I in the understanding and management of thyroid disease and to extensive use of ^{131}I-labeled dyes, fats, drugs, proteins and other substances in diverse areas of medicine. While the role of the "atomic cocktail" in cancer therapy has diminished greatly, in vivo and in vitro radionuclide procedures in medical diagnosis are employed in over one-third of hospital admissions.

The next decade will mark the 100th anniversary of the discoveries of X-radiation and of natural radioactivity. In 1895, Roentgen, while experimenting with cathode rays, observed fluorescence in substances placed at some distance from an opaque-paper covered Crookes tube, an apparatus used to study the conduction of electricity in gases at low pressure. Within a few weeks of intensive effort he was able to demonstrate that he had discovered "a new kind of rays" which he called X-rays. The most dramatic result of this experimentation, which quickly caught the lay mind, was an X-ray picture of his wife's hand recorded on a photographic film. The diagnostic possibilities of X-ray pictures were recognized at once. Almost 1000 papers and many books on the production and use of X-rays were published within the first year after the announcement of the discovery. In fact, the first X-ray journal, Archives of Clinical Skiagraphy, was founded in Great Britain in 1896. That same year Becquerel presented to the Paris Academy of Sciences the results of his discovery of ionizing radiation emitted by uranium compounds. Following up on his

work, Marie Curie, together with her husband, Pierre, purified more highly radioactive materials from large amounts of pitchblende. In 1898 they announced the discovery of two new substances: polonium, named after her native Poland, and radium. For these discoveries Roentgen received the first Nobel Prize in Physics in 1901 and Becquerel and the Curies shared the 1903 Prize in Physics.

It was appreciated almost immediately that X-rays and the radiations from naturally radioactive substances could damage tissue. Becquerel observed a reddening of his skin under the vest pocket in which he was carrying radium. Pierre Curie deliberately exposed part of his arm to an impure radium source for 10 hours and suffered a burn that took months to heal. Since radiation from X-rays and radium could destroy tissue, they were almost immediately used in the treatment of cancer. By 1920 the "War Against Cancer" had considerable public support and it was then thought that radium would provide the cure. Thus in 1921 when Marie Curie made her famous trip to America she was hailed as the "benefactress of the human race" for the "Cancer Cure" that radium was to have made possible and American women raised funds to purchase radium for her laboratory. Radium was also used for the treatment of non-malignant disease. The first case of hyperthyroidism successfully treated by implanting radium directly into the thyroid gland was reported in 1905.[1] Over the next two decades radium therapy for hyperthyroidism was employed.

Unlike the immediate application of X-rays in clinical diagnosis and of radium needles and radon seeds in therapy,[2] other uses of radioisotopes in diagnosis and biomedical investigation were long delayed. In the 1920's two American physicians, Henry Blumgart and Soma Weiss, determined the velocity of blood flow by injecting the radioactive gas radon dissolved in saline into one arm and determining the time it took for the radioactivity to travel to the other arm. They then studied the effect of disease states on that velocity.[3] The natural radioisotopes were of limited value in investigating animal and plant physiology. The major breakthrough was the discovery in 1934 of artificial radioactivity by Irene Curie and her husband Pierre Joliot.[4] This stimulated an enormous period of activity. In the next few years before World War II several hundred radionuclides were produced, principally with the use of the newly invented particle accelerators. Thus the tools became available for using radioisotopes in physiologic studies as well as in clinical diagnosis and therapy. World War II interrupted much of this work. However, in 1948 de Hevesy, who had received the 1943 Nobel Prize in Chemistry for his work on the use of isotopes as tracers in the study of chemical processes, published a remarkable volume entitled "Radioactive Indicators: Their Application in Biochemistry, Animal Physiology and Pathology" in which he reviewed virtually all that was known about the use of radioisotopes in animal and biochemical studies as well as the relatively few studies in humans. He predicted that in the future there would not be many such general surveys restricted to radioindicators, since the results obtained with isotopic tracer methods would be incorporated in textbooks dealing with more restricted aspects of the specific topics concerned.

Among the most common of the radio-isotopes used in humans during this early period were the radioiodines. In 1938 Hertz, Roberts and Evans[5] in Boston published the first paper on the study of thyroid physiology in rabbits employing radioiodine (^{128}I, $T_{1/2}$=25 min; produced by an n,γ reaction using a Ra-α-Be neutron source). That same year, fulfilling a perceived need for a longer-lived radio-iodine, Livingood and Seaborg[6] bombarded tellurium with 8 Mev deuterons and demonstrated the production of two longer-lived radioiodines (^{130}I, $T_{1/2}$-12.5 hour; ^{131}I, $T_{1/2}$-8 day) which were to dominate the early use of radioisotopes in medicine. Hamilton and Soley[7] in Berkeley soon made use of the longer-lived iodines in their human studies. In spite of the problems associated with the war years, several groups initiated studies of the uptake of radio-iodine for the diagnosis of thyroid disease and the treatment of hyperthyroidism. The successful demonstration of the uptake of radioiodine by the thyroid gland led to attempts to demonstrate similar uptake by thyroid cancer tissue. Although the first attempt to find evidence for uptake of radioiodine in metastases from thyroid cancer was not successful,[8] within the next few years there were positive reports[9,10] of radioiodine uptake in well-differentiated thyroid cancer. The radioiodines used in these studies were cyclotron-produced and were a mixture of ^{130}I and ^{131}I. A major report by Seidlin et al.[11] of the successful treatment of metastatic thyroid carcinoma appeared in 1946 - the same year that the Headquarters of the Manhattan Project first announced in Science[12] a program for production and distribution of pile-produced radioisotopes for use in scientific, technical and medical investigations. (It should be noted that over the next decade the terminology changed: "piles" became "reactors"; "radio-isotopes" became "radionuclides".) Within the first year after this announcement 160 institutions received more than 1000 shipments of radioisotopes.[13] What was the importance of the shift from cyclotron-produced to pile-produced radioiodine? Curie amounts rather than millicurie amounts of radioisotopes became readily available. Another major factor was cost. A therapeutic dose for thyroid cancer from a cyclotron was expensive - according to Dr. Seidlin's statements at that time the cost was about $1,500. To avoid wasting any of this precious material, the patient's urines were collected, and the radioiodine was extracted and readministered to the patient. In contrast, the cost of a therapeutic dose of ^{131}I for thyroid cancer from the Oak Ridge reactor was not much more than the cost of shipping and handling. But the major impact was psychologic. The Seidlin et al. article[11] appearing on the fifth anniversary of the bombing of Pearl Harbor made newspaper headlines[14] as "Cancer cure found in the fiery canyons of death at Oak Ridge". The concept of the "Atomic Cocktail" was born. The designation was in such popular usage that it appeared in the title of an article in a respectable medical journal.[15] Once again it was the "War on Cancer" that attracted most attention during the early years following the ready availability of radioisotopes. Within the first 5 years 441 medical groups employed internally administered radioisotopes, presumably principally for cancer therapy.[16] The number of shipments from Oak Ridge increased from 100 per year to 600 per year during this period.[16] Although cancer therapy made the headlines, the most important role for radionuclides was to be in understanding human physiology and clinical diagnosis. In 1954 Nuclear Medicine was identified as a medical specialty and the Society of Nuclear Medicine was born.

Let us return now to the science of the application of ^{131}I in medicine. Of major importance was its use in understanding thyroid physiology and in the diagnosis and therapy of thyroid disease. Since ^{131}I can easily be chemically attached to a variety of molecules, it also was to have an important role as a marker in studies of the distribution, turnover and localization of many substances.

Although the work of Hertz et al.[5] and Hamilton and Soley[7] had pointed the way for using some measure of the thyroidal uptake of radioiodines for the diagnosis of thyroid disease, the ready availability of ^{131}I after 1946 increased enormously the number of patients undergoing such studies. It has been estimated that in the United States alone between 1 and 3 million people had thyroidal uptake studies by 1968. Generally a 15-50% thyroidal uptake of radioiodine at the end of 24 hours was taken to correspond to normal function; lower values signified an underactive gland; higher values an overactive gland. Since the thyroid and kidney compete for removal of radioiodine from blood we demonstrated that a direct determination of the rate of removal of radioiodine by each organ would be a better measure.[17] The usefulness of thyroidal uptake studies for determination of thyroid function decreased by the late 1960's for two separate reasons. The increased use of iodized table salt and the introduction of a new method containing iodine for processing white bread resulted in an increased availability of chemical iodine in the blood. As a consequence there was a decreased fractional extraction and a lower thyroidal uptake of radioiodine.[18] The other, and more important reason, was the development of new simplified techniques for the direct measurement of thyroid-related hormone levels in blood.[19,20]

The treatment of a small group of hyperthyroid patients with radioiodine had been initiated before 1946.[21] However the ready availability of inexpensive ^{131}I led to a dramatic increase in its usage for this purpose thereafter. It had been estimated that in the United States alone by 1968 at least 200,000 people had been so treated.[22]

During the twenty year period after ^{131}I became available from Oak Ridge this radionuclide was extensively used for the diagnosis and treatment of thyroid disease. This experience is important in evaluating whether KI should be needed as a blocking agent in the event of a nuclear power plant accident. It should be noted that at the Three Mile Island (TMI) reactor, in spite of major damage to the fuel rods that resulted in the release of 30% of the radioiodines into the primary coolant, less than 30 Ci of ^{131}I were released to the environment.[23] In contrast, according to Soviet authorities,[24] the Chernobyl accident resulted in a release to the environment of 4.5×10^6 Ci of ^{131}I because of a lack of adequate containment.

How dangerous is exposure to ^{131}I? In the United States alone, several million people had received diagnostic doses of ^{131} before 1968. There has been no systematic follow-up to determine the subsequent incidence of thyroid cancer among these patients. However a Swedish study reported initially[25] on 10,000 patients and subsequently[26] on more than 35,000 patients who had received average tracer doses of 50 μCi ^{131}I which delivered about 50 rem to the thyroid during testing for thyroidal disease. Those patients who received these doses for other than a suspected thyroid malignancy were not at increased risk for thyroid cancer. Compared to a control group their relative risk was only 0.62. The follow-up period averaged 20 years. It should be noted also that in spite of the millions of people who received ^{131}I tracer studies in the United States more than 20 years ago, thyroid cancer deaths number only about 1,000 among the 500,000 annual cancer deaths.[27]

In a report for the Cooperative Thyrotoxicosis Follow-up Study it was noted that a comparison of 36,000 hyperthyroid patients, about 2/3 of whom were treated with 5-15 mCi amounts of ^{131}I and the remainder with surgery, revealed no difference in the incidence of leukemia between the two groups.[22,28] In the ^{131}I-treated patients the radiation dose to the bone marrow from the body distribution of the radionuclide averaged 7 to 15 rem. It should be noted that both groups of hyperthyroid patients, regardless of the method of therapy, showed a 50% higher incidence in leukemia when compared to the age- and sex-corrected United States population-at-large. This emphasizes the importance of a properly defined control group. Had the ^{131}I-treated subjects been compared with the general population, it would have appeared as if there was increased leukemia associated with radioiodine therapy rather than noting the association of leukemia with hyperthyroidism per se.

In 1946 considerable excitement was associated with the "Cancer Cure", that is, the treatment of thyroid cancer with radioiodine. What has happened in the intervening years? Recent reviews[29-31] of the role of ^{131}I therapy in differentiated thyroid carcinoma (the type most likely to show uptake of radioiodine) suggest less enthusiasm for that therapy than was the case four decades ago. It is possible to quote numerous articles concerned with follow-up studies of such patients who were not treated with ^{131}I and who had good survival rates. This type of thyroid cancer progresses slowly and, for those less than 40 at time of diagnosis, the cumulative death rate over a 25 year period may be as low as 10%.[31] At present, the treatment for thyroid cancer in many centers is total thyroidectomy where surgically possible, followed by ablation of the residual thyroid tissue with ^{131}I. The patient is then maintained with suppressive doses of thyroid hormone and restudied at intervals to determine whether the uptake of radioiodine in the metastases is sufficient to warrant further radioiodine therapy. Because of the concern that leukemia may result following administration of large doses of radioiodine, treatment doses now are generally smaller. Less than 300 mCi ^{131}I is now employed[31] compared to the 1000 mCi or greater cumulative doses often used in the early years.[32]

The ready availability of inexpensive ^{131}I and the ease with which it could be easily incorporated chemically into dyes, fats, proteins and other substances led to its early use for a variety of in vivo and in vitro studies completely unrelated to its role in the diagnosis and treatment of thyroid disease. Among the earliest of the agents for detection of brain tumors was ^{131}I labeled sodium diiodofluorescein.[33] With the use of Geiger-Mueller (G-M) counters and a rather primitive technique of counting in multiple symmetrical positions, the "scanning" for detection of tumors[34] and the in vivo behavior of other ^{131}I-labeled substances began. Within the next decade ^{131}I-diodrast[35] and ^{131}I-hippuran[36] were used in the investigation of kidney function and dysfunction, ^{131}I-rose bengal for hepatobiliary scans,[37] ^{131}I-albumin for cardiac scans,[38] etc. However there are a number of reasons why ^{131}I would not remain the radionuclide of choice for these purposes. It has a relatively long half-life which significantly exceeds the scanning time. It emits beta particles which contribute to radiation exposure but not to external detection. This results in more radiation exposure than would be received with other potential radionuclide labels which were to become available. Furthermore the higher energies of its gamma radiation made for less than optimal detection with scintillation coun-

ters as compared to the G-M counters initially employed.

A major breakthrough which provided a greatly improved agent for in vivo studies was the development of the molybdenum-99 technetium-99m generator at the Brookhaven National Laboratory.[39] The Mo parent is reactor-produced and has a half life of 2.7 days; the Tc daughter has a half life of 6 hours, emits no β and only a single γ of 140 Kev, an ideal energy for scintillation detectors. ^{99m}Tc can be eluted from the generator as the pertechnetate which behaves like iodide in physiologic studies. ^{99m}Tc-pertechnetate is trapped by the thyroid but not organified and has become the radionuclide of choice for morphological thyroid imaging. It has also been extensively used to label a variety of other agents such as sulfur-colloid, macroaggregated albumin, phosphonates, and red blood cells, among others, for imaging liver, spleen, bone marrow, lung and other systems. It is probably the least expensive of the now widely used imaging agents.

Radionuclides had proved to be of value in blood volume determinations. Dilution studies of ^{32}P labeled red cells in the circulation were first performed in 1940.[41] Subsequently ^{42}K and ^{51}Cr were similarly employed for labeling red cells. However use of labeled red cells required that the labeling be individually performed for each subject because of the incompatibility of foreign red cells. The use of ^{131}I-serum albumin permitted the same batch of material to be employed for determination of plasma volume in many patients which greatly simplified the procedure.[42] Additional information was gained by monitoring the disappearance of the ^{131}I-labeled albumin from the bloodstream following the 10 minute equilibration period required for blood volume determinations. Such studies permitted determination of the whole body distribution and turnover of albumin[43] and could be applied to turnover studies of other serum proteins. However it was subsequently shown that self-radiation, primarily from the ^{131}I beta particles, could lead to chemical alterations in the molecule, thus artificially decreasing the apparent turnover time of the albumin.[44] It was then appreciated that self-radiation was a general problem which must be taken into account in the preparation of high specific activity labeled proteins and peptides -- particularly in those situations in which the labeled substances were used in studies designed to reflect the turnover of the unlabeled substances.[45]

Studies with ^{131}I-insulin designed to test the hypothesis that adult diabetes is a consequence of abnormally rapid degradation of insulin led to the demonstration that all insulin-treated diabetics develop insulin-binding antibodies.[46] It was soon recognized that the same techniques used for quantifying the concentration of insulin-binding antibody[46] could be used reciprocally for the determination of insulin concentrations in the circulation.[47] The method, radioimmunoassay (RIA), depends on comparing the inhibition of binding of labeled antigen to antibody by the unknown sample with the inhibition by known standards.[47] RIA has been used in thousands of laboratories around the world to measure hundreds of substances of biologic interest in blood and body fluids including, among others, peptidal and non-peptidal hormones, drugs, viruses, etc.[48]

During the first decade after the development of RIA, ^{131}I was the radionuclide of choice for labeling. The ^{131}I label was used most extensively because of its ready availability in institutions in which thyroid studies were commonly employed. However its short half-life and the problems due to its energetic beta particles resulted in a shelf-life too short for the radioiodinated tracers commonly used for RIA. The early work of Myers[49] emphasized the optimal characteristics of ^{125}I ($T_{1/2}$=60 day, 35 Kev γ and no β) and suggested that it be used in place of ^{131}I for a wide variety of applications. ^{125}I became available from Oak Ridge in the 1960's. We then examined the problems associated with the use of ^{131}I or ^{125}I labels for RIA of the peptide hormones in which high specific activity, preferably monoiodinated, peptides are desirable.[50] Theoretically the shorter half life for ^{131}I should make possible higher specific activity monoiodinated peptides. However the observation that reactor-produced ^{131}I was contaminated with ^{127}I and the ^{125}I was carrier-free limited this advantage.[50] As a result by the end of that decade ^{125}I was to become the tracer of choice for RIA and related procedures.

This brief review of the advances in medicine following the discovery of fission was designed to highlight ^{131}I, the most publicized of the radionuclides available in 1946-50 from the Oak Ridge reactor. After four decades ^{131}I remains the radionuclide most widely used for therapy--primarily for a non-malignant condition, hyperthyroidism. Its applications for thyroid function studies and thyroid imaging and for in vitro studies such as radioimmunoassay have been replaced with other radionuclides, some reactor- and others accelerator-produced. Meanwhile Nuclear Medicine, the application of procedures employing a wide variety of radionuclides, has become an independent medical specialty with a primary role of improving medical diagnosis based on better understanding of human physiology and the normal and abnormal functioning of a number of organ systems. As a consequence it has been estimated that in vivo and in vitro radionuclide procedures important to medical diagnosis are now employed in over one-third of hospital admissions as well as in extensive out-patient evaluations.

REFERENCES

1. R. ABBE, "Exophthalmic Goiter Reduced by Radium," Arch. Roentgen Ray 9, 214 (1904-1905).

2. J. MUYR, "Radioactive Substances: Their Therapeutic Uses and Applications," Radiology 8, 223 (1927).

3. H.L. BLUMGART and S. WEISS, "Studies in Velocity of Blood Flow," J. Clin. Invest. 4, (Fifteen separate articles with various co-authors) (1927).

4. I. CURIE and F. JOLIOT, "I. Production Artificielle d'Elements Radioactifs. II. Preuve Chimique de la Transmutation des Elements," J. Phys. et Rad. 5, 153 (1934).

5. S. HERTZ, A. ROBERTS, and R.D. EVANS, "Radioactive Iodine as Indicator in Study of Thyroid Physiology," Proc. Soc. Exp. Biol. Med. 38, 510 (1938).

6. J.J. LIVINGOOD and G.T. SEABORG, "Radioactive Isotopes of Iodine," Phys. Rev. 54, 775 (1938).

7. J.G. HAMILTON and M.H. SOLEY, "Studies in Iodine Metabolism by Use of a New Radioactive Isotope of Iodine," Am. J. Physiol. 127, 557 (1939).

8. J.G. HAMILTON, "The Use of Radioactive Tracers in Biology and Medicine," Radiology 39, 541 (1942).

9. A.S. KESTON, R.P. BALL, V.K. FRANTZ, and W.W. PALMER, "Storage of Radioactive Iodine in a Metastasis from Thyroid Carcinoma," Science 95, 362 (1942).

10. L. LEITER, S.M. SEIDLIN, L.D. MARINELLI, and E.J. BAUMANN, "Adenocarcinoma of the Thyroid With Hyperthyroidism and Functional Metastases:

I. Studies With Thiouracil and Radio-Iodine," J. Clin. Endocrinol. 6, 247 (1946).

11. S.M. SEIDLIN, L.D. MARINELLI, and E. OSHRY, "Radioactive Iodine Therapy: Effect on Functioning Metastases of Adenocarcinoma of the Thyroid," JAMA 132, 838 (1946).

12. Announcement From Headquarters, Manhattan Project, Washington, D.C., "Availability of Radioactive Isotopes," Science, 103, 697 (1946).

13. Isotopes Branch, U.S. Atomic Energy Commission, "The Isotope Distribution Program," Science 106, 175 (1947).

14. M. BRUCER, "The Genesis of Thyroid-Radioiodine," Vignettes Nucl. Med., No. 90, 1 (1978).

15. C.J. COLLICA, W. LENTINO, and S. RUBENFELD, "Some Notes on the Administration of Atomic Cocktails," JAMA 175, 860 (1961).

16. M. BRUCER, "Internally Administered Isotopes for Cancer Therapy," Nucleonics 10, 46 (1952).

17. S.A. BERSON, R.S. YALOW, J. SORRENTINO, and B. ROSWIT, "The Determination of Thyroidal and Renal Plasma I^{131}-Clearance Rates as a Routine Diagnostic Test of Thyroid Dysfunction," J. Clin. Invest. 31, 141 (1952).

18. J.A. PITTMAN, JR., G.E. DAILEY, III, and R.J. BESCHI, "Changing Normal Values for Thyroidal Radioiodine Uptake," N. Eng. J. Med. 280, 1431 (1969).

19. I.J. CHOPRA, D.H. SOLOMON, and G.N. BEALL, "Radioimmunoassay for Measurement of Triiodothyronine in Human Serum," J. Clin. Invest. 50, 2033 (1971).

20. I.J. CHOPRA, "A Radioimmunoassay for Measurement of Thyroxine in Unextrated Serum," J. Clin. Endocrinol. Metab. 34, 938 (1972).

21. E.M. CHAPMAN and R.D. EVANS, "The Treatment of Hyperthyroidism With Radioactive Iodine," JAMA 131, 86 (1946).

22. E.L. SAENGER, G.E. THOMA, and E.A. TOMPKINS, "Incidence of Leukemia Following Treatment of Hyperthyroidism," JAMA 205, 855 (1968).

23. U.H. BEHLING and J.E. HILDEBRAND, Radiation and Health Effects, GPU Nuclear Corp., Middletown, PA (1986).

24. U.S. Department of Energy, Soviet Report on the Chernobyl Accident, English Translation, Wash.D.C., Aug. 16-17 (1986).

25. L.-E. HOLM, G. LUNDELL, and G. WALINDER, "Incidence of Malignant Thyroid Tumors in Humans After Exposure of Diagnostic Doses of Iodine-131. I. Retrospective Cohort Study," J. Natl. Cancer Inst. 64, 1055 (1980).

26. L.-E. HOLM, K.E. WIKLUND, G.E. LUNDELL, N.A. BERGMAN, G. BJELKENGREN, E.S. CEDERQUIST, U.-B.C. ERICSSON, L.-G. LARSSON, M.E. LIDBERG, R.S. LINDBERG, H.V. WICKLUND, and J.D. BOICE, JR., "Thyroid Cancer After Diagnostic Doses of Iodine-131: A Retrospective Cohort Study," J. Natl. Cancer Inst. 80, 1132 (1988).

27. American Cancer Society, "Cancer Statistics, 1989," Ca-A Cancer Journal for Clinicians 39, 1 (1989).

28. E.L. SAENGER, "Radiation and Leukemia Rates," Science 171, 1096 (1971).

29. B. CADY, C.E. SEDGWICK, W.A. MEISSNER, J.R. BOOKWALTER, V. ROMAGOSA, and J. WERBER, "Changing Clinical, Pathologic, Therapeutic and Survival Patterns in Differentiated Thyroid Carcinoma," Ann. Surg. 184, 541 (1976).

30. R.D. LEEPER and K. SHIMAOKA, "Treatment of Metastatic Thyroid Cancer," Clin. Endocrinol. Metab. 9, 383 (1980).

31. Y.K. MAHESHWARI, C.S. HILL, JR., T.P. HAYNIE, III, R.C. HICKEY, and N.A. SAMAAN, "^{131}I Therapy in Differentiated Thyroid Carcinoma: M.D. Anderson Hospital Experience," Cancer 47, 664 (1981).

32. J. SORRENTINO, B. ROSWIT, and R.S. YALOW, "Thyroid Carcinoma With Multiple Metastases and Pathological Fracture, Successfully Treated With Radioiodine. Report of a Case," Radiology 57, 729 (1951).

33. G. GOYACK, G.E. MOORE, and D.F. CLAUSEN, "Localization of Brain Tumors With Radiodyes," Nucleonics 3, 62 (1948).

34. M. ASHKENAZY, L. DAVIS, and J. MARTIN, "Evaluation of Technic and Results

of Radioactive Diiodofluorescein Test for Localization of Intracranial Lesions," J. Neurosurg. 8, 300 (1951).

35. G.V. TAPLIN, O.M. MEREDITH, JR., H. KADE, and C.C. WINTER, "The Radio-isotope Renogram: An External Test for Individual Kidney Function and Upper Urinary Tract Patency," J. Lab. Clin. Med. 48, 886 1956.

36. T.P. HAYNIE, M. NOFAL, E.A. CARR, JR., and W.H. BEIERWALTES, "Scintil-lation Scanning of the Kidney With Radioiodine-131 Contrast Media," Clin. Res. 8, 288 (1960).

37. G.V. TAPLIN, O.M. MEREDITH, and H. KADE, "The Radioactive I-131 Tagged Rose Bengal Uptake Excretion Test for Liver Function Using Gamma Ray Scintillation Counting Techniques," J. Lab. Clin. Med. 45, 665 (1955).

38. A.M. REJALI, W.J. MACINTYRE, and H.L. FRIEDELL, "A Radioisotope Method of Visualization of Blood Pools," Am. J. Roentgen. 79, 129 (1958).

39. W.D. TUCKER, "Radioisotopic Cows," J. Nucl. Med. 1, 60 (1960).

40. P.V. HARPER, R. BECK, D. CHARLESTON, K.A. LATHROP, "Optimization of a scanning method using Tc^{99m}," Nucleonics 22, 50 (1964).

41. L. HAHN and G. HEVESY, "A Method of Blood Volume Determination," Acta Physiol. Scand. 1, 3 (1940).

42. K.R. CRISPELL, B. PORTER, and R.T. NIESET, "Studies of Plasma Volume Using Human Serum Albumin Tagged With Radioactive Iodine," J. Clin. Invest. 29, 513 (1950).

43. S.A. BERSON, R.S. YALOW, S.S. SCHREIBER, and J. POST, "Tracer Experiments With I^{131}-Labeled Human Serum Albumin. Distribution and Degradation Studies," J. Clin. Invest. 2, 746 (1953).

44. R.S. YALOW and S.A. BERSON, "Chemical and Biological Alterations Induced by Irradiation of I^{131}-Labeled Human Serum Albumin," J. Clin. Invest. 36, 44 (1957).

45. S.A. BERSON and R.S. YALOW, "Radiochem-ical and Radiobiological Alterations of I^{131}-Labeled Proteins in Solution. Ann. NY Acad. Sci. 70, 56 (1957).

46. S.A. BERSON, R.S. YALOW, A. BAUMAN, M.A. ROTHSCHILD, and K. NEWERLY, "Insulin-I^{131} Metabolism in Human Subjects: Demonstration of Insulin Binding Globulin in the Circulation of Insulin-Treated Subjects," J. Clin. Invest. 35, 170 (1956).

47. R.S. YALOW and S.A. BERSON, "Immuno-assay of Endogenous Plasma Insulin in Man," J. Clin. Invest. 39, 1157 (1960).

48. R.S. YALOW, "Radioimmunoassay: A Probe for the Fine Structure of Biologic Systems," Science 200, 1236 (1978).

49. W.G. MYERS, "A Gamma Ray Carrier Compound Useful for Clinical Physio-logic Dynamic Studies," Int. J. Appl. Radiat. Isot. 2, 158 (1957).

50. R.S. YALOW and S.A. BERSON, "General Principles of Radioimmunoassay," Radioisotopes in Medicine: In Vitro Studies, U.S. Atomic Energy Commission Symposium in Medicine #11, Tennessee, p. 7 (1968).

NUCLEAR REACTORS AND RESEARCH IN CANCER THERAPY

CORNELIUS A. TOBIAS, Ph.D.
Lawrence Berkeley Laboratory and
Advanced Biomedical Center
450 - 30th Street
Oakland, CA 94609
(415) 451-4900

ABSTRACT

The advent of nuclear reactors made it feasible and practical to produce quantities of radioisotopes for basic biological investigations and for initial therapeutic studies. Intense isotopic radiation sources became available. These events led to the current worldwide use of radioisotopes in medicine. We briefly describe progress in several fields. Among these the initial use of fast neutrons for cancer therapy was based on the high biological effectiveness of recoil particles with high Linear Energy Transfer (LET). The use of a soluble form of 32-P for the treatment of certain blood dyscrasias was pioneered in the late 30's. Soon insoluble radiocolloids such as 198-Au and 90-Y were produced by neutron capture reactions and applied for intracavitary and intraarterial therapy. The biological effects of radioisotopes that decay by internal conversion or by K electron capture is outlined. Local bursts of Auger electrons are more effective in causing DNA lesions and lethal effects than ionization by beta or gamma rays. Brachytherapy was initially based on encapsulation of radium or of radon. Among later developments was the use of platinum-covered tantalum wires. With the discovery of 252-Californium it became possible to deliver localized fast neutron fields to deep tissues. Neutron capture therapy has a 50-year history of research. This method is based on neutron-induced disintegration of 6-Lithium, 10-Boron or 235-Uranium; with the discovery of certain boron compounds and of tumor specific antibodies, it is of continuing interest. The therapeutic use of accelerated heavy ions combines the ability to accurately localize radiation effects deep in the body and the great biological effectiveness of high-LET particles. It appears feasible in the future to combine the high-dose localization that is achieved by particle beams with high selectivity of boron-labeled tumor specific antibodies.

INTRODUCTION

The advent of nuclear science and the discovery of radioisotopes and new forms of radiation in the 30's and 40's filled scientists with a sense of adventure. The idea of dynamic processes was revolutionary. An early pioneer wrote in 1936:

"Make all of the naturally occurring elements radioactive. Give me radio-phosphorus and radio-sulfur, so that I can unravel secrets of cell metabolism, because these radioactive atoms, 'tagged' by their emitted radiation, could be traced wherever they went..."[1]

Today, we know that the advent of radioisotopes has indeed revolutionized biology. But revolution did not stop there. We can paraphrase the cancer therapist's dream:

"Show me by the tools of nuclear medicine where cancer cells are. Synthesize radioactive compounds that will be taken up selectively. Give me neutrons and charged particle beams that can deliver dense ionization into tumors, and we will have powerful new tools for cancer therapy."

As I will describe briefly, the above sentences express the thrust of radiation therapy research. Much progress is being made, but the task is not yet finished.

Soon after the discovery of neutrons by Chadwick,[2] the properties of these neutral particles made a profound impact on cancer research and therapy. Penetrating Radium rays were already used in treatments of cancer, without detailed understanding of the molecular mechanisms involved. It was, however, known since the early investigation of Bergonie and Trilondos in Bordeaux that rapidly proliferating tissues are sensitive to penetrating radiations. Cancer cells were believed to be "rapidly proliferating." Early treatments with penetrating gamma rays from Radium were effective. However, radium was a priceless commodity, available only at Paris, Yachimov and a few other centers.

FAST NEUTRONS

It was demonstrated in 1935 that cyclotron-produced neutron rays had even more severe effects on tissues than gamma rays.[3] Studies of neutron radiation fields with the Wilson cloud chamber contained many dense tracks. Some of these proved to be low energy alpha particles and fast protons. Raymond Zirkle, in his Ph.D. thesis and later at Chicago, proved that alpha particles killed cells much more effectively than any other known agent.[4]

In 1936, working with rodent tumors and with normal tissue slices, John Lawrence demonstrated that tumor tissues (rat sarcoma 180) were much more sensitive to neutrons than to X rays and that tumor tissue seemed more sensitive to neutrons than normal tissue.[5] This prompted them to propose the use of fast neutrons for cancer therapy. Soon after that, in 1938, the first neutron therapy trial began at Berkeley in collaboration with Robert Stone, Professor of Radiology at University of California, San Francisco.[6]

John Lawrence, Paul Aebersold and Ernest Lawrence, Proc.N.A.S. _22_, p.543-557, 1936

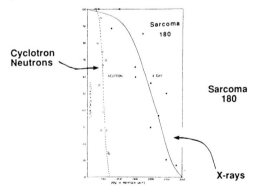

Result of transplantation of Sarcoma 180 after irradiation with various doses of X-rays and Cyclotron neutrons.

Figure 1:Neutrons kill tumors more effectively than X rays. [XBL 8710-4288]

In this first trial, the neutron dosage was determined after carefully documenting the high acute effectiveness of neutrons. Paul Aebersold was the key physicist in these dosimetric studies. Later, he became the head of the Isotope Division of the Atomic Energy Commission. The trial clearly established the ability of fast neutrons to cause lasting tumor regressions. However, some of the patients developed unwanted and deleterious late neutron effects many months after the initial treatment. Our knowledge of neutron action was still incomplete, and more basic biological studies were called for. In the next two decades we learned that neutron damage to living cells was repaired less efficiently than X- or gamma-ray damage.

Soon it was shown that neutrons could kill cells almost equally well either in the presence or the absence of oxygen, whereas anoxic cells were relatively protected from X or gamma rays. In the early 50's L. H. Gray reasoned that tumor cells, in their effort to compete with normal cells for oxygen, often turn hypoxic and hence prone to neutron effect.[7] So a second wave of therapeutic investigations with cyclotron-produced neutrons was started at Hammersmith Hospital in London[8]. Some hoped that the fission neutron spectrum would be ideal for therapy. However, the fission neutrons became rapidly moderated and absorbed by the water component of soft tissues, and it was often not possible to get enough dose into deep tissues where the tumors were located. Currently, a number of neutron therapy trials are in progress in various countries. The beneficial effects of fast neutrons outweigh those of gamma rays, particularly in tumors of the head and neck and in prostate cancer. The exponential absorption of neutrons in deep tissues, however, limits the effectiveness of these particles.

RADIOACTIVE ISOTOPES IN THERAPY

In 1923, Georg Hevesy, initiator of the radioactive tracer method, discovered that there is a transient uptake of radioactive lead in rodent tumors[9]. At the time there were no other effective ways to discover the existence and location of soft tissue tumors and Hevesy's finding raised great interest.[10]

Using a Radium-Beryllium neutron source, Fermi and associates discovered several radioistotpes.[11] Two of the co-chairmen of this 50-year anniversary celebration, E. Amaldi and E. Segre, were both codiscoverers of 32-P. Emilio Segre also participated in early biological investigations with 32-P, in a paper titled: "Rate of Organification of Phosphorus in Animal Tissues."[12]

The advent of the cyclotron and of nuclear reactors allowed the discovery of hundreds of new radioactive isotopes. The Manhattan Project established the Isotopes Division at the Oak Ridge National Laboratory, and the first reactor- produced isotopes were shipped on August 2, 1946. On January 1, 1947, the jurisdiction of this program was turned over to the civilian Atomic Energy Commission. By 1955, 55,000 curies of radioisotopes were shipped annually for various scientific purposes.[13]

The first therapeutic application of artificial radioisotopes was the therapy of Polycythemia Vera with 32-P, initiated in 1937 by John Lawrence.[14] Polycythemia vera is a chronic neoplastic disease of bone marrow. The untreated disease progresses from increased proliferation of bone marrow cells with erythrocytosis, through increased total red cell mass, and later myelofibrosis and myeloid metaplasia. A single dose of soluble 32-P phosphate, a beta emitter of 14.3-days half life, is usually sufficient to produce long lasting remission. The isotope selectively concentrates in mitotically active cells of the bone marrow and in trabecular and cortical bone. Thirty years later, in 1967, Louis Wasserman compared various therapeutic agents and found that at that time 32-P was the best form of treatment for this chronic disease, and 32-P is still in use for the therapy of polychthemia vera. It has been demonstrated, however, that the late manifestations of this disease include leukemia, irrespective of the form of therapy used.

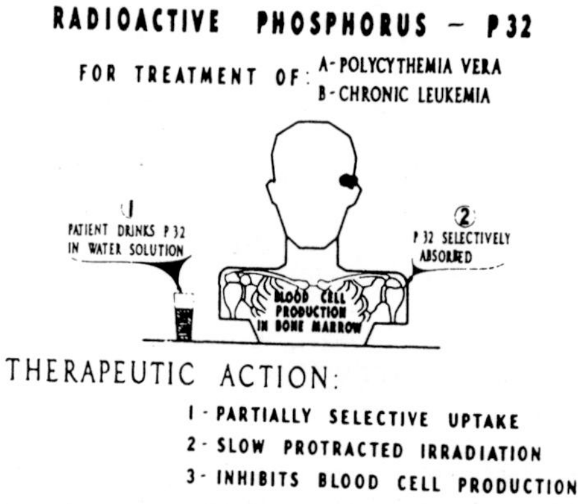

RADIOACTIVE PHOSPHORUS - P 32

FOR TREATMENT OF: A- POLYCYTHEMIA VERA
B- CHRONIC LEUKEMIA

PATIENT DRINKS P 32 IN WATER SOLUTION

② P 32 SELECTIVELY ABSORBED

BLOOD CELL PRODUCTION IN BONE MARROW

THERAPEUTIC ACTION:

1 - PARTIALLY SELECTIVE UPTAKE
2 - SLOW PROTRACTED IRRADIATION
3 - INHIBITS BLOOD CELL PRODUCTION

Figure 2:Schematic of the administration and effects of 32-P. (From Isotopes, p. 24, USAEC, 1955). [ZBL 894-3273]

Many of the new radioisotopes were soon tested for their tumor affinity. Shortly after the discovery of radioiodine (128-Iodine) by Enrico Fermi's group, Joseph Hamilton demonstrated that about 99% of the injected radioiodine was taken up in the thyroid gland.[15,16] The later applications of this startling finding are covered for the symposium by Dr. Rosalyn S. Yalow. Most of the other radioactive isotopes were not enriched in a manner similar to iodine. However, I have shown in 1947 that colloidal gold, labeled with reactor-produced 198-Au (half life 2.7d, produced by neutron capture), is strikingly taken up in kidney cortex. Seymour Kety prepared radioautographs of brain, labeled with the fission product, 133-Xenon (half life 5.27d). Since Xenon is a highly lipid soluble, it is preferentially present in the myelin of white matter. Joseph Hamilton demonstrated that plutonium is taken up in the periosteum of mammals.

EXTERNAL THERAPY SOURCES

In the 40's there were only a few "supervoltage" X-ray generators available that could produce X rays with penetration comparable to radium gamma rays. In 1948, L.G. Grimmett proposed the use of radioactive 60-Cobalt in teletherapy machines.[17] This isotope, discovered by Sampson et al., has a half life of 5.28 years and emits principally gamma rays of 1.2 and 1.3 MeV. Large quantities could be produced from stable 59-Cobalt by the neutron capture reaction. Marshall Brucer and group at Oak Ridge designed the first such source built by the General Electric Co., which contained 1000 curies of 60-Co. The source completed in 1950, was an instant success, but Grimmett did not live to see it. Within ten years, 314 such sources were sold from American reactors. The Canadian Atomic Energy Co. became a major supplier of teletherapy units. In cobalt teletherapy, there is usually a skin-sparing effect: the dose immediately at external body surfaces is relatively small. In the first .3 cm it increases due to a transition in secondary ionization equilibrium. Deeper in the body the rays are gradually absorbed again. The cobalt therapy machines, with their good depth-dose profiles, were generally adopted for use in many countries. Other fission product sources, for example, 137-Cesium, with softer 661 keV gamma rays (half life 30 years) also found biomedical uses.

RADIOCOLLOIDS

When insoluble colloidal particles are injected into the circulation, the cells

552

of the reticulo-endothelial system sequester and hold these locally for considerable time periods. Some migration does occur, however, to the lymph nodes. Most colloids used in medicine have particle sizes ranging from 10 to 1000 nanometers in diameter. The largest particles are usually retained in the lungs and the smallest ones in the bone marrow, with kidneys, liver and spleen holding intermediate sizes. This was first demonstrated by Hardin Jones in 1942, using colloidal 32-P chromic phosphate.[18] The particles are also retained in serosal cavities, such as the peritoneum and the pleura. Colloids are then used as a palliative or preventive form of treatment in these cavities, for example, in ovarian cancer or in lung carcinoma. Among early pioneers were Mueller, who used zinc, Sheppard, who introduced the use of radioactive 198-Aurum.[19,20] Radiogold was discovered by the Fermi group, who made many of their early discoveries with a Radium-Beryllium neutron source.[11] 90-Y was discovered by Stewart, Lawson and Cork.[21] J. Gofman prepared colloids of Yttrium, Zirconium, Columbium and Lanthanum.[22]

beta rays that penetrate into tissue through the wall of the needle.

With the advent of 60-Cobalt, a great variety of radioactive applicators were developed. Several isotopes were utilized for internal applications, among these Yttrium. 90-Yttrium is produced by the decay of the 28-year 90-Sr, a fission product. The beta rays from radon or yttrium needles produce highly localized dose distributions. An important problem is the methodology of accurate placement of the needles in order to obtain a uniform dose distribution in the tumor. Needles must be inserted without causing undue bleeding; free needles placed into tissue can, in time, translocate their position. Warren Sinclair was the first to suggest the use of radioactive tantalum wire. This material is usually coated with platinum for mechanical strength. The wire is eminently suitable for insertion and removal by specially developed "guns" and applicators. Tumors in inaccessible sites, for example, in the head and neck are treated in this manner. Beta rays emitted from the applicators are not suitable for coping with the radiobio-

Table I. A List of the Most Useful Isotopes for Radiocolloids:

Isotope	Half Life	Max Beta Energy	Max Penetration
32 - P	14.3 days	1.71 Mev	.87 cm
90 - Y	64.0 hr	2.27 Mev	1.10 cm
165 - Dy	2.3 hr	1.3 Mev	.59 cm
169 - Er	9.4 d	.34 Mev	.10 cm
186 - Re	90.0 hr	1.07 Mev	.43 cm
198 - Au	2.7 d	.96 Mev	.40 cm

Colloids are also used in the treatment of degenerative joint diseases, such as rheumatoid arthritis. Ansell et al. showed in 1950 that inflammation of the synovial membranes can be reduced for extended periods of time by intraarterial injection of radioactive 198-Au colloid.[23] However, the long-term results do not appear significantly superior to chemotherapeutic or surgical approaches.

INTERSTITIAL RADIATION THERAPY

Brachytherapy, using radium or radon, had its beginning in the 30's. For example, in about 1935, Antoine Lacassagne implanted sealed radon needles in the human pituitary for the purpose of treating tumors and to depress the secretion of hormones.[24] Radon and its decay products produce a complex spectrum of radiations: 214-Lead and 214-Bismuth emit energetic

logical oxygen effect or with highly radioresistant tumor cells.

Figure 3:The distribution of colloidal $235\text{-}UO_2$ in mouse spleen. Right: Histological section. Left: Autoradiograph. The black areas are homopoietic islands, imaged by the emission of alpha particles. (C. Tobias, unpublished, 1947).

The first isotope of element 98, 244-Californium, was discovered by Glenn Seaborg et al.[25] The isotope 252-Californium, discovered by Al Ghiorso and associates, has a half life of 2.65 years.[26] It is a product of sequential neutron captures in nuclear reactors, beginning with 239-Pu and the addition of 13 successive neutrons. It emits energetic alpha particles and, in about 3% of the cases, undergoes spontaneous fission. As a result, there is emission of fast neutrons. Therapeutic 252-Californium sources produced at the Savannah River Laboratory are usually prepared in platinum-iridium capsules. Their radiation field has fast neutrons, slow neutrons and gamma rays. The dose distribution around the source falls off much less steeply than in the case of beta emitters, and neutrons are effective in reducing the sensitivity differences between oxygenated and anoxic tumor tissues.

The initial suggestion for use of Californium in brachytherapy came from Shlea and Stoddard in 1965.[27] The M.D. Anderson Hospital and other centers began human exposures in 1968. However, the administration of this isotope is laborious, and since the patients who carry Cf seeds become neutron sources, there are special health protection problems for the hospital staff.[28] The current leaders of 252-Cf therapy research are Vtyurin at Obninsk (USSR), Tsuya at the Japanese Foundation of Cancer Research (Tokyo), and Maruyama at the University of Kentucky Medical School.[29,30] Tumors of the head and neck and tumors in the abdomen and pelvis are usually candidates for this form of treatment. Californium delivers neutrons at a relatively low dose rate; initial therapy trials suffered from lack of accurate information on the effectiveness of neutrons applied at low dose rate. Whereas lesions produced by low-LET radiations are efficiently repaired, neutron effects remain largely unrepaired, and care must be taken to avoid delayed injury. For example, Todd and Feola found anomalous dose-rate effects.[31]

AUGER EMITTING RADIONUCLIDES

Radionuclides that decay by electron capture or by internal conversion emit a portion of the decay energy as showers of Auger electrons. The ionization and excitation processes by these cause the deposition of high local energy density.

Incorporated into molecules that attach to DNA, Auger processes can cause lesions that are very effective in killing cells. 75-Se, 51-Cr, 201-Tl, 125-I and 77-Br have been used in research studies. The Thymidine analogs, 125-deoxyuridine and 77-Br deoxyuridine, can be taken up in DNA replacing Thymidine. The half life of 77-BrUdR is 57 hours.[32] It appears that DNA lesions produced by 77-BrUdR are not repairable. However, the problem of how to enhance the uptake of such substances in tumor cells, and retard it in normal cells, has not been solved.

Cells of the endocrine system are targets for steroid hormones. There are special receptors that combine with steroid hormones and interact with the DNA of the cell nucleus. The combined hormone and receptor then exert regulatory action on the cell's synthetic apparatus. Attempts have been made to synthesize steroid analogs containing auger-emitting isotopes, in the hope that these will combine with the receptors and, by their decay, cause injury in DNA.[33] Since receptors are often missing in cells of advanced, undifferentiated carcinoma, the hormonal approach may be of limited value.

NEUTRON CAPTURE THERAPY

After the discovery by Enrico Fermi of the properties of slow neutrons and the neutron capture process, Georg Hevesy showed that some substances have very high cross sections for neutron capture. Some of the neutron-induced nuclear transmutations not only had high cross sections, but were also accompanied by the emission of highly ionizing particles. The first suggestion toward neutron capture therapy came from Gordon Locher at Swarthmore College in 1936.[34] Knowing that 10-Boron emits highly ionizing alpha particles, P. Gerald Kruger immersed some tumor tissues

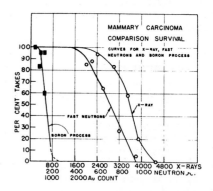

Figure 4: Killing of X rays, fast neutrons and bron capture events. (From the work of Kruger, Reference #35). [XBL 894-1568]

in boric acid and radiated these with slow neutrons from a cyclotron.[35] The samples were then implanted into mice, and the tumor takes were assessed. The results were compared to irradiations without boron and to irradiations with X rays or fast neutrons. The presence of boron markedly increased the killing effect of slow neutrons. Zahl, Cooper and Dunning infiltrated rodent sarcomata in vivo with Li and B compounds and exposed these to slow neutrons; some of the tumors regressed.[36] Table II (from Ref. 25) gives some of the data of interest.

marized the MIT experience.[38] Since neutron beams penetrating through the scalp caused painful ulcerating lesions, the scalp, bone flap and dura of patients being treated with gliomas was removed, and the neutron beam passed through physiological saline solution before reaching the brain. In these early tests, concluded in 1961, it was not possible to achieve a sufficiently high concentration gradient of boron between tumor and normal tissues. In the intervening years, intense research was carried toward suitable boron compounds.[39] A promising method is to

Table II: Disintegration Data

Isotope	6-Li	10-B	235-U
Process	(n,tritium)	(n, alpha)	(n, fission)
Cross section 10^{-24} cm^2	860	3525	420
E liberated, MeV	4.6	2.8	159

Fission recoils are highly ionizing fast atomic nuclei. It was already known in 1947 that uranium has an affinity to cell membranes. In 1946 the author and associates injected colloidal 235-UO_2 into mice, then exposed these animals to a moderated neutron beam at the Oak Ridge reactor.[37] We did succeed in showing that the fission recoils had very high killing efficiency. However, it was not possible to induce significantly high uptake of U in tumors. In this study evidence was obtained that the uptake of radioactive colloids is highly selective in tissue.

To make neutron capture feasible, a great deal needed to be accomplished; it seemed necessary to develop methods to monitor the presence of Li, B or U in tissues and then to find compounds that are taken up in cancerous tumors. It had to be shown that sufficient concentration of the critical isotopes can be present in the tumor. Finally, one had to demonstrate that the biological effects produced by the "capture" reactions are much greater than those produced by neutrons to outweigh the biological effects produced by the neutron beam elsewhere in tissue.

Special facilities at two reactors, one at the medical reactor at Brookhaven National Laboratory and one at MIT, were built in the 50's for boron capture research.[34] Wm. H. Sweet recently sum-

search for compounds that are precursors of molecules manufactured by the tumor cells. A boronated precursor of the pigment melanin, 10-B para-Boronophenylalanine, was synthesized by Snyder et al. and tested by Mishima et al.[40,41] This compound, 10-BPA, is taken up in melanotic melanoma in hamsters and a thermal neutron dose of $1.1 \times 10^{+13}$ neutrons per cm^2 caused complete regression of these tumors. Another important set of compounds are polyhedral boranes, synthesized at DuPont. These show enrichment in tumors; one of these, 10-B $Na_2 B_{12} H_{11} SH$, showed an average ratio tumor/blood of more than 5.[42]

Another promising pathway is the use of boronated polyclonal and monoclonal antibodies. This method can be useful, if there are a sufficient number of antibody binding sites on each tumor cell and if each antibody can carry a sufficient number of 10-Boron atoms. The number of 10-B atoms needed in each cell has been estimated at about 3000. Progress has been achieved with antibodies against human colorectal cancer.

Another problem with the use of thermal neutrons is that these are rapidly absorbed in aqueous tissue. Fairchild et al. developed a method for the use of epithermal neutrons.[43,44] The peak of the biological effect in such columns is several cm below the surface of the body.

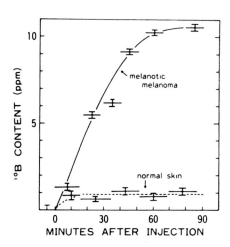

Figure 5: In vivo time course of selective 10-B accumulation in melanotic malignant melanoma proliferating in hamster's subcutaneous tissue revealed by prompt gamma-ray spectroscopy of Kanda and Kobayshi (10-B para Boronophenylalanine). (Based on Fairchild, Reference #43).

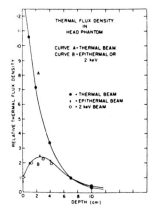

Figure 6: Flux distribution of thermal and epithermal neutrons. (Based on Fairchild, Reference #43, as a function of depth).

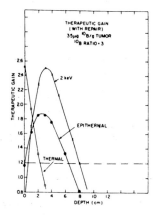

Figure 7: Calculated therapuetic efficiency of thermal and epithermal neutrons as a function of depth. (Based on Fairchild, Reference #43, p. 5).

In 1968, H. Hatanaka of Toyko University, Japan, began a new series of treatments of grade III-IV malignant human glioma tumors. The Hitachi training reactor and the Mushashi Institute reactor were used, and polyhedral boranes were tested. When patients received more than 2.5×10^{12} neutrons/cm^2, and the tumor was at less than 6-cm depth, the 10-year survival was near 30%. Such results have generated renewed interest in neutron capture therapy.[45,46]

HEAVY ACCELERATED NUCLEI IN CANCER THERAPY

Research with neutrons has helped us to understand that good depth localization of the radiation dose and high LET or high ionization energy density at the level of DNA are essential components of good therapeutic agents. However, radioisotopes rarely show sufficiently high local uptake for effective therapy. Externally-applied fast or slow neutrons are hampered because of their rapid absorption in tissue.

The author and his colleagues have applied accelerated beams of light and heavy ions to cancer treatment. The energy of these particles varies inversely with their velocity, culminating in the Bragg ionization curve.[47] The initial suggestion for using accelerated nucleons for cancer therapy came in 1946 from Robert Wilson, who proposed the use of protons.[48] At Berkeley, proton therapy began in 1954 with irradiation of the pituitary gland in patients with advanced metastatic mammary cancer.[49] After the first 30 patients, we changed to the use of helium ion beams. Particles are very effective in the treatment of acromegaly, and good results were achieved for Cushings disease also.[50] Beginning in 1956, The Svedberg and Boerje Larsson started research at the Uppsala cyclotron, culminating in building a new accelerator in 1988.[51] At Harvard University Raymond Kjellberg chose the pituitary and brain as the objects of his studies.[52] H. Suit has achieved excellent results with protons on melanoma of the retinal choroid and on inoperable tumors adjacent to the spine, results that are very similar to those achieved at Berkeley with helium ion beams.[53,54] Very encouraging results are being achieved by Fabrikant in the helium beam treatment of arteriovenous malformations in brain.[55] This is a congenital disease of the blood vessels that can manifest itself in life-threatening hemorrhages. In the USSR, three large accelerators (one at ITEP in Moscow, one at Dubna, and one near Leningrad) all engaged in cancer therapy with protons.

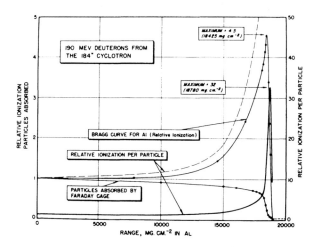

Figure 8:Bragg curve 190 MeV/u deuterons. (Obtained in 1951 by Tobias et al., Reference #47). [JHL 773]

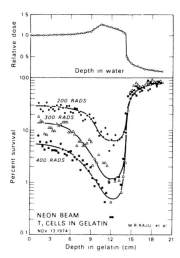

Figure 9:Top: Extended Bragg curve of neon ions obtained with a rotating ridge filter. Bottom: Depth survival curves of kidney cells in the neon beam at various plateau skin doses. (From M. R. Raju, Heavy Particle Radiotherapy, Academic Press, New York, 1980). [XBL 752-4685]

In the late 50's basic cellular studies with heavy accelerated nuclei were carried out at the HILAC, the same accelerator used by Glenn Seaborg and his colleagues in their search for transuranium elements. In 1967 Tobias and Todd proposed a cancer-oriented program with heavy ions accelerated to high enough energy to penetrate deep into the human body.[56] In 1975 the HILAC became a preaccelerator for the Bevatron, and thus the Bevalac was born. An intense biomedical program with heavy ions has been carried out since that time. Since 1983 the capacity of the machine has included acceleration of any of the atomic nuclei in the periodic table.

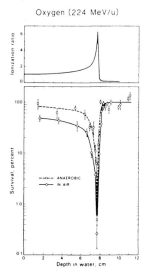

Figure 10:Depth-killing curve of a mono-energetic beam of oxygen ions. The particles have a high biological effectiveness at the peak of the Bragg curve, which is shown on top. (From Tobias and Roisman, Radiology 108, 145-158, 1973). [DBL 733-5080]

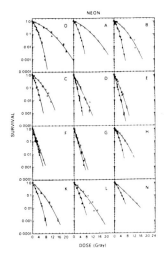

Figure 11:These paired survival curves show the reduction of the difference in survival between aereated and hypoxic cells. T-1 cells were used. E, F, and G are near the Bragg peak. (Based on E. A. Blakely et al., Radiat. Res. 80, 122-160, 1979). [XBL 7710-3937A]

The effectiveness of heavier ion beams, such as neon and silicon, come about because individual particles, unlike X rays or beta rays, can produce multiple chromatin breaks in mammalian cell nuclei. These lead to high lethal efficiency by producing chromosome deletions and rearrangements. Heavy ions are also effective in increasing the sensitivity of cells resistant to X rays and reducing the differences in radiosensitivity between oxygenated and anoxic cells.[57] Current studies at LBL indicate that heavy ions have increased therapeutic effectiveness for soft tissue sarcomas, tumors of the head and neck, brain tumors and prostate carcinoma.[58] The controlled statistical studies will be continued for several more years before we know the exact quantitative relationships. Encouraged by the results to date, heavy-ion accelerators are being built for medical use in Chiba, Japan, and at Darmstadt, Germany; light-ion accelerators are being proposed by the European Economic Community (EULIMA) and in Oakland, California (LIBRA).

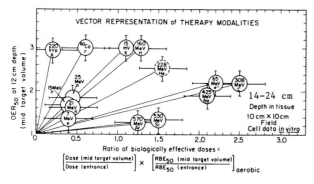

Figure 12: Comparison between various therapy beams. Using depth effectiveness (horizontal axis) and oxygen effect (vertical axis). Carbon and neon, as well as Pi mesons, have the best depth effectiveness; neutrons and X rays are not good. X rays have the greatest oxygen effect and are therefore not suitable to kill anoxic cells. Neutrons of various energies and neon beams are better. Silicon and argon have the smallest oxygen effect. (Indebted to E. A. Blakely for this figure).

MIXED MODALITIES IN CANCER TREATMENT

Heavy ion beams give us the ability to accurately localize treatment deep in the body. The dense ionization near the ends of their tracks helps to minimize tumor sensitivity differences due to heterogeneity of cellular properties and to changes in the humoral environment, such as the availability of oxygen. However, local beams of heavy ions are not adequate to deal with distant metastasis. It would also be helpful to find treatment modalities that can differentiate between normal and cancer cells.

A promising avenue to this seems to be the extended use of immunological pathways. If we could manufacture antibodies against specific classes of tumors, then the body could recognize which are the tumor cells. If these antibodies could carry boron atoms, then under an epithermal neutron beam perhaps a differential in killing efficiency could be established. Even if we had boronated antitumor antibodies, we would probably not be able to saturate each and every tumor cell with the necessary amount of antibodies without deleterious toxic effects. Therefore, it might be more practical to plan heavy ion treatments, to be modulated by neutron capture therapy. We might be able to place enough antibodies into tumors to produce a differential effect between normal and tumor tissue.

Similar scenarios have been proposed for the joint application of accelerated heavy particles with Auger-emitting isotopes and of particles with chemotherapy and hyperthermia.

In closing, I would like to review the past 50 years of cancer research effort as a period of influx of new ideas and new techniques under the stimulation of nuclear science and of modern biology. As we proceed, the advances of technology allow us to use approaches that seemed impossible just a few years ago. Cancer is a natural process of extreme complexity. Nevertheless, progress toward prolonging life and ameliorating symptoms is being made every new day.

REFERENCES

1. J. H. LAWRENCE, "Artificial Radioactivity and Neutron Rays in Biology and Medicine," Handbook of Physical Therapy, A. M. A., Chicago, 1936.

2. J. CHADWICK, "Possible Existence of a Neutron Particle," Nature 129, 312 (1932).

3. J. H. LAWRENCE and E. O. LAWRENCE, "The Biological Action of Neutron Rays," Proc. Nat. Acad. Sci. 22, 124-133 (1936).

4. R. E. ZIRKLE, "Biological Effectiveness of Alpha Particles as Function of Ion Concentration Produced in Their Paths," Am. J. Cancer 23, 558-567 (1935).

5. J. H. LAWRENCE, P. C. AEBERSOLD, and E. O. LAWRENCE, "The Comparative Effects of Neutrons and X rays on Normal and Neoplastic Tissue," Am. Assoc. Adv. Sci. Pub. 4, 215-219 (1937).

6. R. S. STONE, J. H. LAWRENCE, and P. C. AEBERSOLD, "A Preliminary Report on the Use of Fast Neutrons in the Treatment of Malignant Disease," Radiol. 35, 322-327 (1940).

7. L. H. GRAY, A. D. CONGER, M. EBERT, S. HORNSEY, and O. C. A. SCOTT, "Initiation and Development of Cellular Damage by Ionizing Radiation: 32nd Silvanus Thompson Memorial Lecture." Isotopes, pp 357, Eight-year summary of distribution and utilization.

8. M. CATTERALL and D. K. BEWLEY, Fast Neutrons in the Treatment of Cancer, pp 219-234, Academic Press, London, 1979.

9. G. HEVESY, "Absorption and Translocation of Lead by Plants," Biochem. J. 17, 439 (1923).

10. G. HEVESY, "Historical Progress of the Isotope Methodology and Its Influences on the Biological Sciences," Minerva Nucleaire 1, 182 (1957).

11. E. FERMI, E. AMALDI, O. D'AGOSTINO, F. RASETTI, and E. SEGRE, Royal Society of London Proceedings 146A, 483 (1934).

12. G. ARTOM, G. SARZANA, C. PERRIER, M. SANTANGELO, and E. SEGRE, "Rate of Organification of Phosphorus in Animal Tissues," Nature 139, 836 (1937).

13. Isotopes, An Eight-Year Summary of Distribution and Utilization, 357 pp., United States Atomic Energy Commission, March, 1955.

14. D. J. ROSENTHAL and J. H. LAWRENCE, "Radioactive Isotopes in Medicine," Am. Rev. Med. 8, 361-388 (1957).

15. E. AMALDI, O. D'AGOSTINO, E. FERMI, B. PONTECORRO, F. RASETTI, and E. SEGRE, Royal Society of London Proceedings, 149A, 522 (1935).

16. J. G. HAMILTON and M. SOLEY, "Studies in Iodine Metabolism by Use of New Radioactive Isotope of Iodine," Am. J. Physiol. 127, 557-572 (1939).

17. "Progress in Teletherapy," Chapter 23, pp 589-606. Radiation Biology and Medicine (Walter D. Claus, Ed.), Addison Wesley Co., 1958.

18. H. B. JONES, "Method of Distributing Beta Radioactivity to Reticulo-Endothelial System and Adjacent Tissues," J. Clin. Invest. 23, 783 (1944).

19. J. H. MUELLER, Experientia 1, 199 (1945).

20. J. W. SHEPPARD, E. B. WELLS, P. F. HAHN, and J. P. B. GOODELL, "Studies of Distribution of Intravenously Administered Colloidal Sols of Maganese and Gold in Human Beings and Dogs Using Radioactive Isotopes," J. Lab. Clin. Med. 32, 247 (1947).

21. D. W. STEWART, J. L. LAWSON, and J. M. CORK, Physical Review 52, 901 (1937).

22. J. GOFMAN, "Studies with Colloids Containing Isotopes of Yttrium, Xirconium,, Columbium and Lanthanum," J. Lab. Clin. Med. 34, 297 (1949).

23. B. M. ANSELL, A. CROOK, J. R. MALLARD, and E. G. BYWATERS, Am. Rheum. Dis. 22, 435 (1963).

24. Roentgens, Rads and Riddles, Symposium on Supervoltage Therapy (Friedman, Brucer, Anderson, Eds.), USAEC, 1959.

25. S. G. THOMPSON, K. STREET, A. GHIORSO, and G. SEABORG, Physical Review 80, 790 (1950).

26. A. GHIORSO, B. ROSSI, B. G. HARVEY, and S. G. THOMSON, Physical Review 93, 257 (1954).

27. C. S. SHLEA and D. H. STODDARD, "Californium Isotopes Proposed for Intracavity Interstitial Radiation Therapy with Neutrons," Nature 206, 1058-9 (1965).

28. D. H. STODDARD, "Historical Review of Californium-252: Discovery and Development," Nuclear Science Applications 2, 189-199, Harwood Acad. Pub., 1986.

29. Y. MARUYAMA, Opportunities and Challenges with Transuranium Elements (G. Friedlander, Chairman), National Academy Press, Washington D.C., 1983.

30. Y. MARUYAMA and J. R. van NAGELL, "Efficacy of Brachytherapy with California-252 Neutrons Versus Cesium-137 Protons for Eradication of Bulky Localized Cervical Cancer," J. Natl. Cancer Inst. 80, 7 (1988).

31. P. TODD and J. FEOLA, "Inverse Gamma Ray Dose Rate Effect in Californium-252 RBE Experiment with Human T-1 Cells Irradiated In Vitro," Nuclear Science Applications 2, 815-820, 1986.

32. A. I. KASSIS, S. J. ADELSTEIN, and W. D. BLOOMER, Radionuclides in Therapy (R. P. Spencer, Ed.), pp 119-134, 1987.

33. R. H. SEEVERS, pp 145-166 of Ref. 32.

34. L. FARR, "Development of the Nuclear Reactor as a Device for Medical Therapy and Diagnosis," Radiation Biology and Medicine (Walter D. Claus, Ed.), pp 522-540, Addison Wesley Pub., 1958.

35. P. G. KRUGER, "Some Biological Effects of Nuclear Disintegration Products on Neoplastic Tissue," Proc. Nat. Acad. Sci 26, 181-192 (1940).

36. P. A. ZAHL, F. S. COOPER, and J. R. DUNNING, "Some In Vivo Effects of Localized Distintegration Products on Transplantable Mouse Sarcoma," Proc. Nat. Acad. Sci 26, 589 (1940).

37. C. A. TOBIAS, P. P. WEYMOUTH, and L. R. WASSERMAN, "Some Biological Effects due to Nuclear Fission," Science 107, 115 (1948).

38. W. H. SWEET, International Symposium on Neutron Capture Therapy, pp 376-378 (M. Dienes, Ed.), Brookhaven, 1983.

39. A. H. SOLOWAY, "Correlation of Drug Penetration of Brain and Chemical Structure," Science 128, 1572 (1958).

40. H. R. SYNDER, A. J. REEDY, and W. LENNARZ, J. Am. Chem. Soc. 80, 835-838 (1958).

41. Y. MISHIMA, M. ICHIHASHI, T. NAKANISHI, M. TSUJI, and M. UEDA, pp 355-375 of Ref. 32.

42. A. H. SOLOWAY, R. F. BARTH, F. ALAM, and W. E. CAREY, pp 207-214 of Ref. 32.

43. R. G. FAIRCHILD and V. P. BOND, "Enhancement of Tumor Dose via Neutron Beam Filtration and Dose Rate, and the Effects of These Parameters on Minimum Boron Content," Proceedings of the First International Symposium on Neutron Capture Therapy, Oct., 1983 (Fairchild & Brownell, Eds.), pp 1-11.

44. Neutron Capture (Chrien, Ed., Bk. #401665) Plenum Publishers, New York, 1989.

45. Strahlentherapie und Onkologie, Feb.-March, 1989.

46. H. HATANAKA, Acta Neurochirurgica 42, 187-192, Suppl. (1988).

47. C. A. TOBIAS, H. O. ANGER, and J. H. LAWRENCE, "Radiological Use of High Energy Deuterons and Alpha Particles," Am. J. Roentgenol. Rad. Ther. Nuc. Med. 67, 1-27 (1952).

48. R. R. WILSON, "Radiological Use of Fast Protons," Radiology 47, 487-491 (1946).

49. C. A. TOBIAS, J. H. LAWRENCE, J. L. BORN, R. K. McCOMBS, J. E. ROBERTS, H. O. ANGER, B. V. A. LOW-BEER, and C. B. HUGGINS, "Pituitary Irradiation with High-Energy Proton Beams: A Preliminary Report," Cancer Res. 18, 121-134 (1958).

50. J. A. LINFOOT, "Heavy Ion Therapy - Alpha Particle Treatment of Pituitary Tumors," Recent Advances in Diagnosis and Treatment of Pituitary Tumors (J. Linfoot, Ed.), pp 245-269, Raven Press, 1979.

51. S. GRAFFMAN and B. LARSSON, "High Energy Protons for Radiotherapy," Atom Kern Energie 27, 148-153 (1976).

52. R. N. KJELLBERG and B. KLIMAN, "Lifetime Effectiveness - A System of Therapy for Pituitary Adenomas," Recent Advances in Diagnosis and Treatment of Pituitary Tumors (Linfoot, Ed.), pp 269-289, Raven Press, 1979.

53. H. D. SUIT, M. GOITEIN, J. E. TEPPER, L. VERHEY, A. M. KOEHLER, R. SCHNEIDER, and E. GRAGONDAS, "Clinical Experience and Expectations with Protons and Heavy Ions," Int. J. Radiat. Oncol. Biol. Phys. 3, 115-125 (1977).

54. W. M. SAUNDERS, D. H. CHAR, J. M. QUIVEY, J. R. CASTRO, G. T. Y. CHEN, J. M. COLLIER, A. CARTIGNY, E. A. BLAKELY, J. T. LYMAN, S. R. ZINK, and C. A. TOBIAS, "Precision High Dose Radiotherapy: Helium Ion Treatment of Uveal Melanoma," Int. J. Radiat. Oncol. Biol. Phys. 11, 227-233 (1985).

55. J. I. FABRIKANT, J. T. LYMAN, and Y. HOSOBUCHI, "Stereotactic Heavy-Ion Bragg-Peak Radiosurgery for Intracranial Vascular Disorders: Method for Treatment of Deep Arteriovenous Malformations," Br. J. Radiol. 57, 479-490 (1984).

56. C. A. TOBIAS and P. W. TODD, "Heavy Charged Particles in Cancer Therapy," Radiobiology and Radiotherapy, Monograph No. 24, pp 1-21, National Cancer Institute, 1967.

57. C. A. TOBIAS, "The Future of Heavy-Ion Science in Biology and Medicine," (20th Failla Memorial Lecture), Radiat. Res. 103, 1-33 (1985).

58. J. R. CASTRO and M. REIMERS, "Charged Particle Radiotherapy of Selected Tumors in the Head and Neck," Int. J. Rad. Oncol. Biol. Phys. 14, 711-720 (1988).

THE EVOLUTION OF A MASS SPECTROMETRY BASED ON NUCLEAR FISSION

Ronald D. Macfarlane, Texas A&M University,
Department of Chemistry
College Station, Texas 77843
(409) 845-2021

ABSTRACT

An account is given of the events leading up to the first utilization of the spontaneous fission of ^{252}Cf for the mass spectrometry of large molecules. It is based on an observation made 16 years ago that nuclear fission fragments can stimulate the emission of fragile, involatile molecular ions of biomolecules from surfaces. This has led to the design of a new mass spectrometric method that utilizes the unique properties of the fission event. A few examples of some applications to biomedical research are presented. Finally, there is a brief account of what has been learned about the mechanisms of ion emission from nuclear fission tracks.

INTRODUCTION

"Frisch would calculate later that the energy from each bursting uranium nucleus would be sufficient to make a grain of sand visibly jump". This quotation from Richard Rhodes' remarkable account[1] of the first days of the unfolding of the nuclear fission story begun 50 years ago was recounting the realization by Otto Frisch of the enormous energy release in the nuclear fission event; that a process occurring on the microscopic scale could induce an impulse visible in the macroscopic world. This prophetic statement is a fitting beginning to the subject of this paper where the "grains of sand" are high molecular weight proteins and they "visibly jump" when excited by nuclear fission fragments. This seemingly unlikely event is now the basis for one of the most powerful mass spectrometric techniques available in the biotechnology laboratory.

The energy released in the nuclear fission event appears for the most part in the kinetic energy of the fission fragments. It is the loss of the energy of these fission fragments in the surrounding medium that ultimately appears in the heat energy generated in a nuclear reactor. The primary event for the fission fragments is the formation of a fission track in the medium. Much is known about fission tracks in different materials[2] and the radiation damage produced by the intense ionization density is so great that visible craters are formed at the surfaces of the most refractory materials.[3]

Despite the fact that energy dissipation from the fission track is the initial stage of the conversion of nuclear energy to power, we have only fragmentary (so to speak) knowledge of the time evolution of the heavy-ion track. It is known that a microscopic, electrically-conducting plasma is formed in the very early stages.[4] The instantaneous power deposited within a 1 nm segment of the fission track is on the order of 100,000 watts! But in the relaxation of this energy to the surrounding medium, the surface surrounding the fission track is excited to a state that promotes the desorption of complex species such as proteins as intact species. This phenomenon was discovered by accident in the course of a study on the search for second class currents in nuclear beta decay a subject far removed from the world of biomedical mass spectrometry. A brief account is given here of the events leading up to this discovery.

THE DISCOVERY OF ^{252}Cf-PLASMA DESORPTION MASS SPECTROMETRY

The story begins is the early 1970's when there was renewed interest in the fundamental interactions of beta decay and the possible existence of additional components in the weak interaction referred to as second class currents. We had just completed a study of the beta decay of ^{20}Na which decays to alpha particle unstable states in ^{20}Ne where we found a new method to determine the beta/neutrino correlation from the properties of the beta decay recoil[5].

This experiment piqued our curiosity about the properties of beta decay recoils in general. The literature of the previous decade was rich with beta-recoil related studies because they played an important role in determining the nature of the nuclear weak interaction. In early 1972, we decided to set up an experimental program to use the analysis of beta decay recoil ions as a mass spectrometric method for the detection of new short-lived radionuclides produced in nuclear reactions.

The experiment was based on a technique that we had developed a decade earlier for the rapid transport of short-lived nuclides from the high radiation field at the site of production to a low level radiation area where the sensitive methods of detection could be carried out. We called this technique the helium jet recoil transport method[6]. It is still being used for the study of short-lived nuclei, including the new element programs in the USA and USSR.

The developmental problem that had to be solved was to figure out how to form a monolayer source of the short-lived species in steady state and in vacuum. This was accomplished in the following manner which is illustrated in Figure 1. When a nuclear reaction occurs in the target under bombardment from a cyclotron beam, the nuclear reaction recoils are ejected from the target into a helium atmosphere saturated with water vapor. The recoils thermalize in the helium and attach to water clusters generated by the ionizing radiation of the cyclotron beam that passes through the chamber. The recoil/cluster complex is then differentially pumped through a long capillary tube using He as the carrier gas. The capillary terminates in a vacuum chamber, shown on the right in figure 1.

The He stream emerges from the tip of the capillary which acts as a supersonic nozzle. The He expands in a large cone while the heavier water cluster/recoil complex species continue in a highly collimated forward direction through a skimmer that

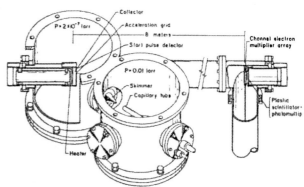

FIG 1 SCHEMATIC OF BETA RECOIL MASS SPECTROMETER

effectively separates the He carrier gas from the recoil/cluster complex. These species enter a second chamber under high vacuum and impinge on a heated surface (labelled collector in Fig. 1) where the water clusters evaporate leaving the radioactive atom on the surface of the collector. When beta decay occurs, the beta particle is detected using a scintillation counter mounted directly behind the collector. The beta decay daughter recoils from the surface and is accelerated through an electrostatic field to a fixed energy. The time-of-flight (TOF) of the beta recoil is measured after it traverses an 8 m path using the pulse from the beta detector as a time-zero marker.

This method worked quite well and a series of studies were initiated to search for new short-lived species in the region of neutron deficient nuclei. As we began to accumulate beta recoil spectra, it became apparent that there were peaks that were common to all spectra and could not be explained as being due to beta decay recoils. Figure 2 shows two beta recoil spectra that illustrate the effect. The spectra are from beta recoils derived from species produced in the bombardment of Ni foils with ^{3}He at 2 different bombarding energies. Note that in both spectra a peak at m/z 45 appears. It also appeared in every spectrum that was recorded no matter what the target/projectile combination. We postulated that this peak was due to ionization of impurity species on the surface by the beta decay with the formation of charged products in coincidence with the detected beta particles.

To test this hypothesis, we inserted a

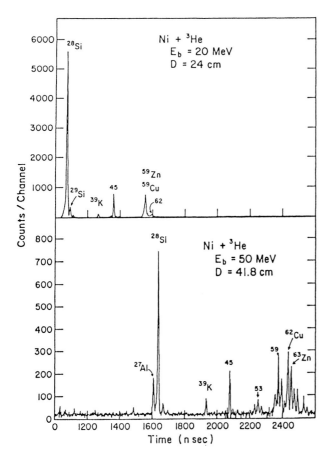

FIG 2 BETA RECOIL MASS SPECTRA

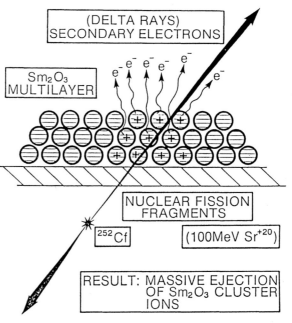

FIG 3 HOW A ^{252}Cf-SOURCE IS USED TO DESORB MOLECULAR IONS FROM THIN FILMS

^{252}Cf was initiated in February, 1973. Over the next several months, we accumulated mass spectra from several matrices including some of biological origin while we continued with our studies with the beta decay recoils.

One of the most important early measurements was the first determination of the mass spectrum of a marine toxin called tetrodotoxin. This molecule is one of a class of biomolecules that is difficult to analyze by mass spectrometry because the molecule is involatile because it is so polar and at the same time, it is thermally unstable which means that it is not possible to make gas phase molecules by heating. Figure 4 shows the ^{252}Cf-PDMS result for this species. We coined the term "^{252}Cf-plasma desorption mass spectrometry (^{252}Cf-PDMS) by analogy with techniques, field desorption which was developed by Beckey.[7]

Our first paper on the method appeared in July, 1974[8] and an article in Science two years later summarized our results on the diversity of molecules that can be analyzed by ^{252}Cf-PDMS.[9] Our results stimulated considerable interest in the mass spectrometry community. Perhaps the most important contribution ^{252}Cf-PDMS made was the demonstration that it was possible to produce gas

^{252}Cf source behind the collector to determine whether the effect could be enhanced by the more heavily ionizing fission fragment. An additional attractive feature of the use of a ^{252}Cf source was that the complementary fission fragment could be used to generate a time-zero signal in the same manner as the beta particles in the original beta recoil measurement. The answer came immediately. Not only was the m/z 45 ion observed with much higher intensity, but a host of other ions was also detected ranging in mass from m/z 1 to 100. We then decided to coat the surface with a thin layer of ^{144}Sm$_2$O$_3$, which we had been using as targets for our nuclear studies, and determine whether any ions could be identified with this matrix. The arrangement is depicted in fig. 3. The fission fragment induced mass spectrum contained not only atomic and small molecular ions of Sm but a cluster of samarium oxide ions extending to molecular weights beyond m/z 2000!

This new aspect of the program, the use of fission fragments from the spontaneous fission of

phase molecular ions of complex, fragile, involatile species.

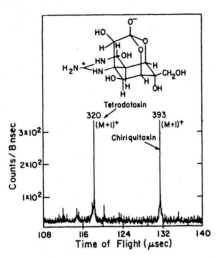

FIG 4 ^{252}Cf-PDMS SPECTRUM OF AN INVOLATILE, UNSTABLE MOLECULE.

It is now recognized that the critical feature of ^{252}Cf-PDMS is the fact that an intense short burst of energy deposited into a matrix can trigger the ejection of surface molecules with low internal excitation. Other researchers soon found that Kev ions and atoms (SIMS[10] and fast atom bombardment, FAB[11]), pulsed lasers (laser desorption[12]) produced similar results and all of these techniques are now part of the arsenal of particle-induced desorption methods. The ^{252}Cf-PDMS method remains as one of the most powerful mass spectrometric methods particularly for the analysis of proteins extending up to molecular weights of 35,000 u.

A commercial version of our first ^{252}Cf-PDMS instrument was introduced by a Swedish firm (Bio-Ion, Nordic. Uppsala) in 1983 and instruments are now operating in leading biotechnology laboratories throughout the world as part of their routine analysis of biopolymers and pharmaceuticals. A recent review of applications of ^{252}Cf-PDMS has been published.[13]

Just 15 years ago, mass spectrometry of simple amino acids was considered to be a difficult measurement. Now the particle-induced mass spectrometric methods are being used in the analysis of the full spectrum of biomolecules: vitamins, biopolymers, antibiotics, the building blocks of cell walls, extending the mass range to

over 100,000 u! Research and development to improve these methods is one of the most active and rapidly changing activities in the field of mass spectrometry. The introduction of ^{252}Cf-plasma desorption mass spectrometry has played a role in this renaissance.

DESCRIPTION OF THE ^{252}Cf-PDMS SYSTEM

Figure 5 shows a schematic of a basic ^{252}Cf-PD mass spectrometer in its current form.

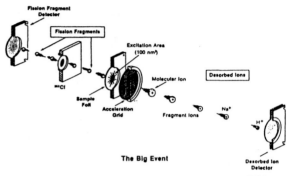

FIG 5 SCHEMATIC DIAGRAM OF THE ^{252}Cf-PLASMA DESORPTION MASS SPECTROMETER.

The sample to be studied is mounted on the surface of a thin foil and inserted into the mass spectrometer. The Bio-Ion system has a wheel onto which many samples can be mounted at one time. The wheel is inserted into a vacuum interlock and analyses can commence within a few minutes of introduction into vacuum. Sample positioning is computer controlled such that the entire set of samples can be analyzed (positive and negative ion spectra) without user intervention. For an analysis, the sample is positioned in front of the ^{252}Cf source, a voltage applied to the sample (positive or negative depending on the polarity of ions to be analyzed) and the measurement commences. The geometry is set up so that for each fission fragment that passes through the sample, the complementary fission fragment is detected by an electron multiplier located behind the ^{252}Cf source. A fission fragment typically ejects 5-10 ions and the TOF for each ion is recorded using a time-to-digital converter which is designed to operate in a "multi-stop" mode so that a single start pulse can initiate the measurement of a set of TOF values for the ions ejected by a single fission fragment. The experiment is repeated 2000 times per second and the data are stored in an array of time interval bins. Data analysis involves generating a calibration curve to convert TOF to m/z using ions of known mass in the spectrum. Masses of other ions in the spectrum are measured from their TOF values using the calibration curve.[13] For a protein with mass 20,000 u, it generally requires 15-30 min acquisition time to determine mass with the desired precision of 1-2 u.

ACCELERATOR STUDIES

Shortly after the first results on ^{252}Cf-PDMS were published, programs were initiated at accelerators at Erlangen, Uppsala, Orsay and Darmstadt to elucidate the role of the projectile in the process. These studies were carried out by nuclear physicists familiar with the notion of measuring excitation functions, angular distributions. Sundqvist has published a recent review of these studies which have now spanned a decade of activity.[15] The advantage of using heavy ion beams from an accelerator is in the control of the incident projectile. Energy, mass, charge state, angle of incidence can all be independently varied.

The conclusions of these studies are as follows. The ion desorption process is directly linked to the electronic stopping power of the incident ion and not to any collision cascade. For an incident ion passing through a thin film, only the energy deposited within 10 layers from the exit surface is contributing to ion emission processes. More oblique trajectories relative to the surface of the target have higher ion emission yields. Ion emission yields peak at the maximum of the dE/dX curve which corresponds to 1 MeV/u. This means that the unattenuated fission fragments have near optimum ion velocities for desorbing ions. Depending on the volatility of the matrix, up to 10 monolayers of material are sputtered from the surface with neutral molecule ejection yields as high as 1500/incident ion. Only a few percent of these are charged. Thus, a rather coherent description of the role of the incident ion has been obtained from these accelerator studies.

DYNAMICS OF ION EMISSION FROM FISSION TRACKS

With the role of the incident ion in the ion emission process established, attention is being directed toward the structure of the fission track as it evolves from the initial track of intense ionization to some final state. One of the questions is where in the track structure ion emission is occurring. A spectacular electron micrograph of a fission track in MoO_3 was taken many years ago by Chatterton.[16] This is reproduced in Fig. 6. It is clear that there are two regions where the damage is quite different. One region is close to the initial trajectory where melting of the crystal has occurred. But the region surrounding this area has preserved much of the crystallinity of the material. We have been able to identify ion emission from these two regions by searching for correlations in the angular distributions of the emitted ions with the angle of the incident track.

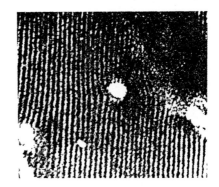

FIG 6 ELECTRON MICROGRAPH OF FISSION TRACK IN MoO_3 SHOWING DISLOCATIONS AROUND TRACK. (REF. 3)

Those ions that are strongly correlated with the direction of the track trajectory are small ions such as H^+, H_2^+, CH_3^+ and appear to be components of the plasma produced in the fission track. Fig. 7 shows the kinetic energy distributions for two of these ions, H^+, and H_2^+. From the measured average energy, the corresponding Maxwell-Boltzmann distribution was calculated. This is the smooth curve superimposed on the data points. The temperature at the exit of the fission track at the time that these ions are emitted is on the order of 27,000 K.

For the emission of heavier molecular ions, the correlation with the axis of the fission track does not exist. This suggests that at the site where the emission of fragile molecular ions occurs, the energy flow has been essentially randomized so that the connection with track geometry is lost. We suggest that this corresponds to the region in the MoO_3 micrograph where there is sufficient energy to produce dislocations but not enough to incur melting.

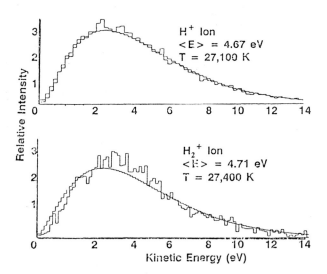

FIG 7　KINETIC ENERGY DISTRIBUTIONS FOR H$^+$ AND H$_2^+$ IONS EMITTED FROM FISSION TRACKS.

Some theoretical work has been carried out by Lucchese on this problem.[18] His simulations show that if the substrate is rapidly heated and there is weak coupling of the surface molecule to the substrate, desorption of the species will occur with minimal transfer of internal energy to the molecule. The kinetic energy distribution of the desorbed species will reflect the surface temperature of the substrate at the site of desorption. We have been able to directly measure the kinetic energy distribution of a small peptide, bradykinin, which has a molecular weight of 1060 u. This is shown in Fig. 8. The average energy corresponds to a temperature of 20,000 K which implies that this is the surface temperature at the site of the desorption. For larger molecules, the attachment of the adsorbate to the substrate becomes stronger which means that considerably more fragmentation occurs. This is what is observed.

In order to be able to desorb larger molecular ions, attention is now being directed toward finding suitable substrates that will result in the desorption of cooler molecular ions. One of these substrates, nitrocellulose, has been found to have this property. In a very recent development in our laboratory, we have found that if the substrate is a collection of small, sublimable molecules and the protein molecule is adsorbed to this substrate, the

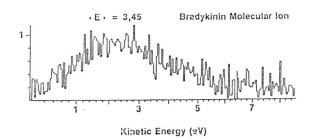

FIG 8　KINETIC ENERGY DISTRIBUTION FOR A LARGE MOLECULAR ION DESORBED FROM A FISSION TRACK.

sublimation of the underlayer carries with it the protein molecular ion with extremely low internal excitation.[18] The development of suitable substrates for moderating the energy from the fission track to the desorption site will be the key to how successful ^{252}Cf-PDMS will be in future applications to higher molecular weight species.

ACKNOWLEDGEMENTS

I wish to thank my colleagues and students, D.F. Torgerson, C.J. McNeal, J. Hill, D. Jacobs, P. Mudgett, and B. Wolf for their very significant contributions to the project over the years. I would also like to express my appreciation to the Department of Energy, National Science Foundation, National Institutes of Health, and R.A. Welch Foundation for their financial support of this project.

REFERENCES

1.　R. RHODES, The Making of the Atomic Bomb. Simon & Schuster, Inc., New York. (1986).

2.　R. L. FLEISCHER, P. B. PRICE, and R. M. WALKER, "Ion Explosion Spike Mechanism for Formation of Charged-Particle Tracks in Solids," J. Appl. Phys., 36, 3645 (1965).

3.　F. P. BOWDEN and L. T. CHADDERTON "Fission Fragment Damage to Crystal Lattices: Dislocation Formation," Proc. Royal Soc. A, 269, 143 (1962).

4.　L. TOMMASINO, N. KLEIN, and P. SOLOMON, "Thin-film Breakdown Counter of Fission Fragments," J. Appl. Phys., 46, 1484 (1975).

5.	R. D. MACFARLANE, N. S. OAKEY, and R. J NICKLES, "Beta-Neutrino Correlations and Longitudinal Nuclear Alignment in the Decay of ^{20}Na," Phys. Lett., 34B, 1333 (1970).

6.	R. D. MACFARLANE and R. D. GRIFFIOEN, "A System for Studying Accelerator-Produced Short-Lived Alpha Emitters," Nucl. Instrum. Meth., 24, 461 (1963).

7.	H. D. BECKEY, A. HEINDRICHS, and H. U WINKLER, Int. J. Mass Spectrom. Ion Phys., 3, 9 (1970).

8.	D. F. TORGERSON, R. P. SKOWRONSKI, and R. D. MACFARLANE, "New Approach to the Mass Spectroscopy of Non-volatile Compounds," Biochem. Biophys. Res. Commun., 60, 616 (1974).

9.	R. D. MACFARLANE and D. F. TORGERSON, Californium-252 Plasma Desorption Mass Spectrometry," Science, 191, 920 (1976).

10.	A. BENNINGHOVEN, D. JASPERS, and W. SICHTERMANN, "Secondary Ion Emission of Amino Acids," Appl. Phys. 11, 35 (1976).

11.	M. BARBER, R. S. BORDOLI, G. J. ELLIOTT, R. D. SEDGWICK, and A. N. TYLER, "Fast Atom Bombardment Mass Spectrometry," Anal. Chem. 54, 645A (1982).

12.	M. A. POSTHUMUS, P. C. KISTEMAKER, H. L. C. MEUZELAAR, and T. N. de BRAU, "Laser Desorption Mass Spectrometry," Anal. Chem. 50, 985 (1978).

13.	B. U. R. SUNDQVIST and R. D. MACFARLANE, "252-Cf Plasma Desorption Mass Spectrometry," Mass Spectrom. Rev., 4, 421 (1985).

14.	R. D. MACFARLANE, "252-Cf Plasma Desorption Mass Spectrometry - Large Molecules, Software, and the Essence of Time," Anal. Chem., 55, 1247A (1983).

15.	B. R. SUNDQVIST, "On the Production of Gaseous Ions of Large Organic Molecules by Energetic Particle Impact Methods," Adv. in Mass Spec. 11, 234 (1989).

16.	D. L. JACOBS, "Initial Kinetic Energy of Secondary Ions Desorbed by ^{252}Cf Fission Fragments," Thesis. Texas A&M University (1988).

17.	S-L. LEE and R. R. LUCCHESE, "Simulation of Heavy Ion Induced Desorption of Biomolecules from Surfaces Using the Popcorn Model," Surf. Sci. 193, 486 (1988)

18.	B. WOLF and R. D. MACFARLANE (unpublished results) 1989.

INDUSTRIAL USE OF FISSION PRODUCTS

Joseph Silverman
Laboratory for Radiation and Polymer Science
Department of Chemical and Nuclear Engineering
University of Maryland, College Park, MD 20742-2111

Perhaps the most disappointing and surprising development in the fifty year history of nuclear fission is the small role fission products play in modern technology. As a large and potentially inexpensive source of ionizing radiation, fission products were expected to offer major practical benefits for the following reasons:

1. The chemical changes produced per unit of absorbed radiation energy are very high. Furthermore the large quanta emitted by radioactive nuclides can initiate endoergic processes at low temperatures. Radiation sterilization of food, crosslinking of plastic wire insulation, initiation of polymerization reactions, etc. could be done, in principle, on an industrial scale with major savings in energy and cost.

2. The transmission and reflection of fission product emissions can be used to measure the thickness and composition of a wide variety of materials. Thickness gauging and radiographic analysis became immediate industrial prospects. Ultimately, tomographic analysis of density and atomic composition distributions in complex shapes were certain to follow.

3. The high sensitivity of the detection of ionizing radiation affords the opportunity of routine use of fission product tracers to monitor the many processes of complex industrial installations such as petroleum and metals refineries.

The attractive opportunities stimulated imaginative efforts to realize their fulfillment, but their direct impact has been minor. Fission products have not fared well, not only in somewhat indirect competition with nonradioactive alternatives, but also in direct competition with other radiation sources, especially electron accelerators and ^{60}Co.

Stable isotopes and modern optical and magnetic resonance techniques no longer lag radioactive tracers in sensitivity; also they often offer the advantage of molecular rather than mere atomic analysis.

There are some 600 accelerators in routine industrial use employing electrons in the 0.2-10 MeV range. Electron energies below 3 MeV are used to cure acrylic coatings and to crosslink plastic wire insulation, electrical connectors, rubber products and food packaging; the higher energies are used mainly for radiation sterilization of single-use disposable medical supplies. About 150 ^{60}Co sources, each in the megacurie range, are used, mainly for sterilization of medical supplies. There are only 5 ^{137}Cs sources of comparable gamma power in industrial use.

X-ray machines tend to dominate radiographic and tomographic applications. Positive ion accelerators produce neutron deficient radionuclides which are often preferable to their neutron rich fission isotopes in medical applications. The oft-proposed use of spent fuel rods as a source of ionizing radiation or thermal power is by now unworthy of serious discussion. Only minor use has been made of ^{90}Sr as a compact heat source in marine and space applications. Chemonuclear reactors and multipurpose reactors with chemonuclear loops have been proposed for the direct absorption of fission product recoils and their decay energy in chemical reagents; the purpose is to produce massive quantities of chemicals such as nitrates and ozone. These efforts have been rejected. The stable precious metals in the accumulating fission product wastes are possibly of long term industrial interest in the unlikely event that these wastes are mined for their values.

There is one major triumph for fission product technology: the application of ^{99}Mo and its daughter ^{99m}Tc as an almost universal tracer system in nuclear medicine. It is the basis of perhaps the only multimillion dollar- per-annum application of fission products to date.

There is also an indirect triumph. Most of the potential applications were known before 1939, but it was fission and its bright promise that made ionizing radiation and radionuclides widely available, and that stimulated the atomic energy research programs which are mainly responsible for the data base and theoretical structure now used so effectively by the competitors it inspired.

REACTORS II

Chairman
Robert E. Carter (NIST)

RESEARCH REACTORS: A PRODUCT OF THE PAST,

THE PATHWAY TO THE FUTURE

W. L. Whittemore
General Atomics
San Diego, California 92138
(619) 455-3000

ABSTRACT

Early experimenters in nuclear research were handicapped by low neutron intensities until neutron sources based on the fission of uranium were developed. This paper treats research reactors which are used as neutron sources for beam ports, in-core irradiations, and isotope production. The development of research reactors has accompanied and further stimulated increasingly complex experiments using neutrons. These reactors evolved rapidly from the first low power graphite pile to reactors operating at tens of megawatts and producing neutron source fluxes up to 10^{15} n/cm^2·s. During the past 40 years, research made possible by modern research reactors has led to notable advances in applied and fundamental science. Even more complex and important results can be expected from research with the newer, special purpose, and ultrahigh flux reactors in the future.

1. INTRODUCTION

The discovery of the neutron by Chadwick in 1932 was followed quickly by the realization that neutrons offer unique possibilities for the investigation of nuclear phenomena. It also became rapidly apparent that the strongest radium-beryllium neutron sources then available were distressingly weak compared to the experimental needs. A partial solution to the problem of weak neutron sources was found in the various accelerators that were developed starting about 1937. However, it was not until the development of the fission chain reactions in the neutron "pile" (later called "reactor") that intensities of neutron sources finally began to approach the needs of experimenters. A recurrent theme throughout the development of research reactors has been the constant request for ever more intense sources of neutrons to supply the needs of increasingly complex experiments.

2. THE RESEARCH REACTOR

The development of the nuclear reactor has progressed along two rather distinct paths that can be designated generally as power reactors and nonpower reactors. Nonpower reactors assume a multiplicity of shapes, sizes, steady state and pulsed power levels, and uses, and they generally separate into test reactors and research reactors. That class known generally as research reactors is the subject of this paper. Research reactors are those reactors used for a broad spectrum of research in areas of physics, engineering, chemistry, biology, and medicine, and are equipped to permit experiments with beams of neutrons and environments of neutrons for irradiations. The power of the research reactors ranges from a few kilowatts to many tens of megawatts. They are generally operated in steady state, although many can be pulsed to very high power levels for brief periods. The research reactor provides beams of neutrons via beam ports that usually extend inward through the biological shield to the core (highest source flux regions). The regions of high intensity fluxes of neutrons occur either within the reactor core or in special regions outside but near the core.

In certain areas of research and nuclear engineering tests, the distinction between test and research reactors becomes somewhat blurred. For the most part, test reactors will be treated in a separate paper in this conference. The research discussed herein involves both the use of neutrons as a tool for investigation as, for example, thermal neutron scattering studies of condensed matter, and, on the other hand, fundamental investigation in which the neutron itself plays the essential role. Examples of the latter are the measurement of the neutron electric dipole moment, the decay of neutrons, the fundamental elementary thermal neutron — neutron scattering cross section, or the neutron-antineutron oscillation experiment.

Glasstone[1] has provided an excellent summary of the early research reactors. The status of research reactors throughout the world has been reviewed and kept up to date by the International Atomic Energy Agency[2] (IAEA). The early research reactors evolved as upscale versions of the first graphite "pile" (i.e., CP-1) where graphite was used as moderator and reflector. The first research reactor at Brookhaven National Laboratory (BNL) was such a reactor (1950)[a] with an operating power up to 28 MW. While its construction specifically accommodated many beam experiments as well as in-pile irradiations and isotope production, the maximum source flux (at about 3×10^{12} n/$cm^2 \cdot s$) was quite low. The NRX research reactor in Canada (1947) was a facility with a high source flux for that early time (2×10^{13} n/$cm^2 \cdot s$), produced with a power of 30 MW using a heavy water moderator and a graphite reflector. Early on, more efficient reactor systems were developed (i.e., larger neutron flux per watt of power) using the concept of heavy water (D_2O) as moderator and with reflectors of D_2O, or D_2O and graphite, or beryllium. An example of this approach was the CP-5 research reactor (1950) which yielded a thermal neutron flux of about 2×10^{13} n/$cm^2 \cdot s$ with a power of only 1 MW. The materials testing reactor (MTR) was developed in Idaho (1952) and served for many years as a research reactor as well as a material testing reactor. More details concerning this important test and research reactor can be found in another paper on Test Reactors to be presented at this conference. The development of the MTR facility is important for another reason. The MTR fuel itself set a standard for many years as fuel suitable for the much smaller research reactors, especially those with maximum power levels of 1 to 3 MW.

Coincident with the development of research reactors in the United States and Canada, similar reactor developments were being pursued in Europe and, at a somewhat later time, in Japan and other sites in Asia. By the early 1950s, increasing numbers of research reactors were operating in national reactor centers in Europe (such as Harwell, England; MOL, Belgium; Kjeller, Norway; Riso, Denmark; Studsvick, Sweden; Petten, the Netherlands; Saclay, France). Typical reactor power levels for these reactors ranged up to 30 MW. In recent years higher power research reactors in the United States and abroad have included the following facilities:

- 20 MW, National Institute of Science and Technology.

- 60 MW, Brookhaven National Laboratory.

- 85 MW, Oak Ridge National Laboratory.

- 57 MW, ILL, Grenoble, France.

- 100 MW, Dimitrovgrad, Russia.

- 120 MW-s (23,000 MW), pulsed facilities at Tokai-Mura, Japan and Pitesti, Romania.

---

[a]The date in parentheses indicate when the facility first came on-line.

In addition to the larger research reactors located at the various national research institutes, the smaller research reactors proliferated. These were multipurpose research reactors with power levels typically up to 1 MW, but with some power levels up to 5 MW. Starting in the mid-1950s, these were located around the world at universities, research institutes, and at industrial sites. Many of these early reactors used MTR-type plate fuel. The early manufacturers of these research reactors included General Electric, Allis Chalmers, Atomics International, Curtiss Wright, Lockheed, and American Standard, to mention a few. Starting in 1958, General Atomics entered the arena with its very successful family of TRIGA reactors. To date, more than 60 TRIGA research reactors have been installed worldwide (23 countries) with steady-state power levels ranging from 16 kW to 15 MW and peak pulsed power levels that range up to 23,000 MW at some installations.

The information summarized by IAEA[2] provides an international perspective on research reactors. Starting in 1955, only 14 countries had research reactors; of these, only 4 were developing countries. By 1988, a total of 61 countries possessed research reactors with more than 35 of these in developing countries. The total number of research reactors grew from about 30 in 1955 to more than 375 worldwide in 1975. Of this number, the Eastern European countries including Russia had a total of 41 research reactors. Unfortunately, the total number worldwide has declined slightly since 1975 to about 300 at present. During the recent period of declining total number of research reactors worldwide, new facilities were being designed and built, and older facilities were being upgraded. Two new 30 MW research reactors are being installed in Indonesia and Korea. Two new research reactors are being completed in the United States, the 1-MW TRIGA Mark II at the University of Texas and the neutron radiographic facility based on a 1-MW TRIGA reactor at the U.S. Air Force Base in Sacramento, California. Older research reactors are being upgraded and modernized at a number of centers in Europe and in Japan. Statistics show, however, that more of the older facilities are being decommissioned than new ones are being added.

The decrease in total number of research reactors is unfortunate for the future of neutron research. When considering the importance of neutrons for research, it is useful to remember that neutrons are neither cheap nor plentiful. If the research can be done by other means, it probably will be. However, the large number of research areas where neutrons do uniquely well is large and demonstrates the real value of neutrons. It is distressing to report that no Nobel prize has yet been awarded for neutron scattering research. And yet, annual funding at a level of hundreds of millions of dollars of very precious research monies is devoted to neutron scattering and allied research just because of the unique value of this type of research. The fact is that modern scientific investigation cannot do without neutrons.

3. ANCILLARY EQUIPMENT

The research reactor is more than simply a high intensity source of neutrons for research. The needs of the experimenter place requirements on the quality and on the energy spectrum of the neutron beams as well as on the intensity of the beams. In many instances, the design of the reactor including choice of fuel will strongly influence the quality of the beam as judged by the content of gamma rays and fast neutrons (both of which are normally considered unwanted background). In certain instances, a combination of reactor design and ancillary equipment is used to control the neutron background in the desired slow neutron beams. An example of this is the use of neutron guide tubes to conduct cold neutron beams from the reactor to the user location with little or no background in the beam. Use of straight, internally reflecting guide tubes for thermal neutrons is a later development. For this application, the content of fast neutrons in the resulting beam, while not eliminated as is the case for bent guide tubes used for cold neutrons, is reduced because of the reduced acceptance angles for the system.

The guide hall is a relatively recent innovation based on the extensive use of guide tubes to conduct numerous beams of thermal and cold neutrons from the reactor source to a distant experimental hall where the background radiation from the reactor is greatly reduced or eliminated for the most part. Combining an intense reactor source of neutrons (20 to 100 MW) with careful use of beam guide tubes has produced an experimental area in which dozens of experiments can be conducted simultaneously. Figure 1 is a photograph of part of the guide hall at the Institut Max von Laue – Paul Langevin (ILL) in Grenoble, France. This guide hall can provide several neutron beams for up to 35 separate experimental setups. Most of these experiments depend for success on additional specialized equipment. Examples of these are: modern versions of the three-axis spectrometers; back scattering spectrometers; neutron spin-echo spectrometers; high resolution powder diffractometers; four-circle diffractometers; diffractometers with photographic detection using modified Laue techniques; polarized neutron spectrometers; small angle scattering instruments including diffuse scattering and low Q, high resolution spectrometers. The above examples of experimental apparatus are used mainly for a broad application of thermal neutron scattering techniques.

Nuclear and fundamental physics experiments frequently use other types of equipment. These typically include the following: fission prod-

Fig. 1. VIEW OF PART OF THE GUIDE HALL AT ILL, GRENOBLE, FRANCE

uct mass separators; conversion electron spectrometers; gamma ray spectrometers; neutron interferometers; ultra cold neutron sources for electric dipole moment and neutron lifetime measurements, and for neutron optics and storage bottle experiments.

Cold and hot neutron sources are two important specialized ancillary modifications. Starting in the mid- to late-1950s, cold sources such as liquid hydrogen or deuterium have been installed in or near the cores of research reactors to improve the intensity of neutrons with energy below the Bragg cutoff of beryllium (≤ 0.005 eV) by rethermalizing to lower moderator temperature. In more recent times, safer cold sources employing solid D_2O or mixtures of solid D_2O and H_2O have been successfully used. Hot sources usually employing high temperature graphite are used to enhance the epithermal neutron spectrum in the narrow energy band (approximately 0.1 to 0.3 eV) where the normal Maxwellian distribution has decreased significantly from the peak thermal flux (0.025 to 0.035 eV) and where the available peak temperatures in the hot moderator can provide useful rethermalization through increased values of moderator temperature.

Specialized types of ancillary equipment permit samples to be irradiated in regions of high neutron flux for activation analysis or isotope production or to undergo neutron irradiations under controlled temperature and environmental conditions.

4. NOTABLE RESULTS

The research reactor has been the focus of a broad range of applications to problems in nuclear science and technology since the 1950s. Scientific research on neutron and nuclear physics, chemistry, biology and medicine, as well as applications on a broad front including the petroleum industry, archaeology, criminology, metallurgy, solid state physics, and materials science exploit the features of the research reactor. The smaller research reactors ($\leq$5 MW) that have been in operation during the past 25 years have made possible the great majority of this excellent research. The principles of neutron research, properties of the neutron, and nuclear applications have been pioneered at these smaller reactor facilities usually associated with a university or an institute. Many of the smaller reactors today are still providing excellent, original research with steady-state power levels ranging from a few hundred kilowatts to a few megawatts. Many of these reactors in the power range up to 2 MW also can be routinely pulsed to high levels of instantaneous power (250 to 2000 MW). Figure 2 is a photograph of a heavily used research reactor at the Johannes Gutenberg University in Mainz, Germany. Their TRIGA reactor has a steady state power of 100 kW and a capability of producing pulses with a peak power of 250 MW. Much of the research is conducted using the pulsed capability to study isotopes with ultrashort half-lives.

While considerable worthwhile research is conducted at the smaller research reactors

Fig. 2. REACTOR HALL FOR MAINZ TRIGA REACTOR SHOWING THE FAST TRANSFER AND RAPID CHEMICAL SEPARATION SETUP FOR SHORT HALF-LIFE ISOTOPES

($<$5 MW), research reactors with power in the range 5 to 30 MW and above are currently providing opportunities to perform extensive original research in many frontier areas of science. A listing of specially notable results coming from the use and application of research reactors regardless of power levels will attest to the value of research reactors in the past and to what can be expected in the future. Two publications[3,4] have included numerous examples of results.

To provide a broad base on which to draw, the writer has contacted more than 35 recognized authorities in all fields of neutron research to seek their opinions on the most important results of nearly 50 years of research with research reactors. As the reader may expect, a number held strong opinions on one or another noteworthy result. These experts commented on the value of:

- Early measurements of Reines and Cowan on neutrinos

- Gravity effects on neutrons

- Cosmology and the formation of elements

- Determination of the capture cross section of protons for neutrons

- Production of plentiful medical isotopes

- Production of significant quantities of transuranic elements

- Neutron lifetime measurement

Other experts listed the results in fundamental neutron physics as being of the greatest value. These include:

- Measurements on the helicity of the neutrino

- Experiments to establish a limit to the electric dipole moment of the neutron

- Precise measurements of the neutron magnetic moment

- Experiments on possible neutrino oscillations

- Experiments on possible neutron-antineutron oscillations

- Experiments on the wave properties of the neutron including the recent measurements of quantum interference with split beams

The largest number of experts expressed almost universal agreement that the greatest value of neutron research lies in the study of both structure and dynamics of condensed materials using the scattering of slow neutrons. In particular, many pointed out that neutrons are uniquely valuable in the study of magnetic structure including that of antiferromagnetic materials and rare earth metals. Most of the present knowledge of high temperature super-conductors has come from neutron scattering research. Polymer physics as well as the study of colloids frequently depend on neutron results to resolve structural uncertainties. An example of the latter is the important result from small angle neutron scattering (SANS) which uniquely resolved the matter of conformation of polymer molecules in bulk materials. SANS measurements confirmed much earlier predictions that the basic molecular structure is the same whether the polymer is in dilute or concentrated form. In fact, neutron scattering experiments will always be needed for the prediction and development of new materials with special physical properties. The results from neutron scattering have led to important findings in structural biology over the past twenty years. These have included the structure of the ribosomal subunit, structure of chromosomes, water structure of proteins, and the biologic function in muscle contraction. From the results set forth herein, it seems clear that no other experimental technique has had the same impact on such a broad variety of solid state and condensed matter problems as has the use of scattered neutrons.

5. THE FUTURE OF RESEARCH REACTORS

As noted earlier in this presentation, the complexity and sophistication of present-day neutron scattering experiments and other neutron beam experiments have continuously placed demands for more intense neutron sources. For example, the development of techniques capable of investigating the structure of tiny organic crystals and to study energy transfers as small as 10^{-8} eV in condensed materials requires high source intensities of neutrons in order that experiment running time shall be kept within manageable limits. To meet these and other needs, the large ILL reactor at Grenoble, France was built and is operated under a multinational charter. Its power level is about 57 MW, producing a source flux of about 10^{15} n/cm^2·s.

In recent years, it has become increasingly clear that a need exists for a source of even higher intensity than 10^{15} n/cm^2·s. Plans for such research reactors are being pursued both in the United States and in Russia. The Russian reactor PIK is under construction with completion planned for 1992. Its power level is set at 100 MW with a source neutron flux of 5×10^{15} n/cm^2·s.

The Advanced Neutron Source (ANS) is in the serious planning stage in the United States.

This is to be a superior neutron source for neutron scattering experiments as well as for sample irradiations and the production of transuranic elements. The proposed power level is about 275 MW producing a source flux of nearly 10^{16} n/cm^2·s. Figure 3 presents a sketch showing a plan view of the ANS facility. The guide hall is an integral part of this facility. The facility will be provided with two cold neutron sources (optimized for different neutron temperatures) and a hot source. According to present plans, this new American facility is to be available for use in the mid- to late-1990s.

The future will see the development of specially designed research reactors for a variety of purposes. The field of neutron radiography is thriving to the extent that special versions of research reactors are being devoted exclusively to neutron radiography. The latest of these is under construction for the U.S. Air Force at Sacramento, California. When commissioned in mid-1989, it will be used exclusively to exploit the unique capability of thermal neutron radiography to detect even small quantities of corrosion in aluminum components of aircraft. In another area, Dr. Hatanaka[5] has had remarkable success in his clinical tests in Japan of boron capture therapy on brain tumors in human patients. Dr. Hatanaka has treated 98 patients between 1968 and 1989 using the Musashi College (Tokyo) 100 kW TRIGA Mark II research reactor. For the class of brain tumors treated (glioblastoma), no other course of treatment including chemotherapy or photon irradiation is effective. His success has reawakened interest worldwide in this most humanitarian of uses for a research reactor. An international society was founded in 1988 for the purpose of promoting boron capture therapy. In many research reactor centers, advanced plans exist for tailoring the neutron beams from several existing research reactors to provide

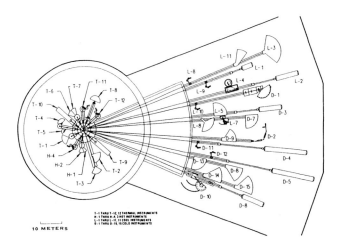

Fig. 3.   PLAN VIEW OF PROPOSED ULTRAHIGH FLUX RESEARCH REACTOR INCLUDING GUIDE HALL FOR THE ADVANCED NEUTRON SOURCE

the optimum penetration of neutrons into tumors within the human brain. At least two special designs for new research reactors have been proposed for this very important application.

Although the recent decrease in total number of research reactors worldwide is disheartening, there is much to encourage guarded optimism for the future of research reactors. Major upgrading efforts have been made or are planned for older facilities in Europe and Japan. New facilities with power levels of 30 MW are being installed in Asia. New very high flux research reactors are either under construction (100 MW PIK reactor in Leningrad) or in an advanced stage of planning (275 MW stage Advanced Neutron Source Reactor, Oak Ridge National Laboratory).

Plans are being pursued for the installation of new research reactors in a number of centers in North Africa, Central Africa, South America, and Asia. Valuable new applications of neutrons such as, for example, for neutron radiography and boron capture therapy can be expected to lead to the construction of new research reactors.

6. CONCLUSION

Since the earliest research reactors in the early to mid-1940s, neutrons from research reactors have become much more readily available for research than from alternative neutron sources such as radioactive sources and accelerators. Not only the properties of the neutron itself as a probe but also the relatively greater source intensities have encouraged wide applications for research reactors in many research domains. In many types of research, neutrons provide an important investi-gative tool. Neutrons are, in fact, indispensable for numerous investigations of condensed media. While the total number of research reactors has declined somewhat in recent years, improvements are being made in existing facilities and new research reactors are being constructed worldwide in all power levels. We can confidently predict that in the next 50 years, neutrons from research reactors will become even more important in modern scientific research than they have been in the past.

REFERENCES

1. S. GLASSTONE, Principles of Nuclear Reactor Engineering, pp. 788-802, D. Van Noshand Co., (1955).

2. Nuclear Research Reactors in the World, Reference Data Series No. 3, International Atomic Energy Agency, Vienna, (1988).

3. Proc. Int. Symp. Use and Development of Lows and Medium Flux Research Reactors, October 16-19, 1983, published in Atomkermenergie, Kerntechnik, 44, Supplement (1984).

4. Proc. Int. Symp. Multipurpose Research Reactors, Grenoble, France, October 19-23, 1987, International Atomic Energy Agency, Vienna (1988).

5. H. HATANAKA, "Clinical Experience with Boron Neutron Capture Therapy," Proc. Int. Symp. Use and Development of Low and Medium Flux Research Reactors, published in Atomkernergie, Kerntechnik, 44 47, Supplement (1984).

TEST REACTOR TECHNOLOGY

D.R. deBoisblanc, Ebasco Services Inc.
2 World Trade Center
New York, N.Y. 10048
(212) 339-3300

ABSTRACT

The Reactor Development Program created a need
for engineering testing of fuels and materials.
The Engineering Test Reactors were developed
around the world in response to this demand.
The design of the test reactors proved to be
different from that of power reactors, carrying
the fuel elements closer to the threshold of
failure, requiring more responsive instrumentation, more rapid control element action, and
inherent self-limiting behaviour under accident
conditions.

The design of the experimental facilities to
exploit these reactors evolved a new,
specialized, branch of engineering, requiring
a very high-level scientific and engineering
team, established a meticulous concern with reliability, the provision for recovery from
their own failures, and detailed attention to
possible interactions with the test reactors.

This paper presents this technology commencing
with the Materials Testing Reactor (MTR) through
the Fast Flux Test Facility, some of the unique
experimental facilities developed to exploit
them, but discusses only cursorily the experiments performed, since sample preparation and
sample analyses were, and to some extent still
are, either classified or proprietary. The
Nuclear Engineering literature is filled with
this information.

INTRODUCTION

It seems incredible that less than ten years
elapsed from the discovery of uranium fission
to the beginning of the construction of the
first experimental reactor whose goal it was to
produce a net output of power. This was the
Experimental Fast Breeder (EBR-I) which also
demonstrated in 1951 that breeding gain was
possible. In the same year, 1948, that EBR-I
was begun, a second reactor, called at first
High Flux Project was also authorized. In
April 1952, this reactor, now called the
Materials Testing Reactor (MTR), commenced its
service at the full power of 30 megawatts.

Originally intended as a research reactor, its
principal facilities for access to the high flux
region were horizontal beam tubes. This
arrangement greatly complicated its use for the
types of power reactor fuels and materials experiments required. Nevertheless, the MTR was
a veritable magnet to the reactor development
community which sought its flux conditions
which were unattainable anywhere else. The in-
genuity that was displayed by the laboratories
and industrial sponsors created a body of design practice that has an influence even today
on materials testing techniques. The use of
the MTR revealed how to make it somewhat more
convenient for experimentalists in the next
generation of test reactors. It is the story
of the unfolding of this technology that is the
subject that I discuss today. Although other
reactors of various types came along to make
their contributions, I will confine my remarks
largely to the MTR type of Test reactors, because this class of reactors, at Idaho and
elsewhere around the world have been so closely
identified with engineering testing of materials.

Power reactor technology applied to military
applications started out near the end of the
decade of the 40's with a substantial legacy
from the weapons program. Theoretical and experimental activities at the various laboratories had explored, in addition to the reactor
needed for the production of plutonium and
other various materials, a wide field of
possible models for power production, lattice
physic studies, and created a generally valid
set of data relating to the fissionable isotopes of uranium. Macroscopic cross-sections,
as well as neutron yields per fission, eta,
spectral distribution of the neutrons, and mass
distribution of the fission fragments had been
measured. Delayed neutron yield, and its implications on reactor kinetics was well enough
described for reactor control systems to be designed. Instrumentation techniques and components were in what might be described as a
good "laboratory" shape. The inventory of
possible materials for moderation, reflection,
and control was almost adequate for firm engineering of reactor systems for serious purposes.

The Naval Reactors Program rapidly set its course toward the development of nuclear propulsion systems. The Aircraft Nuclear Propulsion Program provided its thrust into gas cooled systems and the army had its small power package program. These programs were pursued first in the National Laboratories then in such industrially managed laboratories as Bettis Atomic Power Laboratory and Knolls Atomic Power Laboratory.

In this discussion, I am reliving a period during which it was easy to conceptually design a reactor system to produce power from fissionable material. One knew how to choose nuclear fuel materials, to fabricate fuel elements which could position the fissile materials, clad the uranium with some material to retain fission products, by rolling, coextrusion, isostatic pressing, or one of the many processes known, thereby causing a core containing uranium to be thermally connected to but yet separated from a coolant that could transport heat generated away from the fission source to some device for converting the transported energy into a useful form-perhaps electricity. The physics was well understood, the thermal convection by pumping was easily arranged.

But what was completely unknown was how this nicely contrived system would continue to behave over long periods of operation and in cycling from startup to operating conditions many times during its lifetime. None of the ordinary problems of power producing systems were absent. There were the usual problems of wear, corrosion, vibration, fatigue, and ageing to be expected and dealt with. But there was radiation associated with the fission process, and its aftermath, the fission products. It was the problem created by the need to predict properties affected by radiation fields on materials far beyond what reasonable extrapolation would permit, causing the urge to accelerate the rate at which such information could be acquired, that suggested the use of a high-flux reactor. It was acknowledged that rate effects, spacial gradients, spectral effects, and the ratio of gamma to neutron radiation effects were not going to be the same in the test reactor as in the target reactor, but the advantage of the dramatic change in the time scale of acquisition of information to permit screening candidates dominated the nuclear engineering field. After some time into the testing program had elapsed, these effects began to be understood and steps taken to improve the quality of data by changes in later test reactor designs while also altering test capsule, test loop and other facility designs to be used in the new reactors. The convergence of these two streams are most obvious in the transition in in-pile loop experiments between the MTR in late 1952, the ETR in 1957, and the ATR in 1970. Also, it became clear

that important effect upon cladding and fuel materials in the LMFBR could not be accomplished in thermal test reactors. This led to the design of the Fast Flux Test Facility.

THE MATERIALS TESTING REACTOR

When the Materials Testing Reactor (MTR) went critical in March 1952, it was one of those decisive markings in nuclear technology which becomes even clearer in this retrospective of the developments since the fission process was first discovered. Looking backward reveals the debt owed to this great reactor. Studies carried out in and about the MTR have involved all of the National Laboratories as well as most of the industrial organizations in the nuclear power industry. The choice of core structure and fuel elements of every reactor type designed since 1952 has been influenced by information from the MTR and its programs.

The operation of the MTR was in itself a great experiment. It convincingly demonstrated the feasibility of aluminum uranium fueled reactors, operating at power densities of a megawatt per liter and resulted in a family of later research and test reactors of which the Engineering Test Reactor (ETR) and the Advanced Test Reactor (ATR) are members, as well as others scattered throughout the world. Before its retirement, beside its contribution to the art of materials testing, and its enormous research output utilizing its magnificent beam tubes, the MTR also was employed in several direct experiments. These included demonstration of the feasibility of the 20% enriched uranium core; a special fuel loading which achieved the first sustained operation on plutonium, demonstration of the so-called Phoenix plutonium, which approached a reactivity invariance with almost motionless control rods during the burnup cycle. This mixture of Pu-239, Pu-240, and Pu-241 was expected to be representative of the output of plutonium from commercial reactors at high burnup and was of interest in the Pu-recycle program. The results of all of the experiments demonstrated the practical controllability of a reactor with high excess reactivity on the small delayed neutron fraction of plutonium. The enhanced flux per megawatt arising from the larger value of neutrons per fission was realized, and were it not for other considerations, plutonium would be the preferred fuel for high-flux machines.

The decision to build the MTR was quickly justified by the rapid growth of its burden of experiments which occurred after it went into routine operation. The initial use was confined to static capsules containing samples located in various positions adjacent to the active fuel lattice (Figure 1). The number of reflector pieces of beryllium which were bored to provide for cylindrical samples was increased until a total of 625 separate experimental units were being run by mid-year of 1958.

The demand for the ability to instrument some of the capsule experiments grew, so a modification of the upper tank was made to accommodate two access holes, and by 1958 there were 18 of such experiments operating in a single cycle. (Figures 2, 3, 4).

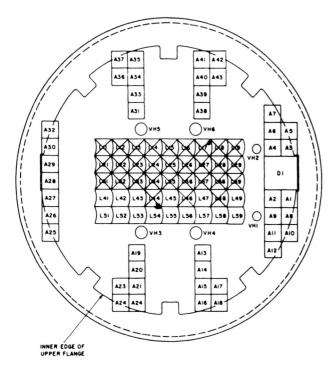

MTR CORE PLAN

X   Reactor Fuel and Shim Rods
VH Spare Control Rod Positions
L   "Core" Experimental Positions
A   Reflector Experimental Positions

FIGURE 1   MTR CROSS SECTION

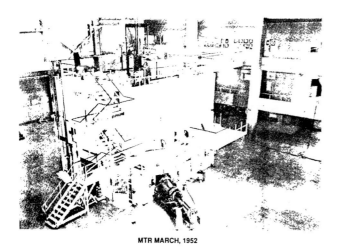

MTR MARCH, 1952

FIGURE 2   A PANORAMA OF MTR AT CRITICALITY

MTR MARCH, 1960

FIGURE 3   VIEW OF MTR NINE YEARS OLD

The quick growth in both the number of experiments and in the number of sponsors brought new problems in controlling the experimental load so as to prevent either an interaction with the reactor or one experiment with the other. To deal with the safety implications of these interactions, a Reactor Safeguard Committee was established at the MTR, which became the watchdog of the entire experimental program. The organization evolved after its institution and became the model upon which many other have been patterned at other installations. The MTR Reactor Safeguard Committee was based upon a four-point philosophy:

    1. Clear definition of the line of supervisory responsibilities in the handling of incidents arising from the malfunction of the reactor or any of the experiments,

    2. An organizational structure, supplemented by various special committees, to insure that no experiment be placed in the reactor without a thorough review of its feasibility or safety,

    3. An organizational structure that guards against long-term changes, in either reactor or experiments, which might produce a serious incident,

    4. Precise definition of the areas of responsibilities of sponsors' representatives, MTR staff supervisors, and MTR committees to eliminate any gaps which might lead to serious incidents.

The Committee was charged to review from time to time the various factors affecting the safe operation of the Materials Testing Reactor, with particular regard to such areas as reactor physics, safety control mechanisms and internal reactor components, and to make recommendations with regard to those things which need to be done to assure that it is possible to continue to operate the reactor with uncompromised safety.

In addition, a Hazards Survey Committee comprising members of Reactor Operations, Project Engineering and the Reactor Safeguard Committee were required to make a periodic review of the entire experimental program, outlining the major hazards of each experiment.

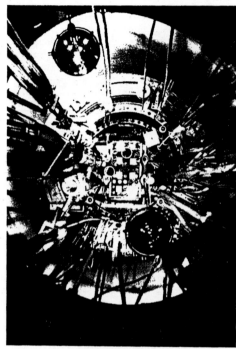

MTR REACTOR TANK SEPT., 1959

FIGURE 4   MTR SHOWING EXPERIMENTAL
                  CONGESTION

Despite the easy availability of irradiation in the MTR the development of the inpile loop became necessary. In its simplest form, a loop could be formed by drawing water from the reactor tank, passing it by the sample and at the outlet, collecting and bringing it outside of the reactor, where various measurements could be made - flow rate, temperature, activity level, water chemistry, etc. Since the reactor inlet water was so precisely controlled and its constants well known, the change produced by its interaction with the sample could be determined. This loop was shaped like a fish-hook, secured within the tank with the long end brought out of the reactor vessel, and with the sample positioned in the short end to received reactor flow. Obviously, the samples were limited to those which were compatible with low-termperature, low pressure water, and were of very high integrity. These could not be used to qualify pins, plates, or tubular elements for operation in a real reactor in which temperature and pressure might be far removed from those of the

test reactor. Double-walled capsules with insulation and NaK coolant could change sample conditions within limits, but still introduced other questions.

The closed loop, with its own water supply, treatment, pumping, and measurement system with high pressure operating capability was used, but a failure of this loop during operation was intolerable, so that only modest pressures were allowed, in non-vulnerable reflector positions, and at lower flux level.

The next development of the engineered process loop provided a permanently installed pressure tube, an annular gas thermal barrier, and a removable inner flow tube containing the sample. From the point of view of the test reactor thereby attention was shifted to the integrity of the pressure tube itself, since it would now accumulate radiation exposure which would ultimately limit its lifetime. The radiation damage data from some of these tubes removed from the ETR later provided the highest exposure values achieved under pressure, and was used to qualify tubes for the next replacement.

The removable flow tube greatly eased the problems of conducting an experimental program. With no penetrations in the bottom plug, and no access from above the core in the MTR (Control drives and fuel holddown device), the in-tank loops, in reflector locations, required modification of the upper tank section, the use of reentrant flow tubes, and clamping devices to inhibit vibration within the reactor tank. The out-of-pile equipment grew in size, complexity, and in functions performed using pumps, motors, valving, pre-heaters, heat exchangers, purge gas systems, water chemistry, shielding, ventilation, instrumentation consoles, thus became elaborate facilities, requiring extensive development engineering, and construction to rigid quality standards. Their operation was itself complex enough to justify special operation and maintenance procedures and extensive operator training.

THE ENGINEERING TEST REACTOR

The pressure of this aggressive program was so great that the conceptual design was begun in 1953 of a new reactor designed to take advantage of the experience of the MTR and the advice of the sponsoring laboratories to produce a reactor specifically oriented towards engineering testing. A gigantic step was taken in the Engineering Test Reactor (ETR), which was approved as a project in 1954 and went critical in 1956. Making use of the fine performance of the MTR fuel fabrication technology, a flat plate element was designed with 36 inches active length versus 24 inches, which increased experimental volume and lowered axial gradients. Burnable poisons were employed to reduce flux variations due to control rod motions, experimental facilities in the active core, bottom control rod drives to delete the need to remove experimental facilities in order to refuel the reactor, and matching top and bottom head penetrations. There were large embedded cylindrical pipes in the biological shield, to permit loop piping from an outlet nozzle trench, to the sub-pile rooms, cubicles were provided in the basement for process equipment, and space was provided for instrument cabinets. Heavy floor bearing capability permitted the addition of special heavy shielding where necessary.

Indeed the ETR lent a new dimension to materials testing technology and was swiftly subscribed. The permanently installed, vertical tubes, with sample and associated components replaceable from above reduced sample damage during the insertion and removal steps. With the longer core, the burnable poisons and the greater core lateral dimension, the sample flux variations during an operating cycle were reduced to about 30 percent versus a factor of 2 in MTR. The contributions of ETR were very great, and with the emergence of commercial power plant interests the programmatic saturation of ETR was reached within a few years. The sophistication of experiments continued to develop so that design criteria for new engineered loops could be commercially subcontracted (Figure 5).

THE ADVANCED TEST REACTOR

It was the heavy demand of the Naval Reactors Program which, although very active in the exploitation of the MTR and the ETR, led to the design of the Advanced Test Reactor. Whereas the ETR had responded to the need to satisfy a diversity of reactor development programs, the ATR was oriented toward an entire, well-documented program from a single sponsor. This permitted optimization in ways that greatly affected the ultimate coordination of the reactor and experimental facilities in the same effort. The result was a remarkable improvement in the quality and precision of the experimental results. Axial flux gradients were reduced to less than 10 percent per foot at the sample, individual fluxes in the experiments were separately controllable to within about three percent through the unique control element disposition (Figure 6).

Power balance in the core is determined by 11 water tubes which have a separate water supply and are located throughout the core plan. These loops flow at constant velocity to detectors which measure the N16 activity in each line giving a relative axially averaged flux pattern. Solution of the matrix of these values allows an assignment of the lobe powers surrounding each experiment. Cross calibration in the ATR Critical Facility confirms the uniqueness of this value. The core length was increased to twice that of the MTR. Nine loop facilities were provided that could be virtually identical if desired.

THE ATR LOOPS

The standardization of the ATR loops, required that provision be made in the design for the cubicle space, floor loading access holes, service water, electric-power, and other utilities required. Conceptual designs and complete Title I designs of a pressurized water loop and a gas-cooled loop were done to reveal these needs. This was done during the original ATR Project and has proved valuable. In Figure 6 the ATR core plan gives the location of the nine positions. Figure 7 shows the vertical disposition of the loops in relation to the core, control drives and access room. Figure 8 indicates the first basement experimental equipment area revealing the lengths to which the design provided for the convenient placement of loop components (Figure 9).

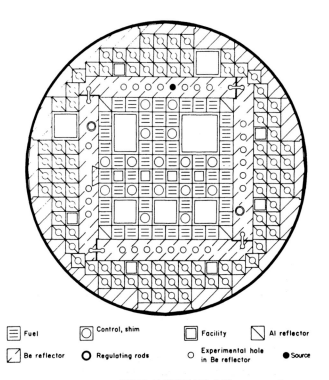

☰ Fuel	⬡ Control, shim	▢ Facility	◇ Al reflector
◁ Be reflector	● Regulating rods	∘ Experimental hole in Be reflector	● Source

ETR CORE PLAN

FIGURE 5   ETR CORE EXPERIMENTAL SPACES

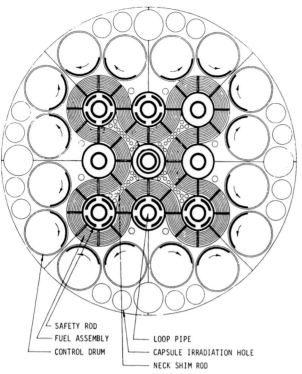

Horizontal cross section of ATR core.

SAFETY ROD
FUEL ASSEMBLY
CONTROL DRUM
LOOP PIPE
CAPSULE IRRADIATION HOLE
NECK SHIM ROD

FIGURE 6   ATR LOOP ARRANGEMENT

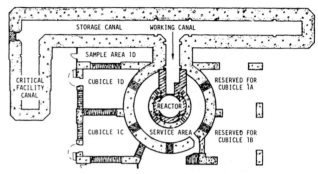

Plan of first basement shows relation of reactor, cubicles, and canal.

STORAGE CANAL
WORKING CANAL
SAMPLE AREA 1D
CRITICAL FACILITY CANAL
CUBICLE 1D
RESERVED FOR CUBICLE 1A
REACTOR
CUBICLE 1C
SERVICE AREA
RESERVED FOR CUBICLE 1B

FIGURE 8   INTEGRATION AT BASEMENT LEVEL

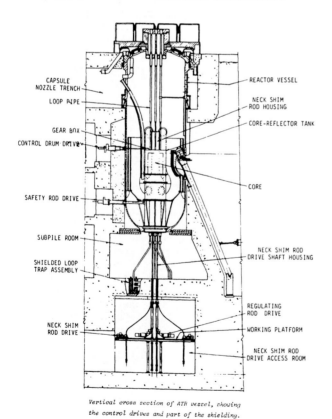

CAPSULE NOZZLE TRENCH
LOOP PIPE
GEAR BOX
CONTROL DRUM DRIVE
SAFETY ROD DRIVE
SUBPILE ROOM
SHIELDED LOOP TRAP ASSEMBLY
NECK SHIM ROD DRIVE

REACTOR VESSEL
NECK SHIM ROD HOUSING
CORE-REFLECTOR TANK
CORE
NECK SHIM ROD DRIVE SHAFT HOUSING
REGULATING ROD DRIVE
WORKING PLATFORM
NECK SHIM ROD DRIVE ACCESS ROOM

Vertical cross section of ATR vessel, showing
the control drives and part of the shielding.

FIGURE 7   ATR SECTION ON VERTICAL AXIS

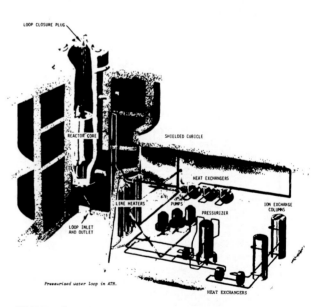

Pressurized water loop in ATR.

LOOP CLOSURE PLUG
REACTOR CORE
SHIELDED CUBICLE
HEAT EXCHANGERS
LINE HEATERS
PUMPS
PRESSURIZER
ION EXCHANGE COLUMNS
LOOP INLET AND OUTLET
HEAT EXCHANGERS

FIGURE 9   ARTISTS SKETCH OF LOOP IN ATR

The pressurized water loop shares the space in the flux trap region between the functions of the pressurized water loop and the reactor safety rods, which are fully withdrawn during operation and hence do not interfere with the flux trap performance relative to the loop which comprises the insulating jacket, a helium annulus, the pressure tube which houses the flow tube and sample (Figure 10).

Servicing the experiment is simply done from the reactor top head. The compatibility throughout this integrated design has resulted in an astonishing record of availability, reported by the Operating Contractor.

It will be noticed that I have not mentioned the other high flux reactors, which are not neglected, because there are two other papers in this conference one of which discusses the use of reactors in research, and the other deals with the historical and ongoing materials testing applications throughout the world.

CONCLUSION

The role of Test Reactor Technology has been crucial in the resolution of fuels and materials development for reactors and so long as anyone dares to work upon a new reactor concept, or to exploit a new fuel system, it will be necessary to go through some of the same studies that used this technology in the first reactors, but with an abundance of technique and previous results to guide him.

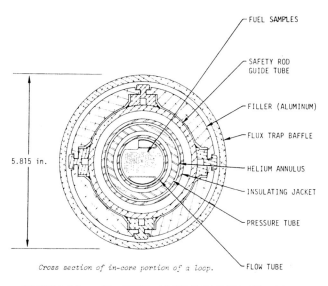

Cross section of in-core portion of a loop.

FIGURE 10   CO-AXIAL ACCOMMODATION OF LOOP
             AND SAFETY ROD.

5.815 in.

FUEL SAMPLES

SAFETY ROD
GUIDE TUBE

FILLER (ALUMINUM)

FLUX TRAP BAFFLE

HELIUM ANNULUS

INSULATING JACKET

PRESSURE TUBE

FLOW TUBE

ASTROPHYSICS AND SPACE APPLICATIONS

Chairman
W. Michael Howard (LLNL)

FISSION BARRIERS FOR r-PROCESS NUCLEI AND IMPLICATIONS FOR ASTROPHYSICS

B. S. Meyer

Institute of Geophysics and

Planetary Physics, L-413

Lawrence Livermore National Laboratory

Livermore, CA 94550

(415) 422-4912

W. M. Howard

Physics Division, L-297

Lawrence Livermore National Laboratory

Livermore, CA 94550

(415) 422-4138

P. Möller

Theoretical Division, MS B279

Los Alamos National Laboratory

Los Alamos, NM 87545

(505) 665-2210

G. J. Mathews

Physics Division, L-405

Lawrence Livermore National Laboratory

Livermore, CA 94550

(415) 422-4265

ABSTRACT

We present calculations of fission-barrier heights, beta decay energies, and neutron separation energies for nuclei with $76 \leq Z \leq 100$ and $140 \leq N \leq 184$. For these nuclear-structure calculations we use the macroscopic-microscopic method with a Yukawa-plus-exponential macroscopic model and a folded-Yukawa microscopic model. The barrier-heights we find are higher than those calculated in previous studies using the droplet macroscopic model. We discuss the implications of the new results on fission-barrier heights for astrophysics.

I. INTRODUCTION

The astrophysical r(apid neutron capture)-process has long been known to be responsible for roughly half of the abundances of nuclei with mass number greater than 80 and for all of the actinides.[1] This nucleosynthesis process occurs in high temperature ($T > 10^8 K$), high neutron number density ($n_n > 10^{20}$ cm^{-3}) environments where neutron captures typically occur more *rapidly* than β-decays. The relative rapidity of the neutron captures causes nuclei to populate an r-process path in the proton-number versus neutron-number plane that is some fifteen to twenty neutrons or more off the line of β-stability. Because the r-process path is so far from the line of β-stability, the nuclear structure data necessary for its study, namely β-decay rates, neutron binding energies, nuclear partition functions, and neutron-capture cross sections, are almost exclusively obtained from theoretical calculations. The use of results from state-of-the-art nuclear-structure calculations in r-process calculations and in many other types of astrophysical calculations is long overdue.

While it is the interplay of β-decay and neutron capture and photodisintegration that plays the dominant role in determining the abundance distribution of r-process nuclei, nuclear fission also has some important consequences. Nuclear fission cuts off the r-process path at large proton number ($Z \sim 90 - -100$). The fission process recycles the two fragment nuclei to a lower point on the r-process path. The r-process abundances in the rare-earth region have been interpreted as fission-cycled material.[2] The viability of this interpretation certainly depends on knowing the location of the fission cut-off of the r-process path. The possibility of superheavy element formation in the r-process is also strongly dependent on the location of the fission cut-off. Finally, β-delayed fission may greatly affect the final abundances of those actinide nuclei with long decay times that are used as cosmochronometers[3] and, consequently, will affect the age of the Galaxy inferred from their abundances.[4]

It is thus clear that accurate theoretical predictions of the properties of the nuclei along the r-process path are crucial for a proper understanding of the r-process abundance distribution. We have emphasized previously in connection with the investigations of β-delayed fission that the predictions of the different quantities should be consistent with each other and, therefore, preferably be obtained from a single nuclear model.[5] It may seem that since all models are expected to reproduce relatively correctly physical quantities, it should be possible to use different models for different quantities. To some extent this is true, but there are many cases where consistency is important. For example, nuclear shape parameterizations are slightly different in different models. Thus, one can not trivially pick a ground-state deformation calculated in one model and use the calculated deformation as input in another model calculation to obtain the ground-state spin. In this paper we present calculations of the nuclear data quantities that are important for a discussion of fission during the r-process. The calculations were obtained within the framework of a consistent nuclear-structure model. We discuss some astrophysical implications of these results.

II. THE NUCLEAR MODEL

The model employed is of the macroscopic-microscopic type. In particular, we use the folded-Yukawa single-particle potential to calculate the microscopic corrections and the Yukawa-plus-exponential model as the macroscopic model. Relative to the standard liquid-drop model in which the surface-energy term is simply proportional to the surface area, the Yukawa-plus-exponential model represents an improvement since it accounts for the reductions in surface tension due to the finite range of the nuclear force, for configurations close to touching in heavy-ion reactions, and for saddle-point shapes with pronounced necks in fission.

It is also expected that the microscopic term is more reliably obtained from the folded-Yukawa single-particle potential than in earlier calculations based on modified-oscillator single-particle potentials. In oscillator potentials the potential goes to infinity at large distances and the spin-orbit and diffuseness parameters vary somewhat unpredictably from region to region of the periodic chart. In contrast, in the folded-Yukawa single-particle potential, the diffuseness parameter remains constant over the periodic system and spin-orbit parameter, which in the model is a linear function of A, only increases by about 25% from oxygen to the heaviest elements.

These changes have led to an improvement in the prediction of nuclear masses since errors in the nuclear mass no longer seem to increase with increasing neutron excess.[6,7] For more details on the nuclear-structure model we refer to ref. 8, which discusses the calculation of ground-state masses, and to ref. 9, which discusses the calculation of fission barriers. In the calculation of nuclear masses no microscopic zero-point energies have been included. Since this term remains fairly constant over the actinide region,

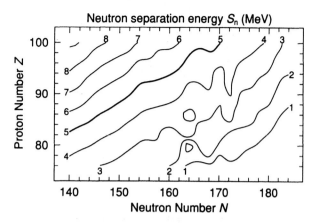

Figure 1: Neutron separation energies in MeV

the omission is of little importance. In the calculation of fission barriers we have limited ourselves to the use of the ϵ-parameterization. Thus, effects associated with the appearance of a new valley in the potential-energy surface, which for nuclei close to ^{264}Fm leads towards compact scission shapes, are not treated here.

There are two types of uncertainties in the current calculation. To fully explore the current version of the model more shape degrees of freedom should be included both at the nuclear ground state and at saddle-point distortions. At the ground-state we expect a maximum change of 1 MeV due to inclusion of additional shape-degrees of freedom. For decay energies the differences would be somewhat less, since correlated errors in neighboring masses partially cancel out.

Another type of error arises from the fact that the current macroscopic model uses expansions in a neutron excess variable, $I = (N - Z)/(N + Z)$, in expressions for the surface and volume energies. We now obtain mass excesses that for neutron-rich nuclei are several 10s of MeV higher than what was obtained by use of the droplet model,[10] and we expect that the new results are more reliable than the old calculations. However, one must ask whether an approach that relies on a perturbation expansion in terms of a neutron excess variable is at all reliable on the neutron dripline. Several groups are currently investigating the feasibility of using a Thomas-Fermi approach that includes a consideration of deformation, instead of a perturbation-expansion approach, for calculating the macroscopic energy.

With our current nuclear model we have calculated neutron separation energies and beta Q-values for nuclei with $76 \leq Z \leq 100$ and $140 \leq N \leq 184$. Figure 1 gives the neutron separation energies in this region. We note the structure at $N = 164$ and at $N = 172$ which arises from fluctuations in the single-particle corrections and isotope to isotope shape changes. For reference, the r-process typically lies along the locus of 2–3 MeV neutron separation

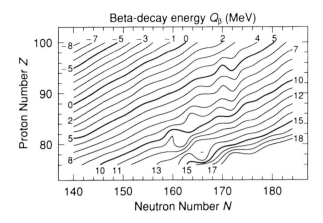

Figure 2: β-decay energies in MeV

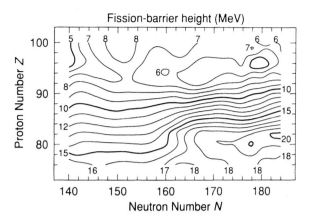

Figure 3: Fission-barrier heights for even nuclei in MeV

energies. Figure 2 gives the beta Q-values for the same nuclei. These also show structure due to the fluctuations in the single-particle corrections.

III. FISSION BARRIERS

One set of nuclear potential-energy surfaces was computed for the 1125 nuclei mentioned previously as a function of ϵ_2 and ϵ_4. Another set of potential-energy surfaces was calculated as a function of a combination of ϵ_2 and ϵ_4 as the symmetric elongation coordinate in the "fission direction" and of a combination of ϵ_3 and ϵ_5 as the mass-asymmetric shape coordinate. Saddle points on these two sets of surfaces were then located. For the mass-symmetric surfaces, the minima and saddle points were simply found by a computer program, since these extrema only occurred on a well-defined fission path. For the mass-asymmetric surface, on the other hand, it was necessary to examine each surface by eye to determine the correct fission path since these surfaces often contained minima and saddle points off the fission path.

To obtain the final fission path, the two sets of saddle points (mass-symmetric and mass-asymmetric) were merged. This was done as follows. The mass-symmetric saddle points on the fission path were used until the first relevant mass-asymmetric saddle was lower in energy than the next mass-symmetric saddle. At this point, the mass-symmetric saddle was replaced by the mass-asymmetric saddle and the fission path was defined to lie in the mass-asymmetric surface from that point on. The ground state of each nucleus was found by requiring that it be the minimum with the maximum fission barrier. Ideally one should at each minimum calculate the half-life with respect to all modes of decay and choose as the ground-state minimum the minimum with the longest total half-life. This was not done, but we expect that the error due to our simplified

definition is small. We expect that in the vast majority of cases the two approaches would give the same minimum as the ground state.

Figure 3 shows fission-barrier heights. Here the fission-barrier height is the difference between the energy of highest saddle point along the fission path and the ground state energy. A constant value of 0.5 MeV was used for the zero-point energy. These fission-barrier heights are typically greater by ~ 1 MeV or more than those of some previous studies.[11,12] The reason for this is that the surface energy term falls off less steeply with increasing neutron excess in the Yukawa-plus-exponential model than in the droplet model used in ref. 11. Since the fission barriers of nuclei increase with increasing ratio of the surface energy to the Coulomb energy, higher surface energies lead to higher barriers. We discuss the implications of these barriers for astrophysics in the next section.

IV. IMPLICATIONS FOR ASTROPHYSICS

We may now consider the implications of our fission-barrier heights for the astrophysical r-process. First let us turn to the question of the fission cut-off of the r-process path. Figure 4 gives the fission-barrier height minus the neutron separation energy for the 1125 nuclei in this study. Where this quantity is negative, the nuclei are unstable to neutron-induced fission. This condition occurs in Figure 4 in the shaded region. As may be seen, this is only found in the extreme upper left corner of the plot, a region well away from the r-process path, which lies roughly along the 2–3 MeV neutron separation energy region of Figure 1. With the fission barriers we have computed, then, neutron-induced fission should not cut off the r-process path before neutron number 184. Furthermore, the numbers in Figure 4 are higher than the corresponding values in previous studies; therefore, it may be possible for the r-process path to pro-

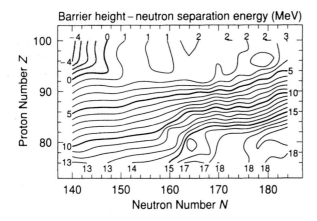

Figure 4: Fission-barrier heights minus neutron separation energies for even nuclei in MeV

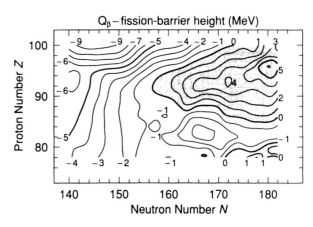

Figure 5: Q_β-value for odd nucleus minus the daughter even fission-barrier height in MeV

ceed beyond the $Z = 96$ cut-off found in refs. 12 and 13 and closer to the region where superheavy element nuclei might be produced.

β-delayed fission may cut off the r-process path well before this, however. In Figure 5 we present beta Q-values of parent nuclei minus the fission-barrier height for daughter nuclei plotted at the location of the daughter nuclei. The shaded regions of this plot indicate where this quantity is positive. Here the nuclei are possibly unstable to β-delayed fission. From the present fission barriers, we conclude that it is possible that β-delayed fission, not neutron-induced fission, cuts off the r-process path, although this conclusion depends strongly on the detailed calculations of β-delayed fission and neutron-emission probabilities. At present, then, we do not have a firm conclusion on the possibility of superheavy element formation in the r-process. If β-delayed fission cuts off the r-process path before or at neutron number 184, we must be pessimistic about superheavy element formation in the r-process. If β-delayed neutron emission competes very favorably with β-delayed fission, however, the r-process may be able to proceed well past $N = 184$ so that superheavy element formation in the r-process is a possibility. Further discussion on this point must await the outcome of new β-delayed fission and neutron emission probability calculations.

Some authors claim that the fission interpretation for the rare-earth abundances in the r-process abundance distribution requires that the r-process path reach a neutron number of about 200.[14] Other authors find that the rare-earth peak can be explained by fission as long as the r-process path reaches neutron number 184.[15] In any case, if β-delayed fission cuts off the r-process path well before neutron number 184, it will be difficult to explain the rare-earth abundances by fission of nuclei near the cut-off of the r-process path. Again we need detailed β-delayed fission and neutron-emission probability calculations to make

a more informed conclusion on this point.

As for decay from the r-process path back to the stability line, β-delayed fission may still affect the abundances of nuclei with mass number greater than roughly 250. Mass number 250 is the highest mass alpha-decaying progenitor of ^{238}U, while mass 252 is the highest mass alpha-decaying progenitor of ^{232}Th; therefore, the new barriers indicate that β-delayed fission may still play a role in affecting the abundances of the cosmochronometers but that this role may be much less than previously thought since at most only one progenitor is affected. It is more likely that β-delayed neutron emission would have an effect on the final abundances of the actinide cosmochronometers. Figure 6 shows where β-delayed one, two, and three neutron emission might occur. Such neutron emission could take place in regions to the right of each line in the plot. Comparison of Figures 1 and 6 show that β-delayed one, two, and three neutron emission can occur for all nuclei on an r-process path represented by the 3 MeV neutron separation energy line. Clearly β-delayed neutron emission may play a crucial role in determining the final abundance of the actinide cosmochronometers.

V. CONCLUSIONS

We have calculated neutron separation energies, beta Q-values, and fission barrier heights for nuclei with $76 \leq Z \leq 100$ and $140 \leq N \leq 184$ from the folded-Yukawa macroscopic-microscopic model. The fission-barrier heights are higher than in previous studies by roughly 1 MeV or more. The implications for astrophysics are 1) that the r-process path may be cut off by β-delayed fission, not neutron-induced fission, 2) that superheavy element formation in the r-process is somewhat more likely than recently supposed, and 3) that β-delayed fission prob-

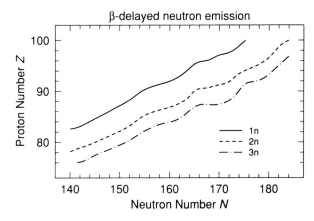

Figure 6: Neutron separation energies in MeV

ably has less of an effect on the abundances of the actinide cosmochronometers than suggested in ref. 4. However, β-delayed neutron emission is likely to have a large effect on the actinide cosmochronometer abundances. We emphasize that all of these conclusions depend on the details of β-delayed fission and neutron-emission calculations.

ACKNOWLEDGEMENTS

This work was performed under the auspices of the U. S. Department of Energy by the Lawrence Livermore National Laboratory under Contract W-7405-Eng-48.

REFERENCES

1. E. M. Burbidge, G. R. Burbidge, W. A. Fowler, and F. Hoyle, "Synthesis of the Elements in Stars," *Rev. Mod. Phys.*, 29, 547 (1957).

2. A. G. W. Cameron, "Nuclear Reactions in Stars and Nucleogenesis," *Pub. Astron. Soc. Pacific*, 69, 201 (1957).

3. F. -K. Thielemann, J. Metzinger, and H. V. Klapdor, "Beta-Delayed Fission and Neutron-Emission: Consequences for the Astrophysical r-Process and the Age of the Galaxy'," *Z. Phys. A*, 309, 301 (1983).

4. F. -K. Thielemann, J. Metzinger, and H. V. Klapdor, "New actinide chronometer production ratios and the age of the Galaxy," *Astron. Astrophys.*, 123, 162 (1983).

5. B. S. Meyer, W. M. Howard, G. J. Mathews, K. Takahashi, P. Möller, and G. A. Leander, "Beta-delayed fission and neutron emission calculations for the actinide cosmochronometers," *Phys. Rev. C4*, 39, to appear May 1989.

6. P. Möller and J. R. Nix, "Nuclear Ground-State Deformations Calculated with a New Macroscopic-Microscopic Model," *At. Data Nucl. Data Tables*, 26, 165 (1981).

7. W. M. Howard, P. Möller, G. J. Mathews, and B. S. Meyer, "New Nuclear Structure Calculations and the Astrophysical r-Process," in *Origin and Distribution of the Elements*, ed. G. J. Mathews, World Scientific, Singapore, (1988).

8. P. Möller and J. R. Nix, "Nuclear Mass Formula With a Yukawa-plus-Exponential Macroscopic Model and a Folded-Yukawa Single-Particle Model," *Nucl. Phys.*, A361, 117 (1981).

9. P. Möller, J. R. Nix, and W. J. Swiatecki, "Calculated Fission Properties of the Heaviest Elements," *Nucl. Phys.* A469, 1 (1987).

10. W. D. Myers, *Droplet model of atomic nuclei.* IFI/Plenum, New York (1977).

11. W. M. Howard and P. Möller, "Calculated Fission Barriers, Ground-State Masses, and Particle Separation Energies for Nuclei with $76 \leq Z \leq 100$ and $140 \leq N \leq 184$," *At. Data Nucl. Data Tables*, 25, 219 (1980).

12. W. M. Howard and J. R. Nix, "Production of Superheavy Nuclei by the Multiple Capture of Neutrons," *Nature*, 247, 17 (1974).

13. G. J. Mathews and V. E. Viola, Jr., "r-Process Nucleosynthesis of Superheavy Nuclei and Nuclear Mass Tables," *Nature*, 261, 328 (1976).

14. E. P. Steinberg and B. D. Wilkins, "Implications of Fission Mass Distributions for the Astrophysical r-Process," *Astrophys. J.*, 223, 1000 (1978).

15. R. Bengtsson and W. M. Howard, "Mass Asymmetric Fission and the Termination of the Astrophysical r-Process," *Phys. Lett.*, 55B, 281 (1975).

FISSION IN THE ASTROPHYSICAL r-PROCESS

Friedrich-Karl Thielemann
A.G.W. Cameron

Harvard-Smithsonian Center for Astrophysics
60 Garden Street, Cambridge, MA 02138

John J. Cowan

Department of Physics and Astronomy
University of Oklahoma, Norman, OK 73019

ABSTRACT

Areas in the nuclear chart where neutron-induced and β^--delayed fission are of importance are identified and methods to predict their values are discussed. Presently available theoretical fission barrier heights seem to overestimate both processes, in comparison to experimental information. Therefore, a judgment of the extent to which they affect r-process calculations can only be preliminary. We expect that the influence on the chronometer ratios ^{232}Th/^{238}U and ^{235}U/^{238}U is small. Whether nuclei heavier than Z=100 can be produced in the r-process can only be decided after calculations with improved mass formulas *and* fission barrier heights.

1. INTRODUCTION

Nuclei up to a nuclear charge of Z$\approx$26-30 are produced in stellar burning stages and explosive burning in supernovae by a sequence of fusion reactions, leading finally to Fe-group nuclei with the maximum binding energy per nucleon. The formation of heavier nuclei is due to a combined process of neutron captures and beta decays. The increasing charge of heavier nuclei, which leads to a stronger repulsion of charged projectiles, does not represent an obstacle for neutrons. The slow neutron capture process (s-process) in He-burning, where neutrons are released by the reactions ^{22}Ne$(\alpha,n)^{25}$Mg or ^{13}C$(\alpha,n)^{16}$O, enables a build-up of heavy elements as far as Pb and Bi. The neutron release and s-process timescale is of the order 10^2 to 10^3 years and the appropriate neutron number densities range from 10^7 to 10^9 cm^{-3}. Therefore, beta-decay of unstable nuclei is almost always preferred over additional neutron capture. For the same reason nuclei heavier than Bi are not produced in the s-process, because the alpha-decay of unstable nuclei is much faster than additional neutron captures.

For much higher neutron densities, neutron capture can be faster than beta-decays for unstable nuclei and very neutron-rich isotopes can thus be produced. With neutron densities in excess of 10^{19}-10^{20} cm^{-3} the line in the nuclear chart beyond which beta decay dominates over neutron capture would be located 15-20 mass units away from stability. Typical beta-decay half-lives of 10^{-2}-10^{-3} sec are encountered, with a few exceptions of the order 10^{-1} sec. Along an r-process (rapid neutron capture) path in this region Fe-nuclei would be transformed to U within a few seconds.

When one makes the simplest assumption that this r-process path is characterized by nuclei with similar neutron capture cross sections, and that these cross sections depend solely on the reaction Q-value, then the r-process path would coincide with a line of constant neutron separation energy. In order to reproduce the solar abundance pattern, the neutron separation energy has to have a value of about 2-3 MeV. This path has kinks at closed neutron numbers where it comes closest to the stability line (see Fig. 1). Only at these locations have a few nuclei have been studied experimentally. These nuclei are ^{80}Zn [12,25] and ^{130}Cd [24].

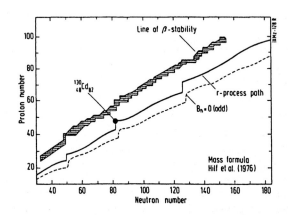

Fig. 1: The position of the r-process path in the nuclear chart. Closed neutron shells cause kinks where the path comes closer to the stability line. Experimental information is presently only available at these locations (^{80}Zn and ^{130}Cd)

Many of these basic ideas were outlined as early as 1957 in papers by Burbidge, Burbidge, Fowler, and Hoyle[6] and independently by Cameron[7]. Since then research has focused on improved input physics and the determination of the associated astrophysical sites [30,41]. The nuclear information needed in order to perform r-process calculations includes neutron capture cross sections, beta decay half lives, and the branching ratios for beta-delayed neutron emission. For nuclei with Z>80 other forms of fission can also become important. Nuclei of main interest here are located in the area of rapid spontaneous fission, referred to as the "bay of shells" [4,20,31]. However, one expects beta-delayed fission and neutron-induced fission to be more important than spontaneous fission, because in both cases the fissioning nucleus is produced in excited states, which results in an effective lowering of the fission barriers [23,32,33,45]. Beta-decay Q-values along the r-process path are of the order 13-15 MeV, much higher than the neutron capture Q-values of 2-3 MeV. Thus beta decay will populate highly excited states above the fission barrier, and therefore delayed fission plays a more important role than neutron-induced fission. Due to the more favorable energetics, the area of delayed or induced fission is more extended in the (N,Z)-plane than the one for spontaneous fission.

Owing to the lack of experimental masses for these neutron-rich nuclei, the nuclear mass formula, which predicts the reaction Q-values, plays a key role. Similar considerations hold true for the prediction of beta-decay half-lives and fission barriers. The only experimental checks on theoretical predictions of beta-delayed and neutron-induced fission (and therefore fission barrier heights) of neutron-rich nuclei have come from the analysis of abundances in explosive nuclear devices [17,18].

Fission enters into r-process calculations in three different ways:

(1) Fission can terminate the r-process path at $Z \approx 92$ and prevent the r-process from producing superheavy elements in nature [19].

(2) In the same way fission can have a strong influence on the total abundances of heavy nuclei by the so-called fission cycling (after fission each of the fission fragments can again capture neutrons until they also fission) [38]. This is especially of importance in environments with a long duration of high neutron densities, and was recently suggested for primordial nucleosynthesis in neutron-rich zones of an inhomogeneous big bang[1].

(3) Following the decrease of neutron densities, when the r-process freezes, nuclei beta-decay back to the stability line. Beta-delayed fission can reduce the flow along a given isobar. The beta-stable nuclei will decay along alpha-decay chains and determine the eventual abundance ratios of very long-lived nuclei like ^{232}Th, ^{234,235}U, and ^{244}Pu. The comparison of these abundance ratios in the solar system with the production ratios in the r-process, when making assumptions about galactic evolution, can help to determine the duration of nucleosynthesis in our galaxy and hence the galactic age (for a discussion of this subject with and without the inclusion of fission see refs. [9,11,32,33,39,45] and references therein).

2. NEUTRON-INDUCED FISSION AND BETA-DELAYED FISSION

In order to calculate cross sections for neutron-induced fission we made use of the statistical model code SMOKER [43,44], and we extended it by including a fission channel.

This code uses microscopic optical potentials for neutrons and protons[22] and a Woods-Saxon potential for alpha particles[28]. The treatment of E1 gamma-transitions incorporates the split of the giant dipole resonance for deformed nuclei, a depression of the Lorentz curve at low energies as also found experimentally, and a natural understanding of the small GDR widths close to magic numbers within a macroscopic-microscopic model, taking also into account coupling to quadrupole surface vibrations of the nucleus[42]. The level density prescription used is a combination of a constant temperature formula for low excitation energies and a back-shifted Fermi gas at intermediate and high energies, where the level density parameter a and the back-shift δ are related to the pairing and shell correction terms of a more recent mass formula[14]. Width fluctuation corrections 40 are also included.

As this code was developed for astrophysical applications which have to cover many unstable nuclei, all physical quantities are *calculated* according to the prescriptions mentioned above rather than being taken from experiment. Additional information, which needs to be employed for the calculation of neutron induced fission, includes only the reaction Q-values and the fission barrier heights. For stable nuclei this information can come from experiment, but for unstable nuclei we have to make use of a mass formula and theoretical predictions of fission barrier heights. In general, the cross section for a reaction $i^o(j,k)l$ from the target ground state i^o to all excited states l^ν of a final nucleus with center of mass energy E_{ij} and reduced mass μ_{ij} is given by

$$\sigma_{jk}(E_{ij}) = \frac{\pi \hbar^2 / (2\mu_{ij} E_{ij})}{(2J_i^o + 1)(2J_j + 1)}$$

$$\times \sum_{J,\pi} (2J+1) \frac{T_j^o(E, J, \pi, E_i^o, J_i^o, \pi_i^o) T_k(E, J, \pi)}{T_{tot}(E, J, \pi)}, \quad (1)$$

E denotes the excitation energy in the compound nucleus, J the spin, and π the parity of excited states. The summation over all excited states ν in the final nucleus is used to calculate $T_k(E, J, \pi)$ in Eq.(1) by

$$T_k(E, J, \pi) = \sum_{\nu=0}^{\omega} T_k^{\nu}(E, J, \pi, E_l^{\nu}, J_l^{\nu}, \pi_l^{\nu})$$

$$+ \int_{E_l^{\omega}}^{E-S_l} \sum_{J_l, \pi_l} T_k(E, J, \pi, E_l, J_l, \pi_l)\rho(E_l, J_l, \pi_l)dE_i. \quad (2)$$

Here the summation over excited states above the highest experimentally known state is changed to an integration over the level density ρ. In the case of an $i(n, f)$ reaction, $T_k(E, J, \pi)/T_{tot}(E, J, \pi)$ is identical to $T_f(E, J, \pi)/T_{tot}(E, J, \pi)$. We make use of a double-humped fission barrier and calculate the fission transmission coefficient in the limit of complete damping [2,26,27]. If one cannot make use of detailed information of the level structure in the second well, this method gives the best results and can be expressed in terms of

$$P_f(E, J, \pi) = T_f(E, J, \pi)/T_{tot}(E, J, \pi)$$

$$P_f(E, J, \pi) = \{1 + \left(\frac{\sum_{k \neq f} T_k(E, J, \pi)}{T_{eff}(E, J, \pi)}\right)^2$$

$$+ 2\frac{\sum_{k \neq f} T_k(E, J, \pi)}{T_{eff}(E, J, \pi)}$$

$$\times \coth[\frac{1}{2}(T_A(E, J, \pi) + T_B(E, J, \pi))]\}^{-1/2} \quad (3)$$

$$T_{eff}(E, J, \pi) = \frac{T_A(E, J, \pi)T_B(E, J, \pi)}{T_A(E, J, \pi) + T_B(E, J, \pi)},$$

with T_A and T_B denoting transmission through the first and second barrier, approximated by individual parabolic Hill-Wheeler type barrier shapes

$$T_A(E, J, \pi) = \int_0^E \rho_A(\epsilon, J, \pi)T_{HW}(\Delta, \hbar\omega_A)d\epsilon$$

$$\Delta = E - E_A - \epsilon - \frac{\hbar^2}{2\Theta}l(l+1). \quad (4)$$

T_B is expressed in equivalent form, $T_{HW}(E, \hbar\omega) = [1 + \exp(-2\pi E/\hbar\omega)]^{-1}$, and the available energy is reduced by the rotational energy with the moment of inertia Θ deduced from $\Theta = 5\Theta_{irr}$ for an irrotational flow model[5]. $\rho_{A,B}$ indicates the level densities above the first and second saddle point, which show an enhancement over the level densities at ground state deformation, due to increased deformation and coupling to low-lying rotational excitations. This enhancement is larger for

the first axially asymmetric barrier than for the second mass asymmetric (axially symmetric) barrier. In the absence of detailed calculations we used a standard enhancement factor of 4 and 2, respectively, over the level density at ground state deformation [3,26]. With a value obtained for P_f and the calculated transmission coefficients T_k ($k \neq f$) for all other channels we can solve $P_f = T_f/(T_f + \sum_k T_k)$ for T_f, and width fluctuation corrections can be included in the usual way[40].

Using all other parameters from global predictions as in the original code SMOKER [43,44], and employing experimental fission barrier heights $E_{A,B}$ and curvatures $\hbar\omega_{A,B}$ from Table XXXI in Bjørnholm and Lynn[3] we obtain very good agreement with experimental cross sections for neutron-induced fission, as indicated in Fig. 2 for ^{238}U.

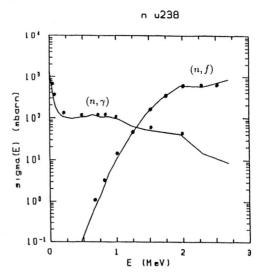

Fig. 2: Predicted cross sections for neutron capture and neutron-induced fission on ^{238}U. Only the reaction Q-values and fission barrier characteristics are taken from experiment. All other quantities like neutron and gamma transmission coefficients and level densities come from global predictions

Beta-delayed fission and neutron emission were calculated in a similar way and have already been described in detail in Thielemann, Metzinger, and Klapdor[45]. The beta-strength distributions were taken from Klapdor, Metzinger, and Oda[23], where the beta-strength function was calculated in the Tamm-Dancoff approximation, using a Gamow-Teller residual interaction. When $B(E_i, J_i, \pi_i)$ denotes the reduced transition probability to a final state with excitation energy E_i in the daughter nucleus, the total beta-decay rate is given by

$$\lambda = ln2/T_{1/2} = 1/D \sum_i B(E_i, J_i, \pi_i)f(Q_\beta - E_i) \quad (5)$$

with $D = 2\pi^3\hbar^7/(g_v^2 m_e^5 c^4)$, g_v denoting the vector coupling constant and $f(E)$ the Fermi function. The 1p1h configurations carrying the beta-strength act as doorway states, spreading their strength into neighboring compound states with a typical width of 0.2-0.3MeV. This can be taken into account by rewriting Eq.(5) with

$$\lambda = \int_0^{Q_\beta} \sum_i \beta_i(E, J_i, \pi_i)dE$$

$$\beta_i(E, J_i, \pi_i) = \frac{1}{\sigma_i(2\pi)^{1/2}}\exp[-(E - E_i)^2/2\sigma_i^2] \quad (6)$$

$$\times B(E_i, J_i, \pi_i)f(Q_\beta - E).$$

After populating excited states in the daughter nucleus, these can subsequently decay by gamma-tansitions to the ground state, neutron emission, or fission. The rates for fission and neutron emission are given by

$$\lambda_f = \int_0^{Q_\beta} \sum_i \beta_i(E, J_i, \pi_i)\frac{T_f(E, J_i, \pi_i)}{T_{tot}(E, J_i, \pi_i)}dE$$

$$\lambda_n = \int_0^{Q_\beta} \sum_i \beta_i(E, J_i, \pi_i)\frac{T_n(E, J_i, \pi_i)}{T_{tot}(E, J_i, \pi_i)}dE. \quad (7)$$

$P_f = T_f/T_{tot}$ is calculated as in Eq.(3) for neutron-induced fission. With knowledge of $T_k(k \neq f)$, T_f and T_{tot} and therefore T_n/T_{tot} can be calculated accordingly. It is customary to introduce the ratios $P_n = \lambda_n/\lambda$ and $P_f = \lambda_f/\lambda$.

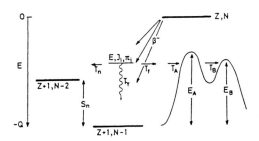

Fig. 3: Schematic representation and energetics of the different beta-delayed decay modes, neutron emission, gamma-deexcitation, and fission

When employing the formalism described above for calculating beta-delayed and neutron-induced fission for very neutron-rich unstable nuclei, three additional physical properties are required: (1) the beta strength function, (2) a nuclear mass formula for determining reaction or decay Q-values, and (3) fission barrier heights and curvatures. Fig. 3 illustrates how (1), (2) and

(3) enter into the result. The beta strength function gives transition strengths for decays to states in the daughter nucleus with respect to the ground state energy of the parent nucleus. The reaction or decay Q-value then determines the corresponding excitation energy in the daughter nucleus. The fission barrier heights are measured with respect to the ground state of the daughter nucleus. In case these quantities are not known experimentally, an appropriate choice from the presently existing literature are beta strength functions from Klapdor, Metzinger, and Oda[23], fission barriers from Howard and Möller[20], and several possible choices for a nuclear mass formula. With respect to the curvatures we utilized the following relations, based on empirical evidence [3,26] for $\hbar\omega_A$ and $\hbar\omega_B$, respectively: 1.04 and 0.6 (even-even), 0.8 and 0.52 (odd-A), and 0.6 and 0.45 (odd-odd).

In the following we present a few results from calculations which make use of this formalism. Table 1 lists the neutron capture and neutron-induced fission cross sections in barns for uranium isotopes at a bombarding energy of 30 keV. In addition it lists the Q-values for the (n, γ)-reaction and the maximum B_f of the two fission barrier heights (A,B) with respect to the ground state of the compound nucleus. Q-values and fission barrier characteristics are taken from experiment [47] and [3] (Table XXXI) if available; otherwise we employed the fission barriers of Howard and Möller[20] and a nuclear mass formula[14]. This means that from ^{240}U onward these quantities are predicted theoretically.

TABLE 1

CROSS SECTIONS AT 30KEV

Isotope	Q_n	B_f	$\sigma(n, \gamma)$	$\sigma(n, f)$
238	4.81	6.46	3.38-1	1.09-5
239	5.93	5.75	1.71-1	4.40-0
240	4.36	6.14	1.25-1	1.25-7
241	5.76	5.91	5.27-1	5.63-1
242	4.07	6.09	6.61-2	7.22-9
243	5.47	5.75	3.42-1	3.38-1
244	3.79	5.80	1.94-2	4.88-8
245	5.18	5.37	1.78-1	5.21-1
246	3.50	5.26	2.11-2	2.13-7
247	4.89	4.86	6.07-2	1.37-0
248	3.22	4.72	1.16-2	5.55-6
249	4.60	4.30	6.33-3	3.13-0
250	2.95	4.18	6.41-3	1.12-4
251	4.32	3.79	6.83-4	3.46-0
252	2.67	3.69	3.70-3	8.66-4
253	4.04	3.33	1.28-4	3.33-0
254	2.40	3.28	2.12-3	1.15-2
255	3.77	2.97	1.49-5	2.47-0
256	2.13	3.00	1.22-4	3.76-1
257	3.49	3.09	4.83-5	2.19-0

In the case of a practically instantaneous exposure of ^{238}U to thermal neutrons of 20-30 keV with a high fluence of 5×10^{24} to 2.4×10^{25} n cm^{-2}, which results in shorter neutron capture half-lives than beta-decay half-lives even for very short-lived nuclei, one would expect a sequence of multiple neutron captures. Such conditions were obtained in a series of thermonuclear explosions in the 1950s and 1960s [10,21,46].

Dependent on the design of the individual device, it has been assumed that neutron captures occur on a mixture of ^{238}U and ^{238}Pa seed nuclei with varying ratios, the latter being initially produced by high energy neutrons in a ^{238}U(n,p)^{238}Np reaction. In the experiment with the highest neutron flux (Hutch) nuclei as heavy as A=257 were found. If we check Table 1 for the possibility of multiple neutron captures, we see that there is only a 5% chance of neutron capture on ^{239}U in comparison to neutron-induced fission. Then follows a series of events where neutron capture wins strongly at even neutron number targets and is comparable to induced fission for odd targets, so that losses are not larger than about 50% for every two mass numbers. But, starting from ^{247}U, induced fission wins by 2 orders of magnitude on odd neutron number nuclei and grows steadily, so that the production of nuclei up to A=257 would be inexplicable. Upon checking our calculations for Pa, we find a similar behavior in that isotopic chain for A=246, 248, 250 etc., which leaves us with the same conclusion. These results are understandable when we consult Fig. 3d in Howard and Möller[20], which shows contours of the neutron energies required for induced fission. Around ^{247}U the energy contours turn negative, i.e., induced fission is already possible for thermal energies. Use of a the mass formula by Hilf, von Groote, Takahashi[14] reduced the effect in comparison to the Howard and Möller[20] masses, as it gives smaller Q_n-values. Therefore, we must conclude from experimental evidence that the theoretical fission barriers are too low for these neutron-rich nuclei.

Thielemann, Metzinger, and Klapdor[45] calculated beta-delayed fission and neutron emission for all nuclei with $75 \leq Z \leq 100$ from stability to the neutron drip line for three different mass formulas, with the methods outlined above. We show their resulting P_f-values in Fig. 4. Their results are consistent with the situation depicted in Fig. 3e of Howard and Möller[20], which shows contours of $Q_\beta - B_f$, a quantity which becomes positive for $N > 152$ and has very large values, up to 7 MeV, in an area around $163 < N < 172$ and $88 < Z < 98$. This area is more extended than the bay of shells which is represented by very short half-lives for spontaneous fission.

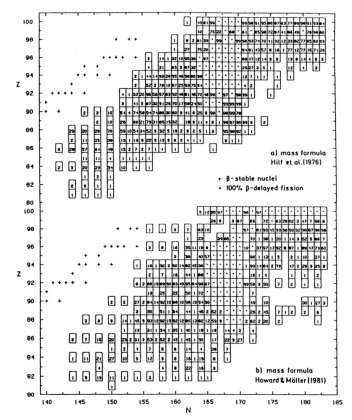

Fig. 4: Ratios for beta-delayed fission P_f in percent, indicated at the position of the daughter nucleus. The fission barriers by Howard and Möller[20] are used, the Q_β-values are taken from different mass formulas. In both cases an area of 100 percent delayed fission is predicted around Z=94 and N=168

Hoff[17,18] did a very careful analysis, testing specifically if the results of the Hutch event are compatible with the predictions for beta-delayed fission. Starting from the observed abundances of beta-stable nuclei up to A=257 after the event, he extrapolated backwards to obtain the required abundances of the uranium isotopes produced in the explosion, taking into account the predicted fission losses in each isobaric chain. A reasonable agreement between predicted abundances [10,21,46] and experiment could only be obtained with the consistent use of the fission barriers *and* nuclear masses from Howard and Möller[20], but still in this case a too large abundance of ^{257}U is predicted. The latter statement seems trivial, as it is always preferable to perform a "consistent" calculation. But in view of the evolution of knowledge of nuclear masses it is important to understand its meaning.

Since the 1976 mass evaluation, which includes formulas like Myers[36] and von Groote, Hilf, Takahashi[13], additional knowledge about the extrapolation of nuclear masses to regions far from stability has emerged. In some regions of the nuclear chart experimental data up to the vicinity of the r-process path are available by now (^{130}Cd, ^{80}Zn). The general result is that a steeper slope of the "mass parabola" is indicated than in most of the 1976 mass formulas. Based on r-process studies, Hilf, von Groote, and Takahashi [14] noticed improved fits with solar system r-abundances when using different droplet model parameters which led to a steeper mass parabola. Its general trend is close to the present experimental findings and the most recent results by Möller *et al.* [35] (finite range droplet model with improved pairing corrections, treatment of nuclear deformations, etc.). The Howard and Möller masses still used a macroscopic part close to the one by Myers[36] which resulted in a too shallow mass parabola. Therefore, the predicted beta-decay Q-values are too small and neutron capture Q-values too large. It is then also understandable that the P_f-values of Thielemann, Metzinger, and Klapdor[45] obtained with a more realistic but steeper mass formula[14] with larger Q_β-values overpredicted the amount of beta-delayed fission substantially. Given the fact, however, that nuclear masses follow that steeper slope, we must conclude — in agreement with our findings from neutron-induced fission of uranium isotopes — that larger fission barriers are needed to explain the experimental results from thermonuclear explosions. This is in agreement with new calculations presented at this meeting [32].

It should be noted that the experiments mentioned above clearly established the effect of beta-delayed fission by not producing an A=256 isotope and isotopes beyond A=257, although in a series of experiments the neutron fluence was progressively increased. It is just at these isobars where the extended bay of shells is encountered. However, with the previously used fission barriers the effect was overestimated.

3. r-PROCESS CALCULATIONS

Astrophysical r-process calculations have one major problem, independent of the nuclear uncertainties discussed above. While low mass type II supernovae are the prime candidates to provide the conditions for r-process nucleosynthesis to occur in their neutron-rich ejecta [29], this is not a proven fact. This uncertainty depends mainly on the incompletely solved type II supernova mechanism and lack of knowledge of the precise location of the mass cut between the neutron star and the ejecta. For alternative scenarios and a general reviews of the r-process see refs. [15,30,41]. Without complete understanding of the astrophysical site, r-process calculations can still be performed with assumed neutron densities and temperatures as a function of time,

varied in order to fit r-process abundances as found in the solar system.

Fission was included in the calculations by Thielemann, Metzinger, and Klapdor[45] and Cowan, Thielemann, and Truran[9]. As mentioned before, fission can influence several aspects of r-process nucleosynthesis. It will determine the fission loss from the r-process path back to beta-stability and the abundance of alpha-unstable short-lived progenitors of the long-lived unstable nuclei ^{232}Th, ^{235,238}U, and ^{244}Pu, which have half-lives comparable to the age of our galaxy and the universe and can therefore be used as cosmic clocks to estimate that age. This situation is illustrated in Fig. 5 which shows the different alpha-decay chains and the percentages of beta-delayed fission which nuclei encounter during their decay from the r-process path. Note however, that the numbers are overestimated as discussed in section 2. In addition, dependent on the location of the r-process path and the detailed P_f-values, fission determines whether nuclei with Z> 100 are produced in the r-process (and therefore in nature). This is also indicated in Fig. 5.

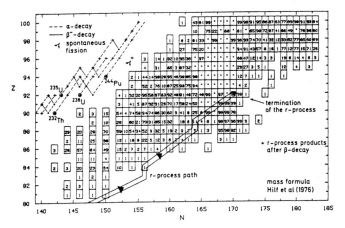

Fig. 5: Location of the r-process path with respect to the region of beta-delayed fission. After freeze-out of the neutron abundance these nuclei will decay back to stability (crosses) and undergo alpha-decay to produce the long-lived nuclei ^{232}Th, ^{235,238}U, and ^{244}Pu. Strong fission losses are encountered on the way to stability but the P_f-values indicated in this figure are overestimated (see text)

The present dilemma is that correct mass formulas describe a relatively steep mass parabola as indicated in Möller *et al.*[35] — which is close in its trends to the one by Hilf, von Groote, Takahashi[14] used in our earlier calculations — but that the fission barriers of Howard and Möller [20] give only reasonable P_f-values when used in connection with the Q-values of a more shallow mass formula [20,36]. In such a situation a "correct" calculation cannot be done but one can take two approaches to estimate the correct behavior: (1) use a mass formula which approximates the correct behavior, and (2) use a more shallow mass formula to be consistent in the calculations for beta-delayed fission. The first approach gives probably a more consistent picture of the overall r-process behavior and the second is probably closer to reality when estimating the influence of fission. The calculations by Thielemann, Metzinger and Klapdor[45] and Cowan, Thielemann, and Truran[9] were performed along these two lines and results are displayed in Fig. 6a and b. In both cases the calculated abundances are displayed in comparison to solar system abundances (only the shape of the curve, not the actual values are of importance). Nuclei beyond A=209 will alpha-decay and produce the enhanced abundances of ^{206,207,208}Pb and ^{209}Bi. In both cases we see a downturn of the curve beyond A=240, which is due to fission, but to a different degree. It can also be noticed that in the first calculation the r-process path terminates in the bay of shells and no superheavy elements are produced. In the second calculation with a different mass formula the r-process runs slightly more neutron-rich and the amount of fission is reduced, so that the bay of shells can be circumvented and nuclei with Z> 100 can be produced. Due to the lack of available fission barriers for nuclei with Z> 100, fission was not included for those nuclei. The abundance curve in Fig. 6b was originally almost flat between A=220 and 320, before beta-decay back to stability from the r-process path. During the decay beta-delayed fission for nuclei with Z< 100 cuts out the abundances between A=240 and 300. This effect could not be considered for nuclei with Z> 100. From the above discussion it is still unclear whether the r-process in nature actually produces superheavies or not. What remains to be done is a calculation with an improved mass formula *and* improved fission barriers.

After decay of the alpha-unstable progenitors of ^{232}Th (^{232}Th, ^{236}U, ^{240}Pu, ^{248}Cm, and ^{252}Cf), ^{235}U (^{235}U, ^{239}Pu, ^{243}Am, ^{247}Cm, ^{251}Cf, and ^{255}Fm), ^{238}U (^{238}U, ^{242}Pu, and ^{246}Cm), and ^{244}Pu (^{244}Pu, ^{248}Cm, and ^{252}Cf) we find the following ratios

TABLE 2

ABUNDANCE RATIOS OF CHRONOMETER PAIRS

^{232}Th/^{238}U	^{235}U/^{238}U	^{244}Pu/^{238}U	REF.
1.40	1.24	0.12	TMK [45]
1.60	1.16	0.40	CTT [9]
1.53	1.26	0.49	no fission
1.71	1.34	0.66	FOW [11]

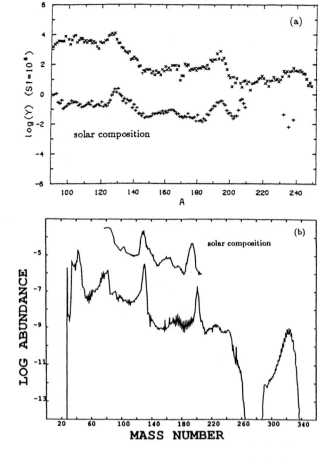

Fig. 6: Resulting r-process abundances in comparison to solar system values from two different calculations. Nuclei beyond A=209 will finally alpha-decay to produce ^{206,207,208}Pb and ^{209}Bi. In both calculations the decline for A>240 is due to the influence of fission. In the first case no nuclei with Z>100 were produced, due to fission, while the second calculation with a different mass formula [20] could circumvent the region of large P_f-values. Delayed fission for nuclei with Z>100 was not included

For comparison we also list the ratios by Fowler[11], who assumes a constant abundance as a function of A and does not include fission. Then one would expect the ratios to be just given by the number of progenitors (6:3=2, 6:3=2, 3:3=1). Since the number of progenitors is not 6 and 3, because some of these nuclei andergo spontaneous fission to an appreciable degree, the ratios 1.71 and 0.66 are obtained. Fowler[11] also introduces a depletion of odd-A nuclei which leads to 1.34. If we compare these numbers with a calculation like Cowan, Thielemann, and Truran (CTT)[9], but without fission, we notice a similar ratio for ^{235}U/^{238}U but smaller values for ^{232}Th/^{238}U and ^{244}Pu/^{238}U. This is due to the fact that r-process calculations (independent of fission) result in a slight abundance maximum around

A=238-240. This automatically reduces the progenitors of ^{232}Th below and above 240 and the progenitors of ^{244}Pu which are all above 240. The "consistent" calculation of CTT with fission barriers and masses from Howard and Möller[20] introduces the effect of fission, but essentially only for A beyond 240, which affects the Pu/U ratio but leaves Th/U almost untouched (in fact, the latter is slightly increased because Th is less affected than U). The TMK calculation with an over-estimated influence of fission also affected abundances below A=240, i.e., important members of the ^{232}Th progenitors and therefore also reduced the Th/U ratio, while the effect on Pu/U is maximized. What we see already from the comparison of calculations without fission and the "consistent" inclusion of fission is that the infuence on the chronometer ratios is not as strong as initially suggested.

After the production of these chronometer pairs in an r-process event, the participating nuclei will decay on long time scales with half-lives of 1.405×10^{10}y (^{232}Th), 4.46×10^9y (^{238}U), and 7.038×10^8y (^{235}U). With the additional knowledge of ongoing new production in galactic nucleosynthesis from a galactic evolution model, one can determine the time at which the appropriate abundance ratios are met which existed in the protosolar nebular, 4.6×10^9y ago, at the formation of the solar system. This leads to a duration time of galactic nucleosynthesis and the age of our galaxy, which is a lower limit to the age of the universe. It would be too elaborate to present the details of such calculations here, and we refer the reader to Cowan, Thielemann, and Truran[9], Clayton[8], and a very thorough and understandable review by Pagel[37]. Here we only quote results, according to the individual entries in Table 2. The last entry, making use of an assumed equal abundance of all progenitor nuclei [11], would result in galactic ages of $9.6 - 10.1 \times 10^9$y. The result from an r-process calculation which neglects fission leads to ages of $13.2 - 15.2 \times 10^9$y. The calculation with the "consistant" inclusion of fission (fission barriers and masses from Howard and Möller[20]) comes to a very comparable range ($12.4 - 14.7 \times 10^9$y). The first entry, which overestimated fission by using an inconsistent set of nuclear data (too small fission barriers from Howard and Möller[20] together with a more realistic steeper mass formula), would result in values of $14.6 - 24 \times 10^9$y.

4. SUMMARY

Theoretical calculations of nuclear properties predict an area of very short half-lives for spontaneous fission, i.e., very small fission barriers, located in the "bay of shells" beyond Z=92 and N=165. This region of large fissibility is extended in neutron-induced and beta-delayed fission, due to the fact that both processes produce nuclei in excited states, which leads to an effective lower-

ing of the fission barriers. These predictions are actually supported by results from thermonuclear explosions where nuclei with A=256 and A> 257 could not be produced from ^{238}U targets, even with increasing neutron fluences. However, the presently existing theoretical predictions for the fission barrier heights overestimate this effect, as can also be deduced from experimental evidence. Therefore, the influence on r-process calculations is still not clearly defined. What is needed are calculations with improved mass formulas *and* fission barriers. Only then it will be possible to determine clearly if the r-process can circumvent the area of strong fission and produce elements with Z> 100. With respect to the production ratios of chronometric pairs a smaller influence than predicted earlier is expected, in fact it might be negligible, but again the final answer can only come from calculations with improved barrier heights.

This research was supported in part by NASA grant NGR 22-007-272 and NSF grants AST 8612647 and AST 8521705. Part of the calculations were performed at the National Center for Supercomputer Applications at the University of Illinois (AST 890009N). This paper contains results from earlier collaborations with H.V. Klapdor, J. Metzinger, and J.W. Truran. We also want to thank S. Becker, W.A. Fowler, M. Howard, G. Mathews, B. Meyer, P. Möller, and B. Pagel for fruitful discussions.

REFERENCES

(1) Applegate, J.H. 1988, *Phys. Rep.* **163**, 141

(2) Back, B.B., Hansen, O., Britt, H.C., Garrett, J.D. 1974 *Phys. Rev.* **C9**, 1924

(3) Bjørnholm, S., Lynn, J.E. 1980, *Rev. Mod. Phys.* **52**, 725

(4) Bengtsson, R., Boleu, R., Larsson, S.E., Randrup, J. 1974, *Phys. Scripta* **10A**, 142

(5) Bohr, A., Mottelson, B. 1975, *Nuclear Structure II*, (Benjamin, New York)

(6) Burbidge, E.M., Burbidge, G.R., Fowler, A.A., Hoyle, F. 1957, *Rev. Mod. Phys.* **29**, 547

(7) Cameron, A.G.W. 1957, Atomic Energy of Canada, Ltd., CRL-41

(8) Clayton, D.D. 1988, *M.N.R.A.S.* **234**, 1

(9) Cowan, J.J., Thielemann, F.-K., Truran, J. W. 1987, *Ap. J.*, **323**, 543

(10) Eccles, S.F. 1970, in *Engineering with Nucl. Explosives*, (American Nuclear Soc.), p. 1269

(11) Fowler, W.A. 1987, *Q. Jl. R. astr. Soc.* **28**, 87

(12) Gill, R.L., Casten, R.F., Warner, D.D., Piotrowski, A. et al. 1986, *Phys. Rev. Lett.* **56**, 1974

(13)Groote, H. von, Hilf, E.R., Takahashi, K. 1976, *At. Nucl. Data Tables* **17**, 418

(14)Hilf, E.R., von Groote, H., Takahashi, K. 1976, in *Proc. 3rd Int. Conf. on Nuclei far off Stability*, CERN-Rep. 76-13, p.142

(15)Hillebrandt, W. 1978, *Space Sci. Rev.* **21**, 639

(16)Hillebrandt, W., Klapdor, H.V., Oda, T., Thielemann, F.-K. 1981, *Astron. Astrophys.* **99**, 195

(17)Hoff, R. 1986, in *Weak and Electromagnetic Interactions in Nuclei*, ed. H.V. Klapdor (Springer, Heidelberg), p.207

(18)Hoff, R. 1987, *J. Phys. G.* **24**, S343

(19)Howard, W.M. 1974, *Phys. Scrypta* **10A**, 138

(20)Howard, W.M., Möller, P. 1980, *Atomic Data Nuclear Data Tables*, **25**, 219

(21)Ingley, J.S. 1969, *Nucl. Phys.* **A124**, 130

(22)Jeukenne, J.P., Lejeune, A., Mahaux, C. 1977, *Phys. Rev.* **C16**, 80

(23)Klapdor, H.V., Metzinger, J., Oda, T. 1984, *At Nucl. Data Tables* **31**, 81

(24)Kratz, K.-L. et al. 1986, *Z. Phys.* **A325**, 483

(25)Lund, E., Aleklett, K., Fogelberg, B., Sangariyavanish, A. 1986, *Phys. Scripta* **34**, 614

(26)Lynn, J.E. 1980, in *Nucl. Theory for Applications*, ed. A.Salam, IAEA-SMR-43 (Intl. Atomic Energy Comm., Vienna), p.353

(27)Lynn, J.E., Back, B.B. 1974, *J. Phys.* **A7**, 395

(28)Mann, F.M. 1978, Hauser 5, A Computer Code to Calculate Nuclear Cross Sections, Hanford Engineering (HEDL-TME 78-83)

(29)Mathews, G.J., Cowan, J.J. 1989, in *Heavy Ion Physics and Nuclear Astrophysical Problems*, eds. S. Kubono, M. Ishihara, T. Nomura, (World Scientific, Singapore), p.143

(30)Mathews, G.J., Ward, R.A. 1985, *Rep. Prog. Phys.* **48**, 1371

(31)Meldner, H.W., Nuckolls, J., Wood, L. 1974, *Phys. Scripta* **10A**, 149

(32)Meyer, B.S., Howard, W.M., Mathews, G.J., Möller, P. 1985, in *Nuclei off the Line of Stability*, ACS Symposium Series **324** (American Chemical Society, Washington D.C.), p.149

(33)Meyer, B.S., Howard, W.M., Möller, P., Leander, G.A. 1989, *Phys. Rev.* **C39**, in press

(34)Meyer, B.S., Möller, P., Howard, W.M., Mathews, G.J. 1989, this conference

(35)Möller, P., Myers, W.D., Swiatecki, W.J., Treiner, J. 1988 *At. Nucl. Data Tables* **39**, 225

(36)Myers, W.D. 1976, *At. Nucl. Data Tables* **17**, 411

(37)Pagel, B.E.J. 1988, in *Evolutionary Phenomena in Galaxies*, eds. J.Beckman and B.E.J. Pagel, (Cambridge Univ. Press), p.

(38)Seeger, P.A., Fowler, W.A., Clayton , D.D. 1965, *Ap. J. Suppl.* **97**, 121

(39)Symbalisty, E.M.D., Schramm D.N. 1982, *Ap. J. Lett.* **22**, 143

(40)Tepel, J.W., Hoffmann, H.M., Weidenmüller, H.A. 1974, *Phys. Lett.* **49B**, 1

(41)Thielemann, F.-K. 1989, in *Nuclear Astrophysics*, ed. M. Lozano, M.I. Gallardo, J.M. Arias (Springer: Berlin), p.106

(42)Thielemann, F.-K, Arnould, M. 1983, in *Proc. Int. Conf. on Nucl. Data for Sci. and Technology*, ed. K. Böckhoff (Reidel, Dordrecht), p.762

(43)Thielemann, F.-K., Arnould, M., Truran, J.W. 1987, in *Advances in Nuclear Astrophysics*, eds. E. Vangioni-Flam et al., (éditions frontières: Gif sur Yvette), p.525

(44)Thielemann, F.-K., Arnould, M., Truran, J.W. 1988, in *Capture Gamma-Ray Spectroscopy*, eds. K. Abrahams, P. van Assche (IOP, Bristol), p.730

(45)Thielemann, F.-K., Metzinger, J., and Klapdor, H.V. 1983, *Z. Phys.* **A309**, 301

(46)Truran, J.W., Cameron, A.G.W. 1966, *Arkiv Fys.* **36**, 509

(47)Wapstra, A.H., Audi, G., Hoekstra, R. 1988, *At. Nucl. Data Tables* **39**, 281

FISSION FRAGMENT ROCKETS - A NEW FRONTIER

G. F. Chapline and W. M. Howard
Lawrence Livermore National Laboratory
P.O. Box 808
Livermore, CA 94550
415-422-4106 or 415-422-4138

B. G. Schnitzler
Idaho National Engineering Laboratory
P.O. Box 1625
Idaho Falls, ID 83415
208-526-9794

ABSTRACT

A new reactor concept is described which would enable fission fragments to be continuously extracted from the reactor. Such a reactor has the potential of enabling extremely energetic and ambitious deep space missions. In this talk the basic physics issues involved in the operation of this type of reactor are outlined, and some possible applications to space exploration are described.

INTRODUCTION

As we're sure most of your are aware fission fragments come in two varieties: a) "heavy" fragments with a kinetic energy of approximately 0.5 MeV per AMU, and b) "light" fragments whose kinetic energy is approximately 1.0 MeV per AMU. In this talk we wish to discuss the possibility that these fission fragments can be used directly to propel a spacecraft.[1] The usual figure of merit for rocket propellants is specific impulse - the length of burn for which an acceleration of 1 g can be maintained. In a rocket exhaust fission fragments would give a specific impulse of 10^6 seconds. The best chemical rocket propellants currently in use have specific impulses of about 300 seconds. Thus the use of fission fragments could lead to burn-out velocities 3000 times those currently attainable. In terms of the speed of light this corresponds to velocities in excess of .05c!

Obviously the attainment of velocities on the order of .05c will open up new possibilities for the exploration of space beyond the solar system. Of course, the realization of these possibilities will depend on how easy it is to design a nuclear reactor that allows the fission fragments to escape. In ordinary solids or liquids fission fragments travel only a few microns before losing their energy. Thus the average density of material in the reactor core must be much smaller than solid density if the fission fragments are to escape.

Our basic conception for how a fission fragment rocket would work is very simple. The reactor core is in a vacuum and the fissile material is placed in the reactor core in the form of a coating on very thin (i.e., few micron) diameter fibers. The fission fragments are then guided out of the reactor core with magnetic fields. In a vacuum the mean free path for a fission fragment will be comparable to the size of the reactor core if the spacing between the fuel wires is sufficiently large. The fission fragment escape probability from an array of wires will be determined by the escape probability from a single fiber and the thickness of the array of fibers. In Fig. 1 we show the escape probability for fission fragments from a fiber coated with uranium carbide as a function of coating and fiber thickness. Escape probabilities were calculated using a integral transport code developed at the Idaho National Engineering Laboratory. Evidently with UC coating thicknesses of less than 0.5 µm, it is possible to achieve fiber escape probabilities exceeding 70%. The escape probability from a layer of wires will be determined by the product of the volume averaged density of material in the layer, ρ, and thickness of the layer, Δx. The range of fission fragments is about 2 mg/cm^2. Therefore, $\rho\Delta x$ for a fuel layer cannot exceed about 1 mg/cm^2.

While it is clear that it is possible in principle to achieve criticality with low fuel densities, one might guess that the reactor core size would be prohibitively large or that excessively large magnetic fields would be required to guide the fission fragments out of the reactor core. However, initial investigations of this concept resulted in two surprises. First, if one uses a good moderator-reflector and highly fissile isotopes then relatively small amounts of fissile material are required for criticality, and the reactor core need be only one or two meters across. Second, the magnetic fields needed to

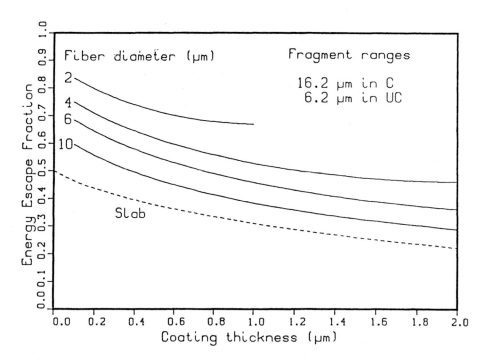

Figure 1. Fission fragment escape probability for uranium carbide coated graphite fibers.

guide the fission fragments out of the reactor can be generated with currently available technology. To illustrate this last point we note that the magnetic rigidity of fission fragments with atomic weight A will be given by

$$Br = \frac{14.AE^{1/2}}{Z_{eff}} \text{ Tesla-cm} \qquad (1)$$

where E is the kinetic energy of the fragment in units of MeV/amu and Z_{eff} is the effective charge. In estimating the effective charge we used a formula given by Srivastava and Mukherji, which corresponds to Bohr's idea that the effective charge is equal to the number of orbital electrons whose velocities are less than the ion velocity v. For the heavy fission fragments $v \simeq .03c$ and $Z_{eff} \simeq 22$. For nascent fission fragments the rigidity is about 0.5 Tesla-meters.

Our notion then for how a fission fragment rocket would work is that the fuel wires would be grouped into thin layers inside the reactor core while current carrying elements just outside the moderator would create magnetic fields between the layers. The magnetic field serves to both insulate the moderator and transport the fission fragments out of the reactor core (Fig. 2). The magnetic field strength must be such that the cyclotron radius is smaller than the distance between fuel layers but larger than the thickness of a fuel layer. The distance between layers of fuel wires will be determined by the escape probability desired and the average density of

material inside the core. For example, if an escape probability of 50% is desired and the average density of material in the core is 1.0×10^{-4} gm/cm^3, then the maximum allowable distance between fuel layers will be approximately 10 cm.

REACTOR PHYSICS

It is clear that the best chances for achieving a satisfactory level of performance lie with the utilization of fissile isotopes with the largest fission cross-sections. Because of the tenuous density of fuel in the core, the neutrons will make several passes into and out of the reflector; thus the fission fragment rocket will operate as a thermal reactor. The thermal neutron fission cross-section and neutron multiplicities for some candidate actinides are shown in Table I. Because of their large thermal fission cross-sections and neutron multiplicities the best fuels for a fission fragment rocket are ^{242}Am metastable (^{242*}Am) and ^{245}Cm. However, it should be possible to build a prototype reactor that uses ^{239}Pu or even ^{235}U. In Table II we show the critical mass for these isotopes for a 5-m long by 1-m diameter core surrounded by 3m of D$_2$O moderator.

The 500-g critical mass for ^{242*}Am corresponds to a density $\rho = 1.2 \times 10^{-4}$ g/cm^3. If the ^{242*}Am were uniformly dispersed in the core at this density, the range for fission fragments inside the core would be about 18 cm. This means that 60% of the fuel is within a fission fragment range of the edge of the core.

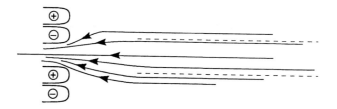

Figure 2. Fuel layers and schematic magnetic field for fission fragment extraction.

TABLE I

CANDIDATE FISSILE FUELS

Material	ν	σ_f	ρ	$\nu\sigma_f\rho$
U^{233}	2.453	497	18.6	23,000
U^{235}	2.398	515	18.7	23,000
Pu^{239}	2.844	725	19.6	40,000
Am^{242m}	3.210	6694	19.9	427,000
Cm^{245}	3.600	1937	13.4	93,000
Cf^{251}	3.870	3168	13.5	165,000

TABLE II

CRITICAL MASS FOR 5-m x 1-m DIAMETER CORE

$^{242*}Am$	0.5 kg
^{245}Cm	1.1 kg
^{239}Pu	5.6 kg
^{235}U	11. kg

By segmenting the fuel into layers and using magnetic fields between the layers (cf. Fig. 2) we hope to achieve extraction efficiencies $\gtrsim$ 50%.

For spacecraft applications it is crucial that the reactor mass be kept as small as possible; therefore there is a strong incentive to use $^{242*}Am$ or ^{245}Cm as the fuel and to operate with the highest fuel density that is consistent with good fission fragment extraction efficiency. In Table III we show the results of some initial attempts to estimate the amount of moderator-reflector in fission fragments rockets using $^{242*}Am$ as the reactor fuel. The reactor core was assumed to be a cylinder surrounded by a uniform layer of moderator. Only prompt neutrons were included in the calculation. The fuel (consisting of 1 atomic part $^{242*}Am$ and 5 atomic parts ^{13}C) was uniformly distributed in the core. λ_{FF}/R is the ratio of the fission fragment range in the uniformly distributed fuel to the fuel radius.

The parameters for these critical assemblies were calculated using ALICE, a Monte-Carlo neutronics code developed at the Lawrence Livermore National Laboratory. The

TABLE III

MODERATOR REQUIREMENTS FOR $^{242*}Am$-FUELED PROMPT CRITICAL CONFIGURATION

Core Dimensions (m)	Fuel Density (mg/cm^3)	λ_{FF}/R	Moderator-Reflector Thickness/ Mass (cm)/ (metric tons)
10 x 1	0.12	.33	40/18.5
10 x 1	0.10	.40	50/26
10 x 2	0.05	.40	30/27
7 x 1.5	0.05	.53	55/30

average fuel densities and core diameters were chosen to make it plausible that a fission fragment extraction efficiency of at least 50% is achievable. The moderator-reflector was chosen to be $^{13}CD_2$, which is about as good as D_2O as a moderator-reflector. In practice we have in mind using as a moderator/reflector some organic material such as a deuterated heavy wax. The potential advantage of using an organic material for the moderator is that the equilibrium vapor pressure of such a material may be much smaller than D_2O. For example, with the use of catalysts one might be able to shift the equilibrium towards non-volatile materials. One will still need a pressure vessel, but our hope is that the pressure will be low enough to be able to use graphite for the pressure bearing walls. To our knowledge graphite is the only structural material which can survive the large neutron fluence during the required operating life. In the case of ^{239}Pu calculations similar to those shown in Table III suggest that the minimum moderator mass will be approximately 100 tons.

The power that can be generated with a fission fragment rocket will be limited by the rate at which waste heat can be radiated away. Indeed, the mass of a spacecraft powered with a conventional reactor will generally be determined by the mass required for heat rejection. Fortunately, fission fragment rockets offer an extraordinary opportunity for heat rejection. The small diameter of the fuel wires means that the fuel has a large surface area, and the fuel itself can be used to radiate away waste heat. If we assume the fuel wires are 3-μm carbon fibers with a 0.4-μm thick coating of americium, then one metric ton of fuel wires will have an area of 2×10^9 cm^2. At a temperature of 1100 K this is sufficient area to radiate away 20 GW! Thus if the fuel wires are dispersed over a sufficiently large area they will radiatively cool themselves. This does not completely eliminate the need for conventional cooling, but one of the unique features of fission fragment rockets is that almost all the energy produced is either carried away by the fission fragments that escape the core or is deposited in the fuel wires.

Another factor that will limit the power that can be generated in a fission fragment rocket is the necessity of keeping the fuel elements in the reactor core from melting. As noted above one metric ton of fuel wires can radiate away 20 GW; however, only a few kilograms of fuel are inside the reactor core at any given time. Therefore, one is faced with the problem of rapidly circulating the fuel wires through the reactor core in order to keep them from melting. One way this might be accomplished is to string the fuel wires on a very large wheel which is rapidly rotating. To get some idea of how rapidly the wheel must rotate let us note that the heat input necessary to take americium up to its melting point (1449 K) is 10.5 kcal/mole or 182 kJ/kg.[2] If we assume that the heat capacity of the fuel wires is approximately 1 MJ/kg, a 2-meter diameter by 10-meter long reactor core in which the average density of fuel wires is 1×10^{-4} gm/cm^3 will have a heat capacity of approximately 3 MJ. The heat loading on the fuel wires inside the reactor core will be 4.5 GW. Thus at a total power of 10 GW and a 50% fission fragment extraction efficiency the fuel wires could spend no more than 10^{-3} s inside the reactor core. This means that the fuel must be circulated through the reactor core with a velocity of at least 1 km/s. If the fuel wires are rotated through the reactor core one must be careful that the centrifugal loading on the fuel wires does not exceed their strength. For example, if the wheel diameter is 200 meters and the wheel rim has a velocity of 1 km/s, then the centrifugal loading on a 3-μm diameter carbon fiber coated with 0.4 μm is americium is 4×10^4 MPa. This loading is a factor 10 less than the tensile strength of the strongest few micron diameter carbon fibers currently available. Therefore there is some room for optimism with respect to being able to operate fission fragment rockets at powers possibly as high as 10 GW. If we assume that the total mass of the fission fragment powered spacecraft is 100 metric tons, then 10 GW corresponds to a power-to-weight ratio of 100 kW/kg!

APPLICATIONS TO SPACE EXPLORATION

To illustrate the extraordinary possibilities opened up by the fission fragment rocket let us consider a mission to the nearest star, Alpha Centauri, 4.1 light-years from the solar system. The mission should start in a sufficiently high orbit so that the fission fragment exhaust will not harm earth satellites. Let us assume that we have an americium fueled rocket and include a device such that the fission fragments that are trapped on the carbon wires, along with the spent wires, are discarded periodically. We also assume a 10-GW reactor operating for about 40 years, the spacecraft coasting thereafter. For a fission fragment escape probability of 50% we can deliver a mass of payload plus structure of fifteen metric tons in 121 years or thirty metric tons in 148 years. If we could increase the escape fraction to 70%, we can deliver ten metric tons in 87 years, twenty metric tons in 101 years, or thirty metric tons in 113 years. Thus an americium-powered fission fragment rocket holds the potential of a less than 150-year mission to the nearest star if the payload and structure mass can be kept sufficiently small.

Of perhaps more immediate interest would be a scientific mission to a 10^3 AU (1 AU = earth-sun distance).[2] If we assume that the fission fragment extraction efficiency is 50% then a Pu fueled 1 GW fission fragment rocket could provide an acceleration on the order of 10^{-4} g for a 100 ton spacecraft. If the reactor operated for 10 years, then one would consume about 5 metric tons of ^{239}Pu and reach 10^3 AU in 20 years. One really exciting objective of such a mission would be to attempt to use the sun as a gravitational lens.[3] At radio wavelengths below 1 cm useful focal lengths for the sun as a gravitational lens lie in the range 550-2000 AU. Using radio receives no more sensitive than have already been developed for interplanetary spacecraft, it should be possible to image planets at a distance of 20 light years with a resolution of 15 km.[3] Needless to say, such a project would attract widespread interest.

Fission fragment rockets may also be useful for solar system missions. In particular, it may be possible to achieve significant reductions in solar system transit times; e.g. a 4 month transit time to Mars. For these missions, though, it would be advantageous to directly convert the fission fragment energy to electricity, which is used to power a more conventional ion propulsion system (e.g. using xenon as the propellant).

CONCLUSION

It should be noted that none of the components of the fission fragment rocket requires a new technology, except for the organic moderator if that is used. Of course, a significant infrastructure development would be required to produce large amounts of ^{242*}Am. However, less stressing missions, such as the TAU mission or rapid interplanetary travel, could be done with a plutonium-fueled, or maybe even a uranium-fueled rocket. Indeed, we believe that with sufficient funding a prototype fission fragment rocket using ^{239}Pu as the fuel could be flown by the end of the century or shortly thereafter.

ACKNOWLEDGMENTS

The authors are grateful to Ron Cohen, Paul Dickson, James Jones, Yoshi Matsuda, and Ernie Plechaty for suggestions and help with calculations.

Work performed under the auspices of the U.S. Department of Energy by the Lawrence Livermore National Laboratory under contract number W-7405-ENG-48.

REFERENCES

1. G. Chapline, Nucl. Instruments and Methods in Physics Research A271 (1988) 202.

2. K. T. Nock, TAU-A Mission to a Thousand Astronomical Units, AIAA reprint 87-1049 (1987).

3. V. R. Eshleman, Science 85 (1979) 1133.

NATIONAL INSTITUTE OF STANDARDS AND TECHNOLOGY PLENARY: NUCLEAR FISSION — A PROSPECTIVE

Chairman
W. W. Havens, Jr. (APS)

NUCLEAR FISSION: PAST, PRESENT AND FUTURE

H. H. BARSCHALL

University of Wisconsin
Department of Physics
1150 University Avenue
Madison WI 53706
(608) 262-9569

During the past three days we have reviewed the events that led to the discovery of fission and the impact of the discovery on nuclear physics. We also heard summaries of the applications of the discovery on other fields of science and engineering. In closing the conference I was asked to say a few words to put our gathering into a broader context.

As Glenn Seaborg mentioned last night, our conference is not the only one which commemorates the 50th anniversary of the discovery of fission. The commemorations started last November at Castle Gaussig in the DDR, and Fig. 1 is a photograph showing the participants at that meeting. The participants sent us greetings reproduced in Fig. 2. This was followed by an event in

FIG. 1. PARTICIPANTS AT MEETING ON "PHYSICS AND CHEMISTRY OF FISSION" HELD AT SCHLOSS GAUSSIG, DDR, IN NOVEMBER 1988.

best compliments from

Gaussig 1988 to

Gaitherburg 1989

FIG. 2. GREETINGS FROM GAUSSIG TO GAITHERSBURG.

FIG. 3. PARTICIPANTS AT WORKSHOP ON THE SOCIAL AND HISTORICAL AS-
PECTS OF THE DISCOVERY OF FISSION, HELD IN MARCH 1989 IN BERLIN.

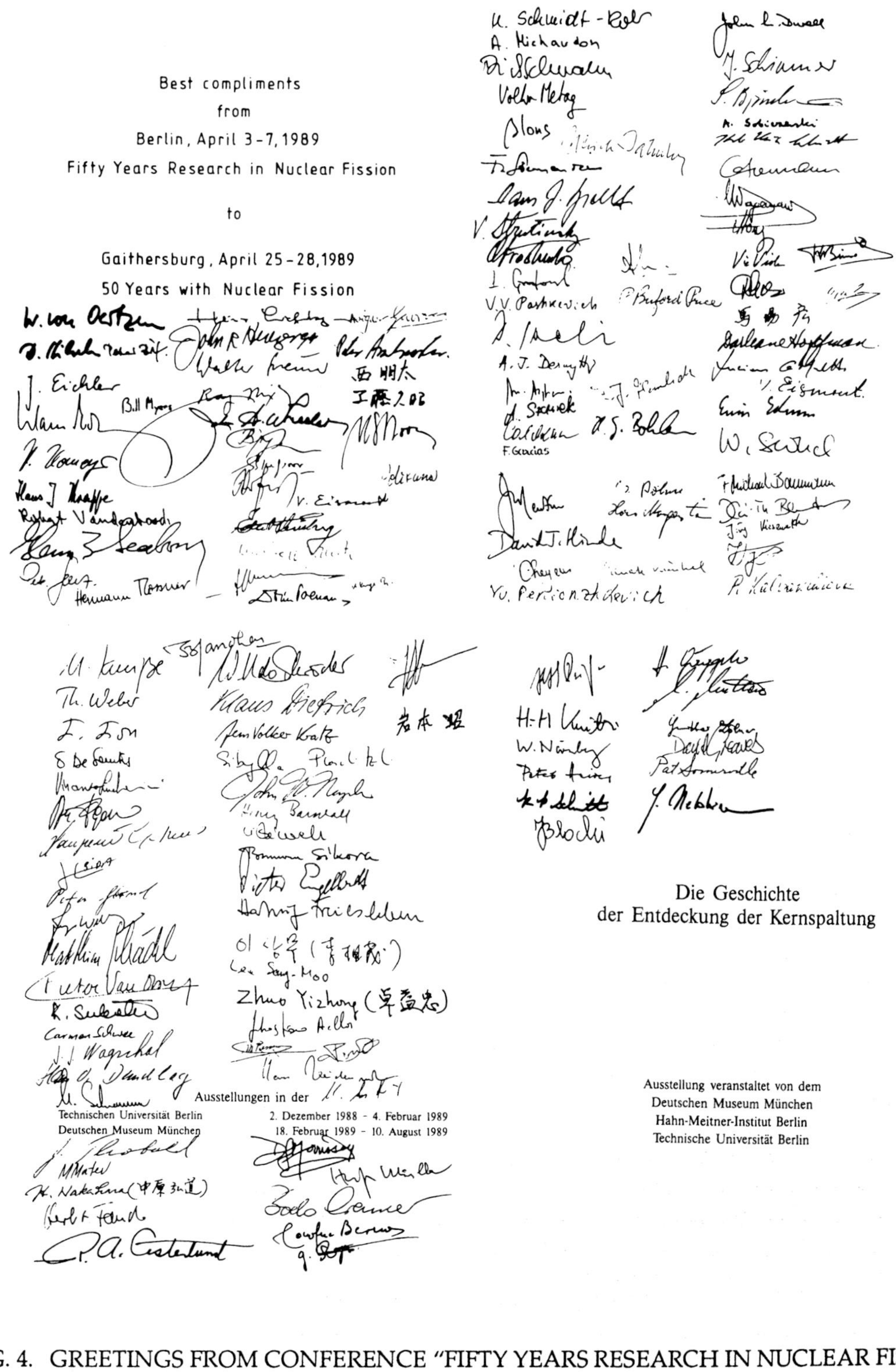

Best compliments
from
Berlin, April 3-7, 1989
Fifty Years Research in Nuclear Fission

to

Gaithersburg, April 25-28, 1989
50 Years with Nuclear Fission

Die Geschichte
der Entdeckung der Kernspaltung

Ausstellung veranstaltet von dem
Deutschen Museum München
Hahn-Meitner-Institut Berlin
Technische Universität Berlin

Ausstellungen in der
Technischen Universität Berlin   2. Dezember 1988 - 4. Februar 1989
Deutschen Museum München   18. Februar 1989 - 10. August 1989

FIG. 4.   GREETINGS FROM CONFERENCE "FIFTY YEARS RESEARCH IN NUCLEAR FIS-
SION," HELD IN APRIL 1989 IN BERLIN, TO GAITHERSBURG CONFERENCE.

611

Berlin on the actual anniversary date of the discovery. That was a traumatic event in that some radicals tried to reenact the notorious Kristallnacht by completely destroying the exhibit that showed the equipment used 50 years ago. Fortunately funds have been found to reconstruct the exhibit, and it will be shown at the Deutsche Museum in Munich. There was a session on 50 years of fission in January at the joint meeting of the American Physical Society and the American Association for the Advancement of Science in San Francisco. At the end of March there was a workshop in Berlin which was concerned with historical and social aspects of the discovery, and Fig. 3 is a photograph showing the participants at that workshop. The following week, also in Berlin there was an International Conference on the nuclear physics of fission, and Fig. 4 shows the greetings from the participants of this conference to our meeting. The last of the series of commemorations that I know about will be held in Leningrad this fall, and we are preparing a message from the participants in the present conference to the Leningrad gathering.

I am not aware of any other discovery in physics whose anniversary has been recognized by so many observances even though this discovery changed physics far less than many other discoveries. The typical reaction was that attributed to Niels Bohr when Frisch[1] told him the news of the discovery: "Oh what idiots we all have been!... This is just as it must be!" Bertrand Goldschmidt told us that Joliot used a word stronger than "idiots" when he heard the news. The discovery fitted perfectly with what was known about the nucleus, and really did not provide any new insights, nor did it require any radical revisions of existing nuclear models. Denys Wilkinson[2] wrote about 30 years after the discovery: ".. Had nature chosen her constants a little differently, we should have been deprived of its potential for social good and spared its power for social evil...It has remained a phenomenon very much of its own, finding its explanation in the rest of nuclear physics, but giving little in return." The study of fission has made important contributions to nuclear physics, for example in revealing details of the fission barrier and in the discovery of fission isomers, topics which were discussed in detail by many speakers at our conference, but the reason for the interest in fission is of course that it produced the chain reaction. At the workshop in

Berlin in March John Rigden said: "If the dynamics of the fission process produced only one neutron, the 1939 discovery of fission would have significance only to nuclear physicists and it would not be recognized in 1989 as an event of historic proportions." Since more than two neutrons are given off per fission, even *The New Yorker*[3] calls the discovery of fission "a fair candidate for the single most significant discovery of the twentieth century."

There have been a series of separate commemorations of Fermi's accomplishment of the chain reaction at Chicago on December 2, 1942, just four years after the discovery of fission. These took place in 1952, 1967, and 1982.

The fact that Hahn and Strassmann discovered fission during the darkest period of German history, just before Germany started World War II, was unfortunate in that it led to the development of destructive applications before the development of beneficial applications. As a consequence many people view fission as an evil. Unfortunately we have persuaded only some of our fellow citizens that nuclear reactors cannot produce nuclear explosions. Hardly any mention of nuclear explosives has been made at any of the commemorative events. An exception was the workshop in Berlin, where John Rigden criticized the military activities of U.S. scientists during World War II, especially after the collapse of Germany. In contrast, Yao Shuping of the Chinese Academy of Science in Beijing said at the same workshop: "Whereas scientists in many countries were condemning themselves for taking part in making nuclear weapons, Chinese scientists were excited and elated over their participation in making such weapons."

Since the principal reason for our gathering is the importance of beneficial applications of the chain reaction, I will devote the rest of my remarks to this topic.

The main useful products of the chain reaction are heat, radionuclides, and neutrons. Heat is used primarily to generate electric power. In this country 20% of the electric power is at present produced by fission; in some parts of the U.S. the fraction is as high as 80%, for example in the Chicago area. In some other countries the fraction is much higher than in the U.S., more than 70% in France. As several speakers pointed out, world-wide about one-sixth of the electrical power is produced in fission reactors.

Many of us consider nuclear power as environmentally more benign than other methods of electricity generation. Nevertheless no new nuclear power plants have been ordered in this country for over ten years, and there has been a similar cessation of the deployment of nuclear power in many other countries. This is often explained as the result of popular opposition to nuclear power. Although there is indeed a vocal and effective opposition, it is only one of the factors that has stopped nuclear power development. In this country many referenda have been held whose purpose was to shut down nuclear plants. To-date not one of them has passed. The latest, last fall in Massachusetts, where one might have expected the strongest opposition to nuclear power, since Massachusetts has prevented the Seabrook plant in neighboring New Hampshire from operating, the proposition calling for a closing of nuclear plants lost by a two-to-one margin. The principal reasons why the utilities do not order new nuclear plants are economic. Twenty-five years ago power from nuclear plants was much cheaper than from coal-fired plants, but now the cost of building nuclear plants has increased, at least in the U.S., to the point where nuclear-generated electricity is no longer economical. The reasons for the change are complicated, and I will not try to discuss them here.

Alvin Weinberg used the term coined by David Lilienthal "The Second Nuclear Age" to describe a period when new nuclear plants will again be ordered. I agree with the view expressed in Edward Teller's paper presented this morning and Bertram Wolfe's remark made yesterday that, in the long run, we cannot get along without power generated in nuclear reactions, but I do not expect the Second Nuclear Age to occur in my lifetime or in the twentieth century.

Now I would like to turn to the use of radionuclides produced in fission reactors, either as fission products or by neutron activation. One of the earliest applications was the use of these radionuclides in the treatment of malignant disease, especially the use of ^{60}Co. For many years almost every hospital had such radiation therapy facilities, and during that period a large fraction of the cancer patients have benefitted from treatments with radionuclides. In recent years, at least in the U.S., linear accelerators have largely replaced radionuclide sources in radiation therapy. The advantage of accelerators is that they can be turned off, hence there is no danger from installing, changing, or discarding the sources. More importantly, the more energetic radiation available from modern Linacs has great clinical benefits. For particular applications, especially for brachytherapy, i.e., for implanted sources, reactor-produced radionuclides continue to be used, and today we heard reports on the use of reactor-produced ^{90}Y and ^{131}I in cancer therapy.

The use of radiation in food preservation could have enormous benefits both in increasing the food supply and in preventing infections from food. The use of irradiated foods has not been adopted, except for a few products. In many countries, including the U.S., irradiated foods may be sold, but the perception that the irradiated foods may contain either radiation or radiation-induced hazards has prevented their wide use. Even if the sale of irradiated foods becomes more widely accepted, accelerators will probably serve as radiation sources because of the hazards associated with the handling of intense radionuclide sources and because of the burdensome regulations applicable to reactor-produced radionuclides. We heard from Joseph Silverman this morning that modern electron accelerators produce equivalent radiation intensities at a cost which is comparable with the cost of using radionuclides, such as ^{60}Co, and that these accelerators have 99% availability.

Similarly there is a preference for using accelerators rather than reactor-produced radionuclides in commercial manufacturing, for example in the processing of tires and of plastic wire insulation.

The entire field of nuclear medicine was developed to take advantage of reactor-produced radionuclides. Radionuclides, especially ^{99}Tc, are used in a great variety of diagnostic procedures. In fact, one can hardly visualize a modern hospital without a nuclear medicine department. Rosalyn Yalow told us this morning that radionuclide procedures are now used in over one-third of hospital admissions. There is, however, here also a trend away from reactor-produced radionuclides towards accelerator-made radionuclides. Even if the same radionuclide is produced with an accelerator, the regulations for its use are in most states less restrictive than if the same radionuclide is made in a nuclear reactor. Although the regulatory problems encourage such a shift, the main reason is that for many diagnostic procedures radionuclides are useful which cannot be made in reactors. In particular, the subfield of nuclear medicine known as Positron Emission Tomography relies on accelerator-made positron emitters.

The revolutionary developments in molecular and cellular biology during the period since the first chain reaction were made possible through the use of radionuclides as tracers, especially the elucidation of metabolic pathways. For this application isotopes of H, C, P, and S were needed. ^{3}H and ^{14}C became available cheaply and abundantly. They continue to be a vital tool for biological research.

I would like to discuss the use of reactor-produced neutrons in research in physics and in biology only briefly, since this topic was treated very completely by William Whittemore this afternoon. He emphasized how valuable a tool cold neutrons are and the importance of small-angle neutron scattering, especially for condensed matter physics. I should mention also the use of reactor neutrons in the preparation of transuranic elements, a topic which Glenn Seaborg described so well this morning.

In summary, while forty years ago the hopes and expectations for the peaceful uses of fission may have been too optimistic, the benefits to science, to health care, to power generation have been enormous, and this conference has helped us to learn of many new facts about fission and its applications.

I would like to use this opportunity to thank the organizers of this conference for all their efforts which enabled us to learn of recent developments, to exchange information with our colleagues many of whom we had not met before, to meet again old friends, and to recognize the accomplishments of the exciting scientific developments that occurred fifty years ago. In particular we should thank Jim Behrens, Allan Carlson, and Oren Wasson of the National Institute of Standards and Technology. They put in an enormous amount of time and effort to make this conference a success and to accommodate the often unreasonable wishes of the participants.

REFERENCES

1. O. R. Frisch "What little I remember" Cambridge University Press, 1979, p. 116.

2. D. H. Wilkinson, Comments Nucl. Part. Phys. 2, 146 (1968).

3. The New Yorker, Dec. 26, 1988, p. 21.

POSTER SESSION:
THEORY AND EXPERIMENTS
IN SUPPORT OF THEORY

WERNER-WHEELER DYNAMICS OF CLUSTER EMISSIONS AND COLD FISSION

D.N. POENARU, M. IVASCU, I. IVASCU, M. MIREA
Central Institute of Physics
P.O. Box MG-6
RO-76900 Bucharest, Romania
806840, 807040/2190

W. GREINER, K. DEPTA, W. RENNER
Institut für Theoretische Physik
Postfach 111932
D-6000 Frankfurt/Main, F.R. Germany
(069) 798-2332

ABSTRACT

Cluster radioactivities, α-decay and cold fission are described in a unified manner by using the analytical superasymmetric fission model. Halflives for C-14, Ne-24, Mg-28 and Si-32 emissions have been confirmed within 1.5 orders. The measured most probable cold fission fragments and α-decay lifetimes of 385 emitters are reproduced. Werner-Wheeler inertias corrected for center of mass motion are calculated. From the dynamical point of view, cluster-like shapes are better than the more compact ones if the emitted particle is lighter than Si-34. In a threedimensional parametrization the components of the effective mass tensor show the contribution of the neck degree of freedom in the prescission stage. The elongation coordinate plays the main role for a constrained mass asymmetry.

INTRODUCTION

The fission fragment mass asymmetry is the result of a subtle interplay of collective and single-particle properties of the nucleons motion.[1-5] In order to study different decay processes[6] in a wide range of mass asymmetry, it was necessary to extend the liquid drop (LDM)[1] and Yukawa-plus-exponential (Y+EM)[7] models to systems with different charge densities.[8] A phenomenlogical shell correction and two center shape parametrization have been employed.

It was shown that α-decay, cluster radioactivities and cold fission phenomena, taking place by quantum-mechanical tunneling, can be explained in a unified manner.[9,10] A unified theory of particle evaporation and fission from excited states above the barrier was developed[11] on the basis of statistical considerations.

[14]C radioactivity of [222,224]Ra had been one of the eight new decay modes predicted in 1980 by our group. The emitter [223]Ra was studied[12] in the first experiment, reported in 1984. The technique of charged particle identification with a ΔExE telescope has been replaced by magnetic spectrometers[13,14] and solid state track detectors,[15 17] with which branching ratios relative to α-decay as low as 10^{-16} has been measured.

The analytical superasymmetric fission model (ASAFM) developed and improved since 1980, has been used to search systematically for the new decay modes and to predict halflives in the whole chart of nuclides.[18,19] The estimated values have been confirmed by the measurements of ^{14}C, [24]Ne, [28]Mg and [32]Si radioactivities, in the range 10^{11}-10^{26} sec. Transitions to excited states of the final fragments[20], multiple cluster decays (including double α-decay) and emission from excited states under barrier[18], have not been observed until now. Other theories [21-26] fall in two categories (fission or emission of a preformed cluster) considered by our group[10] in 1980.

In the following we shall present briefly the main results obtained within ASAFM, and a dynamical study based on the hydrodynamical inertia tensor calculated in the framework of the Werner-Wheeler approximation.

PREDICTIONS AND CONFIRMATIONS

The analytical relationship for the lifetime has been obtained by using LDM, which is known to give a too large barrier height for a constrained mass asymmetry. It was taken into account by subtracting a correction energy containing both shell and pairing effects. Since 1980, the stability of all nuclides with known mass values against cluster emissions, α-decay and cold fission, was studied within ASAFM.

Transzirconium nuclei, including the "stable" ones, are metastable with respect to several cluster emissions. The region of new radioactivities extends below that of α-decay. Highest emission rates are expected for combinations parent-emitted nuclei leading to a doubly magic daughter [208]Pb, or to its neighbours. Several tables have been published (see the last ones in refs. 27, 19), which have been used to guide subsequent experimental and theoretical

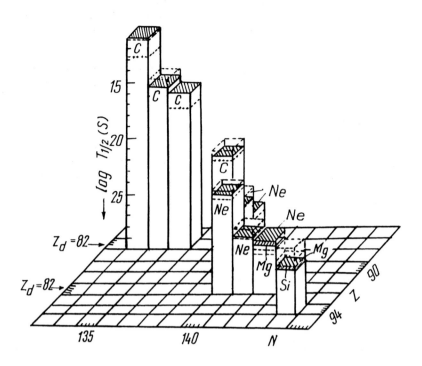

FIGURE 1   EXPERIMENTAL HALFLIVES (HATCHED AREAS) COMPARED WITH EARLY
ASAFM PREDICTIONS (DOTTED LINES) AND ESTIMATIONS INCLUDING
AN EVEN-ODD EFFECT (DAHSED LINES)

investigations.

In this region, the estimated halflives are shorter than 10^{23} years for more than 150 kinds of cluster emissions, but the number of those with branching ratios relative to α-decay in the observable range $b > 10^{-16}$, is not very large. In the first experiment of ^{14}C emission from ^{223}Ra, the highest branching ratio (10^{-9}) has been determined.

The measured lifetimes of ^{14}C, ^{24}Ne, ^{28}Mg, and ^{32}Si emissions from $^{222,224,226}Ra$; ^{230}Th, ^{231}Pa, $^{232,234}U$; ^{234}U, ^{238}Pu; and ^{238}Pu, respectively, are lying in the range $10^{11} - 10^{26}$ sec., in agreement with early ASAFM predictions within 1.5 orders of magnitude. The agreement was improved by taking into account an even-odd effect.[28,27,19] The results of successful experiments are plotted in Fig. 1. One can see the variation of the lifetime with the neutron number of the daughter for ^{14}C emission from Ra isotopes and the variation with both proton and neutron numbers of the daughter for ^{24}Ne radioactivity : when $Z_d = 82$ the halflife is minimum for $N_d = 126$, and when $N_d = 126$, the minimum is found for $Z_d = 82$.

For ^{14}C and some of the ^{24}Ne emitters, other cluster radioactivities are several orders of magnitude less probable. In other cases two

emitted ions are so close in intensity that it was not possible to be resolved (for example $^{24,25}Ne$ from ^{233}U and $^{28,30}Mg$ from ^{238}Pu), or two different decay modes have been measured (Ne + Mg from ^{234}U and Mg + Si from ^{238}Pu).

The best illustration of the unified description of various fission processes in a wide range of mass asymmetry is a halflife spectrum[18] including α-decay, cluster radioactivities (Ne+ Mg) and cold fission (with the most probable light fragment ^{100}Zr) of the parent nucleus ^{234}U, for which all three groups of decay modes have been measured.

Experimental data on cold fission have been collected in two regions of nuclei : $1°$) thermal neutron induced fission on $^{233,235}U$, ^{238}Np, $^{239,241}Pu$, and ^{245}Cm targets and spontaneous fission of ^{252}Cf; $2°$) bimodal fission of ^{258}Fm, $^{258,262}No$ and $^{259,260}Md$.[9,29,31] From the measured mass distributions one can see, for example, that ^{100}Zr, ^{104}Mo and ^{106}Mo are the most probable light fragments in the cold fission of $^{234,236}U$ and ^{240}Pu, respectively. The same fragments correspond to local minima in the halflife spectrum calculated within ASAFM, by assuming that cold fission is a cluster emission process.

In many cases cold fission properties are dominated by the magic number of neutrons and protons N = 82, Z = 50 in one or both fragments. Consequently the best conditions for symmetric cold fission are fulfilled by ^{264}Fm, leading to identical doubly magic fragments ^{132}Sn. The transition from asymmetry to symmetry around Z = 100 is very sharp and that from symmetry to asymmetry (Z > 100) is much smoother. Unlike the former region, where the cold fission is very weak in intensity relative to the usual mechanism, in the latter (Z ≃ 100) they become comparable, leading to the bimodal character.

Of course, neither liquid drop binding, nor the shell effects of ^{132}Sn are as strong as those of ^{208}Pb, which is responsible not only for already detected cluster radioactivities, but also for cold fusion reactions effectively used to produce the heaviest elements.

WERNER-WHEELER INERTIA

The informations concerning the reaction of a nuclear system to the generalized forces acting on it during a fission process are contained in the inertia tensor, {B_{ij}}, which depends on the arbitrarily chosen set of shape coordinates {q_i}, (i = 1,2,.......,n). The hydrodynamical or the cranking models have been used frequently to study fission halflives and heavy ion scattering. It is not known how to apply the cranking model to extremely large mass asymmetry. For the shape parametrizations of two intersected spheres (Fig. 2), the hydrodynamical methods solving the irrotational problem by expansion of the velocity potential in a series of Bessel functions or solid harmonics,[3] lead to numerical difficulties.

The Werner-Wheeler approximation (WWA) to irrotational flow motion[32] can be used. It allows us to obtain analytical relationships for the particular parametrizations mentioned above.[33] The method is excellent for shapes involved in the early stages of fission. It should be cautiously applied in view of the discussion concerning its accuracy[32] as compared to the exact irrotational flow, for small distortions about a spherical equilibrium shape. For spheroidal shapes and for the quadrupolar deformation the flow produced by WWA is irrotational, but for higher multipolarities it overestimates the diagonal elements of the inertia tensor. Nevertheless, for two touching spheres, WWA gives exactly the well known result.

Viscosity effects seem to be less important in cold rearrangement processes than in the usual fission mechanism, as evidenced by the high total kinetic energy of the fragments. In the following we shall assume that they are negligibly small.

The velocity components $\dot{z}$, $\dot{\rho}$, in cylindrical coordinates for axially symmetric systems, are generally both functions of z and ρ. In the Werner-Wheeler approximation $\dot{z}$ is supposed to be independent on ρ, and $\dot{\rho}$ - proportional to ρ :

$$\dot{z} = \Sigma X_i \dot{q}_i \; ; \; \dot{\rho} = (\rho/\rho_s)\Sigma Y_i \dot{q}_i \qquad (1)$$

where $\rho_s=\rho_s(z)$ is the surface equation with z' and z" intercepts on the symmetry axis. The components of the inertia tensor are expressed as

$$B_{ij} = \pi\sigma \int_{z'}^{z''} \rho_s^2(X_iX_j + \frac{1}{2}Y_iY_j)dz+B_{ij}^C \qquad (2)$$

$$B_{ij}^C = -(\pi^2\sigma/V) \int_{z'}^{z''} \rho_s^2X_i dz \int_{z'}^{z''} \rho_s^2X_j dz \qquad (3)$$

in which B_{ij}^C (the correction due to the center of mass motion) is different from zero if the origin of z is not placed in the center of mass. The functions X_i, Y_i of (z,q) are calculated for the left(l) and right(r) side of the shape:

$$X_{il} = -\rho_s^{-2} \frac{\partial}{\partial q_i} \int_{z'}^{z} \rho_s^2 dz \qquad (4)$$

$$X_{ir} = \rho_s^{-2} \frac{\partial}{\partial q_i} \int_{z}^{z''} \rho_s^2 dz \qquad (5)$$

$$(Y_i)_{l,r} = - \frac{\rho_s}{2} \cdot \frac{\partial}{\partial z} (X_i)_{l,r} \qquad (6)$$

V is the volume of the system, assumed to be conserved, $\sigma = 3m/(4\pi r_o^3)$ is the mass density, m is the nucleon mass and r_o is the radius constant r_o = 1.16fm.

We have frequently used the parametrization of two intersecting spheres with constant

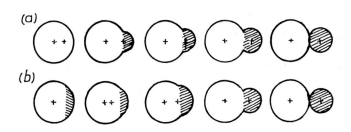

FIGURE 2   TWO PARAMETRIZATIONS OF INTERSECTED SPHERES: CLUSTER-LIKE (a) AND MORE COMPACT SHAPES (b)

radius, R_2, of the light fragment (Fig. 2a) to describe cluster radioactivities, α-decay and cold fission. For a constrained mass asymmetry one needs only one shape coordinate (for example the separation distance of the geometrical centers of the spheres, $q=R=z_2-z_1$, or the distance between the centers of masses of the fragments, $q=z_m=z_{c2}-z_{c1}$). More compact shapes (Fig. 2b) are obtained by taking V_2=constant.[22]

The contribution of the left (B_1) and right (B_2) fragments to inertia,[34] and the correction (B_c) are given by the following general analytical relationships:

$$4r_o^3B_i(R)/3m = (R_iR_i')^2[2R_i^2/H_i -$$

$$- 4.5R_i-3.5D_i+6R_i\ell n(2R_i/H_i)]+(\bar{z}_i')^2V_i/\pi+$$

$$+(-1)^i2z_i'R_iR_i'(R_i+D_i)^2 \quad , \quad (i = 1,2) \qquad (7)$$

$$4r_o^3B_c(R)/3m = -(3/4R_o^3)\{\textstyle\sum_i z_i'V_i/\pi +$$

$$+(-1)^iR_iR_i'(R_i+D_i)^2]\}^2 \qquad (8)$$

where R_o, R_1, R_2 are the radii of the parent, daughter and emitted nuclei, $D_1=z_s-z_1$, $D_2=z_2-z_s$, $H_i=R_i-D_i$, z_s is the position of intersection plane, and V_i are the volumes of the fragments. The superscript prime means derivative with respect to R. Eqs. (7) and (8) are very simple when the origin is in the center of the first sphere ($z_1'=o$). When the origin is in the separation plane or in the center of mass, z_i' should be replaced by $-D_i'$ and $(z_1-z_c)'$, respectively, in which z_c-z_1 is the distance of the center of mass relative to the center of the first sphere.

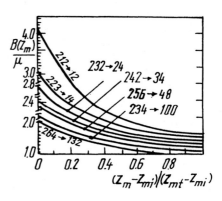

FIGURE 3   INERTIA FOR EMISSION OF DIFFERENT PARTICLES FROM VARIOUS PARENT NUCLEI. V_2 = CONSTANT

For R_2=constant, both $B(R)$ and $B(z_{mc})$ are increasing when the shape parameter increases. On the contrary, $B(z_m)$ decreases (Fig. 3), but $B(R)$ increases for V_2'=constant. In this way one has a qualitative justification for the empirical law used by Fiset and Nix to study almost symmetrical fission. As we shall see below, the parametrization with V_2=constant is not suitable for cluster radioactivities with $A_2 \lesssim 34$, hence a better choice in ref. 23 would be an increasing law of $B(z_m)$. Many diagrams illustrating the correct behaviour of B/μ (where μ is the reduced mass) reaching unity at the touching point, and some wrong results obtained by ignoring the center of mass motion[22] are plotted elsewhere.[35]

One can take into consideration the neck degree of freedom, by introducing a third surface

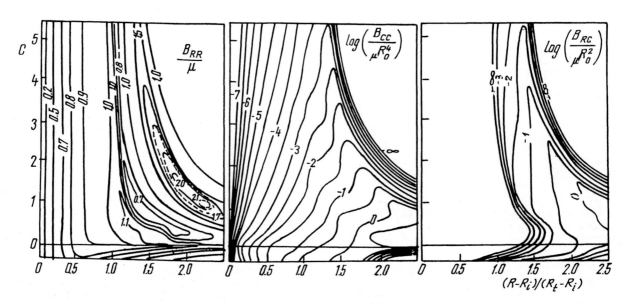

FIGURE 4   CONTOUR PLOTS OF THE INERTIA COMPONENTS B_{RR}, B_{CC} AND B_{CR} FOR EMISSION OF ^{24}Ne FROM ^{232}U.

smoothly joining the two spheres.[36] This is obtained by rotating around the symmetry axis a third circle with radius R_3, and the center position (z_3, ρ_3). When ρ_3 is in the same quadrant with the generated area (s=1), one has a necked-in shape; otherwise (s=-1) one can change the convexity, leading to "diamond" shapes. There are three coordinates: R; $C = sR_o/R_3$ and $\eta = (A_1 - A_2)/A$. The symmetric inertia tensor has correspondingly six distinct components. Fig. 4 shows a typical result for two diagonal and one nondiagonal elements B_{RR}, B_{CC} and B_{RC}. One has to divide B_{CC} with R_o^4 and B_{RC} with R_o^2 in order to have the same units as for B_{RR}. A log scale is convenient for B_{CC} and B_{RC} because they take very small values for low R.

A cut at a given C, through the three quantities in Fig. 4, is plotted in Fig. 5 showing clearly that the neck contribution is non

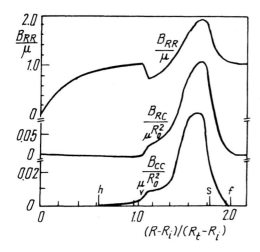

FIGURE 5   VARIATION WITH R, AT C=2.14 OF THE INERTIAS SHOWN IN FIGURE 4

negligible essentially around the scission point (s). Other "special" points are labelled with h, v and f meaning the volume of the small fragment equal to half (h) or, to final value (v) and $R_f = R_1 + R_2 + 2R_3$, which corresponds to spherical fragments. A sudden drop of inertia at $R = R_v$ is due to the fact that the light fragment being deformed has to reduce its radius R_2 in order to conserve the volume. Consequently, this parametrization uses the condition R_2=constant for $R < R_v$ and V_2=constant for $R > R_v$. When $R < R_v$, B_{RC} takes small negative values.

SHAPES SUITABLE FOR PARTICLE EMISSION

Let us assume again parametrizations with one degree of freedom. Within semi-classical Wentzel-Kramers-Brillouin theory the halflife of a parent nucleus relative to spontaneous emission of heavy ions depends exponentially on

the action integral

$$K = \frac{2}{\hbar} \int_{R_i}^{R_b} \{2B(R)[E(R)-Q]\}^{1/2} dR \qquad (9)$$

where $\hbar$ is the Planck constant, $E(R)$ is the deformation energy, Q is the released energy and R_i, R_b are the turning points given by $E(R_i) = E(R_b) \equiv Q$. In spite of the fact that B depends strongly on the chosen shape coordinate, one can prove easily that K is independent on this choice.

It is interesting to compare the values K_1 and K_2 of the action integral along the two fission paths shown in Fig. 2, for different cluster radioactivities and cold fission.

According to the Y+EM[7] extended for different charge densities,[8] the nuclear, E_y, and Coulomb, E_c, energies are expressed as a sum of three terms : two self energies of the fragments and their interaction :

$$E_y/E_y^o = (c_{s1}/c_s)B_{y1} + (c_{s2}/c_s)B_{y2} +$$

$$+ \{(c_{s1} c_{s2})^{1/2}/c_s\} B_{y12} \qquad (10)$$

$$E_c/E_c^o = (\rho_{1e}/\rho_{oe})^2 B_{c1} + (\rho_{2e}/\rho_{oe})^2 B_{c2} +$$

$$+ (\rho_{1e} \rho_{2e}/\rho_{oe}^2)B_{c12} \qquad (11)$$

where E_y^o and E_c^o correspond to spherical shapes,

$$c_{si} = a_s[1 - \varkappa(N_i - Z_i)^2/A_i] \qquad (12)$$

$$\rho_{ie} = 3eZ_i/(4\pi r_o^3 A_i) \qquad (13)$$

and a_s, $\varkappa$, r_o are the parameters of the model.

In the prescission region of axially symmetric systems, the shape dependent terms B_{yi}, B_{ci} are expressed[8] by triple and double integrals, respectively, computed by Gauss-Legendre quadrature. Analytical relationships are available for separated spherical fragments.

In the range of mass numbers of emitted clusters, $A_e \equiv A_2$, from 4 to 50, we have considered $A_1 = 208$, $Z_1 = 82$ and for each A_e, the proton number Z_e leading to the highest emission rate.[18] The results of the calculations are plotted in Fig. 6. The full and dashed lines were obtained with and without a correction allowing to have $E(R_i) = Q_{exp}$. Both curves show that cluster-like shapes are more suitable from the dynamical point of view for cluster radioactivities with $A_e < 34$. The transition from one fission path to another is not so sharp when the corrections to experimental Q-values are introduced.

621

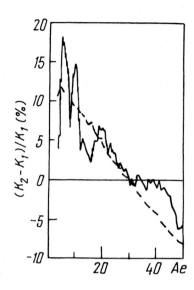

FIGURE 6   ACTION INTEGRALS ALONG
             CLUSTER-LIKE (K_1) AND MORE
             COMPACT (K_2) SHAPES

In conclusion, when the hydrodynamical Werner-Wheeler inertia tensor is computed, it is important to consider the center of mass motion. Analytical results are obtained for two parametrizations of intersected spheres with R_2=constant and V_2=constant. A decreasing law for the inertia $B(z_m)$ is justified in the latter case, which is suitable for low mass asymmetry or symmetry. The action integral is independent on the arbitrarily chosen shape parameter. For $A_e < 34$, cluster-like shapes, frequently used within ASAFM, lead to lower values of the action integral, compared to more compact shapes better suited for cold fission processes.

REFERENCES

1. W. D. MYERS, and W. J. SWIATECKI "Nuclear Masses and Deformations", Nucl. Phys., 81, 1 (1966).

2. V. M. STRUTINSKY, "Shell Effects in Nuclear Masses and Deformation Energies", Nucl. Phys. A95, 420 (1967).

3. J. R. NIX, "Calculation of Fission Barriers for Heavy and Superheavy Nuclei", Ann. Rev. Nucl. Sci., 22, 65 (1972).

4. J. A. MARUHN, W. GREINER, and W. SCHEID, "Theory of Fragmentation in Fission, Fusion and Heavy Ion Scattering", in Heavy Ion Collisions, Vol. 2, R. Bock, Ed., North Holland, Amsterdam, 399 (1980).

5. R. VANDENBOSCH, and J. R. HUIZENGA, Nuclear Fission, Academic Press, New York, 1973.

6. PARTICLE EMISSION FROM NUCLEI. Vol. I: Nuclear Deformation Energy. Vol. II: Alpha, Proton and Heavy Ion Radioactivities. Vol. III: Fission and Beta-Delayed Decay Modes, D. N. Poenaru, and M. Ivascu, Eds., CRC Press, Boca Raton, Florida, 1988.

7. H. J. KRAPPE, J. R. NIX, and A. J. SIERK, "Unified Potential for Heavy-Ion Elastic Scattering, Fusion, Fission and Ground-State Masses and Deformations", Phys. Rev., C20, 992 (1979).

8. D. N. POENARU, M. IVASCU, and D. MAZILU, "Deformation Energies for Nuclei with Different Charge-to-Mass Ratio", J. Phys. G., 5, 1093 (1979), and "Folded Yukawa-plus-Exponential Potential Energy Surfaces for Nuclei with Different Charge Densities", Comp. Phys. Commun., 19, 205 (1980).

9. D. N. POENARU, M. IVASCU, and W. GREINER "Unified Approach of Alpha-Decay, Heavy Ion Emission and Cold Fission", Chapter 7, in ref. 6, Vol. III.

10. W. GREINER, M. IVASCU, D. N. POENARU, and A. SANDULESCU, "Cluster Radioactivities", in Treatise on Heavy Ion Science, Vol. 8, D. A. Bromley, Ed., Plenum Press, in print.

11. L. G. MORETTO, and G. J. WOZNIAK, "The Role of the Compound Nucleus in Complex Fragment Emission at Low and Intermediate Energies", Progress in Particle and Nucl. Phys., in print.

12. H. J. ROSE, and G. A. JONES, "A New Kind of Natural Radioactivity", Nature, 307, 247 1984.

13. E. HOURANI, and M. HUSSONNOIS, "Discovery of the Radioactive Decay of ^{223}Ra by ^{14}C Emission and Experiments with the Magnetic Spectrometer SOLENO", Chapter 6, in ref. 6, Vol. II.

14. W. HENNING, and W. KUTSCHERA, "Measurement of Spontaneous ^{14}C Emission from ^{223}Ra with an Enge Split-Pole Magnetic Spectrograph", Chapter 7, in ref. 6, Vol. II.

15. P. B. PRICE, and S. W. BARWICK, "Experimental Studies of Heavy Ion Radioactivities", Chapter 8, in ref. 6, Vol. II.

16. P. B. PRICE, "Cluster Radioactivity and Nuclear Fission", invited talk at this Conference.

17. D. HASEGAN, and S. P. TRETYAKOVA, "Spontaneous Emission of ^{24}Ne and Heavier Ions", Chapter 9, in ref. 6, Vol. II.

18. D. N. POENARU, and M. IVASCU, "Heavy Ion Radioactivities", Chapter 5, in ref. 6, Vol. II.

19. D. N. POENARU, M. IVASCU, D. MAZILU, I. IVASCU, E. HOURANI, and W. GREINER, "Unified Model for Alpha-Decay, Cluster Radioactivities and Cold Fission", invited talk at Int. Symp. on Developments in Nuclear Cluster Dynamics, Sapporo, Japan, August 1-3, 1988.

20. M. GREINER and W. SCHEID, "Radioactive Decay into Excited States via Heavy Ion Emission", J. Phys. G., 12, L229 (1986).

21. Y. J. SHI, and W. J. SWIATECKI, "Estimates of the Influence of Nuclear Deformations and Shell Effects on the Lifetimes of Exotic Radioactivities", Nucl. Phys., A464, 205 (1987).

22. G. A. PIK-PICHAK, "A New Mode of Natural Radioactivity", Sov. J. Nucl. Phys., 44, 923 (1986).

23. G. SHANMUGAM, and B. KAMALAHARAN, "Application of a Cubic Barrier in Exotic Decay Studies", Phys. Rev., C38, 1377 (1988).

24. M. IVASCU, and I. SILISTEANU, "The Microscopic Approach to the Rates of Radioactive Decay by Emission of Heavy Clusters", Nucl. Phys., A485, 93 (1988).

25. R. BLENDOWSKE, and H. WALLISER, "Systematics of Cluster-Radioactivity-Decay Constants as Suggested by Microscopic Calculations", Phys. Rev. Lett., 61, 1930 (1988).

26. **F. BARRANCO**, R. A. BROGLIA and G. F. BERTSCH, "Exotic Radioactivity as a Superfluid Tunneling Phenomenon", Phys. Rev. Lett., 60, 507 (1988).

27. D. N. POENARU, M. IVASCU, D. MAZILU, R. GHERGHESCU, K. DEPTA, and W. GREINER, "Most Probable Cold Fission Fragments and Heavy Ion Radioactivities", NP-54-86, Central Institute of Physics, Bucharest (1986).

28. D. N. POENARU, W. GREINER, M. IVASCU, D. MAZILU, and I. H. PLONSI, "Odd-Even Staggering of Heavy Cluster Spontaneous Emission Rates", Z. Phys., A325, 435 (1986).

29. F. GÖNNENWEIN, B. BÖRSING, and H. LÖFFLER, "Cold Fragmentation", in Dynamics of Collective Phenomena, P. David, Ed., World Scientific, Singapore, 29 (1987).

30. D. C. HOFFMAN, and L. P. SOMERVILLE, "Spontaneous Fission", Chapter 1, in ref. 6, Vol. III.

31. E. K. HULET et al., "Bimodal Symmetric Fission Observed in the Heaviest Elements", Phys. Rev. Lett., 56, 313 (1986).

32. K. T. R. DAVIES, A. SIERK, and J. R. NIX, "Effect of Viscosity on the Dynamics of Fission", Phys. Rev., C13, 2385 (1976).

33. D. N. POENARU, and M. IVASCU, "Dynamics of Cluster Radioactivities in a Wide Range of Mass Asymmetry", invited talk at 5th Int. Conf. on Clustering Aspects in Nuclear and Subnuclear Systems, Kyoto, Japan, July 25-29, 1988.

34. I. IVASCU, "Nuclear Hydrodynamics", St. Cerc. Fiz., in print.

35. D. N. POENARU, J. A. MARUHN, W. GREINER, M. IVAŞCU, D. MAZILU, and I. IVAŞCU, "Inertia and Fission Paths in a Wide Range of Mass Asymmetry", Z. Phys., in print.

36. K. DEPTA, R. HERRMANN, J. A. MARUHN, W. GREINER, M. GREINER, and W. SCHEID, "Nuclear Deformation, Cluster Structure, Fission and Cluster Radioactivity", International Symposium on Nuclear Fission and Heavy-Ion Induced Reactions, Rochester, April 20-22, 1986.

PRELIMINARY CALCULATIONS OF MEDIUM-ENERGY FISSION

CROSS SECTIONS AND SPECTRA

M. Bozoian, E. D. Arthur, D. C. George, D. G. Madland, P. G. Young
Theoretical Division
Los Alamos National Laboratory
Los Alamos, New Mexico 87545
(505) 665-0093

ABSTRACT

Nucleon-induced fission cross sections determined from a statistical preequilibrium model are used in conjunction with a new scission-point model of fission fragment mass, charge and excitation energy distributions to produce evaporation model calculations of particle and gamma spectra and multiplicities from fission. Comparisons are made to experiment for the 14.5-MeV neutron-induced fission of ^{238}U. In addition, calculated particle and gamma spectra will be compared with the ENDF/B library for 2- and 5-MeV neutron-induced fission of ^{235}U and ^{238}U, respectively. Initial preditions for these same quantities for proton-induced fission reactions at energies up to 100 MeV will be presented and discussed.

INTRODUCTION

The GNASH[1] preequilibrium-statistical nuclear model code is used to calculate neutron-induced fission cross sections over the incident energies of a few MeV to 100 MeV for ^{238}U and ^{237}Np, as well as p + ^{238}U fission cross sections over a similar energy range. These calculated compound system fission cross sections and their excitation energies are then used as input to a scission-point model, which determines fission fragment masses, their yields, and excitation energies. The latter are used in an evaporation model version of GNASH to calculate neutron emission spectra resulting from de-excitation of the fragment masses.

DETERMINATION OF (n,f) AND (p,f) CROSS SECTIONS

As described in an accompanying paper[2] to this conference, the GNASH preequilibrium-statistical model code was used to produce cross sections for fission of the respective compound nuclei that are involved in medium-energy nucleon-nucleus fission processes. Two versions, a multistep Hauser-Feshbach and Weisskopf-Ewing evaporation theory formulation, were used in this process. Both incorporate preequilibrium corrections and contain relatively sophisticated fission models. As described in Ref. 2, calculations were made to compare with new (n,f) data from which fission parameters required for neptunium and uranium compound systems occurring in p + ^{238}U fission were determined. From this procedure, fission cross-section components for the compound systems (up to 25-30 occurring for higher incident energies) appropriate for the neutron or proton-induced reaction process of interest were determined. Simultaneously, average excitation energies associated with each fissioning compound system were determined by weighting populations occurring during particle emission that produced systems that fissioned. As described below, these data were used with a scission point model to determine fission fragment excitation and kinetic energies.

THE SCISSION-POINT MODEL[3]

The basis of this model is the recovery of a fission fragment mass distribution from its given fission-product mass distribution. In the current version of the model, the fission fragment mass distributions are reconstructed from measured fission-product distributions by correcting the (stable) heavy fission-product mass peak using one-half of the total average neutron multiplicity, $\bar{\nu}$:

$$\bar{\nu}_H = \frac{1}{2}\bar{\nu} = \frac{1}{2}\frac{E^* - <E_\gamma^{tot}>}{<S_n> + <\eta>} , \qquad (1)$$

where E^* is either the excitation energy or average excitation energy of a fragment pair at the scission point in first-chance or multiple-chance fission, respectively; $<E_\gamma^{tot}>$ is the Hoffmans'[4] expression for the average total gamma-ray energy per fission; $<S_n>$ is the average neutron separation energy; and $<\eta>$ is the average neutron kinetic energy. An iterative procedure continues until the difference between the current $\bar{\nu}_H$, and the previous $\bar{\nu}_H$ is less than 1.

The fission fragment charge distribution is described by a narrow Gaussian and each fragment mass is associated with two isobars. The charges are determined from the Unchanged Charge Distribution (UCD) hypothesis, which requires the charge densities of the fragments to equal that of the fissioning nucleus, apart from a small correction.

The excitation energy of the fission fragment pair, E^*, is found in terms of ε, the excitation energy of the compound nucleus prior to fission; E_r, the energy release per fission; and E_f^{tot}, the total fission fragment kinetic energy:

$$E^* = \varepsilon + E_r - E_f^{tot} . \qquad (2)$$

The superscript up-and-down arrows differentiate between the two charges associated with each fragment mass.

The excitation energy, $E^{*\uparrow\downarrow}$, is partitioned between the two fragment masses according to, *e.g.*,

$$E_H^{*\uparrow} = E^{*\uparrow} \Big/ \left(1 + \frac{a_L^{\downarrow}}{a_H^{\uparrow}}\right) , \qquad (3a)$$

$$E_L^{*\uparrow} = E^{*\uparrow} \Big/ \left(1 + \frac{a_H^{\uparrow}}{a_L^{\downarrow}}\right) \qquad (3b)$$

where the subscripts H and L refer to heavy and light members of each fission fragment pair and the a's are the Fermi gas level-density parameters of Gilbert-Cameron.[5] Similar expressions hold for $E_H^{*\downarrow}$ and $E_L^{*\downarrow}$.

The binary fission hypothesis assumes identity of the heavy and light mass distributions. Each mass yield is then partitioned between the two charges for each mass according to the Gaussian charge distribution.

The GNASH evaporation model is provided with these calculated fission fragment masses, excitation energies, yields, and kinetic energies per nucleon. The de-excitation of the fragments allows calculation of the multiplicities as well as neutron and gamma-ray emission spectra.

COMPARISONS TO EXPERIMENT AND INITIAL PREDICTIONS

The medium-energy fission model is compared with neutron emission, mass distribution and energy data for 14.5-MeV neutron-induced fission of ^{238}U.[6] Our expression for average total fragment kinetic energy agrees with Ref. 6's experimental value to within 0.06%. The average total fragment kinetic energy formula as a function of pre-neutron emission fragment mass tracks the data reasonably well (see Fig. 1). We also obtain good agreement with the data for average number of emitted neutrons as a function of pre-neutron emission fragment mass (the so-called "saw-tooth curve") except for the lightest and heaviest fission fragment masses using the original Gilbert-Cameron parameters in Eqs. (3a) and (3b). Multiplying the ratio of these parameters, as seen in the above-mentioned equations, by a factor allowed to vary about 1.0, we obtain modifications to the parameters that result in better agreement to the saw-tooth data. For all but the heaviest fission fragment masses, the Fermi gas parameters are plus/minus 10 to 20% of their original values. For the heaviest fission fragment masses, these parameters can change by up to 40%. The two calculated saw-tooth curves are compared with data in Fig. 2.

After converting the calculations done in GNASH from the center-of-mass frame to the Lab frame, neutron spectra for 2 MeV n + ^{235}U are compared with ENDF/B library data, Fig. 3. We conclude this summary with a composite figure, Fig. 4, showing neutron spectra for 5 MeV n + ^{238}U compared with ENDF/B data, and predictions of neutron spectra for 15 MeV n + ^{238}U and 70 MeV p + ^{238}U. The neutron spectra in Fig. 4 are determined from the de-excitation of the fission fragments only and do not include pre-fission neutrons from multiple-chance fission.

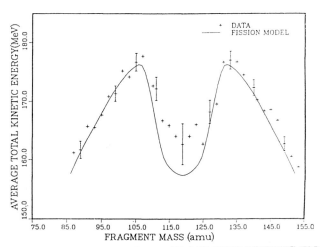

FIG. 1. AVERAGE TOTAL FRAGMENT KINETIC ENERGY AS A FUNCTION OF PRE-NEUTRON EMISSION FRAGMENT MASS. (DATA ARE FROM REF. 6).

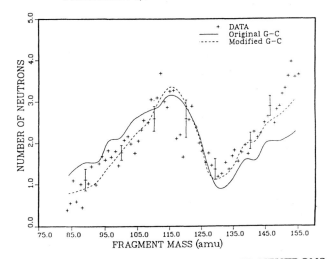

FIG. 2. AVERAGE NUMBER OF EMITTED NEUTRONS AS A FUNCTION OF PRE-NEUTRON-EMISSION FRAGMENT MASS. (DATA ARE FROM REF. 6.)

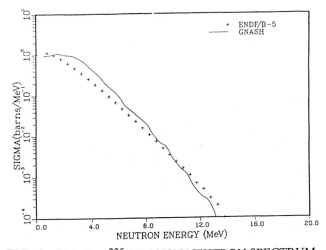

FIG. 3. 2 MeV n+^{235}U FISSION NEUTRON SPECTRUM.

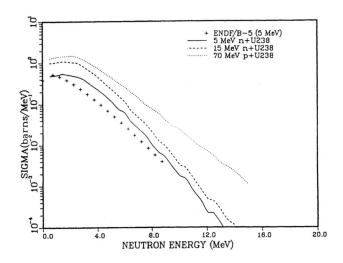

FIG. 4.   NEUTRON SPECTRA FROM FISSION OF ^{238}U.

REFERENCES

1.   P. G. YOUNG AND E. D. ARTHUR, "GNASH: A Preequilibrium, Statistical Nuclear-Model Code for Calculation of Cross Sections and Emission Spectra," Los Alamos National Laboratory report LA-6947 (November 1977).

2.   E. D. ARTHUR AND P. G. YOUNG, "Calculated Medium-Energy Fission Cross Sections," submitted for presentation at the American Nuclear Society Conference, April 26-28, Gaithersburg, Maryland.

3.   D. G. MADLAND, "Scission-Point Fission Model for Calculating Particle and Gamma Spectra and Multiplicities Associated with Medium-Energy Fission," Los Alamos National Laboratory informal report T-2-IR-88-1, May 1988.

4.   D. C. AND M. M. HOFFMAN, Ann. Rev. of Nucl. Sci. 24, p. 151 (1974).

5.   A. GILBERT AND A. G. W. CAMERON, "A Composite Nuclear-Level Density Formula with Shell Corrections," Can. J. Phys. 43, 1446 (1965).

6.   H. YAMAMOTO et al., "Neutron Emission, Mass Distribution and Energetics in 14.5-MeV Neutron Induced Fission of Uranium-238," Jour. Nucl. Sci. and Tech. 16 [11], pp. 779-791 (November 1979).

THE ETFSI METHOD: A NEW APPROACH TO FISSION-BARRIER CALCULATIONS

F. TONDEUR
Institut d'Astronomie et Astrophysique,
Université Libre de Bruxelles,
CP 165, B1050 Bruxelles, Belgium

and

Institut Supérieur Industriel de Bruxelles

A. K. DUTTA and J. M. PEARSON
Laboratoire de Physique Nucléaire,
Université de Montréal,
Montréal, Qué. H3C 3J7 Canada

ABSTRACT

We summarize our two-part approach to fission barriers and nuclear masses based on the extended Thomas-Fermi (macroscopic) and Strutinsky integral (microscopic) methods. Our final set of parameters for the Skyrme + δ-pairing force, fitted to 516 nuclear masses, is presented; the rms error for this sample is 0.693 MeV. A complete mass table is currently being generated with this force, and here we give our results for the fission barriers of four experimentally known nuclei, and of $262U$, a nucleus which plays a crucial role in the r-process of stellar nucleosynthesis.

INTRODUCTION

The ETFSI (extended Thomas-Fermi + Strutinsky integral) method that we have developed[1, 2] for the systematic calculation of fission barriers and nuclear masses is a high-speed approximation to the Hartree-Fock (HF) method, with pairing treated by the BCS method. Much of the motivation for this method lies in the fact that the late stages of stellar nucleosynthesis, particularly the r-process, depend crucially on the fission barriers and binding energies of heavy nuclei lying so close to the neutron(n)-drip line that there is no possibility of being able to measure them in the laboratory. It thus becomes of the greatest importance to be able to make reliable extrapolations of fission barriers and masses away from the known region, relatively close to the stability line, out towards the n-drip line.

Any mass formula will fit all the available data if it has enough free parameters, but if one is to have any confidence in its ability to extrapolate reliably the formula must not only give a good fit to the data but also have a sound theoretical base. Clearly, if two different mass formulas give comparable fits to the data but extrapolate differently, the one with the better theoretical foundation would be preferred. Generally speaking, the theoretically superior of the two would be characterized by a smaller number of parameters.

Hitherto, the systematic calculation of barriers and masses has usually been based on the so-called macroscopic-microscopic approach, i.e., the combination of the drop(let) model (DM) with Strutinsky shell corrections and BCS pairing corrections. Now while the DM mass formulas can give good fits to the data, they do so only with a relatively large number of parameters. For example, the most recent and most sophisticated version, the so-called "finite-range" droplet model (FRDM)[3], has rms errors of 0.769 MeV for 1593 masses, but requires some 29 parameters, as compared to 9 in the present work. At the same time, all DM mass formulas are open to theoretical criticism on two different counts:

a) In the usual forms of the drop(let) model (ref. 4, for example) the characteristic "leptodermous" expansion in powers of $A^{-1/3}$ is truncated prematurely[5-7]. This difficulty appears to be rectified as far as masses are concerned in the FRDM[8], but there may still be a problem beyond the saddle point[9]. More serious is the premature truncation of the expansion in powers of $I = (N-Z)/A$. It was found[8] that when the FRDM model is fitted to the data, errors of as large as 15 MeV can result out at the n-drip line.

b) It is difficult to relate the DM and shell-model parts coherently. To be specific, the calculation of the microscopic corrections involves the use of a s. p. potential, and since this must be generated by the distribution of nucleons in the nucleus it constitutes a link between the microscopic and macroscopic parts of the mass formula. Now the actual way in which the s. p. potential is generated from the nucleon distribution is by folding some two-body force over the latter, but in no form of the drop(let) model is there an unambiguous prescription for choosing this force. Furthermore, the density distribution itself is determined only in a very crude way in the drop(let) model.

Both these classes of difficulty are avoided when the binding energy is calculated by the HF+BCS method. In the first place there is no approximation based on a power-series expansion. Secondly, there is no separation of the total energy into macroscopic and microscopic parts, so complete consistency between the two is automatically guaranteed. A mass formula based on the HF+BCS method will, therefore, be more secure theoretically than one based on a drop(let) model. This method represents, in fact, the most fundamental approach to the mass formula that has any chance of succeeding, even though it is much less rigorous than an approach based on the "real" nuclear forces.

The ideal procedure to be followed with this method would consist in taking some suitable form of effective interaction and fitting its parameters, along with those of the pairing force, to all the data on masses, fission barriers, radii, etc., as in the published DM fits. Unfortunately, the method suffers from the defect of requiring a very large amount of computer time, especially for deformed nuclei, with the result that its systematic application has been somewhat limited. In particular, the available HF effective forces have been fitted to relatively few of the available data, and even then not always very well, thereby detracting from the reliability of the method as a means of extrapolating.

We have shown[1,2] that our ETFSI method is essentially equivalent to HF in the sense that when the underlying Skyrme-type force is fitted to the data the extrapolations out to the n-drip line are very close to those given by the HF method, the discrepancy being less than 1 MeV both for masses and barriers. Nevertheless, the method is computationally so much more rapid than HF that it offers a practical approach to the systematic calculation of fission barriers and nuclear masses. The ETFSI method has been fully described in refs.1 and 2, and the object of the present paper is two-fold: i) We present the final set of force parameters with which we are currently constructing a complete mass table. ii) We give preliminary results of fission-barrier calculations with this force, including the astrophysically interesting case of ^{262}U.

RESUME OF THE ETFSI METHOD

We recall here just the main features of the method, full details having been given in refs. 1 and 2.

The basis of the method is the Skyrme-type force

$$
\begin{aligned}
v_{ij} = & \, t_0(1+x_0 P_\sigma)\delta(\vec{r}_{ij}) \\
& + t_1(1+x_1 P_\sigma)[\vec{p}_{ij}{}^2\delta(\vec{r}_{ij}) + h.\,a.]/(2\hbar^2) \\
& + t_2(1+x_2 P_\sigma)\, \vec{p}_{ij}.\delta(\vec{r}_{ij})\,\vec{p}_{ij}/\hbar^2 \\
& + t_3(1+x_3 P_\sigma)\,[\rho_{qi}(\vec{r}_i)+\rho_{qj}(\vec{r}_j)]^\gamma \delta(\vec{r}_{ij})/6 \\
& + (i/\hbar^2)W_0(\vec{\sigma}_i+\vec{\sigma}_j).\vec{p}_{ij}\times\delta(\vec{r}_{ij})\,\vec{p}_{ij}
\end{aligned}
$$

(1)

with (t_2, x_2) fixed by (t_1, x_1) in such a way that the effective mass is equal to the real mass, $M^* = M$, this being appropriate for masses and fission barriers[1,2].

In approximating the HF method by the ETF method we adopt simple Fermi-type parametrizations for the density distributions in the case of spherical nuclei. As for deformed nuclei, we adopt the u-parametrization of BGH[7], with the reference surface described by the (c, h) parametrization[10].

Since the ETF method loses the shell effects the energy E_{ETF} will vary smoothly from one nucleus to another, and we are obliged to add shell corrections, i.e., we are forced back to a macroscopic-microscopic approach. However, compared to the DM mass formulas there is an important difference, since we can now determine quite unambiguously the fields appearing in the s.p. Schrödinger equation,

$$[(-\hbar^2/2M)\nabla^2 + U_q(\vec{r}) + \vec{W}_q(\vec{r}).\{-i\vec{\nabla}\times\vec{\sigma}\}]\phi(\vec{r}) = \epsilon\phi(\vec{r}) \ , \tag{2}$$

the solutions to which are required for the calculation of the shell (and pairing) corrections: one simply folds the same Skyrme-type force involved in the ETF functional over the density distribution emerging from the macroscopic (ETF) part of the calculation. There is thus a high degree of coherence between the macroscopic and microscopic parts, the unifying factor being the Skyrme force that underlies both; this presumably accounts for the excellent agreement with the HF method[1,2].

The smoothed term $\tilde{\Sigma}\epsilon_\mu$ appearing in the shell correction, given by the Strutinsky theorem as

$$\delta = \Sigma\,\epsilon_\mu - \tilde{\Sigma}\epsilon_\mu, \tag{3}$$

could have been calculated by the conventional Strutinsky averaging procedures, as in refs 3 and 4, for example. However, it is well known that this method contains some ambiguities, mainly because of the continuum s.p. states, which means that they could become especially troublesome towards the drip lines. One of the great advantages of the ETF representation of the macroscopic term is that the usual smoothing procedure can be replaced by what we call the Strutinsky-integral (SI) method[11]:

$$\tilde{\Sigma}\,\epsilon_\mu = \sum_{q=n,p}\int d^3r\,(\,\frac{\hbar^2}{2M}\,\tau_q + \rho_q\,U_q + J_q\,.\,W_q\,) \tag{4}$$

where ρ_q, τ_q and J_q are the various ETF densities.

We adopted this prescription, since it is very easy to apply and is quite unambiguous, even at the drip lines. Calculating the shell-model corrections

in this way is essentially equivalent to one iteration of HF, which means that our method is an order of magnitude faster than HF.

We handle pairing by doing BCS with a δ-function force,

$$v_{ij} = V_p\delta(r_{ij}) \tag{5}$$

Although this increases the computer time as compared to the "constant-G" model, it allows a good fit to the data with a single parameter, the constant strength V_p, thereby leading us to expect a more reliable extrapolation from the data out to the exotic regions.

For deformed nuclei and fission barriers we subtract from the total computed energy the spurious rotational energy

$$E_{rot} = \frac{\hbar^2}{2\mathcal{J}}\,<\hat{J}^2> \tag{6}$$

A special feature of the ETFSI method is that the total energy can be expressed in terms of quantities that vary smoothly with N, Z, and deformation. This means that in the construction of the mass table and in the calculation of fission barriers extensive use of interpolation can be made, both in the N-Z and c-h planes, gaining thereby two more orders of magnitude in computation time.

THE FIT

The data sample to which we fitted our force included 491 spherical nuclei, essentially all known cases with $Z\geq20$; to avoid problems with the Wigner effect we excluded nuclei with $N\approx Z$. Our sample also contained 25 deformed nuclei with $100 \leq A \leq 260$. The masses of these 516 nuclei were taken from the 1988 compilation[12]. We also required a good fit to charge radii.

The parameters of our final fit are: $t_0 = -1788.59$ MeV. fm^3, $t_1 = -t_2 = 282.623$ MeV. fm^5, $t_3 = 12775.3$ MeV. fm^4, $x_0 = 0.72$, $x_1 = x_2 = -0.5$, $x_3 = 1.04564$, $\gamma = 0.333333$, $W_0 = 126.997$ MeV. fm^5, $V_p = -220.0$ MeV. fm^3. The corresponding nuclear-matter coefficients are: $a_{vol} = -15.85$ MeV, $k_F = 1.335$ fm^{-1}, symmetry coefficient $J = 27.5$ MeV, incompressibility $K = 234.8$ MeV.

The rms error of the fit is 0.693 MeV, with deformed nuclei fitted almost as well as spherical nuclei. Given the wide dispersion of these nuclei over the nuclear chart, we have here reason to expect that our final mass table, currently under construction with this force, will have a fit to the totality of mass data comparable to, if not better than, that of the FRDM[3], and this with just 9 parameters.

On the other hand, we already have indications that the extrapolation out to the n-drip line given by this force might be significantly different from that of the FRDM: for the doubly-magic nucleus ^{266}Pb we find 5.9 MeV more binding with our force (we thank Dr. P. Möller for sending us his extrapolated results before publication). This is precisely the kind of "malacodermous" effect anticipated in ref.8: because of the omission of higher-order surface-symmetry terms, the FRDM, and presumably all previous forms of the drop(let) model, underestimate the softening of the neutron skin as the n-excess grows.

FISSION BARRIERS

We show in Table 1 our results for four experimentally known barriers, comparing with the DM results of ref.4 (the FRDM barriers are not yet available). Left-right (l-r) asymmetry is included. Our results are quite different from those of ref. 4, but the overall quality of the fits is similar in the two cases. (For the last two nuclei it is the outer of the two barriers that we show, this being the most model-sensitive.)

Uranium-262. This nucleus lies on the r-process path, and it has been suggested[13] that nucleosynthesis might terminate at this point, because of the low fission barrier of 3.36 MeV predicted by the DM calculation of Howard and Möller[14]. We show in Fig. 1 the potential-energy surface that we obtain with our force for the case of l-r symmetry. The shaded areas "g.s", "I", and "II" correspond to the ground state, first and second isomers, respectively; it is to be noted that unlike ref. 14 we find the ground state to be the least deformed of the three minima. The energy contours (in MeV) do not contain the rotational correction (6). The small triangles labelled "1", "2", and "3" represent the three saddle points; the barrier heights are 2.0, 6.0, and 12.1 MeV, respectively (here the rotational correction is included). The fact that it is the outermost barrier that is the highest is characteristic of highly neutron-rich nuclei.

Releasing the constraint of l-r symmetry shifts the third saddle point to 3′, the corresponding barrier falling to 8.4±0.4 MeV (the value of the asymmetry parameter α here is 0.07). However, allowing triaxiality, which we cannot handle at present, is not expected to reduce this barrier much further, since it is the outermost one[14, 15].

Thus, on the basis of the ETFSI method, we conclude that the r-process path is much less likely to terminate at ^{262}U than the DM calculations suggest, and that the prospects for superheavy production are consequently improved.

TABLE 1. Fission Barriers

	ETFSI	DM	Expt.	
^{186}Os	25.6	20.6	23.4±0.5	MeV
^{210}Po	21.7	22.3	20.4±0.5	
^{240}Pu	3.4	4.8	5.45±0.2	
^{250}Cm	3.4	5.4	3.9±0.3	

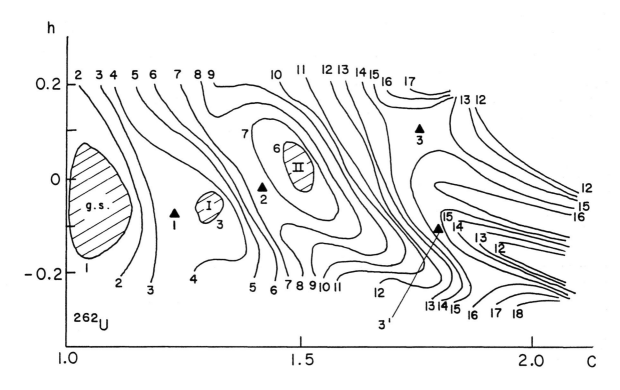

FIG. 1 Potential-energy surface for ^{262}U (l-r symmetry)

REFERENCES

1. A. K. Dutta, J.-P. Arcoragi, J. M. Pearson, R. Behrman, and F. Tondeur, Nucl. Phys. A458 (1986), 77

2. F. Tondeur, A. K. Dutta, J. M. Pearson, and R. Behrman, Nucl. Phys. A470 (1987), 93

3. P. Möller, W. D. Myers, W. J. Swiatecki, and J. Treiner, Atomic Data and Nuclear Data Tables 39 (1988), 225

4. P. Möller and J. R. Nix, Nucl. Phys. A361 (1981), 117

5. J. M. Pearson, Nucl. Phys. A376 (1982), 501

6. F. Tondeur, J. M. Pearson, and M. Farine, Nucl. Phys. A394 (1983), 462

7. M. Brack, C. Guet, and H.-B. Håkansson, Phys. Reports. 123 (1985), 277

8. A. K. Dutta, J.-P. Arcoragi, J. M. Pearson, R. Behrman, and M. Farine, Nucl. Phys. A454 (1986), 374

9. J. Treiner, R. W. Hasse, and P. Schuck, J. Physique Lett. 44 (1983), L-733

10. M. Brack, J. Damgaard, A. S. Jensen, H. C. Pauli, V. M. Strutinsky, and C. Y. Wong, Rev. Mod. Phys. 44 (1972), 320

11. Y. H. Chu, B. K. Jennings, and M. Brack, Phys. Lett. 68B (1977), 407

12. A. H. Wapstra, G. Audi and R. Hoekstra, Atomic Data and Nuclear Data Tables 39 (1988), 281

13. F.-K. Thielemann, J. Metzinger, and H. V. Klapdor, Zeit. f. Phys. A 309 (1983), 301

14. W. M. Howard and P. Möller, Atomic Data and Nuclear Data Tables 25 (1980), 219

15. J.-F. Berger, M. Girod, and D. Gogny, J. Physique. Lett. 42 (1981), L509

CALCULATION OF FISSION NEUTRON SPECTRUM INCORPORATING
NEUTRONS FROM ACCELERATING FRAGMENTS

R. L. WALSH
Australian Nuclear Science & Technology
Organisation, Lucas Heights Res. Laboratories,
Private Mailbag 1, Menai, NSW 2234, Australia
Fax 61(02)543-7726

G. CHIRCU
University of New South Wales
PO Box 1
Kensington, NSW 2033 Australia
Fax 61(02)663-2188

ABSTRACT

We have incorporated a component of neutron emission from accelerating fragments into our calculation of the fission neutron spectrum of ^{252}Cf using the spin-dependent Madland-Nix model. The calculation now gives good agreement with evaluated data in the low energy region below 0.5 MeV. Previous calculations using this model, which assumed all neutron emission to be from fully accelerated fragments, were 10% lower than the evaluated data below 0.5 MeV.

I. INTRODUCTION

For many years, the existence of a 'scission' component in the neutron emission from fission has been assumed. These scission neutrons were thought to be emitted near the moment of snapping of the neck forming the two fragments, and to have an angular distribution which is isotropic in the laboratory system. The experimental results indicated that, for ^{252}Cf(sf), 5-10% of the total neutrons were scission neutrons[1-5] and for ^{235}U(n,f), 10-15%.[6-8]

Recent data[9-12] have found little or no evidence for scission neutrons. The results could be explained by assuming all neutron emission to be from fully accelerated fragments[10,12] or by including as well a small component of neutrons emitted whilst the fragments are still accelerating, that is before the fragments have attained their full velocities.[9]

This work examines the effect on the fission neutron spectrum (FNS) of ^{252}Cf of incorporation of such a component of neutrons from accelerating fragments. In particular, the work attempts to fit the low energy FNS data for ^{252}Cf below 0.5 MeV, using the Madland-Nix model.[13] Hitherto, only the Complex Cascade Evaporation model[14,15] and Hauser-Feshbach type models[16] had been able to satisfactorily reproduce these low energy data.

II. CALCULATION OF FNS IGNORING NEUTRONS FROM ACCELERATING FRAGMENTS

We assume that all the neutron emission occurs from fully accelerated fragments and calculate the FNS for ^{252}Cf using the Madland-Nix model (MNM).[13] Furthermore, we have extended the MNM formalism to take account of the spin of the fission fragment (b = 0.1)[17,18,19], and have used fission energy release values calculated from the recent mass table of Wapstra and Audi.[20] The nuclear level density parameter 'a' was chosen by chi-square minimisation with respect to the evaluated data points of Mannhart.[21] This gave a = A/(9.3 MeV) and a chi-square value of 3.8 per degree of freedom. Our calculation and the Mannhart data are shown in Fig.1, relative to a Maxwellian spectrum with TM = 1.42. (The solid curve includes fragment spin, the dashed curve neglects fragment spin).

Above 0.5 MeV there is good agreement between the calculation and the data. Below 0.5 MeV the calculation is some 10% below the data. This has also been reported by Madland.[22] It is interesting to ask whether inclusion of neutrons from accelerating fragments might improve this agreement at low energy. Several authors have discussed the effect of these neutrons on the FNS for ^{252}Cf[15] and the possibility of their improving agreement between theory and data at low energies.[16,23]

III. CALCULATION OF FNS WITH INCORPORATION OF NEUTRONS FROM ACCELERATING FRAGMENTS

A. Using Parameters of Riehs

Riehs measured neutrons emitted from ^{252}Cf fission fragments at 0° and 90° to the fragment flight direction.[9] He concluded that 13.2% of the total neutrons are emitted at a time

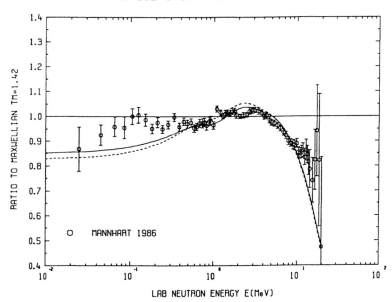

FIG. 1 FISSION NEUTRON SPECTRUM (FNS) FOR ^{252}Cf(sf) CALCULATED USING SPIN-DEPENDENT MADLAND-NIX MODEL (MNM). NUCLEAR DENSITY LEVEL a = A/(9.3 MeV). SOLID CURVE INCLUDES FRAGMENT SPIN (b = 0.1); DASHED CURVE NEGLECTS FRAGMENT SPIN. EVALUATED DATA POINTS OF MANNHART[21] ALSO SHOWN. χ^2 = 3.8 PER DEGREE OF FREEDOM.

when the fragments have a fraction b_v = 0.2 of their final velocity.

Therefore, we have extended the (spin-included) Madland-Nix model by incorporating a neutron emission component identical to that found by Riehs. Both neutron components are assumed to have an evaporation energy spectrum in the CMS and the fragment spin is included in each. The FNS thus calculated for ^{252}Cf is shown by the solid curve in Fig.2. The value of a is a = A/(9.3 MeV), as for Fig.1. The dashed curve shows the FNS without inclusion of neutrons from accelerating fragments (but with fragment spin included). It is seen that the inclusion of neutrons from accelerating fragments has 'overshot' the low energy data by about 7% and produces 5-10% worse agreement with the data above 3 MeV. However, the fact that the 'flat' shape of the data below 0.5 MeV is now better reproduced gives some encouragement.

B. Optimisation of Parameters

We next try to get the best fit possible by simultaneous variation of the parameters b_v and a to find a minimum in chi-square. This was done assuming the arbitrary values of 5% and 10% for the relative component of neutrons from accelerating fragments. The resulting parameter values found were b_v = 0.5, a = A/(9.8 MeV), and 10% for the low energy neutron component. The resulting FNS curve is shown by the solid curve in Fig.3. The value of χ^2_{min} is 1.5 per degree of freedom. The agreement with the data below 0.5 MeV is now good. At the same time, the agreement with the data above 0.5 MeV (of Fig.1) has been maintained. (The dashed curve shows the calculated FNS for a = A/(9.8 MeV) but without inclusion of neutrons from accelerating fragments).

That is, the above implies a scenario where ten percent of the total neutrons are emitted at a time when the fragments have attained fifty percent of their final velocity.

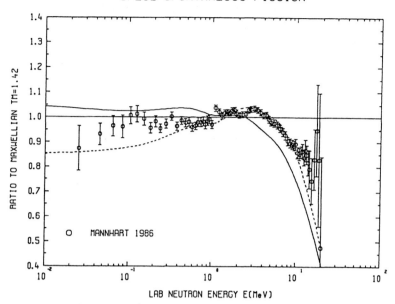

FIG. 2   FISSION NEUTRON SPECTRUM CALCULATED WITH INCORPORATION OF NEUTRONS FROM ACCELERATING FRAGMENTS, USING PARAMETERS OF RIEHS[9] (VIZ. LOW ENERGY NEUTRON COMPONENT = 13.2%, b = 0.2). SHOWN BY SOLID CURVE. DASHED CURVE SHOWS FNS WITHOUT NEUTRONS FROM ACCELERATING FRAGMENTS (SAME AS SOLID CURVE IN FIG. 1).

IV.   DISCUSSION

The assumption that the neutrons from the accelerating fragments are all emitted at a fixed point in time is almost certainly an over-simplification. A distribution of emission times during the acceleration stage would be a truer picture, as discussed in Ref.[15] Further, the mechanism of neutron emission from accelerating fragments and thus the theoretical validity of the value b_v = 0.5, are not well understood.

However, the simplified, fixed-time version presented in the present work serves as a useful exercise and shows that calculations of the FNS for ^{252}Cf using the Madland-Nix model can, with the above assumptions, reproduce the flat behaviour of the evaluated data[21] below 0.5 MeV, whilst at the same time maintaining a perfectly reasonable value for the nuclear level density parameter (a = A/(9.8 MeV)). Hitherto, only the CEM[14] and Hauser-Feshbach type models[16] for the FNS were able to reproduce the low energy data. (The fragment spin is included in all three models).

A significant point, of course, is that the CEM and Hauser-Feshbach type models achieved their agreement with the low energy data without inclusion of a neutron component from accelerating fragments. The result of inclusion of such a component in these models would throw further light on an intriguing question.

V.   REFERENCES

1.   H.R. BOWMAN, S.G. THOMPSON, J.C.D. MILTON and W.J. SWIATECKI, *Phys. Rev.* 126, 2120 (1962).

2.   E. CHEIFETZ and Z. FRAENKEL, *Phys. Rev. Lett.* 21, 36 (1968).

3.   C.J. BISHOP, I. HALPERN, R.W. SHAW and R. VANDENBOSCH Jr. *Nucl. Phys.* A198, 161 (1972).

4.   Z. FRAENKEL, I. MAYK, J.P. UNIK, A.J. GORSKI and W.D. LOVELAND, *Phys. Rev.* C12, 1809 (1975).

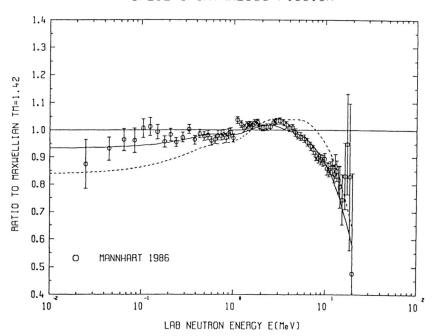

FIG. 3   FISSION   NEUTRON   SPECTRUM   FOR ^{252}Cf(sf)
CALCULATED WITH INCORPORATION OF NEUTRONS FROM
ACCELERATING   FRAGMENTS.   SOLID   CURVE   SHOWS
BEST FIT OBTAINED BY SIMULTANEOUS VARIATION OF
b   AND   a   TO FIND MINIMUM IN χ^2.   LOW ENERGY
NEUTRON COMPONENT = 10%, b = 0.5, a = A/(9.8
MeV). χ^2 = 1.5 PER DEGREE OF FREEDOM.   DASHED
CURVE   SHOWS   FNS   FOR   a = A/(9.8   MeV)   BUT
WITHOUT NEUTRONS FROM ACCELERATING FRAGMENTS.

5.   D. WARD, R.J. CHARITY, D.J. HINDE, J.R.
     LEIGH and J.O. NEWTON, *Nucl. Phys.* A403, 189
     (1983).

6.   S.S. KAPOOR, R. RAMANNA and P.N. RAMA RAO,
     Phys. Rev. 131, 283 (1963).

7.   K. SKARSVAG and K. BORGHEIM, *Nucl. Phys.* 45,
     72 (1963).

8.   J.C.D. MILTON and J.S. FRASER, *Proc. IAEA
     Symp. Physics and Chemistry of Fission*,
     Salzburg, Austria, Vol.2, p.39, 1965.

9.   P. RIEHS, *Acta Physica Austriaca*, 53, 271
     (1981).

10. H. MARTIN, W. NEUBERT, D. RICHTER and D.
     SEELIGER, *Proc. Int. Conf. Nucl. Data*,
     Santa Fe, USA, Vol.1, p.377, May 1985.

11. C. BUDTZ-JORGENSEN and H.-H. KNITTER, ibid,
     Vol.1. p.341.

12. O.I. BATENKOV, A.B. BLINOV, M.V. BLINOV and
     S.N. SMIRNOV, *Proc. IAEA Group Meeting on
     Neutron Sources*, Leningrad, U.S.S.R, p.201.
     June 1986.

13. D.G. MADLAND and J.R. NIX, *Nucl. Sci. Eng.*,
     81, 213 (1982).

14. H. MÄRTEN and D. SEELIGER, *Proc. Int. Conf.
     Nucl. Standard Ref. Data*, Geel, Belgium,
     p.255, 1984. Also, *J. Phys.* G10, 349
     (1984).

15. H. MÄRTEN, D. RICHTER and D. SEELIGER, *Proc.
     XV Int. Symp. Nucl. Phys.*, Gaussig, GDR, p.1
     Nov. 1985.

16. B.F. GERASIMENKO and V.A. RUBCHENYA, loc. cit. (12), p.208.

17. R.L. WALSH, *Report NEANDC(E) 241/L, INDC(FR) 70/L* (1987).

18. R.L. WALSH and G. CHIRCU, *Proc. Int. Conf. Neutron Physics*, Kiev, U.S.S.R. September 1987.

19. R.L. WALSH, *Journal of Nuclear Science and Enineering*, in press (1989).

20. A.H. WAPSTRA and G. AUDI, *Nucl. Phys.* A432, 1 (1985).

21. W. MANNHART, loc. cit. (12), p.158.

22. D.G. MADLAND, *Proc. Int. Conf. Nucl. Data for Science and Technology*, Mito, Japan 30 May - 3 June, 1988.

23. M.V. BLINOV et al., *Report INDC(CCP) - 238* (1984).

COUPLING OF THE PAIRING VIBRATIONS WITH THE FISSION MODE

S. PIŁAT, A. STASZCZAK, K. POMORSKI
Dept. of Theoretical Physics, M. Curie-Skłodowska University,
20-031 Lublin, POLAND
0048(081)376168

ABSTRACT

The influence of the collective pairing
vibrations on the spontaneous fission life-
-time is studied. The Nilsson single particle potential plus two-body long-range
forces in the local approximation and the
pairing residual interaction is used. The
collective hamiltonian is obtained within
the generator coordinate method and gaussian overlap approximation. The coupling
of the pairing vibrations with the fission mode (elongation and neck) decreases
the action integral by 13 % on average
and reduces the WKB estimates of the fission life-times a few orders of magnitude.

INTRODUCTION

The coupling of the pairing degrees
of freedom with the fission mode was studied within the cranking model[1,2]. In this
approach one starts from the time-dependent Schrödinger equation even when the
process is evidently stationary, e.g. the
nuclear vibrations. Then, a classical Hamilton function is obtained and a somewhat arbitrary "second quantization" is
necessary to derive a quantal collective
hamiltonian. Moreover the nuclear wave
function depends on a overcomplete set of
the variables containing both single-particle and collective variables. This over-
completness can produce spurious effects
in some cases.

The idea of the present work is to
study the influence of the pairing vibrations on the spontaneous fission in a more
advanced model. Using the generator coordinate method (GCM) with the extended
gaussian overlap approximation (GOA)[4,5],
the quantal collective hamiltonian for
the coupled shape and pairing vibrations
(for protons and neutrons) is obtained
directly[3]. Moreover it was shown in Ref.[6]
by comparison with an exactly soluble model that the collective pairing hamiltonian derived in the GCM+GOA gave much
better results than the cranking method.

The model is presented in the first
chapter. It can be applied to describe
the coupling of the pairing vibrations
with the shape vibrations or with the
fission mode. The second chapter contains the details and results of the numerical estimations of the spontaneous
fission half-lives for the transplutonium elements[3]. The probability of the
barrier penetration was evaluated in the
WKB approximation of the solution of
the collective GCM hamiltonian. It was
not our aim to reproduce exactly the
experimental data but to estimate the
pairing vibrations effect on the spontaneous fission probability and to illustrate that our model works. Conclusions

are drawn in the end of the paper.

THE MODEL

The set of the generator coordinates we choose to describe coupled shape and pairing modes contains the pairing gaps (Δ_p, Δ_n) the gauge angles (φ_p, φ_n) and the deformation parameters (β_i). We assume the generator function $|q\rangle$ to be the product of the BCS-type functions for protons (p) and neutrons (n):

$$|q\rangle = |\beta_i; \Delta_p, \varphi_p, \Delta_n, \varphi_n\rangle$$
$$= \prod_{\tau=p,n} \exp\left\{-i(\hat{N}-N_\tau)\varphi_\tau\right\}|BCS\rangle_\tau . \quad (1)$$

The microscopic many-body hamiltonian we use has the form:

$$\hat{H} = \hat{H}_o(\beta_i^o) - \frac{1}{2}\sum_{ij}\chi_{ij}\hat{F}_i^+\hat{F}_j$$
$$+ \hat{H}_{pair} - \lambda(\hat{N}-\langle\hat{N}\rangle) , \quad (2)$$

where the deformed single-particle mean field hamiltonian $(\hat{H}_o)$ and the pairing $(\hat{H}_{pair})$ hamiltonian are the sum of the proton and neutron parts. The two-body long-range residual interaction is taken in the local approximation what is a rather natural extension of the concept of QQ forces[7]:

$$\hat{F}_i(\beta_i) = \frac{\partial\hat{H}_o}{\partial\beta_i}\bigg|_{\beta_i=\beta_o} - \langle\beta|\frac{\partial\hat{H}_o}{\partial\beta_i}|\beta\rangle_{\beta_o} . \quad (3)$$

The strength χ_{ij} is determined by the self-consistency condition[7]

$$(\chi^{-1})_{ij} = \frac{\partial\langle\beta|\hat{F}_j|\beta\rangle}{\partial\beta_i}\bigg|_{\beta_o} . \quad (4)$$

The last term in (2) express the constraints for the particle numbers. The choice (1) of the generator function (with the gauge angle φ_τ) ensure the approximate particle number projection[8] when the collective hamiltonian is derived.

Following the GCM+GOA method[4,5] we obtain the collective hamiltonian of the form:

$$\hat{\mathcal{H}}_{coll} = -\frac{1}{2\sqrt{\tau}}\sum_{ij}\frac{\partial}{\partial q_i}\sqrt{\tau}(B^{-1})_{ij}\frac{\partial}{\partial q_j}$$
$$+ V(q) \quad (5)$$

with the collective inertia:

$$(B^{-1})_{ij} = \frac{1}{2}\sum_{kl}(\tau^{-1})_{ik}\left\{\langle q|\frac{\overleftarrow{\partial}}{\partial q_k}\hat{H}\frac{\overrightarrow{\partial}}{\partial q_l}|q\rangle_L\right.$$
$$\left. -\langle q|\hat{H}\frac{\partial^2}{\partial q_k\partial q_l}|q\rangle_L\right\}(\tau^{-1})_{lj} . \quad (6)$$

Here τ stands for the determinant of the width tensor of the generator function overlap:

$$\tau_{ij} = \langle q|\frac{\overleftarrow{\partial}}{\partial q_i}\frac{\overrightarrow{\partial}}{\partial q_j}|q\rangle . \quad (7)$$

The collective potential:

$$V(q) = \langle q|\hat{H}|q\rangle - \mathcal{E}_o(q) \quad (8)$$

is equal to the Hartree-Fock energy corrected by the so-called zero-point energy:

$$\mathcal{E}_o(q) = \frac{1}{2}\sum_{ij}(\tau^{-1})_{ij}\langle q|\frac{\overleftarrow{\partial}}{\partial q_i}\hat{H}\frac{\overrightarrow{\partial}}{\partial q_j}|q\rangle_L .$$
$$(9)$$

The matrix elements entering formulae (6-9) have to be evaluated microscopically[3] and depend on the single-particle hamiltonian used in the practical calculations.

RESULTS AND DISCUSSION

The model was applied to estimate the effect of the coupling between pairing and fission modes in three-dimensional space $(\varepsilon_{24}, \Delta_p, \Delta_n)$[3]. Here $\varepsilon_{24} = (\varepsilon_2, \varepsilon_4 = 0.2 \, \varepsilon_2 - 0.06)$ corresponds to the average path to fission on the $(\varepsilon_2, \varepsilon_4)$ plane. Our microscopic many-body hamiltonian (2) is based on the deformed Nilsson single-particle potential with the parameters "A~242" from Ref.[9]. The pairing forces strength was taken as[3,12]:

$$G_P \cdot Z^{2/3} = 0.241 \, \hbar\mathring{\omega}_0 \, ,$$
$$G_N \cdot N^{2/3} = 0.227 \, \hbar\mathring{\omega}_0 \quad (10)$$

to reproduce the experimental values of Δ_p, Δ_n in the minimum of the collective potential (8).

The spontaneous fission half-lives (T_{sf}) for the even-even transplutonium elements were evaluated within the WKB approximation[9]:

$$T_{sf} [yr] = 10^{-28.04} [1 + \exp S(L)] \, , \quad (11)$$

where $S(L)$ is the action integral along the fission path L

$$S(L) = \frac{2}{\hbar} \int_{q_1}^{q_2} [2|V(q) - E|B_{eff}]^{1/2} dq. \quad (12)$$

The static expectation value $\langle q|\hat{H}|q \rangle$ in the collective potential V (8) was obtained in the Strutinsky macroscopic-microscopic prescription (see e.g.[9]). For the macroscopic part we chose the droplet energy calculated with respect to the spherical shape. The effective inertia along the fission path B_{eff}[2] was con-

structed using the mass parameters obtained with the formula (6). E is the energy of the fissioning nucleus assumed to be $V_{eq} + 0.5$ MeV[9]. The action integral was evaluated along two paths to fission in $(\varepsilon_{24}, \Delta_p, \Delta_n)$ space. The first, static one corresponds to the bottom of the fission valley, i.e. minimal potential energy and is used in the most of the papers on spontaneous fission life-times (e.g. Ref.[10]). The second one is the dynamic path which minimizes the action integral[11].

In the Fig. 1 a typical Δ-dependence of the collective potential V and the dominant part $B_{\varepsilon_{24}\varepsilon_{24}}$ of the effective inertia B_{eff} for ^{250}Fm is shown as an example. One can see that due to the strong

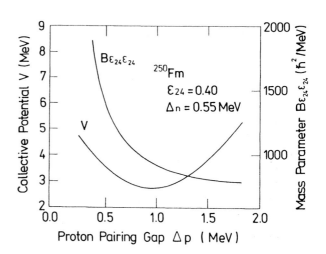

FIG. 1 $B_{\varepsilon_{24}\varepsilon_{24}}$ MASS PARAMETER AND COLLECTIVE POTENTIAL V AS FUNCTIONS OF Δ_p FOR ^{250}Fm. THE CROSS-SECTION WAS MADE AT THE POINT $\varepsilon_{24} = 0.40$ CORRESPONDING TO THE TOP OF THE BARRIER AND $\Delta_n = 0.55$ MeV

dependence of inertia on Δ the minimal value of the action (12) is achieved for Δ larger than that corresponding to the minimum of the potential[1]. This effect can be very well observed in Fig. 2,

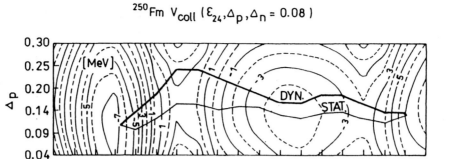

^{250}Fm V_{coll} (ε_{24}, Δ_p, $\Delta_n = 0.08$)

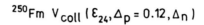

^{250}Fm V_{coll} (ε_{24}, $\Delta_p = 0.12$, Δ_n)

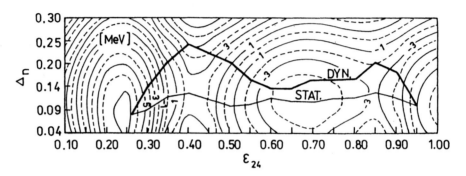

FIG. 2 THE STATIC AND DYNAMIC PATHS TO FISSION ON THE MAP OF
THE COLLECTIVE POTENTIAL V FOR ^{250}Fm

where the static and dynamic paths to fission are plotted on the map of the collective potential for ^{250}Fm. It is easily seen that because of the coupling between pairing and fission modes the distance between these two trajectories reaches even 100 % of the static values of Δ.

The influence of this effect on the spontaneous fission half-lives (T_{sf}) is shown in Fig. 3. We plotted here T_{sf} for transplutonium elements calculated for the static and dynamic trajectories compared with the experimental data quoted in Ref.[10]. One can see that the GCM+GOA estimates in our simplified model (one deformation parameter ε_{24} only) are reasonable. The dynamic estimate of T_{sf} are closer to the experimental data and smaller than static T_{sf} by six orders of magnitude on average for Z = 96 and about one order only for Z = 106. These results are on line with the previous calculations in the cranking model[2].

Although the differences between dynamic and static T_{sf} change with the Z-number what is due to the width of the fission barrier, we found the relative difference between the static and dynamic action integrals (12) to be approximately constant for all cases studied both in GCM+GOA and in the cranking model[3]:

$$\frac{S_{stat} - S_{dyn}}{S_{stat}} 100\% \approx 13\% . \qquad (13)$$

This result means that the coupling with the pairing vibrations is important and has to be taken into considerations in the calculations of the spontaneous fission half-lives.

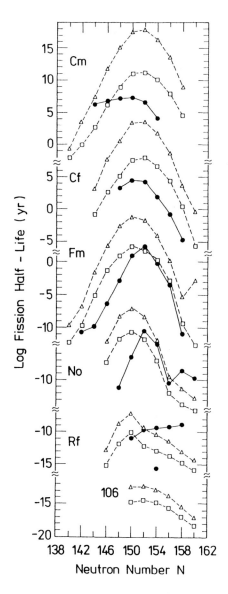

FIG. 3   THE DYNAMIC ($\square$) AND STATIC (Δ) ESTIMATES OF T_{sf} COMPARED WITH EXPERIMENTAL DATA ($\bullet$)

In the paper[10] the static T_{sf} for the heaviest elements were evaluated in a more advanced macroscopic-microscopic model with a semi-empirical inertia. Authors used the Yukawa-plus-exponential model for the macroscopic part and the folded-Yukawa single-particle potential.

In this model a potential-energy surfaces contain the two valleys leading to elongated and compact scission shapes. According to (13) we have reduced the static action integrals from[10] by 13% and we have obtained the estimates of T_{sf} corrected by the pairing vibrations effect. The closest to experimental data ($\bullet$) T_{sf} from[10] for elongated ($\square$) or compact (Δ) shapes as well as the corrected values of T_{sf} for elongated ($+$) and compact ($\times$) shapes are plotted in Fig. 4. One can see

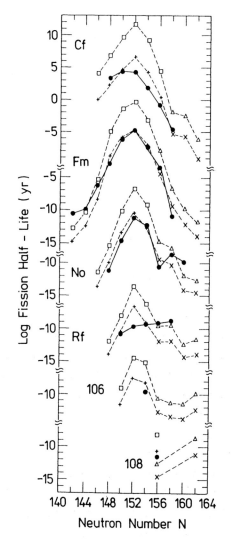

FIG. 4 THE ESTIMATES OF T_{sf} FROM REF.[10] ($\square$ -- Δ) AND CORRECTED BY THE PAIRING VIBRATIONS EFFECT ($+$ -- $\times$) COMPARED WITH EXPERIMENT ($\bullet$)

what after this correction the agreement of the theory with the experimental T_{sf} is much better.

CONCLUSIONS

The results of our study demonstrate that:

  (i) the GCM+GOA model may give a reasonable estimates of T_{sf},
 (ii) the dynamic trajectory to fission differs significantly from the static one because of the strong dependence of the mass parameters on pairing gaps (see also[1,2]),
(iii) the inclusion of the pairing vibrations reduces the WKB estimates of the T_{sf} by 6 orders of magnitude on average for Z = 96 while about 1 order of magnitude only for Z = 106; this decrease is mainly due to the change of the width of the fission barriers.
 (iv) the coupling between the pairing and fission modes decreases the action integral by 13 % on average.

It has been demonstrated that the pairing degrees of freedom play an important role and have to be taken into account in any theoretical estimation of the spontaneous fission half-lives.

This work was supported in part by the Polish Ministry of National Education under Project CPBP 01.06.

REFERENCES

1. L. G. MORETTO, and R. B. BABINET, "Large Superfluidity Enhancement in the Penetration of Fission Barrier," Phys. Let., 49B, 147 (1974).

2. A. STASZCZAK, A. BARAN, K. POMORSKI, and K. BÖNING, "Coupling of the Pairing Vibrations with the Fission Mode," Phys. Lett. 161B, 227 (1985).

3. A. STASZCZAK, S. PIŁAT, and K. POMORSKI, "Influence of Pairing Vibrations on Spontaneous Fission Probability" - submitted to Nucl. Phys., A.

4. D. M. BRINK, and A. WEIGUNY, "The Generator Coordinate Theory of Collective Motion," Nucl. Phys., A120, 59 (1968).

5. A. GÓŹDŹ, K. POMORSKI, M. BRACK, and E. WERNER, "The Mass Parameters for the Average Mean-Field Potential," Nucle. Phys., A442, 26 (1985).

6. A. GÓŹDŹ, K. POMORSKI, M. BRACK, and E. WERNER, "Collective Pairing Hamiltonian in the GCM Approximation," Nucl. Phys., A442, 50 (1985).

7. A. BOHR, B. R. MOTTELSON, "Nuclear Structure," vol. 2, Benjamin 1975.

8. A. GÓŹDŹ, and K. POMORSKI, "Restoring of Broken Symmetries in the Generator-Coordinate Method," Nucl. Phys., A451, 1 (1986).

9. S. G. NILSSON, C. F. TSANG, A. SOBICZEWSKI, Z. SZYMAŃSKI, S. WYCECH, CH. GUSTAFSON, I.-L. LAMM, P. MÖLLER, and B. NILSSON, "On the Nuclear Structure and Stability of Heavy and Superheavy Elements," Nucl. Phys., A131, 1 (1969).

10. P. MÖLLER, J. R. NIX, and W. J. SWIATECKI, "New Developments in the Calculation of Heavy-Element Fission Barriers," LA-UR-88-2266, Los Alamos National Laboratory (1988).

11. A. BARAN, "Some Dynamical Aspects of the Fission Process," Phys. Lett., 76B, 8 (1978).

12. S. PIŁAT, K. POMORSKI, and A. STASZCZAK, "New Estimate of the Pairing Coupling Constant," Z. Phys., A332, (1989).

THEORY OF SPONTANEOUS FISSION AND CLUSTER RADIOACTIVE-DECAY

RAJ K. GUPTA, S. KUMAR, S.S. MALIK, R.K. PURI and S. SINGH

Department of Physics, Panjab University, Chandigarh -160014, India

091(172)22741

ABSTRACT

A new model for two-step mechanism of clustering formation and tunneling of confining nuclear interaction barrier is discussed for spontaneous cluster decay of radioactive nuclei. The clustering formation is calculated as the quantum mechanical fragmentation probability at $R_0 < R < R_1 + R_2$ and the tunneling probabilty is the WKB penetrability, solved analytically. The heavy cluster-decay is also treated as fission process, using two-centre shell model parametrization of nuclear shape in the quantum mechanical fragmentation theory. Applications of the decay-model are also made to "stable" nuclei and success of the quantum mechanical fragmentation theory is demonstrated for the fine structure in fission charge distribution yields.

I. INTRODUCTION

Radioactive nuclei not only fission but also decay spontaneously via emission of heavy clusters[1,2] like C-14, Ne-24-26, Mg-28,30, Si-34 and Ca-48. The heavy clusters, no doubt, could also be considered as cases of strongly asymmetric fission. Theoretically, both the possibilities have been studied.[3-8] The cluster-decay is essentially a two-step process of cluster formation that escapes the parent nucleus after making many assaults on the confining interaction barrier. On the other hand, in fission theories the preformation factor is taken to be unity for all the decay products, and only the WKB penetrability is calculated. Some calculations also allow decay into excited states of daughter nucleus.[8] An alternative and very successful approach to fission phenomenon is the quantum mechanical fragmentation theory (QMFT),[9,10] where the probability of finding the fission fragments is given by the solution of stationary Schrödinger equation in an appropriate mass or charge division coordinate, at a fixed R near the saddle.

In this paper, we discuss the exotic cluster-decay process on the basis of our new decay-model[6] and also study this phenomenon as a strongly asymmetric fission process by using the QMFT. This answers the question whether all the observed cluster-decays belong to one class of exotic cluster-decay process or some of them are simply the cases of normal fission. An associated question is: at what stage or stages of the fission process the mass and charge distributions

of two fission fragments are decided and at what stage of the decay process the clustering formation takes place in nuclei.

II. THE QUANTUM MECHANICAL FRAGMENTATION THEORY

Introducing the dynamical collective coordinates of mass and charge asymmetries[9,10],

$$\eta = (A_1 - A_2)/A \quad \text{and} \quad \eta_z = (Z_1 - Z_2)/Z \quad (1)$$

along with the other commonly used coordinates of relative separation $\vec{R}$ (or equivalently length λ of the nuclear system), the deformations β_i and the neck parameter ϵ in the asymmetric two centre shell model (ATCSM) nuclear shape (see Fig. 1), the collective Hamiltonian is written as

$$H = T(\vec{R}, \dot{\beta}_i, \dot{\eta}, \dot{\eta}_z; \vec{R}, \beta_i, \eta, \eta_z) + V(\vec{R}, \beta_i, \eta, \eta_z) \quad (2)$$

The potential V is calculated in Strutinsky way, where the shell effects δU are obtained by renormalizing the sum of the ATCSM single particle energies to an appropriate liquid drop model (V_{LDM}). The mass parameters, giving the kinetic energy part of the Hamiltonian, are obtained consistently from the adiabatic cranking model or simply from the classical model. Using two spheres approximation, the potential is given as

$$V(\eta, R) = -\sum_{i=1}^{2} B_i(A_i, z_i) + \frac{Z_1 Z_2 e^2}{R} + V_P \quad (3)$$

with charges Z_i fixed by minimizing (3) with $V_P = 0$ in η_z coordinate. In (3), V_P refers to additional nuclear proximity potential.

For temperature effects on the potential, we use the well accepted relation

$$V = V_{LDM} + \delta U \exp(-\theta^2/2.25) \quad (4)$$

where θ is the nuclear temperature (in MeV) and is related to the excitation energy E^* as

$$E^* = \frac{A}{9} \theta^2 - \theta \quad (5)$$

The mass parameters should also vary with θ but no usable prescription is available to date.

Considering that, in first approximation, the coupling between η and η_z is weak, we quantize the motions in each of these coordinates separately. Then, the stationary Schrödinger equation in, say, η is

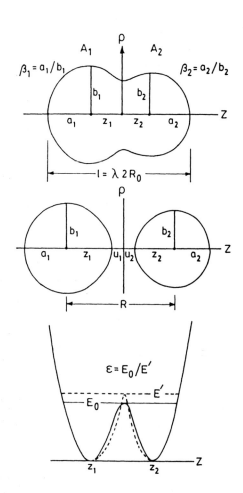

$$\beta_1 = a_1/b_1 \qquad \beta_2 = a_2/b_2$$

$$l = \lambda 2R_0$$

$$\varepsilon = E_0/E'$$

FIGURE 1 ASYMMETRIC TWO-CENTRE SHELL MODEL POTENTIAL AND THE ASSOCIATED NUCLEAR SHAPES.

$$\left[-\frac{\hbar^2}{2\sqrt{B_{\eta\eta}}}\frac{\partial}{\partial\eta}\frac{1}{\sqrt{B_{\eta\eta}}}\frac{\partial}{\partial\eta}+V(\eta)\right]\psi_R^{(\Lambda)}(\eta)=E_R^{(\Lambda)}\psi_R^{(\Lambda)}(\eta) \quad (6)$$

Solving (6) numerically, $|\psi_R|^2$ gives the probability of finding the mass (or charge) fragmentations at R, which on proper scaling gives the fractional mass yield for, say, fragment A_1:

$$Y(A_1)=|\psi_R(\eta(A_1))|^2\sqrt{B_{\eta\eta}(A_1)}\frac{2}{A} \quad (7)$$

Here we have allowed the effects of the vibrational states $\Lambda = 0,1,2,3...$ through a Boltzmann-type of occupation of excited states:

$$|\psi_R|^2=\sum_{\Lambda=0}^{\alpha}|\psi_R^{(\Lambda)}|^2\exp\left(-E_R^{(\Lambda)}/\theta\right) \quad (8)$$

Such a prescription gives the fission charge distribution yields independent of $\theta \leqslant 7$ MeV, though for mass distribution yields the peak-to-valley ratio changes as θ is added.

III. CLUSTER-DECAY MECHANISM

The cluster-decay process involves[6] coupled motions in mass asymmetry η and the relative separation R coordinates, which in decoupled approximation give two steps of (i) clustering formation in the ground state (with probability Po) and (ii) tunneling of the confining nuclear interaction barrier (with probability P) after making ν attempts per second. Then decay constant or half-life time for a metastable system is

$$\lambda = P_o \nu P \qquad or \qquad T_{1/2}= Ln2/\lambda \quad (9)$$

In our model[6], the clustering formation probability Po is defined as a quantum mechanical probability of finding the fragments A_1 and A_2 (with fixed Z_1 and Z_2, respectively), at a fixed R, given by ground state solution of (6):

$$P_o(A_1)=|\psi_R^{(o)}(A_1)|^2\sqrt{B_{\eta\eta}(A_1)}\frac{2}{A} \quad (10)$$

For the assault frequency ν, we use

$$\nu = \frac{\upsilon}{R_o} = \left(2E_2/\mu\right)^{1/2}/R_o \quad with \quad E_2=\frac{A_1}{A}Q \quad (11)$$

where Ro is radius of the parent nucleus and E_2 is the kinetic energy of emitted cluster. $Q= E_1 + E_2$ for clusters produced in ground state.

P is the WKB penetrability of the interaction barrier, illustrated in Fig. 2 (solid lines) as calculated from (3) for $R \geqslant R_1 + R_2 (= R_t)$ and joined smoothly for $R < R_t$ to the Q-value at $R = Ro$. Since our calculations below suggest to use $R = R_t$ for the evaluation of Po, with turning points at $R = R_t$ and $R = R_b$ (defined by $V(R_b) = Q$), the transmission probability P (as shown in Fig. 2) is given by

$$P= P_i W_i P_b \quad (12)$$

The deexcitation probability W_i is scaled exponentially with the excitation energy[8], as

$$W_i = \exp\left(-bE_i\right) \quad (13)$$

with parameter $b \approx 0$ for heavy cluster emission. Thus $W_i =1$ and P_i and P_b in WKB theory are

$$P_i = \exp\left(-\frac{2}{\hbar}\int_{R_t}^{R_i}\left\{2\mu\left[V(R)-V(R_i)\right]\right\}^{1/2}dR\right) \quad (14)$$

$$P_b = \exp\left(-\frac{2}{\hbar}\int_{R_i}^{R_b}\left\{2\mu\left[V(R)-Q\right]\right\}^{1/2}dR\right) \quad (15)$$

The integrals here are solved analytically by parametrizing V(R) properly, as illustrated in Fig. 2 (the dots). For explicit analytical expressions, see Ref.6.

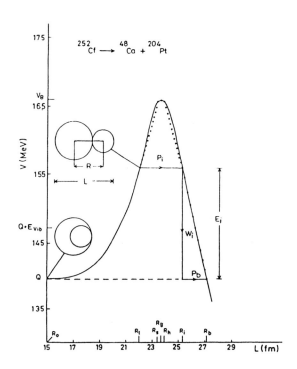

$^{252}Cf \longrightarrow {}^{48}Ca + {}^{204}Pt$

FIGURE 2 NUCLEAR INTERACTION POTENTIAL FOR CLUS-
TERING IN Cf-252 --> Ca-48+Pt-204.
TUNNELLING PATH IS ALSO INDICATED.

IV. CALCULATIONS

In this section we present our calculations
for (i) the cluster decay phenomena and (ii) the
spontaneous fission using the QMFT. This allows
us to identify the predominant phenomena for the
observed heavy cluster decays.

A. Cluster-decay Process

We first look at our calculated fragmentation potentials $V(\eta)$ at various R- values, starting from touching configuration to a large overlap of two spheres (Fig. 3, illustrated for Ra-
222). Apperently, the positions and depths of all
the potential energy minima are almost independent of the R- value, which allowed us to take R
= R_t for the calculations of $V(\eta)$ for a number of
nuclei.[11] In every case, deep potential energy
minima are found to occur at the usual fission
fragments (e.g. Kr-88 and its complementary fragment Te-134 in Ra-222) and at He-4, Be-10, C-14
and Ca-46-50 clusters. For U-232-234, Np-237, Am-
241 and Cf-252, additional deep minima occur at
Ne-24-26, Mg-28,30, Si-34 and Ca-48, respectively. Adding of the proximity potential does not
bring any alteration in these minima. This means,
the potential energy minima, determining the
possible cluster formation (and decay) channels,
are due to shell effects only.[11]

TABLE 1 CLUSTER PREFORMATION PROBABILITIES,
Po(cluster), RELATIVE TO ONE, AND THEIR
RATIOS FOR Ra-222, AT VARIOUS R-VALUES.

R (fm)	$P_o({}^{14}C)$	$P_o(\alpha)$	$P_o({}^{14}C)/P_o(\alpha)$
R_1+R_2	1.40×10^{-14}	9.93×10^{-8}	1.41×10^{-7}
$R_1+R_2 -0.5$	4.12×10^{-15}	1.12×10^{-7}	0.37×10^{-7}
$R_1+R_2 -1$	2.33×10^{-6}	9.33×10^{-1}	0.25×10^{-7}
$R_1+R_2 -2.2$	0	3.93×10^{-10}	$-$

Our calculated Po for C-14 and α-particle at
different R-values are given in Table 1 for Ra-
222. We notice that for a very large overlap (R =
$R_1+R_2 -2.2$) the formation probability for C-14 is
zero. However, as the overlap decreases, though
Po(C-14) and Po(α) depend strongly on R, their
ratios remain constant upto the touching configuration. Interpreting this result in terms of the
zero-point vibration energy E_{vib}, introduced
empirically by Poenaru et al[7], we find that the
configuration of larger overlap (R=$R_1+R_2 -2.2$)
refer to an excitation energy below E_{vib} but the
ones with smaller overlap above it. This suggests
that clustering formation in our model also begins at R-value corresponding to $V(R) \approx Q+E_{vib}$.
However, since the relative clustering formation
probability remains constant upto R=R_t, we
choose R_t as our starting point for the tunneling
process.

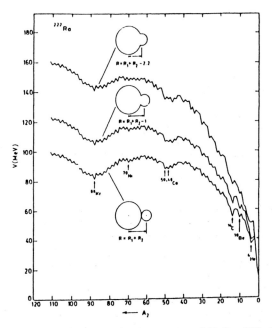

FIGURE 3 FRAGMENTATION POTENTIALS FOR Ra-222 AT R
$\leqslant R_1 + R_2$, USING EQ. (3) WITH V_p =0.

TABLE 2   RELATIVE CLUSTERING FORMATION PROBABILITIES WITH RESPECT
TO α-PARTICLE, Po(cluster)/Po(α).

NUCLEUS	EMITTED CLUSTER	PRESENT WORK	REF.1	REF.4	REF.3	REF.5
221 Fr	14 C	8.77×10^{-10}				
221 Ra	14 C	4.08×10^{-8}			9.61×10^{-6}	
222 Ra	14 C	1.41×10^{-7}		$\sim10^{-7}$	1.09×10^{-5}	3.05×10^{-10}
223 Ra	14 C	5.47×10^{-8}	7×10^{-5} -4×10^{-7}		9.61×10^{-6}	2.78×10^{-10}
224 Ra	14 C	1.69×10^{-8}			7.29×10^{-6}	1.94×10^{-10}
226 Ra	14 C	1.54×10^{-10}			5.29×10^{-6}	
230 Th	24 Ne	3.54×10^{-13}			2.56×10^{-10}	
231 Pa	24 Ne	4.50×10^{-13}			3.24×10^{-10}	
232 U	24 Ne	1.91×10^{-11}			4.0×10^{-10}	
233 U	24 Ne	1.30×10^{-12}			2.56×10^{-10}	
	25 Ne	8.32×10^{-12}			1.69×10^{-10}	
234 U	24 Ne	3.76×10^{-20}				
	26 Ne	4.06×10^{-18}				
	28 Mg	6.22×10^{-21}				
237 Np	30 Mg	1.42×10^{-14}			1.69×10^{-12}	
241 Am	34 Si	2.20×10^{-13}				
252 Cf	48 Ca	2.03×10^{-12}				

Table 2 gives a comparison of our relative cluster formation probabilities with other authors. Our calculations agree, within an order of magnitude, with all the authors, except with Blendowske et al[5] Furthermore, our calculations show a decrease in pre-formation probability with increase of the cluster size, though it is not as systematic as is shown by Iriondo et al.[3]

Our calculated half-life times $T_{1/2}$ for decay of some radioactive nuclei and their comparisons with other calculations and experimental data are given in Table 3. We notice that for C-14 decay, our calculations and that of Blendowske et al[5], using both the steps of clustering formation and barrier penetration, are in better agreement with experiments than the fission calculations.[7] On the other hand, for heavier clusters like Ne-24,25, Mg-28,30, Si-34 and Ca-48, the fission calculations[7] compare better with experiments (see also the next sub-section).

Finally, Table 4 for heavy "stable" nuclei, show that, in agreement with other calculations[1,2], $T_{1/2}$ for some cluster decays are even smaller than for α-decay and in some cases whereas the nucleus is stable against α-decay it is infact metastable with respect to heavy cluster decays. For Zr-80, the most deformed nucleus ($\beta=0.4$) in nature, Po are found to be largest for α-nuclei and for clusters with $A_2 \geqslant 16$, $Q > 0$ having $T_{1/2}$ of the same order as for other heavy stable nuclei. Mg-24 decay of Zr-80 is most probable, with $\log T_{1/2} = 43.4$.

B.   Spontaneous Fission Process

In this section, we study applications of the quantum mechanical fragmentation theory to the measured charge and mass distributions in fission of various nuclei. Both the mass and charge distributions are assumed to be fixed at a point just past the saddle shape. This assum-

TABLE 3 CALCULATED AND EXPERIMENTAL HALF-LIFE TIMES FOR CLUSTER-DECAY OF RADIOACTIVE NUCLEI.

NUCL.	CLUS.	EXPT. LOG($T_{1/2}$)	CALCULATED LOG($T_{1/2}$)		
			PRESENT WORK	REF.5	REF.7
221 Fr	14 C	>13.8	15.0		15.1
221 Ra	14 C	>12.8	12.6		13.8
222 Ra	14 C	10.9-11.1	11.2	11.0	12.6
223 Ra	14 C	14.9-15.5	14.1	15.2	14.8
224 Ra	14 C	15.8-16.0	15.0	15.9	17.4
226 Ra	14 C	21.2	21.2		22.4
230 Th	24 Ne	24.6	21.2		24.8
231 Pa	24 Ne	23.2	19.3		22.0
232 U	24 Ne	21.3-21.5	16.5		20.4
233 U	24 Ne	24.8	20.3		23.0
	25 Ne	24.8	19.2		23.0
234 U	24 Ne	25.1	32.0		25.7
	26 Ne	25.1	28.9		26.2
	28 Mg	25.5	29.5		24.6
237 Np	30 Mg	>27.2	21.0		25.4
241 Am	34 Si	>21.6	16.3		22.6
252 Cf	48 Ca	>15.9	11.3		21.5

TABLE 4 CALCULATED HALF-LIFE TIMES FOR CLUSTER-DECAY OF "STABLE" NUCLEI, LOG($T_{1/2}$).

NUCL.	PRESENT WORK					REF.12	
	α	14 C	16 O	18 O	24 Mg	α	16 O
80 Zr	stable	stable	77.4		43.4		
154 Gd	52.1	53.8	49.2	66.2		60.4	48.5
156 Gd	stable	70.4		64.1			
160 Dy	89.4	81.7		69.0			
164 Er	38.2	86.9	69.0	73.7			

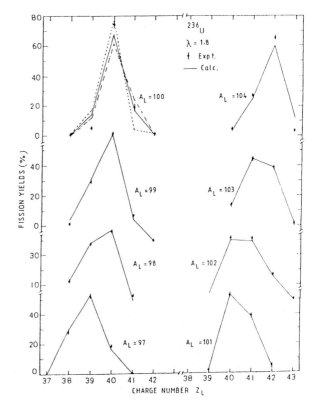

FIGURE 4 CALCULATED CHARGE-DISTRIBUTION YIELDS.

ption, supported by the near constancy of the potentials $V(\eta)$ and the calculated fission mass yields at later stages of R,[9,10,13] has also an experimental verification. More quantitatively, Saroha et al[14] solved the time dependent Schrödinger equation analytically, for charge fragmentation potential $V(\eta_z)$ parametrized as a simple harmonic oscillator. Starting with initial condition of a narrow Gaussian distribution, the final charge distribution is also a Gaussian distribution, calculated at scission time obtained classically from Newton's equation of motion. Applications of this model to spontaneous fission of U-236 and Cf-252 support the result that charge distribution is fixed already near the top of the barrier.

Fig. 4 illustrates[13] the calculated charge distribution yields for various mass chains A_L

=97-104 of U-236, compared with the experimental data.[15] The effects of neutron evaporation are also included in the calculations. It is interesting that both the symmetric as well as asymmetric distributions are reproduced without any fitting parameter in our theory. The role of shell effects in both the potential and cranking mass parameters is clearly depicted in giving the fine structure of the yields.

Fig. 5 shows our calculations, in good agreement with empirical data[15] for δ_P:

$$\delta_P\left(Z+\frac{3}{2}\right) = \frac{1}{8} \ (-1)^{Z+1} \left[(L_3-L_0) - 3(L_2-L_1) \right] \quad (16)$$

where $L_n = log(Y(Z+n))$; $n=0,1,2,3$ with $Y(Z+n)$ as the isotonic yields multiplied by the mass yields and normalized for each isotone. Apparently, (16) gives the proton odd-even effects. As another quantitative measure of this quantity, we define the difference between the sum of even-Z and odd-Z yields:

$$\Delta_P = Y_e - Y_o \quad (17)$$

For the interval $38 \leqslant Z \leqslant 43$, our calculated $\Delta_P = 17.21\%$, which is close to the empirical value[15] $(23.7+0.07)\%$ for a large interval $31 \leqslant Z \leqslant 43$. For the observed decrease of odd-even effect with excitation energy, we first set $\delta U = 0$ in the potential. This reduces Δ_P from 17.21 to 10%, in agreement with experiments.[15] The odd-even effect is further reduced to almost zero (giving a Gaussian form of charge distribution) when the averaged cranking mass $\overline{B}_{\eta\eta}$ is used.

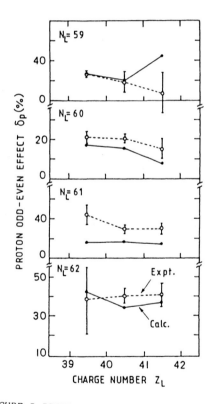

FIGURE 5 PROTON ODD-EVEN EFFECT $\delta_P(Z)$.

Mass distribution yields have also been calculated for fission of a number of nuclei. The shell corrections in the potential energy $V(\eta)$ are found to be responsible for the tripple, double and single humped distributions observed, respectively, in fission of Ra-226, U-236 and Fm-258 and also for asymmetric distribution (double humped) becoming symmetric (single humped) in going from Fm-253 to Fm-260. In the following, we discuss an illustrative case of Cf-252, where the shell effects in adiabatic cranking masses are found to give the observed asymmetric distribution.

Fig.6 shows the measured[16] mass yield distribution of Cf-252 (fragment masses 85-165), compared with our calculations using cranking masses $B_{\eta\eta}(\eta)$ and the liquid drop potential V_{LDM} with and without shell effects δU in it. Also V_{LDM} and averaged masses $\overline{B}_{\eta\eta}$ are used. We notice good comparisons between theory and experiments with δU in potential playing no significant role. The double hump in the distribution is obtained due to shell effects in mass parameters. Extending these calculations to the strongly asymmetric region (mass 40-212), we find that, using V_{LDM} and $B_{\eta\eta}(\eta)$, the ground state mass yield for Ca-48 emission from Cf-252, $Y(Ca-48) = 1.56\times10^{-14}$ or $logT_{1/2} = 13.6$ (here $\lambda = Y(A_i)$) which compares more favourably with experiments than the cluster-decay value in Table 3. In this context, it may also be relevant to note that for Ne-24 decay of U-232, the measured[17] spontaneous fission branching ratio $\lambda(Ne-24)/\lambda(\alpha) = 1.2\times10^{-12}$ is comparable with the recently measured[2] cluster decay ratio $\lambda(Ne-24)/\lambda(\alpha) = (2.0\pm0.5)\times10^{-12}$.

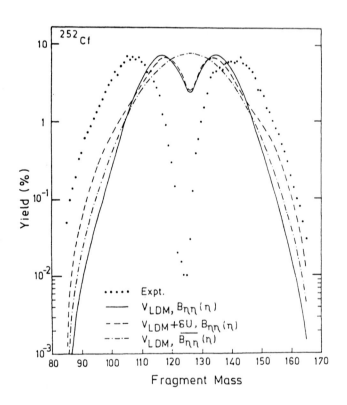

FIGURE 6 CALCULATED MASS-DISTRIBUTION YIELDS.

V. SUMMARY

We have shown that clustering formation in nuclei is given by the quantum mechanical fragmentation process at $Ro < R < R_1+R_2$ and the cluster decay of radioactive nuclei for C-14 is best interpreted as a two-step mechanism of clustering formation and tunneling of the confining nuclear interaction barrier. For heavier clusters, like Ca-48, the fission process is more predominant, calculated as the quantum mechanical fragmentation process occuring at a point past the saddle shape, near the top of the barrier. Success of this theory is also demonstrated in predicting correctly the proton odd-even effects in fission charge distribution yields. Furthermore, cluster-decay of "stable" nuclei present interesting possibilities of being stable against α-decay but metastable with respect to some heavy clusters.

REFERENCES

1. H.J.ROSE and G.A.JONES, "A New Kind of Natural Radioactivity," Nature, 307, 245 (1984).

2. S.W. BARWICK et al, "Radioactive Decay of U-232 by Ne-24 Emission," Phys. Rev., C31, 1984 (1985).

3. M. IRIONDO et al, "Cluster Radioactivity and Clustering Formation in Nuclei," Nucl. Phys., A454, 252 (1986).

4. S. LANDOWNE and C.H. DASSO, "Novel Aspects of the Carbon-Decay Mode of Radium," Phys. Rev., C33, 387 (1986).

5. R. BLENDOWSKE et al, "Microscopic Calculations of the C-14 Decay of Ra Nuclei," Nucl. Phys., A464, 75 (1987).

6. S.S. MALIK and R.K. GUPTA, "Theory of Cluster Radioactive Decay and of Cluster Formation in Nuclei," Phys. Rev., C39, No.4(1989)

7. D.N. POENARU et al, "Calculated Half-Lives and Kinetic Energies for Spontaneous Emission of Heavy Ions from Nuclei," At. Data Nucl. Data Tables, 34, 423 (1986).

8. M. GREINER and W. SCHEID, "Radioactive Decay into Excited States via Heavy Ion Emission," J. Phys. G: Nucl. Phys., 12, L229 (1986).

9. R.K. GUPTA et al, "Fragmentation Dynamics in Nuclear Fission and in Heavy Ion Collisions, J. Phys. (Paris) Coll., 45, C6-477 (1984).

10. J.A. MARUHN et al, Heavy Ion Collisions ed. R. BOCK North Holland, 1980, Vol.2.

11. R.K. GUPTA et al, "Exotic Emission of C-14 and Other Heavy Clusters in the Fragmentation of Ra-222-224 and U-232," J. Phys. G: Nucl. Phys., 13, L27 (1987).

12. D.N. POENARU et al, "Heavy Cluster Decay of Trans-Zirconium Stable Nuclides," Phys. Rev., C32, 2198 (1985).

13. D.R. SAROHA and R.K. GUPTA, "Fine Structure in Nuclear Fission Charge Distribution Yields and the Odd-Even Charge Effects as the Dynamical Fragmentation Process," Phys. Rev., C29, 1101 (1984).

14. D.R. SAROHA et al, "Analytically Solvable Model of Charge Dispersion in Nuclear Fission," Phys. Rev., C27, 2720 (1983).

15. W. LANG et al, "Nuclear Charge and Mass Yields for U-235(n_{th},f) as a Function of the Kinetic Energy of the Fission Products," Nucl. Phys., A345, 34 (1980).

16. H.N. ERTEN and N.K. ARAS, "Charge Distribution in the Spontaneous Fission of Cf-252," J. Inorg. Nucl. Chem., 41, 149 (1979).

17. A.H. JAFFEY and A. HIRSCH, (unpublished results) quoted in R. VANDENBOSCH and J.R. HUIZENGA, Nuclear Fission (A P 1973).

A STATISTICAL MODEL FOR NEUTRON AND ALPHA INDUCED FISSION

B. Compani-Tabrizi
Lockheed Missiles and Space Co.
3251 Hanover Street
Palo Alto, CA 94301-1191

M. A. Hooshyar
Mathematics Department
The University of Texas
at Dallas
P.O. Box 830688
Richardson, TX
75083-0688

F. Bary Malik
Physics Department
Southern Illinois University
Carbondale, IL 62901-4401

ABSTRACT

We have calculated mass and kinetic energy spectra for thermal, 5.5 MeV and 22.0 MeV neutron induced fission of ^{239}Pu, 15.5 MeV neutron induced fission of ^{235}U and 27.5 MeV alpha induced fission of ^{232}Th. Calculated spectra are in good agreement with data. We have further provided an explanation of cold fission and calculated cold fission probabilities relative to the most probable decay probabilities for thermal neutron induced fission of ^{235}U and alpha induced fission of ^{226}Ra to a number of daughter pairs. Calculations in all cases are based on a statistical model with an external barrier between saddle and scission points. Such a barrier is expected from a many body approach using realistic two nucleon interaction.

INTRODUCTION

One of the interesting features of particle induced fission is that the percentage yields of daughter fragments change significantly with the variation of incident energy of the projectile. For example, in neutron induced fission of ^{235}U, the percentage yields around symmetric modes change form a very small fraction of 0.1% for thermal neutrons to about 2% for 22.0 MeV incident neutrons. This change in mass yield spectra is also accompanied by a somewhat less drastic change in total kinetic energy spectra. Using an empirical external barrier between saddle and scission points, it has been possible to account for this change for neutron induced fission of ^{235}U (ref.1). We extend here the model to analyze neutron induced fission of ^{239}Pu and alpha-induced fission of ^{232}Th along with neutron induced fission of ^{235}U. The latter two cases are chosen because the compound nucleus in each case is ^{236}U and the incident energies of alpha and neutron are such that the compound system formed in each case is at about the same excitation energy. A part of this analysis is reported in ref. 2.

Another very interesting feature established recently but predicted in 1976 by us is the observation of cold fission. We shall present here the reason for cold fission and provide examples for such a phenomenon for neutron induced fission of ^{235}U reported in refs. 1 and 2 and alpha induced fission of ^{232}Th. In fact, the theory predicts that each fragment of a particular daughter pair could be at various excitation energies, the maximum being dictated by the energy conservation.

THEORY

In this model we assume that the incident projectile forms a compound system which decays into two fragments. Within the framework of the statistical theory (See ref. 3 for a summary) the differential cross section for the process (α and α', denote, respectively, the incident and final channel) is given by the following expression:

$$\frac{d\sigma_{\alpha\alpha'}}{d\Omega} = \sum_{I,\ell} (\pi/k^2)(2\ell+1)T_\ell(\alpha)$$

$$\left[\frac{P_{\alpha'}(I,U,\vec{n})}{\sum_{\alpha''}\int P_{\alpha''}(I,U,n)\,d\Omega}\right] \qquad (1)$$

where I and U are, respectively, the angular momentum and excitation energy of the compound system, k and $T_c(\alpha)$, are respectively, the wave number and transmission coefficients of the 1th partial wave and P(I,U,n) is the probability of decay of the compound system in a given direction n making an angle θ with the incident beam. The latter may be written as:

$$P_{\alpha'}(I,U,\vec{n}) = \int_o^u P_{\alpha'}(I,\vec{U},n,\varepsilon)d\varepsilon \qquad (2)$$

where $P(I,U,n,\varepsilon)$ is the probability of decay into two fragments having different excitation energies and total kinetic energy ε. Following Ericsson[3], we get the expression

$$P_{\alpha'}(I,U,\vec{n},\varepsilon) = (1/\hbar)(1/\sqrt{2})(1/\pi)^{5/2}$$

$$(T_o(\varepsilon)/\rho_c(I,U))$$

$$\int_o^{Q+T-\varepsilon} \rho_1(U_1)\rho_2(U_2) \frac{(\sigma_1\sigma_2)^3}{(\sigma_1{}^2+\sigma_2{}^2)^{1/2}}$$

$$\exp(\frac{I^2\sin^2\theta}{4(\sigma_1{}^2+\sigma_2{}^2)})J_o(i\frac{I^2\sin^2\theta}{4(\sigma_1{}^2+\sigma_2{}^2)}) \quad dU_1 \qquad (3)$$

Here $\rho_1(U_1)$ and $\rho_2(U_2)$ are nuclear level density functions of the final fragments 1 and 2 at excitation energies U_1 and U_2, respectively. $\rho_c(I,U)$ is the level density function of the compound nucleus with spin I and excitation energy U_c. $T_o(\varepsilon)$ is the transmission function for the two fragments for a given total center-of-mass kinetic energy ε.

To evaluate (3), we use the level density function of Gadioli and Zetta[4].

$$\rho(I,u) = \frac{\hbar^3}{12\sqrt{8}}(2I+1)\exp(\frac{I(I+1)}{2\sigma^2})$$

$$a^{1/2}g-3/2 \frac{\exp(2\sqrt{au})}{(u+t)^2}; \qquad u\geq 5MeV$$

$$= \delta \text{ function (i.e.discrete); } u<5MeV \qquad (4)$$

where u is the effective excitation energy which, in the superfluid model of nuclear excitation, is related to U by[5] $u=U-\Delta+70/A$, Δ being the gap parameter. $\sigma^2=(g/\hbar^2)[(u+t)/a]^{1/2}$ is the nuclear spin cut-off parameter, g, the nuclear moment of inertia = (0.7) the rigid body moment $=0.7(\frac{2}{5}AR^2)$; R = 1.5 $A^{1/3}$, A being the nucleon number. a is taken to be 0.127 MeV^{-1} in all cases.

The kinetic energy ε, associated with two final fragments of mass $M(A_1)$ and $M(A_2)$ is related to the incident projectile energy E(P) by the following relation:

$$E=U_1+U_2+\varepsilon=Q+E(P)=M(P)+M(T)$$

$$-M(A_1)-M(A_2)+\varepsilon \qquad (5)$$

where Q is the energy released for the decay to the ground state of a daughter pair and E is the maximum available energy that could be distributed between excitation energies of a particular daughter pair and their relative kinetic energy. Effective excitation energies of each fragment is then related as follows:

$$u_2=Q+E(P)-\varepsilon-\Delta_2+(70/A_2)+\Delta_1-(70/A_1)-u_1 \qquad (6)$$

Experimental measurements are usually averaged over angles. Decay probabilities averaged over all angles are given by Here ρ_c is the level density function of the compound nucleus and we have used $u=at^2-t$, t being the temperature.

$$P(I,u,\varepsilon)=\frac{\sqrt{\pi}\hbar^6}{\rho_c(I,U)}$$

$$(a_1a_2)^{1/2} \frac{1}{(12)^2(2\sqrt{2})}\sqrt{2} \; (g_1g_2)^{-3/2}$$

$$T(\varepsilon)\int_o^{E-\varepsilon} \frac{(\sigma_1\sigma_2)^3}{(\sigma_1{}^2+\sigma_2{}^2)^{1/2}}$$

$$\frac{\exp(2\sqrt{a_1u_a})}{(u_1+t_1)^2}$$

$$\frac{\exp(2\sqrt{a_1u_2})}{(u_2+t_2)^2} \quad dU_1 \qquad (7)$$

Here ρ_c is the level density function of the compound nucleus and we have used $u=at^2-t$, t being the temperature.

Decay width $\Gamma(I,u,\varepsilon)$ is related to decay probability by $\Gamma(I,u,\varepsilon) = \hbar P(I,u,\varepsilon)$. Total decay width is, therefore,

$$\Gamma(I,u) = \int_o^E \Gamma(I,u,\varepsilon)d\varepsilon \qquad (8)$$

651

E the available energy in a given final channel, is distributed among excitation energies of each fragment and their relative kinetic energy. The decay probability to various excited states of each member of a particular daughter pair depends on this distribution. In principle, the decay is possible to all excited and ground states subject to the energy conservation (5).

Thus, cold fission and extremely hot fission corresponding to minimum allowed ϵ are two key features of the theory.

Calculation of percentage yields involves relative decay probabilities and do not require any knowledge of ρ_c and many other constants. In fact, neglecting the difference between U_i and u_i (i=1,2), one can simply write

$$\Gamma(I,U,\epsilon) \sim T(\epsilon) \int_0^{E-\epsilon} dU_1$$

$$\frac{\exp(2\sqrt{a_1 U_1})}{(U_1+t_1)^2} \frac{\exp(2\sqrt{a_2(E-\epsilon-U_1)})}{(E-\epsilon-U_1+t_2)^2} \qquad (9)$$

The most probable kinetic energy, TKE, associated with the decay to a particular daughter pair can be obtained by plotting $\Gamma(I,U,\epsilon)$ as a function of ϵ. Maxima in such plots are TKEs for decay to various pairs.

Up to now we have not consider any other constraint in the decay or the distribution of energy to excitation of individual partner of a pair. We impose the condition that the distribution be such that the change of entropy, $\Delta s \geq 0$. This is insured[1] by setting the lower limit of integration in (8) and (9) from the condition that at that limit $u(t) = u_1(t) + u_2(t)$ and setting entropy of that state to be zero. This condition means that the temperature of a daughter pair is equal to that of the compound nucleus when the scission process starts. Furthermore, if Δs is to remain positive in the entire domain of integration, the upper limit is $E-\epsilon-U_2(t)$ where $U_2(t)$ is the minimum amount of excitation energy needed in the other partner to insure that the change in entropy is always positive.

Calculation of $T(\epsilon)$ requires specification of an interaction between a daughter pair.

Calculation of potential energy surface based on liquid drop models with constant density distribution does not provide any attraction between the two fragments in the region between saddle and scission points. On the other hand, all scattering data for energies higher than the Coulomb barrier of two colliding nuclei demands at least some attraction between them. The key physical factor leading to this attraction is the relatively large nuclear surface where the density is less than the central density of a nucleus. A simple extension of that to the fission case leads to an attraction between saddle and scission points[6]. Detailed calculations[7] based on energy density functional method confirm this. As noted in ref. 8, the dynamic properties of fission such as half-lives, mass, charge and TKE spectra are sensitive to the details of this external barrier and not to the internal Bohr-Wheeler-Strutinski part of the potential. We use here the empirical barrier of refs. 9, 10 which has been successful in accounting for (a) correct spontaneous and isomer half-lives with proper average kinetic energies, (b) correct mass, charge and TKE distribution in spontaneous and thermal neutron induced fission, (c) in predicting proper mass and TKE in isomer fission and (d) in predicting correctly extremely short or zero half-lives of superheavy elements. The parameters of this empirical potential are determined from one of the fastest decay modes in the spontaneous fission of ^{240}Pu and have been left unchanged. This potential is

$$V(R) = V_D(R) + V_c(R)$$

$$V_D(R) = 200 \text{ MeV} \qquad ; R < R_c$$
$$= V_{Coul} - 60 \text{ MeV} \qquad ; R_c \leq R < R_b$$
$$= V_{Coul}\exp[(r-R_0)/d] \quad ; R_b < R < R_0$$
$$= Z_1 Z_2 e^2/R \qquad ; R_0 < R \qquad (10)$$

with R_c = 8 fm. and $R_b = R_0 + (d)\log(V_0/V_{Coul})$ with d = 5.0 fm. and $V_{Coul} = Z_1 Z_2 e^2/R_0$. The effective potential originating from multichannel coupling V_c is parametrized as

$$V_C = \lambda \exp\{-|(R-R_0)/C|^3\} \qquad (11)$$

with $\lambda = 4.56 + (36.1) \exp(-|(175-A)/75.3|^{9.5}$ MeV
with $C = 4.8 - 0.6 \exp[-0.036(|A_1 - A_2|)^{1.6}]$

It is interesting to point out that if $T(\varepsilon)$ is set equal to one i.e., the case of having no barrier between saddle and scission points, the calculated most probable kinetic energy is zero and the kinetic energy spectra will be that of evaporation. Clearly, this is in sharp contradiction with observation. Observation of cold fission[16,17] which means that the relative kinetic energy is almost equal to $(Q + E(P))$, lends considerable support to the existence of an external behavior.

RESULTS AND DISCUSSION

A. Calculation of TKE and Cold Fission

As noted earlier, TKE i.e., the most probable kinetic energy for the decay to a particular daughter pair can be obtained by plotting $\Gamma(I,u,\varepsilon)$ as a function of ε. In Fig. 1 we have plotted $\Gamma(I,u,\varepsilon)$ for neutron induced fission of ^{235}U for the case (a) $T(\varepsilon) = 1$. i.e., no external barrier (on the left) and (b) $T(\varepsilon)$ calculated using the barrier (10) (on the right). As expected, the decay probabilities for the no barrier case exhibit evaporation like spectra and cold fission is not possible. On the other hand, the decay probabilities for the case of an external barrier exhibit sharp maxima corresponding to the most probable kinetic energies i.e., TKE, at about the observed values. In addition, decays to all possible excited states of a particular daughter pair is allowed within the constraint of the conservation of energy. In particular, cold fission is accounted for. Yields for the cold fission case are expected to be one or two orders of magnitudes lower compared to the maximum yields. As noted in ref. 1, the quantitative number depends on the details of the barrier. Experimental study of yields for a particular daughter pair at different excitation energies will provide considerable information on the details of this external barrier. A knowledge of TKE alone for a given decay mode gives information only on the structure near the top of the barrier.

In Fig. 2, we show another example of the kinetic energy spectrum for 30.8 MeV alpha induced fission of ^{226}Ra to three daughter pairs.

Once again cold fission as well as fission to different excitation energies of a particular daughter pair is allowed.

B. n + ^{239}Pu

The barrier used here is essentially the same as the one used in ref. 9 (note that near asymmetric decay modes which basically determine half-lives, g→0) and reproduces spontaneous fission and isomer fission half-lives of ^{240}Pu at correct average kinetic energy. The observed half-lives of 1.34×10^{11} year and average kinetic energy of (177.7 ± 1.8) MeV for spontaneous fission compare well with the theoretical calculations of 10^{10} year and 178.9 MeV, respectively. Similarly the observed half-lives of $(3.8 \pm 0.3) 10^{-9}$ sec. for isomer fission is in reasonable agreement with the calculated value of 9.0×10^{-10} sec.

In thermal neutron induced fission of ^{239}Pu, the compound system ^{240}Pu is at 6.455 MeV excitation energy before fission. Thus, 6.455 MeV extra energy is available for integration in (7)-(9) which means that in principle, there should be slight difference in percentage mass yield pattern and TKE spectra in two cases. This is, indeed, the case experimentally. Perfect theoretical fits obtained in both cases imply that the theory can account for this quantitatively.

In Fig. 3 we have plotted observed[11] percentage mass yield curve and TKE for thermal neutron induced fission of ^{239}Pu by solid lines. Theoretically calculated mass yield curve along with TKE and Q-values used to obtain the best fit are drawn as solid dots and dashed line, respectively. Calculated Q-values obtained from Meyers and Swiatecki mass formula[12] which has a typical error of a few MeV are noted as solid triangle. The agreement is excellent.

As noted earlier, it is possible to calculate theoretically the most probable kinetic energy, i.e., TKE associated with the decay to a particular daughter pair. This can be accomplished by plotting $\Gamma(I,u,\varepsilon)$ or $P(I,u,\varepsilon)$ as a function of ε. Such a plot yields[1,2] a maximum for the decay to each daughter pair and its location is then the calculated TKE. These calculated TKE are noted as open circles in the upper insert of Fig. 3. The good agreement obtained provides a reasonable insight to the process.

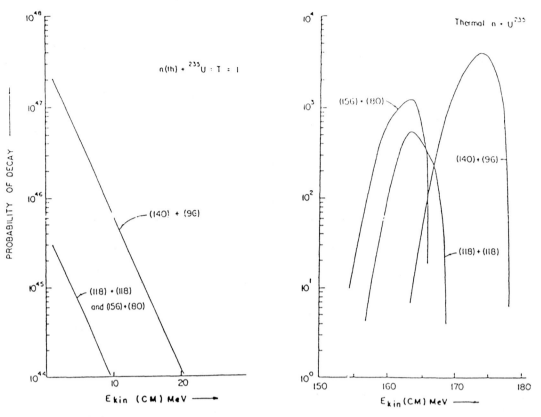

Figure 1--Calculated yields for the no barrier case (on left) and the case with the barrier (on right).

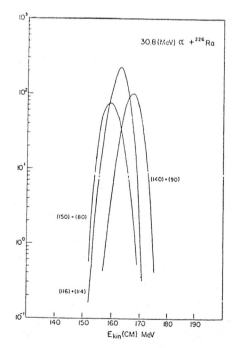

Figure 2--Calculated yields for alpha induced fission in three daughter pairs.

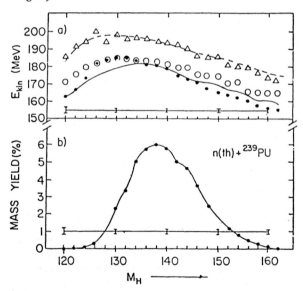

Figure 3--Observed data (solid line), calculated best fit (solid dots) and calculated TKE from the maxima of decay probabilities (open circle). Q-value used and calculated from mass formula are shown as dashed line and open triangles.

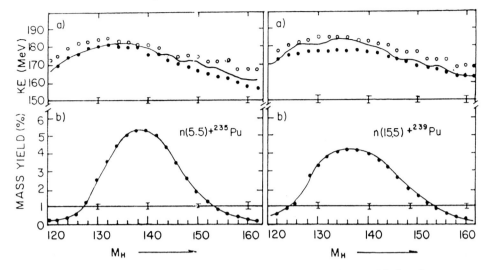

Figure 4--Observed (solid lines) and calculated (solid dots) percentage yields and TKE. Open circles are calculated TKE.

Solid lines in Fig. 4 denote experimentaly observed percentage yields and TKE for various decay modes of the compound nucleus ^{240}Pu. Observed percentage yields are significantly different for the two cases. For example, the percentage yields to symmetric modes increase substantially and to asymmetric modes decrease by one or two percentage points for the 15.5 MeV case compared to these for the 5.5 MeV case. TKE spectra, however, do not change substantially. This implies that the additional 10 MeV energy available for the 15.5 case is distributed randomly among all nucleons resulting into very little change in the location of maximum for a particular decay mode. Calculated yields and TKE used to obtain the best fits are shown as dots in Fig. 4. Open circles in the same figure represent theoretical values of TKE obtained from the maxima in yield curves. Theoretical TKE are in good agreement with the observed ones within the error bars which are typically 0 to 5 MeV.

C. n(15.5 MeV) + ^{235}U and α(27.5 Mev) + ^{232}Th

One of the assumptions of the theory is the formation of an intermediate compound nucleus. If this assumption is correct, compound nuclei that are formed at about the same excitation energies by bombarding different projectiles should decay to fission products having about the same mass and TKE spectra. Compound nuclei formed in the neutron induced fission of ^{235}U and alpha induced fission of ^{232}Th, is the same, namely ^{236}U. Q-values of the reactions (n+ ^{235}U → ^{236}U) and (α + ^{232}Th → ^{236}U) are, respectively, 6.47 and (-4.57) MeV. Thus, 15.5 MeV neutron and 26.54 MeV α particle bombarded on ^{235}U and ^{232}Th, respectively, form ^{236}U at the same excitation energy. Unfortunately, no data on 26.54 MeV alpha particle are available

but there are mass yield data on 27.5 MeV α-particle which, for our purpose, is reasonably close.

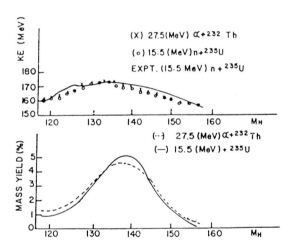

Figure 5--Observed and calculated mass yield (they are indistinguishable) are shown at the bottom. Solid curve, crosses and open circles at the top are, respectively, experimental, and theoretical TKE used to fit the yields.

Solid and dashed lines in the lower insert of Fig. 5 represent observed[14,15] and calclated percentage yields for neutron and alpha-induced fission of ^{235}U and ^{232}Th, respectively. Within the accuracy of the drawing, calculations and data are the same. TKE obtained from this theoretical fits to the yield curves are denoted by open circles and crosses for the neutron and alpha case, respectively, in the upper insert.

Solid curve in the upper insert represent observed TKE for the neutron case. No data for the alpha case is available. The data for the neutron case are very close to the theoretical TKE expected from the best fit to the mass spectrum. We have used exactly the same barrier as the one for the (n + ^{239}Pu) case and Q-values which are consistent with those obtained from Meyers and Swiatecki's mass formula.

CONCLUSION

The ability of the theory to account for both the TKE and percentage mass yield spectra in each of the cases, along with its success to account for half-lives mass and TKE spectra of spontaneous and isomer fission with proper average kinetic energy as well as charge distribution lends strong support for the existence of an external barrier between scission and saddle points. Such a barrier is clearly expected from a many body calculation using appropriate nuclear density distribution function but not in a liquid drop theory using a constant density. The theory provides a reasonable explanation for the observation of cold fission which lends further credence to the existence of a barrier between saddle and scission points.

REFERENCES

1. F. B. Malik, M. A. Hooshyar and B. Compani-Tabrizi, Proc. V. Int'l Conf. on Nucl. Reaction Mechanism ed. E. Gadioli (The University of Milano Press 1988) p. 310.

2. F. B. Malik, M. A. Hooshyar and B. Compani-Tabrizi, Proc. Int'l Conf. on the Interaction of Neutrons with Nuclei held at Lowell, Mass. ed. E. Sheldon (Energy Research and Development Office No. 1976) p. 725.

3. T. Ericson, Adv. Phys. 9, 425 (1960).

4. E. Gadioli and L. Zetta, Phys. Rev. 167, 1016 (1968).

5. A. G. W. Cameron, Cand. J. Phys. 36, 1040 (1958).

6. B. Block, J. W. Clark, M. D. High, R. Malmin and and F. B. Malik, Bull. Am. Phys. Soc. 15, 646 (1970); Ann. Phys. (N.Y.) 62, 464 (1971).

7. I. Reichstein and F. B. Malik, Ann. Phys. (N.Y.) 98, 322 (1976); Superheavy Elements ed. M. A. K. Lodhi (Pergamon Press 1978).

8. P. C. Sabatier and F. B. Malik, Helv. Phys. Acta 46, 303 (1973).

9. M. A. Hooshyar and F. B. Malik, Phys. Let. 38B, 495 (1972).

10. M. A. Hooshyar and F. B. Malik, Helv. Phys. Acta 45, 567 (1972); 46, 720, 724 (1973).

11. H. W. Schmitt, J. H. Neiler and F. J. Walter, Phys. Rev. 149, 896 (1966).

12. W. D. Meyers and W. J. Swiatecki, Nucl Phys. 81, 1 (1966).

13. V. M. Surin, A. I. Sergachev, N. I. Rezchikov and B. D. Kuz'minov, Sov. J. Nucl. Phys. 14, 523 (1972).

14. P. P. D'yachenko and B. D. Kuz'minov, Sov. J. Nucl. Phys. 7, 27 (1968).

15. A. F. Pavlov et al. Yad. Fiz. 17, 1143 (1973).

16. W. M. Gibson, T. D. Thomas and G. I. Miller, Phys. Rev. Lett. 7, 65 (1961).

17. P. Koczon et al. Phys. Lett. 191, 249 (1987) and G. G. Clerc et at. Nuc. Phys. A452, 277 (1986).

KINETIC SHELL CORRECTION AND

DDM PREDICTIONS FOR SUPERHEAVY NUCLEI

Krishna Kumar
Tennessee Technological University
Physics Department, Box 5051
Cookeville, TN 38505
(615) 372-3477

ABSTRACT

The Shell correction anomaly in the masses of
magic nuclei like ^{208}Pb and ^{126}Sn is attributed
to a kinetic shell correction, which is automatically included in the Dynamic Deformation
Model (DDM).

Additional dynamic effects are included in the
calculation of nuclear fission and it is predicted
that the next proton magic number, with respect
to fission stability, is not shifted from 126 to
114. α- and ϵ-decay shift the predicted super-
hearvy peak to $Z = 116$ ($N=184$) with a total
half-life of 1,079 years. New heavy-ion fusion
experiments are suggested.

INTRODUCTION

Brack et al.[1] and Chasman[2] have pointed out
that when the shell correction method (SCM) of
Strutinsky[3] is employed to calculate nuclear
masses, then the empirical single particle level
(SPL) spacings give reasonable agreements with
experiment in most cases but there is a substantial discrepancy in the case of doubly-magic
nuclei. This discrepancy is 7.5 MeV for ^{208}Pb
and 2.5 MeV for ^{132}Sn. This will be called
below the shell correction anomaly (SCA).

It is argued below that the SCA arises from
the fact that a kinetic shell correction (KSC)
has been neglected in most previous calculations
based on the SCM. The KSC is automatically included in the DDM[4,5]. Some of the DDM results
for the SCA are given and compared with experiment.

Since the KSC is included in the DDM, it
is not necessary to adjust the SPL spacings in
order to remove the SCA. Additional dynamic
effects are included in the DDM calculation of
fission barriers and lifetimes. Comparison
with experiment and predictions for superheavy
nuclei are presented.

KINETIC SHELL-CORRECTION (KSC)

The "empirical' shell correction energy is
defined as

$$\delta E_{esc} = E_{exp} - E_{SLD} \tag{1}$$

where E_{exp} is the experimental atomic-mass
energy and E_{SLD} is the spherical liquid drop
(or droplet model[6] without the empirical shell
correction) energy. Usually, this quantity is
identified with δU_{shell}, the microscopically
calculated shell correction of the potential
energy of deformation. However, this is not
correct. All three terms of Eq. (1) include
the potential as well as the kinetic energy of
the nucleus. Instead, we must compare the empirical shell correction of Eq. (1) with the
microscopically calculated total shell correction

$$\delta E_{msc} = \delta U_{shell} + \delta K_{shell} \tag{2}$$

where δK_{shell} is the kinetic shell correction
which may be defined as

$$\delta K_{shell} = E_{ZPM}(\text{micro.}) - E_{ZPM}(LD) \tag{3}$$

where $E_{ZPM}(\text{micro.})$ is the microscopically calculated zero-point energy and $E_{ZPM}(LD)$ is the
zero-point energy of the liquid drop nucleus.
We deduce the later from Eq. (6A-24, 6A-31) of
Bohr and Mottelson[7] except for a factor of 5/2
in their Eq. (6A-31), in order to take into
account the fact that the observed mass parameter is larger than the "irrotational" value
by a factor of 2-3.

Before making the comparison of the microscopic and the empirical quantities, we must
point out another possible correction or inter-
pretational difference. Since the shell-
correction of Eq. (1) is defined with respect
to the spherical liquid-drop, the microscopic
shell correction for a certain deformation
(def) must be defined as

$$\delta U_{shell} = \delta U(def) + E_{LD}(def) - E_{SLD} \quad . \quad (4)$$

Comparison is given in Table I for several spherical, deformed, and doubly-magic nuclei. Note that the "correction" of Eq. (4) changes the shell correction by as much as 0.77 MeV, while that of Eq. (2, 3) makes a change of as much as 11.94 MeV. The DDM shell corrections agree with those of the Droplet Model[6] within 1.4 MeV in the case of the crucial nuclei ^{208}Pb, ^{298}[114], and ^{310}[126]. The differences are larger in other cases, but one has to keep in mind that no special effort has been made in the DDM to fit the nuclear masses and that the discrepancies with respect to the "empirical" values are smaller than 0.017 MeV per nucleon.

FISSION AND SUPERHEAVIES

The DDM has recently been extended so that the configuration space is large enough for transuranic and for superheavy nuclei. A matching procedure is employed so that the Hill-Wheeler[8] y-family shapes allowing for scission can be taken into account, and so that barrier penetration to thousands of decay channels ranging in mass asymmetry from α-decay to heavy-ion-emission to symmetric-fission can be included. Reasonable agreement with the experimental fission barriers and lifetimes of 12 transuranic even-even nuclei have been obtained.[5]

These microscopically calculated results are combined with some semi-empirical relations in order to calculate the fission, α-, β-, ε-, and total half-lives of nuclei with Z=90-130, A=207-368. Comparison with experiment and with the Folded Yukawa model[9] is shown in Fig. 1, 2.

We predict the next proton magic number, with respect to stability against fission, to be 126, and the associated neutron number to be 184. In terms of the total half-life, we predict a magic island surrounding a major peak of 1,079 years at ^{300}[eka-Polonium, 116] and three minor peaks of 70 y at ^{297}[eka-Thallium, 113], 9 y at ^{331}[eka-Neptunium, 125], and 5 y at ^{302}[eka-Radon, 118].

We suggest in Fig. 3 a magic trail to the magic mountain. This trail was arrived at as follows:

Because of the extreme neutron excess in ^{300}[116], it is not possible to find a projectile-target combination where both are stable. Hence, a search was made for a heavier and more accessible nucleus which would decay to the desired one. One way to increase neutron excess is to go down via α-decay, another is to go down via ε-decay (electron-capture). These processes suggested the unique trail from ^{308}[130] to ^{300}[116], as shown in Fig. 3. Each step of this trail has 100% decay-probability except for that from ^{308}[130] to ^{308}[129] which

has only 51% probability. That step has been included only to indicate that the nice unique segment of the proposed trail essentially ends there.

The upper part of this trail starts with the heavy-ion fusion of ^{140}Ce and ^{nat}W. Additional reactions leading to the same compound nucleus, ^{324}[132], have been proposed elsewhere[5]. However, the reaction listed in Fig. 3 appears to be the most promising one: (i) The projectile is semi-magic (82 neutrons) and, hence, has a better chance of surviving fission before fusion. (ii) The target (often used as a beam stopper because of its durability) has the best chance of surviving the long exposures which would probably be needed for a successful experiment.

The upper part of the trail indicated in Fig. 3 does involve a greater uncertainty. A fusion calculation[5] based on the Extra Push Model[10] suggests that a projectile energy of ∼ 3.2 MeV/n (excitation energy of ∼ 300 MeV) would be needed in order to fuse the heavy-ions with a reasonable cross-section (∼10 mb). Then, the extrapolation from the available data on particle production suggests that about 10-14 neutrons would be evaporated before the system cools down to a region near a nuclear ground state. Also, about 2-12 protons may be evaporated. Hence, a number of paths starting from the heavy-ion fusion reaction are suggested.

It may seem from the above discussion that the proposed trail is much too uncertain. But it is not that bad as far as the final destination is concerned. If you land anywhere on the "electron-capture" segment of the trail, then you can't miss the magic mountain!

CONCLUSION

The neglect of Kinetic Shell Correction led previous theorists to predict the next proton magic number to be 114. With the inclusion of this correction in the DDM, this number remains 126. The calculated fission and total half-lives are much closer to experiment. New predictions for superheavy nuclei have been presented. Magic trails to the predicted magic mountain of total half-life of 1,079 years at ^{300}[Eka-Polonium, 116] have been suggested.

REFERENCES

1. M. BRACK et al., Rev. Mod. Phys., 44, 320 (1972).

2. R. R. CHASMAN, in Superheavy Elements, ed. M. A. K. Lodhi. Pergamon Press, New York, pp. 363-86 (1978).

3. V. M. STRUTINSKY, Nucl. Phys. A, 122, 1 (1968).

4. K. KUMAR, Nuclear Models and the Search for Unity in Nuclear Physics. Oxford University Press, New York, (1985).

5. K. KUMAR, Superheavy Elements. Adam Hilgers Limited, Bristol, in press.

6. W. D. MYERS, Droplet Model of Atomic Nuclei. IFI/Plenum Data Company, New York, (1977).

7. A. BOHR and B. R. MOTTELSON, Nuclear Structure, Vol. 2. W. A. Benjamin, Inc., Reading, (1975).

8. D. L. HILL and J. A. WHEELER, Phys. Rev., 89, 1102 (1953).

9. E. O. FISET and J. R. NIX, Nucl. Phys A, 193, 647 (1972).

10. W. J. SWIATECKI, Nucl. Phys. A. 428, 199C (1984).

11. J. K. TULI, Nuclear Wallet Cards. Brookhaven Laboratory, Upton, (1985).

12. R. VANDENBOSCH and J. R. HUIZENGA, Nuclear Fission. Academic Press, New York, (1973).

13. F. P. HESSBERGER et al., in Nuclei Far From Stability, ed. I. S. Towner. American Institute of Physics, New York, (1988).

Table I. Microscopic and empirical shell corrections in selected spherical, deformed and doubly magic nuclei.

Nucleus	Potential shell corrections		Kinetic shell corrections		Total shell corrections		
	$\delta U(def)$	δU_{shell}	E_{ZPM} (micro.)	δK_{shell}	DDM	DM[a]	Empirical[b]
^{126}Sn	− 9.00	− 8.52	6.52	2.73	− 5.79	− 4.80	− 4.07
^{204}Hg	−15.70	−15.34	3.80	1.48	−13.87	− 8.26	−10.53
^{206}Hg	−17.31	−17.17	4.93	2.60	−14.57	− 9.85	−11.17
^{208}Pb	−22.26	−22.26	14.18	11.94	−10.32	−11.17	−13.45
^{240}Pu	− 4.28	− 3.58	1.41	− 0.37	− 3.95	− 1.53	− 2.17
^{254}Fm	− 5.77	− 5.00	0.84	− 0.72	− 5.72	− 2.66	− 3.79
^{256}Fm	− 5.85	− 5.10	2.48	0.92	− 4.18	− 2.62	− 3.12
^{298}[114]	− 9.68	− 9.68	2.36	1.28	− 8.40	− 7.02	
^{310}[126]	−18.80	−18.80	5.30	5.30	−13.50	−12.76	

[a]Droplet Model, Ref. 6.

[b]Ref. 6.

FISSION HALF-LIFE ALONG THE LINE OF FISSION-STABILITY

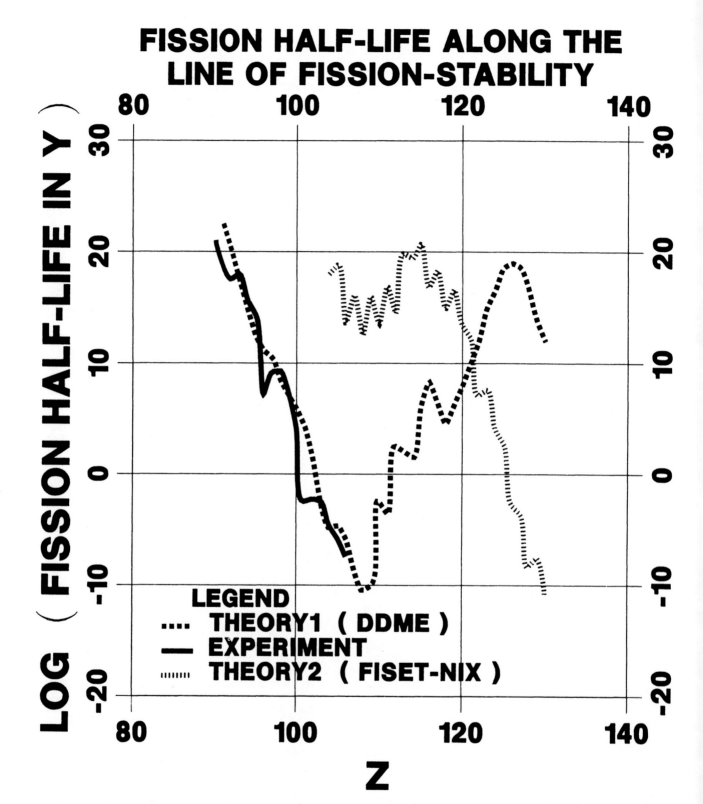

Figure 1. Fission Half-Life Along the Line of Fission-Stability. The experimental values are taken from Ref. 11-13, while Theory 1 is from Ref. 5, and Theory 2 from Ref. 9.

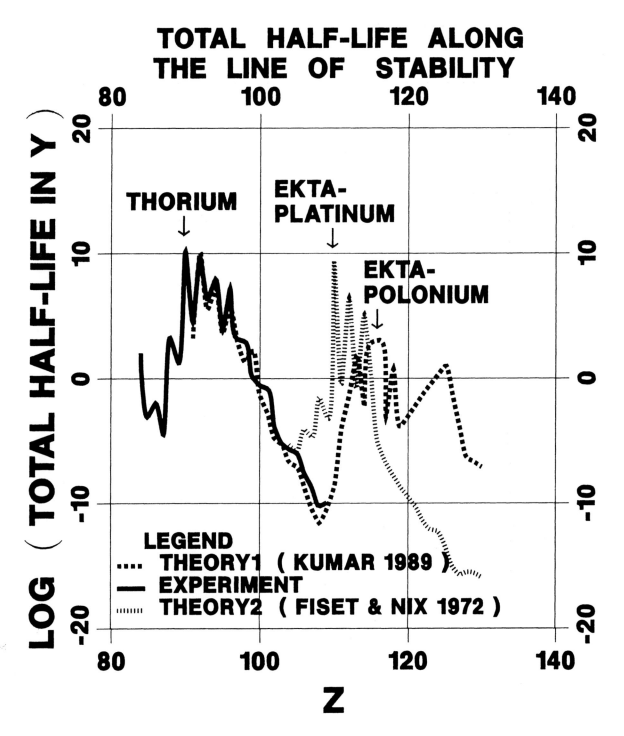

Figure 2. Total Half-Life Along the Line of Total-Stability. See Fig. 1 caption for the references.

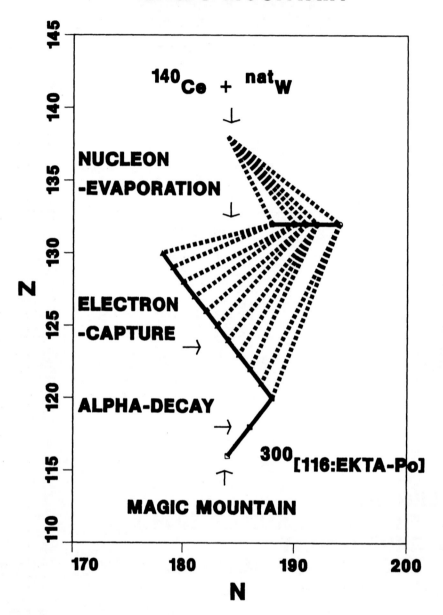

Figure 3. Trails to the Magic Mountain.

MULTIDIMENSIONAL FISSION BARRIER OF Th-232

A. CHIKHI, N.H. ALLAL, M. FELLAH and B. FAID
L.P.T / C.D.T.N.
2, Bd Frantz Fanon,
ALGER, ALGERIA

ABSTRACT

This paper reports an investigation of the left - right asymmetry nuclear shape influence on the Th-232 fission path, particulary the remarquable one that concern height of the fission barrier. The deformation potential energy is determined by the hybrid model using the liquid drop model as well as the generalised WOODS-SAXON potential. The fission barrier reveals the existence of a third well which turn out to be shallow in comparison and for which the nucleus would take a space parity asymmetric form.

INTRODUCTION

It is a well known fact that the 'Thorium anomaly'[1] has already led people to suggest many iceas on how its solution should by terms of a third shallow potential well[2] at the point of deformation where the nucleus mass symmetry breaks down. This solution has been first extented to the transition elements (Ra,Ac)[3] as well as to the light actinides Th isotopes and Pa[4], and later generalized to all nuclei containing a number of neutrons which does exceed the limit of 160[5]. For nuclei whose number of neutrons is less than 143, the third potential well becomes gradually more shallow as neutrons tend to be less abondant. The fission barrier for these is then reduced to the double hump and the structures that are observed throughout the energy dependence of the fission probability are to be related to the spectrum of the transition occuring above the axially asymmetric external barrier [6,7]. The objectiof the present paper is to study the energy deformation of the Th-232 ; in a first step, the fission path for this nucleus is find out by imposing both the left-right and axial symmetries during the deformation process ; then, a left-right symmetry breaking is introduced which enables to establish the deformation energy extrema along the fission path.

FRAME-WORK MODEL

The calculation was carried out within the frame-work of the MYERS-SWIATECKI-STRUTINSKY hybrid model in its more general version. The deformation has been described using three independant parameters : the elongation c, the striction h and the mass asymmetry α, under condition of strict conservation of nuclear volume ; the Pauli parametrization[1] of the nuclear surface has allowed to carry out an analytical evaluation of the liquid drop energy ; the individual nucleon energies are computed by mean of the generalized WOODS-SAXON potential energy levels ; the energy fluctuations from microscopic origin have been evaluated on the basis of both the STRUTINSKY model and BCS theory.

RESULTS ANALYSIS

A - Symmetric shape

The Th-232 fission path as described by the liquid drop model is deduced from the potential energy surfaces drown as function the c and h parameters ; it is roughly given by the curve $h \approx 0$. The fission barrier obtained by combining both the classical and quantal aspects of the nucleus, shows a deformed fundamental state and two maxima separated by a potential well. The first and the second symmetrical humps have respectively the coordinates :

$$c = 1.33 \quad , \quad h = 0.075 \quad , \quad E = 4.4 \text{ MeV}$$
$$c = 1.65 \quad , \quad h = 0.0 \quad , \quad E = 9.2 \text{ MeV}$$

and the fundamental and isomeric states are situated at the following deformations :

$$c = 1.18 \quad , \quad h = -0.3$$
$$c = 1.42 \quad , \quad h = -0.075$$

These results are consistent with all the other theoritical results but they do not reproduce what has been established experimentally ; this is the so-called "thorium anomaly".

B - Asymmetric shape

The assymetric fission calls on the introduction of a third degree of freedomα.
The calculations have enabled us to detect a gradual decrease of the height of the second barrier and the appearance at the same time of a depression at its peak, thus giving evidence of the presence of two symmetric fission valleys with respect to the α parameter. On the other hand the total shell correction changes in sign with respect to the one obtained for symmetric fission in the region of the second symmetric saddle point. This total shell correction digs in a third minimum in the Th-232 fission barrier.

Moreover, this investigation has shown that the first barrier as well as the second minima are stable with respect to α. In the region of the second barrier, the nucleus undergoes an asymmetric shape along one of the two valleys that correspond to these two possible orientations. This property leads to each state degenerating into two opposite parity states in total accord with the experimental results[8,9]; each valley displays a third shallow minimum (0.7 MeV) surrounded by two barriers of roughly the same height. These new asymmetric barriers have coordinates.

(c = 1.56 , h = 0.1125 , α = 0.13 , E = 7.2 MeV)
and
(c = 1.65 , h = 0.075 , α = 0.12 , E = 7.0 MeV)

respectively.

The third minimum (6.5 MeV) is found at the deformation given by

(c = 1.59 , h = 0.09375 , α = 0.13)

Comparing these values with the ones obtained elsewhere[2,10] shows clearly that there is an agreement between the two sets of results as for as existence and the depth of the third well are concerned. There is however a slight desagreement as to what should now be the heights of both the asymmetric fission barriers and the third minimum. This is due perhaps to our different way of evaluating the Th deformation potential energy as compared to what is in reference[2] and also to the use of an infinite edge potential as in reference[10]. Despite these slight differences, the heights when normalized with respect to the fondamental state are very consistent with the experimental results to within an error bar of the order of 1 MeV.

REFERENCES

1. H.C. PAULI, T. LEDERBERGER Nucl. Phys. A 175 (1979) 545

2. P. MOLLER, J.R. NIX proc. AIEA, ROCHESTER VI (1974) 133

3. J. WEBER et al. Phys. Rev. C13 (1976) 2413

4. S. BJORNHOLM, J.E. LYNN Rev. Mod. Phys. 52 (1980) 725

5. W.M. HOWARD, P. MOLLER Atom. Data and Nucl. Data Tables 25 (1980) 219

6. A. NEMILOV et al. Sov. J. Nucl. Phys. 37 (1983) 488

7. S.A. EGOROV et al. Sov. J. Nucl. Phys. 46 (1987) 38

8. D. PAYA Proc. IAEA-JULICH-VI (1980) 207

9. A. SIGRE Nucl. Phys. A 445 (1985) 462

10. S. ABERG, S.E. LARSSON, P. MOLLER Proc. IAEA-ROCHESTER-VI (1980) 303

A NEW METHOD FOR A SIMULTANEOUS SHELL AND PAIRING CORRECTION

N.H. ALLAL and M. FELLAH
L.P.T / C.D.T.N
2, Bd Frantz Fanon
ALGER, ALGERIA

ABSTRACT

A new level density has been derived with an explicit inclusion of pairing correlation in the context of the BCS theory. As in the Strutinsky method, this level density has been developped in terms of Hermite polynomials. The mean energy of a system is obtained by limiting this development to a certain order. The procedure helps one to determine analytically the total microscopic shell and pairing corrections simultaneously. This method has been used to calculate the ground state energy of Pb-208 and the isomeric state of Pu-240 with the deformed Woods-Saxon potential. The energy correction presents a plateau for $1 \leq \gamma \leq 2$ $\hbar w_o$ and the mean value of gap parameter $\bar{\Delta}$ is different from that for the BCS theory. In the case of Pb-208, the microscopic energy correction calculated with this method $\delta E = -13.21$ MeV is very close to the experimental value of $\delta E = -12.8$ MeV. The correction to the macroscopic energy of fissionning nuclei evaluated by the present method would lead to a better determination of the fission path.

INTRODUCTION

The microscopic shell and pairing corrections to the deformation energy of a system in the context of macroscopic and microscopic model are determined separately using different methods[1,2]. Although the shell correction is based on the Strutinsky method[3,4], the correction due to pairing is determined only phenomenologically through different techniques[5,6]. Since both the corrections have the same microscopic origin, it would be worth-while to calculate them simultaneously from the same independent particle model. This means that the Strutinsky level density distribution should include the pairing correlations. The self-consitent Hartree-Bogoliubov method for T=O and T≠O [7,8] and the semi-classical methods[11] account for these two corrections simultaneously. However, these methods are very time consuming.

In this contribution, we develop an analytical method, a generalisation of Strutinsky method, based on a level density distribution that includes explicitely the pairing correlation, which allows us to calculate the shell and pairing corrections simultaneously.

PRINCIPLE OF METHOD

One knows that for a given spectrum, the number of levels in an energy interval $d\varepsilon$ is $dn = g(\varepsilon) d\varepsilon$, where $g(\varepsilon)$ is the level density. For a doubly degenerate independent particle spectrum $g(\varepsilon)$ is :

$$g(\varepsilon) = 2 \sum_m \delta(\varepsilon - \varepsilon_m) \qquad (1)$$

where ε_m are the energies of discreet levels. The Fermi energy λ for a system of N particles is determined from the relation :

$$N = F(\lambda) \qquad \text{where}$$

$$F(\lambda) = \int_{-\infty}^{\lambda} dn = \int_{-\infty}^{\lambda} g(\varepsilon) d\varepsilon \qquad (2)$$

When one includes the pairing correlations, the condition of conservation of mean number of particles in the BCS theory leads to expression of $F(\lambda)$ which is :

$$F(\lambda) = \sum_m \left\{ 1 - \frac{\varepsilon_m - \lambda}{\sqrt{(\varepsilon_m - \lambda)^2 + \Delta^2}} \right\} \qquad (3)$$

where Δ is the gap parameter.

The eq(2) allows to define a level density $g(\varepsilon, \Delta)$ such that

$$g(\varepsilon, \Delta) = \sum_m \frac{\Delta^2}{[(\varepsilon_m - \varepsilon)^2 + \Delta^2]^{3/2}} \qquad (4)$$

It has already been shown[9] that the generalised level density $g(\varepsilon, \Delta)$ reduces to that of eq.(1) when $\Delta \to O$. The total microscopic energy correction δE can be obtained by a procedure similar to that of Strutinsky. To do this, it is sufficient to define with the help eq.(4), a mean energy $\bar{E}(\bar{\Delta})$. Then $\delta E = E(\Delta) - \bar{E}(\bar{\Delta})$, where $E(\Delta)$ is the usual BCS energy and $\bar{\Delta}$, the mean gap parameter corresponding to the level density $\bar{g}(\varepsilon, \bar{\Delta})$.

In order to make possible an analytical and numerical comparison of the correction δE obtained from eq.(4) with that calculated with the Strutinsky method, one develops $g(\varepsilon,\Delta)$ in a series of Hermite polynomials by introducing an averaging parameter γ such that

$$g(\varepsilon,\Delta) = \sum_m g_m(\varepsilon,\Delta) \qquad \text{with}$$

$$g_m(\varepsilon,\Delta) = \frac{1}{\gamma}\frac{\Delta^2/\gamma^2}{\left[\left(\frac{\varepsilon-\varepsilon_m}{\gamma}\right)^2 + \frac{\Delta^2}{\gamma^2}\right]^{3/2}} \qquad (5)$$

$$= \frac{1}{\gamma}\frac{a^2}{[x_m^2 + a^2]^{3/2}}$$

where $a = \Delta/\gamma$ and $x_m = (\varepsilon-\varepsilon_m)/\gamma$

Then one looks for a development of the form

$$g_m(\varepsilon,\Delta) = \frac{1}{\gamma\sqrt{\pi}}\sum_k c_{2k}(\Delta)\,H_{2k}\left(\frac{\varepsilon-\varepsilon_m}{\gamma}\right) \qquad (6)$$

where the $c_{2k}(\Delta)$ are given by

$$c_{2k}(\Delta) = 2(2k+1)\sum_{p=0}^{k}\frac{(-1)^p I_{2k-2p+2}}{2^{2p}\,p!\,(2k-2p+1)!}$$

with

$$I_{2p} = \int_{-\infty}^{+\infty}\frac{x^{2p}e^{-x^2}}{[x^2+a^2]^{3/2}}\,dx$$

and $H_{2k}(x)$ are the Hermite polynomials of order 2k. The integrals I_{2p} can be evaluated in terms of modified Bessel fonctions. Now, one defines the level density by limiting the series development of eq.(6) to order p :

$$\bar{g}_m(\varepsilon,\bar{\Delta}) = \frac{K}{\gamma\sqrt{\pi}}\sum_{k=0}^{P}c_{2k}(\bar{\Delta})\,H_{2k}\left(\frac{\varepsilon-\varepsilon_m}{\gamma}\right) \qquad (7)$$

where $K = 1/c_0(\bar{\Delta})$ is a factor of normalisation.

The mean occupation and non occupation probabilities defined as

$$\bar{v}_m^2 = \frac{1}{2}\int_{-\infty}^{\bar{\lambda}}\bar{g}_m(\varepsilon,\bar{\Delta})\exp\left(-\left(\frac{\varepsilon-\varepsilon_m}{\gamma}\right)^2\right)d\varepsilon$$

$$\bar{u}_m^2 = \frac{1}{2}\int_{\bar{\lambda}}^{+\infty}\bar{g}_m(\varepsilon,\bar{\Delta})\exp\left(-\left(\frac{\varepsilon-\varepsilon_m}{\gamma}\right)^2\right)d\varepsilon \qquad (8)$$

where $\bar{\lambda}$ is determined with the help of $\bar{g}(\varepsilon,\bar{\Delta})$ become :

$$\bar{v}_m^2 = \frac{1}{2}(1+erf(x_m)) - \frac{1}{\sqrt{\pi}}\sum_{k=1}^{P}\frac{c_{2k}(\bar{\Delta})}{c_0(\bar{\Delta})}H_{2k-1}(x_m)e^{-x_m^2} \qquad (9)$$

$$\bar{u}_m^2 = \frac{1}{2}(1-erf(x_m)) + \frac{1}{\sqrt{\pi}}\sum_{k=1}^{P}\frac{c_{2k}(\bar{\Delta})}{c_0(\bar{\Delta})}H_{2k-1}(x_m)e^{-x_m^2}$$

where $X_m = (\bar{\lambda}-\varepsilon_m)/\gamma$

This treatment leads to the mean energy of the system, whose form is similar to that of the BCS energy, and this helps us to define the energy correction.

$$\delta E = 2\sum_m \varepsilon_m(\vartheta_m^2 - \bar{\vartheta}_m^2) - (\Delta^2 - \bar{\Delta}^2)/G - G\sum_m(\vartheta_m^4 - \bar{\vartheta}_m^4) \qquad (10)$$

where $\bar{\Delta} = G\sum_m \bar{u}_m\bar{v}_m$ will be taken as a parameter and determined simultaneously with γ in order to ensure the stationnarity of δE :

$$\partial(\delta E)/\partial\gamma = \partial(\delta E)/\partial\bar{\Delta} = 0 \qquad (11)$$

NUMERICAL RESULTS AND DISCUSSION

We tested and applied this method to the ground state of Pb-208 and the isomeric state of Pu-240 using the deformed Woods-Saxons potential[1].

First we determined the parameters γ and $\bar{\Delta}$ and the order p of the sum of eq.(7) that ensure the condition of stationnarity of δE as figs.1 and 2 show, the δE for Pu-240 presents a plateau for $1 \leqslant \gamma \leqslant 2$ $\hbar w_0$ for both neutrons and protons. The plateau becomes sharper p $\geqslant$ 3. Similar results were found for Pb-208. Furthermore, we compared the energy correction δE, the pairing strength G and $\bar{\Delta}$ obtained with the present method with the existing values. For Pu-240, the δE (-5.59 MeV for neutrons and 1.13 MeV for protons) is $\approx$1 MeV lower than with the usual Strutinsky method. The $\bar{\Delta}$ that satisfies condition(11) is very close to that given by the BCS method in the case of neutrons ; however, it is much smaller for protons. In the case of Pb-208, our method gives δE=-13.21 MeV compared to -17.6 MeV from the usual Strutinsky method, in both cases with a deformed Woods-Saxon potential [10]. Our value is very close to the experimental value of -12.8 MeV. Apparently, the well-known "lead-anomaly" that shows up with the usual

666

Strutinsky method[10] does not exist when our method is used to calculated δE. Furthermore, for Pb-208, the value of the gap parameter $\bar{\Delta}$ is very small and $\approx 10^{-2}$ and 10^{-4} for neutrons and protons respectively as in the case of the BCS method.

As a conclusion, we feel that our method of calculation of microscopic correction, may be considered to be a generalisation of the Strutinsky method. It should, as a rule, allow us to calculate more precisely the nuclear masses and the fission barriers.

Acknowledgements :

The authors wish to express their gratitude to Prof. Asghar for his kind interest in this work and for useful suggestions.

REFERENCES

1. H.C. PAULI, Phys. Rep 7C (1973) 35

2. S. BJORNHOLM and J.E. LYNN Rev. Mod. Phys. 52 (1980) 725

3. V.M. STRUTINSKY, Nucl. Phys. A95 (1967) 420

4. V.M. STRUTINSKY and F.A. IVANYUK Nucl. Phys. A255 (1975) 405

5. M. BOSTERLI et al., Phys. Rev. C5 (1972) 1050

6. A.S. JENSEN and J. DAMGAARD, Nucl. Phys. A203 (1973) 578

7. M. BRACK and P. QUENTIN, Nucl. Phys. A361 (1981) 35

8. M. DIEBEL et al., Nucl. Phys. A355 (1981) 66

9. N.H. ALLAL and M. FELLAH, Proc." Journees d'études sur la fission" (1986) 9, Arcachon (France)

10. M. BRACK et al., Rev. Mod. Phys. 44 (1972) 320

11. M. BRACK et al., Phys. Rep. 123 (1985) 275

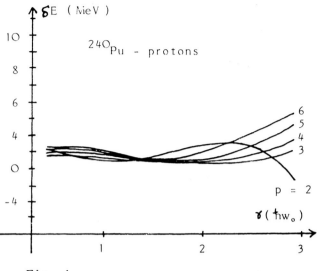

Fig. 1

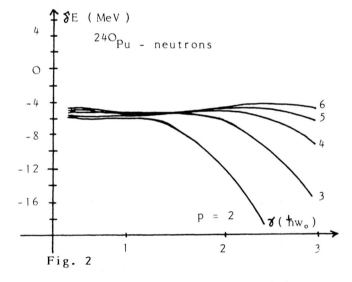

Fig. 2

Fig. 1 and 2 : Dependence of microscopic energy correction E upon smoothing parameter γ for different orders p.

FISSION AS A MULTI-DIMENSIONAL BROWNIAN MOTION

Zhong Yun-xiao   Hu Ji-min
Department of Technical Physics
Peking Univesity, Beijing 100871, China

ABSTRACT

Fission of ^{213}At at 100MeV excitation is studied as
a mnltidimensional Brownian motion. The potential
energy surface is calculated with Nix's modified liquid drop model.The kinetic energy is calculated by
Werner-Wheeler's method. Swiatecki's one body wall
formula is applied to calculate the dissipation function, with Nix's reduction factor.With the usual (c,
h, α) deformation parameters,the resulting coupled
Langevin equation is solved by Monte-Carlo method
for one (h= α =0),and two(h=0) dimensional cases.The
calculated average fragment kinetic energy and the
rms dispersions are in accordance with experiments
while the rms dispersions of mass distributions obtained from two dimensional calculation is considerably larger than experimental results.

I. INTRODUCTION

From classical point of view, the fission process can be considered as a series of changes of nuclear shapes from ground state to scission configurations under the joint influences of the collective
driving force and the coupling with the motion of
individual nucleons. This is the main idea of the
Brownian motion model of nuclear fission. It is expected that such a picture will hold for fissions at
moderately high excitations.The problem can be treated with the application of the Fokker-Planck equation
and several attempts has been made in this approach.
In the one dimensional case numerical solution of the
Fokker-Planck equation can be obtained with simplified potential barriers and constant inertia and
viscosity parameters. Actually fission probabilitis
for different barrier forms can be obtained much
easier from the Smoluchowski equations which is a
good approximation to the Fokker-Planck equation
with sufficiently high viscosity.[1] However in order
to extract more reliable and detailed informations,it is necessary to treat fission as a multidi-
mentional Brownian motion.For fission probabilities,
Kramers' method can be generalized to calculate the
quasi-steady fission rate for multidimensional case.[2]
Starting from the saddle point, approximate solution of the two dimensional Fokker-Planck equation
has been performed by Scheuter et al to calculate
the fission fragment kinetic energy distribution.[3]
Similar work has been attempted by Adeev and

Gonchar with an assumed parabolic potential
barrier.[4] These calculations are subjected to
the objection that the distribution at the saddle
point was assummed arbitrarily, So far as we
know, a multidimensional Brownian motion study
of the whole fission process has not been published. In this paper, we shall describe our preliminary attempt to study the whole fission process
(from a spherical nucleus to the scission point)
as a two dimensional Brownian motion,with realistic
potential energy surface,inertia and dissipation
tensors. It would be a formidable problem to solve
the resulting Fokker-Planck equations with 5 vari-
bles. Direct solution of the Langevin equation with
Monte Carlo simulation of the random force is a
more straight forward approach to the problem. In
the second section, we shall show with a simple one
dimensional model, that such an approach will yield
approximately the same results as that obtained from
the direct solution of the Fokker-Planck equation.
In the third section the method of calculation is
described.Results of calculation and comparison with
empirical data is discussed in the last section.

II. A SIMPLE ONE DIMENSIONAL MODEL

As a check to our method of calculation,we have
studied a simple one dimensional model suggested by
Grange et al[5] with all the parameters unchanged.
In this model,the potential energy takes the following form

$$U(x) = \zeta gx^2(x-c)(x+b)$$

where ζ =0.25 m Ao is the mass parameter, Ao is the
mass number of the fissioning nucleus and m is the
mass of the nucleon. The constant c,b,g are adjusted so that the potential gives two valley and one
peak, the first valley serves as the ground state
and the peak as the barrier, 4 MeV higher than the
first valley, and the second valley serves as a
dump of the Brownian particles.
The Langevin equation can be written as

$$(d^2x/dt^2) = -\beta (dx/dt) + R(t)/\zeta + F(x) \qquad (1)$$

where $F(x) = -(dU/dx)/\zeta$, β is the damping coefficent
and R(t) is the random force. To solve equation (1),
the time is divided into many equal intervals Δt, In

each interval, the random force has varied many times, while F(x) can be taken as a constant. Solve equation (1) in the (n+1)th interval, one obtains the recursion formulae for V and X

$$V_{n+1} = V_n \exp(-\Delta t/\tau) + D \exp(-\Delta t/2\tau)$$
$$+ F_{n+1} \tau [1 - \exp(-\Delta t/2\tau)]$$
$$+ F_n \tau [\exp(-\Delta t/2\tau) - \exp(-\Delta t/\tau)]$$

$$X_{n+1} = X_n + \tau V_n [1 - \exp(-\Delta t/\tau)]$$
$$+ D \tau [1 - \exp(-\Delta t/2\tau)]$$
$$+ F_n \tau [\Delta t - \tau \{1 - \exp(-\Delta t/\tau)\}] \qquad (2)$$

where V_n, X_n and F_n are the values of (dx/dt), x, $F(x)$ at the time $t_n = n\Delta t$, $\tau = 1/\beta$ and

$$D = \int_0^{\Delta t} R(t) dt$$

can be taken as Guassian random numbers with mean square root deviation

$$\sigma = (2T\Delta t/\zeta \tau)^{1/2} \qquad (3)$$

where T is nuclear temperature. With D given by Monte-Carlo sampling, equation (2) can be solved for any number of time intervals with initial distribution givin by

$$(\zeta \omega_1/2T_0) \exp\{\zeta [V_0^2 + \omega_1^2 (X_0 - X_{10})^2]/2T_0\}$$

where X_{10} is the position of the bottom of the first valley, ω_1 is the vibration frequency in that valley and $T_0 = 0.3$ MeV, the value given in Ref.5. The across of any particle over the peak of the barrier is considered as a fission event. With a large number of testing particles(10^4 in our calculation), the fission probability per unit time, Y, is given by negative of the slope of $\ln(n)$--t curve, where n is the number of particles remaining in the first valley at time t,

As in Ref. 5, we have taken $A = 248$, $T = 1,4$ Mev and several values of τ. The results of calculation are not sensitive to the value of Δt if it is smaller than $\tau/5$. We have taken $\Delta t = \tau/10$ in the final calculation. Comparison of our results with that of Ref. 5 is shown in Fig 1. Considering the statistical errors of our method (not shown in the figure), the agreement is satisfactory.

III. METHOD OF MULTIDIMENSIONAL CALCULATIONS

In the multidimensional case, the Langevin equation is given by

$$\Sigma M_{ij} \ddot{q}_j + (\partial U/\partial q_i) + \Sigma W_{ij} \dot{q}_j = R_i(t) \qquad (4)$$

where q_i's are the deformation parameters, M_{ij} and W_{ij} are inertia and dissipation tensors, U the potential energy function and R_i the random force. In order to apply this formula to a realistic fission problem, we have to face with three difficulties, namely, the choice of deformation parameters, calculation of the parameters appeared in (4) and the solution of (4). A brief discussion of these problems is given in the following.

A. Choice of Deformation Parameters

Any choice of deformaton parameters is a restriction on the form of the nucleus. In a dynamical calculation, such restrictions may lead to serious diffculties. To reduce the number of parameters, we have adopted the usual (c, h, α) parametization, with the surface equation given by

$$\rho^2 = Q(z) = (c^2 - z^2)[A + B(z/c)^2 + \alpha(z/c)] \qquad (5)$$

where ρ and z are cylindrical coordinates and

$$A = 1/c^3 - 0.5h - 0.1(c-1)$$

$$B = 2h + 0.5(c-1)$$

with the spherical radius R_0 of the fissioning nucleus as the unit of length. This parametrization of nuclear shape is all-right for small values (say less than 0.3) of α and h. It may leads to unreasonable shapes for large absolute values of α and h. To avoid this difficulty, we have in this preliminary work limited our calculation to one ($\alpha = h = 0$) and two dimensional (h=0) cases, in the two dimensional case, the potential energy is suitably raised to prevent the value of α to become too large. This artifice may be considered as the price paid for the simplicity of this parametrization. It is also rather difficult to define the precise scission point for a given shape parametrization. In fact, scission may occur when the neck is thin enough. The

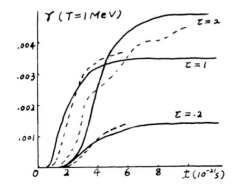
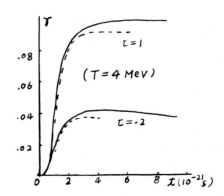

Fig.1 Comparison of the fission probabilities per unit time calculated in the present paper (solid curve)and that of Ref(5). (dotted curve). The unit of time is 10^{-21}s.

669

geometrical scission occurs when

$$\xi = A - \alpha^2/4B = 0 \qquad (6)$$

We have arbitrarily fixed the value $\xi = .01$ for the dynamical scission point, corresponding to neck radius smaller than $0.2R_0$.

B. Calculation of Potential Energy Surface, Inertia and Dissipation Tensor.

The potential energy surface is calculated from the macroscopic model of Moller and Nix with the parameters given by them.[6] We have not take into account the change of these constant with nuclear temperature. It is estimated that no serious errors will be incurred in this respect. To avoid laborious repeated calculations, the calculated potential energy is fitted with the simple formula (for the fissioning nucleus ^{213}At).

$$U = 0.7(.8/c)^{10} - [142.5(C^3/3 - 1.425C^2 + 1.85C - .7584 - .05\alpha^2) + 7(1-\alpha^2)(C/2)^6](1 + 10\alpha^2 + 50\alpha^4) \qquad (7)$$

The potential energy given by (7) is compared with that obtained from direct calculation in Fig.2. It may be seen from the figure, that the agreement is satisfactory for $\alpha = 0 - .3$. For $\alpha > 0.3$, the potential given by (7) is artificially raised to keep the absolute value of α from getting too large.

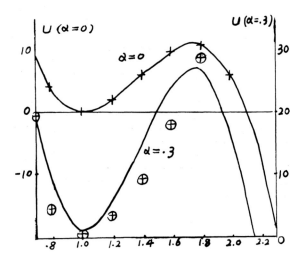

Fig.2 Potential energy as a function of the elongation parameter c, solid line indicate values from (7), crosses are the values obtained by direct calculation.

There is some reason to expect that if the short range correlation between the nucleons can be neglected for an excited nucleus, irrotational flow model might be applied to calculate the inertia parameters. Hence, we have applied Werner Wheeler's method, which yields similar results

with much simplified calculation.[7] For dissipation function, Swiatecki's one-body dissipation mechanism is adopted.[8] However, his pure classical consideration may lead to the over estimation of the dissipation energy. We have therefore inserted in his wall formula a correction factor k, which is taken to be 0.27 according to Nix's estimation.[9] Accordingly, the inertia and dissipation tensor may be calculated from the following formula (in MeV, 10^{-22}s)

$$M_{ij} = 1.0545A_0^{5/3}\int_z^c dz\{Q[A_i - (\partial\bar{z}/\partial q_i)][A_j - (\partial\bar{z}/\partial q_j)] + [Q_z A_i + (\partial Q/\partial q_i)][Q_z A_j + (\partial Q/\partial q_j)]/8\} \qquad (8)$$

$$W_{ij} = 1.5765 A_0^{4/3}\int_z^c dz[(\partial Q/\partial q_i) + Q_z(\partial\bar{z}/\partial q_i)] [(\partial Q/\partial q_j) + Q_z(\partial\bar{z}/\partial q_j)]/[4Q + Q_z^2]^{1/2} \qquad (9)$$

$$A_i = (1/Q)\int_z^c (\partial Q/\partial q_i)dz, \quad \bar{z} = \alpha c^4/5, \quad Q_z = (\partial Q/\partial z)$$

It is to be noted, that for deformations with obvious necks, both the Werner Wheeler's method and the wall formula become less applicable. Actual calculation shown that both M_{ij} and W_{ij} become very large for $c > 1.6$. Hence the formula (8) and (9) are applied only in the region $c <= 1.6$. For $c > 1.6$, the deformation is already near the scission point, M_{ij} and W_{ij} are fixed at the values for $c = 1.6$.

C. Solution of the Langevin Equation

For two dimensional case, the equations are

$$M_{11}\ddot{q}_1 + M_{12}\ddot{q}_2 + W_{11}\dot{q}_1 + W_{12}\dot{q}_2 = R_1(t) + f_1$$

$$M_{12}\ddot{q}_1 + M_{22}\ddot{q}_2 + W_{12}\dot{q}_1 + W_{22}\dot{q}_2 = R_2(t) + f_2 \qquad (10)$$

where 1,2 stands for deformation parameter c, and α, and $f_i = -(\partial U/\partial q_i)$ are the driving forces. To solve (10) it is more convenient to transform the matrices M and W into diagonal form. Forturnately, the transformation which transform M into diagonal form, transforms W also approximately into diagonal form. Neglecting the remaining small non-diagonal term of W we obtain the decoupled equations

$$M_1\ddot{B}_1 + W_1\dot{B}_1 = R_1 + F_1 \qquad M_2\ddot{B}_2 + W_2\dot{B}_2 = R_2 + F_2 \qquad (11)$$

where $\quad B_1 = aq_1 + bq_2 \qquad B_2 = -bq_1 + aq_2$

$$M_1 = .5(M_{11} + M_{22}) + (.25(M_{11} - M_{22})^2 + M_{12}^2)^{1/2}$$

$$M_2 = .5(M_{11} + M_{22}) - (.25(M_{11} - M_{22})^2 + M_{12}^2)^{1/2}$$

$$a = -M_{12}/[(M_{11} - M_1)^2 + M_{12}^2]^{1/2} \qquad b = (1 - a^2)^{1/2}$$

To solve the above equation, we must chose a time interval Δt large enough so that the random force R_i fluctuates many times inside this time interval. The results of calculation is not very sensitive to the actual value of Δt. We have chosen the value 0.5×10^{-22}s through try and error, which is of the same order of magnitude as the period of motion of individual nucleons inside the nucleus. Due to the smallness of M_2, even for such a small time interval, the change of α and $\dot{\alpha}$ inside the interval can not be neglected. Inside each time interval, the random force $R_i(t)$ can be replaced by $D_i/\triangle t - (1/\triangle t)\int R_i(t)dt$, and D_i are random impulses which obey Gaussian distribution with mean square root deviation $\sigma_i = (2TW_i\triangle t)^{1/2}$. In each interval, inertia and dissipation tensors can be taken as constants, but the driving force on the α degree of freedom is approximated by a harmonic force. With these approximations and D_i obtained from Monte-Carlo sampling, the Langevin equations (11) can be solved inside the time interval $\triangle t$. The motion of any test particle is given by the accumulated motion of successive time intervals.

IV. RESULTS OF CALCULATIONS

We have chosen ^{213}At at 100 MeV excitation as the fissioning system to be studied. As a result of reaction ^{209}Bi(α,f), this is an experimentally will studied system. The angular momentums carried by α-particles is not very large, and has been neglected in the calculations. The excitation is high enough so that the macroscopic classical approximation can be applied. The initial distribution is taken to be

$$(M_1\omega_1/2T_0)\exp\{[M_1C^2+M_1\omega_1^2(C-1)^2]/2T_0\}$$

with $\alpha = \dot{\alpha} = 0$. T_0 is taken to be 1 MeV. Practically, the results of calculation is almost indenpendent of the of the value of T_0 less than 2 MeV. The nuclear temperature at any instant is given approximately by

$$T = [(E_0-E_c)/a]^{1/2}$$

where $E_0 = 100$MeV is the total excitation energy and

$$E_c = U(c,\alpha) + 0.5\sum_{ij}M_{ij}\dot{q}_i\dot{q}_j \qquad (12)$$

is the total energy of collective motion, $a=16$ MeV^{-1}

For comparison, we have performed calculations for one ($h = \alpha = 0$) and two ($h=0$)dimensional cases. In the one dimensional case, we have made two kinds of statistics to determine the fission probabilities per unit time. In the first case, the cross over the barrier peak is considered as a case of fission. and the particle is considered as lost from the sampling particles and the fission probability γ_1 is evaluated just as described in the second section. In the second case, only the pass of the scission point(defined by $\xi = .01$) is considered as a fission event, and the fission probability γ_2 is calculated in the same way. The value of γ_1 and γ_2 so determined are plotted as a function of time in Fig.3. From the figure, it can be seen that the values of γ_2 are smaller than γ_1 in the transcient interval, but approach the same quasi-steady value. This is what one would expect as there should not be any accumulation of particles beyond the barrier, and the probability for the particle to cross back the barrier is very small.

The velocity of each particle passing the scission point is also recorded and the total fragment kinetic energy is given by

$$E_k = \mu\dot{r}^2/2 + V_c \qquad (13)$$

where μ is the reduced mass, equal to $.25A_0M$ for symmetrical fission, r is the distance between centers

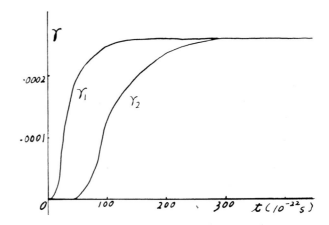

Fig.3 Fission probability in one dimension

of mass of two fragments and $\dot{r}$ their relative velocity, can be calculated from c and $\dot{c}$, and

$$V_c = Z_1Z_2 \, e^2/r \qquad (14)$$

is the Coulomb energy between the fragments if they are replaced by two charged spheres centered at their centers of mass. It is to be noted that the the value of V_c given the (14) is not the total potential energy between two fragments. However, the interchange of potential energy, deformation energy, internal energy and kinetic energy of the fragments continues after the scission. Formula (14) is equivalent to the assumption that only the monopole interaction energy between two charges transforms into the kinetic energy of the fragment On the average, it may be a reasonable assumption, but may lead to the underestimation of rms deviation of fragments kinetic energy up to a few MeV. In the one dimensional case, the calculated average total fragment kinetic and rms deviation are given in the first column of table 1.

For two dimensional calculation, the fission probability can be obtained in the same way and the steady value of γ_2 is given in table 1. In this case,

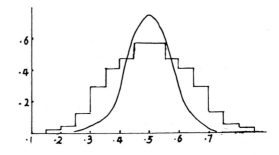

Fig.4 Comparison of calculated mass distribution with the empirical distribution.[10]

the value of c and α at the scission points are recorded. And the volumes of the complementary fragments and the distance between their center of mass can be calculated. Since the masses and charges are proportional to their volumes, the fragments mass and total kinetic energy distribution can be obtained. Their average values and rms deviations are listed in the second column of table 1. The calculated mass distribution is also shown in histogram form in Fig.4,together with the experimental distribution.[10] One may notice that the calculated distribution is indeed symmetrical, though much broader than the empirical distribution.

Table 1

	1-dimen.	2-dimen.	empirical value[10]
fission probability (10^{20}sec^{-1})	.026	.013	
mean kinetic energy (MeV)	157	145	149
rms dispersion of kinetic energy (MeV)	7	12	10
rms dispersion of mass distribution		28	14

From the table,it can be seen that the general agreement of our calculation and the empirical results is satisfactory. Although some necessary approximations are made in the calculation,no adjustable parameters are introduced to fit the empirical values. Comparing the corresponding results of one and two dimensional calculations, one may notice that although they are of the same order, the numerical values differ considerably.One may conclude that reliable numerical predictions can be made only through suitable multidimensional calculations.

The most significant deviation of the present results from the empirical results is that the calculated mass distribution is much broader than the empirical distribution. This discrepancy may arise from the following reasons. Firstly the improper treatment of the inertia and dissipation tensors in the asymmetry degree of freedom and the artificial adjustment of the potential energy may lead to too large variations on the values of parameter α. Secondly, a three dimensional calculation may improve the results. Thirdly, the most fundamental defects of the present calculation may lie in the improper shape parametrization. From this preliminary investigation, it is clear that there is still a long way to go to make a satisfactory multidimensional calculation for the fission process.

REFFERENCE

1. Zhong Yun-xiao: "The Rate of Escape of Brownian Particles over Potential Barriers",Chinese Phys. 6, 57 (1986)

2. Hu Ji-min and Zhong Yun-xiao: "Broownian Motion Model of the Fission Process",Chinese Phys. 2, 157 (1982)

3. F.Scheuter,C.Gregoire,H.Hofmann and J.R.Nix: "Fission Fragment Kinetic Energy Distributions from a Two Dimensional Fokker-Planck Equation" Phys. Lett. 149B, 303(1984)

4. G.D.Adeev and I.I.Gonchar," A Simplified Two-Dimemsional Diffusion Model for Calculating the Fission-Fragment Kinetic Energy Distribution", Zeit. fur Phy. A322, 479 (1985).

5. P.Grange,Li Jun-Qing,and H.A.Weidenmuller, "Induced Nuclear Fission Viewed as a Diffusion Process:Transients",Phys. Rev. C27, 2063 (1983).

6. P.Moller and J.R.Nix,"Nuclear Mass Formula with a Yukawa-Plus-Expotential Macroscopic Model and a Folded-Yukawa Single-Particle potential", Nucl. Phys. A361, 117(1981).

7. K.T.R.Davies,A.J.Sierk,and J.R.Nix,"Effect of Viscosity on the Dynamics of Fission", Phys. Rev.C13 ,2385 (1976).

8. J.Blocki,Y.Boneh,J.R.Nix,J.Randrup,M.Robel, A.J. Sierk,and W.J.Swiatecki,"One-Body Dissipation and the Super-Viscidity of Nuclei",Ann. Phys. 113, 330 (1978).

9. J.R.Nix and A.J.Sierk,"Mechanism of Dissipation in Heavy-Ion Reactions",For presentation at the 6th Adriatic Interational Conference on Nuclear Physics, Preprint LA-UR-87-1705, Los Alamos National Laboratory (1987).

10. F.Plasil,D.S.Burnett,H.C.Britt,and S.G.Thompson, "Kinetic Energy-Mass Distributions from the Fission of Nuclei Lighter than Radium",Phys. Rev. 142, 696 (1966).

MASS AND KINETIC ENERGY DISTRIBUTIONS FOR ^{232}Th(γ,f)

M.PIESSENS, E.JACOBS, D.DE FRENNE, S.POMME AND A.DE CLERCQ
Nuclear Physics Laboratory
Proeftuinstraat 86
B-9000 Gent (Belgium)
091/228731

ABSTRACT

Mass and kinetic energy distributions were obtained for ^{232}Th(γ,f) with 6 bremsstrahlung endpoint energies between 7 and 14 MeV by γ-ray spectrometry of fission products and energy correlation measurements. For the highest excitation energies a triple humped mass distribution is observed. The small symmetric component decreases very fast with decreasing excitation energy. Two asymmetric mass components are observed : one in the vicinity of $M_H^* = 143$ and a smaller one in the vicinity of $M_H^* = 135$. The contribution of the latter becomes higher with increasing excitation energy. An overall increase of $<TKE^*>(M_H^*)$ with increasing excitation energy is observed with a maximum in the vicinity of $M_H^* = 130$. The experimental results are interpreted in the framework of the fission channel model of Brosa et al.

INTRODUCTION

In the past the fission of thorium isotopes has been subject to several experimental and theoretical studies. The famous 'thoriumanomaly' problem which arises from a disagreement between the theoretical and the experimental heights of the first fission barrier for the thoriumisotopes is still actual. A solution of this problem was first proposed by Möller and Nix[1] who found for the thoriumisotopes a shallow third minimum in the fission barrier at a deformation corresponding to the second barrier. This third minimum then takes over the role of the usual second minimum, which, because of the low inner barrier for the thorium isotopes, would not play an important role in the determination of the fission cross sections.

Also the fission characteristics of the thoriumfragments compared to the other actinides seem to exibit a peculiar behavior with respect to the excitation energy in the vicinity of the fission barrier. The most intensively studied fissioning system in this respect is ^{232}Th(n,f). Strong fluctuations in the average total kinetic energy $<TKE^*>$ and the average total number of emitted neutrons $<\nu_{tot}>$ have been observed by several authors[2-5]. Besides those fluctuations there seems to be a global increase of $<TKE^*>$ by a few MeV with increasing excitation energy for E_n approximately between 1 and 5 MeV. This increase is mainly caused by increasing TKE^* for particular

mass splits and less by changing mass distributions. At this point though there is no agreement between the results of different authors. An equal increase of TKE^* for all mass splits (except for heavy masses between 126 and 130 where a decrease of TKE is observed) was observed by Holubarsch et al.[2], while a more expressed increase for heavy masses in the vicinity of 132 was observed by Sergachev et al.[3] and on the contrary a less expressed increase for the same mass splits was observed by Trochon et al.[4]. Usually for the neutron induced fission an explanation is given in terms of transition states at the saddle point. For the lowest excitation energies it seems that $<\nu_{tot}>$ does not increase or even decreases with increasing excitation energy. For higher excitation energies the normal increase of $<\nu_{tot}>$ is observed (see ref.6 and references therein). Also for the ^{232}Th(α,α'f) fissioning system David et al.[7] observed a strong increase of $<TKE^*>$ for excitation energies between 6 and 8 MeV. For higher excitation energies $<TKE^*>$ remains approximately constant. Caldwell et al.[8] observed for ^{232}Th(γ,f) with monoenergetic photons for $<\nu_{tot}>$ a decrease between 6 and 8 MeV and an increase for higher excitation energies, in contrast with the behavior of the heavier actinides where a linearly increasing $<\nu_{tot}>$ over the whole excitation energy range studied is observed.

On theoretical basis the experimentally obtained fission characteristics of a whole range of nuclei can be reasonably explained within the framework of the scissionpoint model[9]. More recently Brosa et al.[10] extended the idea of independent fission modes in his multi-exit channel model coupled with random neck rupture at the scission point. We will restrict here the interpretation of our results to a discussion in the framework of this model.

EXPERIMENTAL PROCEDURE

Two different experimental methods were used : γ-ray spectrometry and energy correlation measurements. Both experiments were performed for 7, 8, 9, 10, 12 and 14 MeV bremsstrahlung induced fission of ^{232}Th.

The γ-ray spectrometry method was used to determine postneutron mass distributions. The cumulative yield of about 40 mass chains was obtained for the 6 bremsstrahlung endpoint energies. The bulk of information was obtained by γ-ray spectroscopy of aluminum fission product catcherfoils. In addition, to obtain the lowest mass yields (mostly in the symmetric mass region) chemical separations of e.g. Sb, Ru, Cd were carried out from irradiated thorium nitrate powder.

Energy correlation measurements with Si-surface barrier detectors yield spectra of provisional mass and postneutron kinetic energy N(μ,TKE). For the calibration of the detectors we used the Schmitt-method[11] together with the revised detector constants of Weissenberger et al.[12] for ^{252}Cf(sf). By combining the results of the γ-ray spectrometry and the energy correlation measurements we deduced the preneutron mass and preneutron kinetic energy correlations N(M*,TKE*).

The experiments were performed at the 15 MeV linac of our laboratory. Bremsstrahlung was produced in a thick carbon convertor. The corresponding bremsstrahlung spectra N(E$_e$,E) were calculated with the aid of the computercode EGS4[13]. The average excitation energy corresponding with each endpoint energy was obtained via

$$\langle Eexc(E_e) \rangle = \frac{\int_0^{E_e} N(E_e,E)\ \sigma_f(E)\ E\ dE}{\int_0^{E_e} N(E_e,E)\ \sigma_f(E)\ dE}$$

with σ_f(E) the photofission cross section for ^{232}Th measured by Caldwell et al.[14]. In our experiments an average excitation energy range between 6.2 and 9.5 MeV was covered.

EXPERIMENTAL RESULTS

The postneutron massdistributions are presented in fig.1. Only the asymmetric mass wings for 7 MeV and 14 MeV bremsstrahlung are completely shown in order not to overload the figure. The asymmetric mass wings for 8 to 12 MeV bremsstrahlung follow the same systematic behavior. Above 9 MeV bremsstrahlung a small but distinct peak is present for symmetric fission. This symmetric peak decreases very fast with decreasing excitation energy. For 8 MeV bremsstrahlung only an upper limit for symmetric fission can be given. For 7 MeV bremsstrahlung the fission cross section is to low to determine experimentally any symmetric contribution. Also the asymmetric mass wings show a striking behavior with respect to the excitation energy. For all excitation energies studied the heavy mass wing shows a maximum in the vicinity of M$_H$ = 142 and a shoulder in the vicinity of M$_H$ = 134. This shoulder increases systematically with increasing $\langle$Eexc$\rangle$, causing a shift of the heavy mass wing towards more symmetric mass splits. The same (complementary) shift is also observed for the light mass wing.

The results of the energy correlation measurements N(μ,TKE) are shown in a two dimensional representation in fig.2 for 9, 10 and 14 MeV bremsstrahlung. This figure clearly demonstrates the appearence of a symmetric component for higher excitation energies. For 7 MeV bremsstrahlung no

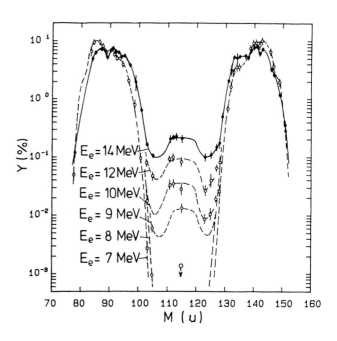

Fig.1 Postneutron mass distributions for 7-14 MeV bremsstrahlung. The asymmetric mass wings for 8 to 12 MeV bremsstrahlung (not shown in the figure) show the same systematic behavior.

symmetric fission events were detected and for 8 MeV only a few events were registrated which might be ascribed to symmetric fission. Fig.2 also shows that the symmetric fission component has on the average a relatively low kinetic energy compared to the asymmetric component(s).

The preneutron massdistribution for 7 MeV bremsstrahlung shows a sharp peak for heavy fragments in the vicinity of 144 and a shoulder in the vicinity of mass 135. In analogy with the postneutron massdistributions this shoulder increases with increasing $\langle$E$_{exc}\rangle$. With increasing $\langle$E$_{exc}\rangle$ the kinetic energy distributions show a systematic broadening and a shift towards higher energies. Between 7 and 14 MeV an increase of $\langle$TKE$^*\rangle$ by 2.5 MeV is observed. This increase of $\langle$TKE$^*\rangle$ is partly due to changes in the mass distributions and partly to increasing fragment kinetic energies.

Fig.3 shows the kinetic energy as a function of the fragment mass $\langle$TKE$^*\rangle$(M$_H^*$) for 7 and 14 MeV bremsstrahlung. A maximum of TKE* in the vicinity of mass 130 and a dip for symmetric fission is observed. Going from 7 to 14 MeV bremsstrahlung a systematic increase of $\langle$TKE$^*\rangle$ is observed for all asymmetric mass splits. This increase is most expressed for M$_H$ = 130. In fig.4 the kinetic energy averaged over selected mass areas is shown. This figure shows that for mass splits between 129 and 133 the largest changes are observed : a total increase of about 3 MeV is observed between 7 and 14 MeV bremsstrahlung. For more asymmetric mass splits this increase becomes less pronounced.

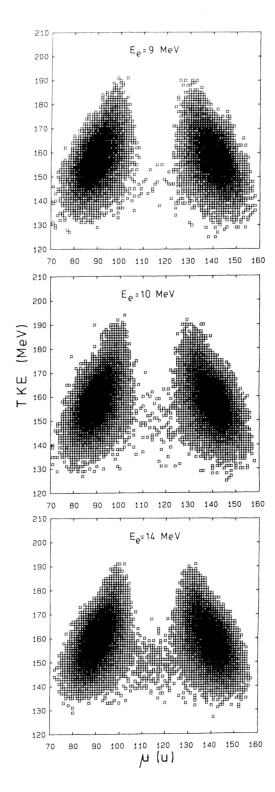

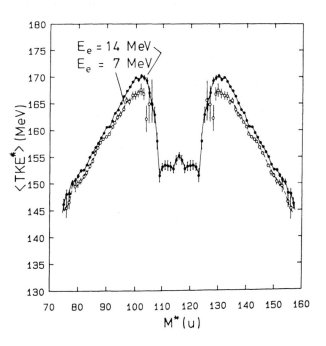

Fig.3 Total kinetic energy as a function of the
fragment mass for 7 and 14 MeV
bremsstrahlung.

Fig.2 A two dimensional representation of the
results of the energy correlation measurements
for 9, 10 and 14 MeV bremsstrahlung. The
darkest areas correspond with the highest
yield. In each distribution, equal steps of
relative yield were taken.

INTERPRETATION OF THE OBSERVED
DISTRIBUTIONS WITH THE CALCULATIONS OF
BROSA

Calculations of Brosa yield three fission channels
in the potential energy surface for ^{232}Th from the
groundstate upto the scission point[15]. The 'superlong'
path, which bifurcates from the 'standard' path in the
vicinity of the second minimum, proceeds over the highest
barrier and gives rise to a mass symmetric, highly
deformed scission configuration. In the vicinity of the
second saddle point the standard path bifurcates into the
standard I path with $M_H^* = 132$ and with a high total kinetic
energy and the standard II path with $M_H^* = 138$ and with
intermediate total kinetic energies. The two standard paths
proceed over the same main barrier and hence yields of
the same order of magnitude are expected, independect of
the excitation energy.

Qualitatively this prediction of three fission
components is in agreement with the experimental results.
The postneutron massdistributions as well as the results of
the energy correlation measurements show the presence
of a distinct symmetric fission component. The lower TKE
for symmetric fission can be seen from fig.2 and 3. The
fast decreasing yield of symmetric fission with decreasing
excitation energy is an indication of a hindrance by a
higher barrier for symmetric fission. The contribution of
symmetric fission to the total yield was estimated from the
experimental data in two independent ways. On one hand

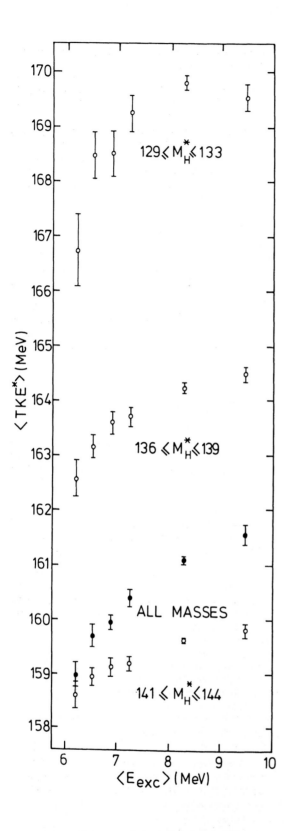

Fig.4 Total kinetic energy as a function of the average excitation energy for selected mass splits.

we deduced the symmetric yield from the $N(\mu,TKE)$ plots by counting the events situated in the area of symmetric fission, wich was determined by the results for 12 and 14 MeV, where the distinction between symmetric and asymmetric fission can be easily made by following the contourlines. On the other hand the symmetric yields were determined from the postneutron massdistributions. Therefore we fitted 5 gaussians (two asymmetric ones for the light mass wing, two for the heavy mass wing and one for the symmetric component) to these distributions. The dispersion of the symmetric component for 8 and 9 MeV bremsstrahlung was then determined by extrapolation from the results for 10, 12 and 14 MeV bremsstrahlung, where the symmetric peak is well determined. The results of the two methods are shown in fig.5. Good agreement

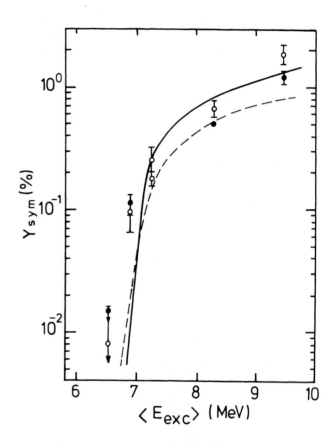

Fig.5 The symmetric yield deduced from the energy correlation measurements (closed points) and the postneutron massdistributions (open circles). The dotted line and the full line are the corresponding Hill-Wheeler penetration-fits to the data. The results of this fit are $E_f = 8.5$ MeV and $\hbar\omega = 0.33$ MeV for the first data set and $E_f = 8.7$ MeV and $\hbar\omega = 0.39$ MeV for the second data set.

exists between those two sets of results. A possibility to estimate the height of the symmetric fission barrier is by fitting the Hill-Wheeler barrier penetration expression to the experimental results taking into account the use of bremsstrahlung :

$$W_3(E_e) = \frac{\int_0^{E_e} \dfrac{W_0}{1+\exp\left\{\dfrac{2\pi(V_s-E)}{\hbar\omega}\right\}} N(E,E_e)\sigma_f(E)\,dE}{\int_0^{E_e} N(E,E_e)\sigma_f(E)\,dE}$$

with $W_3(E_e)$ the experimental symmetric yield and V_s and $\hbar\omega$ the height and curvature of the symmetric barrier. The results of this fitting are also shown in the fig.6. We find for the height of the symmetric fission barrier for the two methods resp. 8.5 and 8.7 MeV, i.e. about 2 MeV higher than the asymmetric fission barrier.

The existence of two asymmetric components is also supported by the experimental data. Both the post and the preneutron massdistributions show a shoulder in the vicinity of heavy mass 135 and a peak yield in the vicinity of heavy mass 143. An attempt to give a more qualitative description of the experimental data in terms of three fission channels was performed by fitting a two dimensional function to the experimental $N(M_H^*, TKE^*)$ distributions :

$$N(M_H^*, TKE^*) = \sum_i W_i \left\{ \frac{1}{\sqrt{2\pi}\,\sigma_{M_i}} e^{-\frac{(M_H^*-M_i)^2}{2\sigma_{M_i}^2}} \right\}$$

$$\cdot \left\{ \frac{1}{\sqrt{2\pi}\,\sigma_{TKE_i}} e^{-\frac{(TKE^*-TKE_i(M_H^*))^2}{2\sigma_{TKE_i}^2}} \right\}$$

with W_i the weight, M_i the average mass, σ_{M_i} the dispersion of M_i for the ith component. The average kinetic energy (in

MeV) for a certain mass split for the ith component is given by the coulombrepulsion

$$TKE_i(M_H^*) = \frac{1.44}{D_i} \left[\frac{Z_f}{M_f} M_L^* + 0.5\right]\left[\frac{Z_f}{M_f} M_H^* - 0.5\right]$$

The nuclear charges of the two fragments being given by the equal charge displacent hyphothesis with a small correction (-0.5 for the heavy fragments and +0.5 for the light fragments). D_i (given in fm) is the distance between the two centers of gravity. The parameters left to fit are W_i, M_i, σ_{M_i}, D_i and σ_{TKE_i} for i = 1,2,3. Of course the mass for the symmetric fission component is fixed to $A_f/2$.

The results of this procedure are summarized in table 1 and are compared with the theoretical values given by Brosa. The results of this fitprocedure for the mass yield, the total kinetic energy and the dispersion of the kinetic energy distribution as a function of the heavy fragment mass are shown for 7 and 14 MeV bremsstrahlung in fig.6. Between 7 and 14 MeV the contribution of standard I increases from about 20 % to 30 %. The shift of the positions of the average masses is small : about 0.5 u between 7 and 14 MeV bremsstrahlung. Also the total increase of the width of the distributions is small : about 0.4 u.

To give a good description of $<TKE^*>(M_H^*)$ is it necessary that the average kinetic energies corresponding with the two asymmetric components increase with increasing excitation energy : $<TKE^*>$ for standard I should increase by 3 MeV, while $<TKE^*>$ for standard II should increase by about 1.5 MeV between 7 and 14 MeV bremsstrahlung. Also the behavior of the dispersion of the kinetic energy as a function fragment mass can be well reproduced, when for each of the three component the dispersion on TKE remains constant for all mass splits. The larger dispersion for masses between 130 and 135 compared to those for masses larger than 140 is explained by a higer dispersion for the standard I component. The maximum in the dispersion around mass 125 for 14 MeV and its absence for 7 MeV is explained by the contribution of symmetric fission. The average kinetic energy for symmetric fission differs by about 20 MeV from that for standard I and so for 14 MeV a maximum of the dispersion

TABLE 1. Parameters obtained from the fit to the experiments. The lower part is from theory[15].

Channel	W_i(%)	M_i(4)	σ_{M_i}	TKE_i(MeV)	σ_{TKE_i}(MeV)
		Experimental Results (7 → 14 MeV bremsstrahlung)			
Superlong	0 → 1.2	116		- → 153.3	- → 9.4
Standard I	19.8 → 29.2	135.7 → 135.2	3.2 → 3.6	165.1 → 168.3	9.3 → 9.6
Standard II	80.2 → 69.6	143.3 → 142.7	4.0 → 4.3	156.6 → 158.1	7.3 → 7.7
		Theoretical Results (7 → 10 MeV mono energetically)			
Channel	W_i(%)	M_i(4)	σ_{M_i}	TKE_i(MeV)	σ_{TKE_i}(MeV)
Superlong	small	116	6.9 → 8.9	159 ± 5	-
Standard I	≈ 50%	132 ± 5	2.1 → 3.6	180 ± 5	-
Standard II	≈ 50%	138 ± 5	4.0 → 6.2	165 ± 5	-

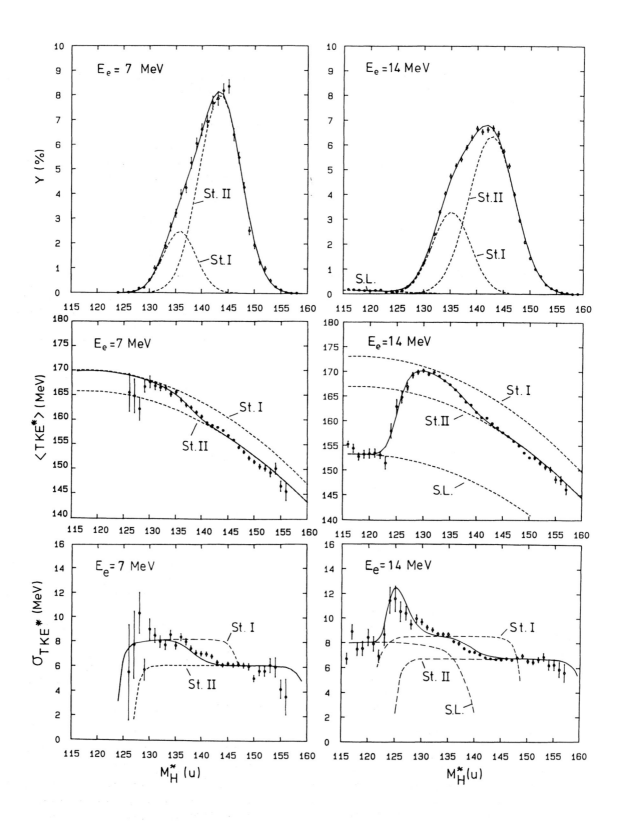

Fig.6 Comparison of the experimental distributions and the results of the fitting procedure discussed in the text. The results of the massdistributions (upper part), the kinetic energy as a function of the fragment mass (middle part) and the dispersion of the kinetic energy as a function of the heavy fragment mass (lower part) for 7 and 14 MeV bremsstrahlung are shown.

is expected near the mass splits corresponding with equal yields for the two components. For 7 MeV, with no symmetric fission, no maximum in the dispersion is observed. With increasing excitation energy the dispersion for each component increases only weakly.

CONCLUSIONS

We have measured the mass and kinetic energy distributions for the photon induced fission for ^{232}Th with 7-14 MeV bremsstrahlung, covering an average excitation energy region between 6.2 and 9.5 MeV. With increasing excitation energy the massdistributions change from a narrow peaked asymmetric massdistribution with a maximum yield of almost 10% in the vicinity of heavy mass 144 to a broader mass distribution with the position of the heavy mass peak shifted towards more symmetric mass splits. At te same time a small but distinct symmetric mass hump appears for the highest excitation energies. The average total kinetic energy increases by about 2.5 MeV between 7 and 14 MeV bremsstrahlung. This increase is partly due to the shift in the mass distributions and partly by an overall increase of the fragment kinetic energy, which is most striking for the heavy fragments in the vicinity of 132.

For the interpretation of our results we restricted ourselves to the model of Brosa et al.. This model gives an explanation for the existence of a small symmetric component and its fast decreasing yield with decreasing excitation energy by the existence of the 'superlong path' in the potential energy surface of ^{232}Th, corresponding with symmetric fission and proceeding over a higher barrier. A satisfying description of the asymmetric mass components can be given as a composition of a standard I and a standard II component. However, an explanation of the relative contributions of both components and the increasing contribution of the standard I component with increasing excitation energy is not yet proposed. Also the increasing kinetic energy (very expressed for the standard I and less expressed for the standard II component) can not be explained.

The behavior of the fragment mass and kinetic energy with respect to the excitation energy is completely opposite to the observation for the other actinides. An unambigious explanation can upto now not be given. An explanation may be found in increasing fragment shell corrections for low scission point temperatures. The increasing TKE could also partly be ascribed to an adiabatic behavior of thorium for the lowest excitation energies, where not much excitation energy is available for pairbreaking and hence a large part of the suplementary excitation energy is converted into prescission kinetic energy of the fragments with increasing excitation energy. Possibility the very asymmetric mass distributions for the lowest excitation energies in the vicinity of the fission barrier may be related to a third minimum in the potential energy surface for asymmetric deformations, leading to resonant barrier penetration.

ACKNOWLEDGEMENT

Thanks are expressed to Dr. U. Brosa for making availible his results for ^{232}Th prior to publication.

REFERENCES

1. P.MOLLER and J.R.NIX, 'Calculation of Fission Barriers', Physics and Chemistry of Fission (IAEA, Vienna,1973) Vol.I, p.103.(1974)
2. W.HOLUBARSCH, E. PFEIFFER and F. GONNENWEIN, 'Fragment Kinetic Energies in MeV neutron-induced fission of ^{232}Th', Nuclear Physics A171, p.631 (1971)
3. J.TROCHON, H.ABOU YEHIA, F.BRISARD and Y.PRANAL, 'Fission Properties of ^{233}Th', Nucl.Phys.A318 ,p.63 (1979)
4. A.I.SERGACHEV, V.G. VORAB'EVA, B.D.KUZ'MINOV, V.B. MIKHAILOV and M.Z.TARASKO, 'Influence of intermediate states of fissioning Th^{233} nucleus om the mass and kinetic energy distributions of the fragments', Sov.J.Nucl.Phys.7(4),P.475 (1968)
5. N.P.D'YACHENKO, B.D.KUZ'MINOV, V.F.MITROFANOV and A.I.SERGACHEV,'Effect of transition states of the fissioning nucleus ^{233}Th on fragment kinetic energy', Sov.J.Nucl.Phys.26(4),p.365 (1977)
6. J.CARUANA, J.W.BOLDEMAN and R.L.WALSCH,'The ν_p values for neutron fission of ^{232}Th near threshold', Nucl.Phys.A285,p.2119 (1977)
7. P.DAVID, J.DEBRUS, H.JANSZEN, J.SCHULZE, M.N.HARAKEH, J.VAN DER PLICHT and A.VAN DER WOUDE,'The study of the $(\alpha,\alpha'f)$ reaction at 120 MeV on ^{232}Th. (III)Total kinetic energies and mass distributions for excitation energies below 12 MeV',Nucl.Phys.A380,p.27(1982)
8. J.T.CALDWELL, E.J.DOWDY, R.A.ALVAREZ, B.L.BERMAN and P.MEYER,'Experimental Determinations of Photofission Neutron Multiplicities for ^{235}U,^{236}U,^{238}U and ^{232}Th Using Monoenergetic Photons',Nuclear Science and Engineering 73,p.153(1980)
9. B.D.WILKINS, E.P.STEINBERG and R.R.CHASMAN,'Scission-point model of nuclear fission based on deformed-shell effects',Phys.Rev.C14,p.1832(1976)
10. U.BROSA,'Multimodal fission and neutron evaporation',Phys.Rev.C38 ,p.1944, and references therein(1988)
11. H.W.SCHMITT, W.M.GIBSON, J.H.NEILER, F.J.WALTER and T.D.THOMAS,'Absolute energy calibration of solid-state detectors for fission fragments and heavy ions',Physics and Chemistry of Fission, IAEA Vienna,p.531,(1965)
12. E.WEISSENBERGER, P.GELTENBORT, A.OED, F.GONNENWEIN and H.FAUST,'Energy calibration of surface barrier detectors for fission fragments', Nuclear Instruments and Methods in Physics Research A248,p.506 (1986)
13. W.R.NELSON, H. HIRAYAMA and D.W.O.ROGERS,'The EGS4 Code System',SLAC-report-265 (1985).

14. J.T.CALDWELL, E.J.DOWDY, B.L.BERMAN,
    R.A.ALVAREZ and P.MEIER,'Giant resonance for the
    actinide nuclei : Photoneutron and photofission cross
    sections for ^{235}U,^{236}U,^{238}U and ^{232}Th',
    Phys.Rev.C21,p.1215(1980)
15. U.BROSA, private communication.

NEUTRON EMISSION AS A FUNCTION OF FRAGMENT ENERGY IN THE SPONTANEOUS FISSION OF ^{260}Md

J. F. Wild, J. van Aarle,* W. Westmeier,* R. W. Lougheed, E. K. Hulet, K. J. Moody,
R. J. Dougan, R. Brandt,* and P. Patzelt*

University of California
Lawrence Livermore National Laboratory
Nuclear Chemistry Division
P. O. Box 808, L-232
Livermore, CA 94551

*Phillips Universität
D-3550
Marburg/Lahn
Federal Republic of Germany

ABSTRACT

We have made the first measurement of the number of neutrons emitted in the spontaneous fission of a nuclide in which very high fragment energies dominate the fission process. In bombardments of ^{254}Es, we produced 28-d ^{260}Md, which was neutron-counted in a 1-m-diam spherical tank containing a Gd-doped scintillator solution. The average number of neutrons emitted per fission is only 2.58 ± 0.11, substantially less than for other actinides. A direct correlation of neutron multiplicity with fragment excitation energy is clearly demonstrated.

Introduction

In nuclear fission, the total energy released, known as the Q-value for fission, is determined by the mass difference between the fissioning species and the fragments. A large part of this total energy is given up as kinetic energy of the fragments (total kinetic energy, TKE). The remainder exists in the form of excitation energy of the fragments and is dissipated mostly with the emission of gamma rays and the evaporation of prompt neutrons.

The number of prompt neutrons emitted in a fission event is directly related to the excitation energy of the fragments. The fragments at scission are deformed to some degree; following scission, the potential energy of deformation is rapidly converted to internal excitation energy. The closer the TKE of a fission event is to the fission Q-value, the lower is the amount of energy available for fragment excitation. The spontaneous fission (SF) of ^{260}Md offers the first good test of this relationship in the regime of low fragment excitation energies.

The SF of ^{260}Md is markedly bimodal,[1] with about two-thirds of the fissions having TKEs in a distribution that peaks at 235 MeV, while the remainder peak at lower TKEs (see Fig. 1). The low-TKE fissions are expected to arise from elongated scission shapes in which the fragments are highly deformed. The high-TKE fissions are expected to arise from more compact scission shapes in which the fragments are nearly spherical.

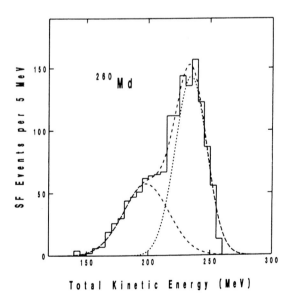

Fig. 1. The TKE distribution for the SF of ^{260}Md obtained from this experiment. The two Gaussian curves represent the low- and high- TKE regions of bimodal fission; the high- TKE region contains approximately 63% of the events.

Because of this compact scission shape, the Coulomb repulsion between the fission fragments is greater, which results in a higher TKE. There is less fragment deformation energy at scission and, hence, less excitation energy available for the emission of neutrons and gamma rays. Consequently, a measurement of the number of neutrons emitted at the time of fission should show an inverse relationship with fragment kinetic energy. In addition, because ^{260}Md provides a major proportion of high-energy fission events in which the fragment excitation energy should be low, we wanted to determine if this manifested itself in a substantially lower neutron-emission rate.

Experimental

We produced a sample of about 3000 atoms of ^{260}Md from the bombardment of ^{254}Es with ^{22}Ne ions. After extensive chemical purification, we electroplated the mendelevium on a thin (25- to 30-μg/cm^2) polyimide film and sent it to Marburg for the neutron-multiplicity measurement. This sample was counted for about three months. We made background, dead time, and counter-efficiency corrections to the observed neutron-multiplicity distribution from 1207 fission events, according to the method outlined by Spencer et al.[2] We used a standard of ^{252}Cf, mounted in a manner identical to that of the mendelevium sample, to calibrate the response of surface-barrier detectors to the fission-fragment energy and to determine the efficiency of the neutron counter.

Results and Discussion

The corrected (true) neutron-multiplicity distribution is shown in Fig. 2. We found the average multiplicity to be 2.58 ± 0.11 neutrons per fission. This number is more than one neutron per fission lower than that of other nuclides in

the heavy-actinide region for which neutron measurements have been made. More than 25% of the SF events from ^{260}Md emit fewer than two neutrons while, in comparison, only about 3% of fissions from ^{252}Cf emit fewer than two neutrons. The distribution variance, 2.57 ± 0.13, is considerably higher than that of ^{252}Cf (1.62). This is a result of the sum of the breadths of the individual distributions from the two modes of fission from ^{260}Md .

The bimodal nature of the SF of ^{260}Md is amply demonstrated by the data in Fig. 3, which shows two partial neutron-multiplicity distributions. The dashed histogram fitted to the triangular data points was obtained from SF events with TKE > 224 MeV. This distribution has a low average multiplicity of 1.58 ± 0.10 neutrons per fission. This indicates that there cannot be much fragment excitation energy and strongly suggests that the fragments at

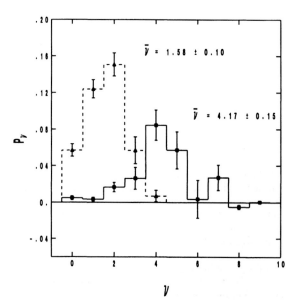

Fig. 3. Partial neutron-multiplicity distributions from the SF of ^{260}Md. The dashed-line histogram (triangular data points) is derived from fission events with TKE > 224 MeV, while the solid-line histogram (square data points) is obtained from fission events with TKE < 210 MeV.

scission must be nearly spherical. The solid histogram that fits the square data points represents SF events with TKE < 210 MeV and has an average multiplicity of 4.17 ± 0.15 neutrons per fission. This latter distribution is more typical of the heavier actinides that undergo "conventional" unimodal SF, such as ^{252}Cf ($\bar{\nu} = 3.773$) (Ref. 2), and indicates the presence of considerably more fragment-deformation energy from an elongated scission shape.

The fragment-excitation energy for fission can be estimated by calculating the Q-value for a given distribution of fragment masses and subtracting from it the measured average TKE for events with the same mass distribution. We calculated Q values and determined the average TKE for several ranges of TKE in the SF of ^{260}Md and plotted Q − TKE against the average number of neutrons emitted by fissions in each energy range (see Fig. 4). Higher values of Q − TKE result from the lower-TKE

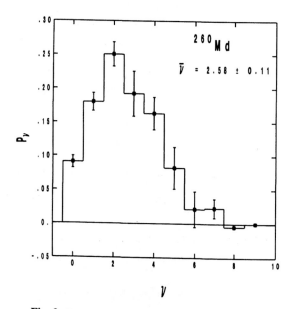

Fig. 2. The total neutron-multiplicity distribution from the SF of ^{260}Md, corrected for background, dead time, and counter efficiency. The average multiplicity is 2.58 ± 0.11 neutrons per fission.

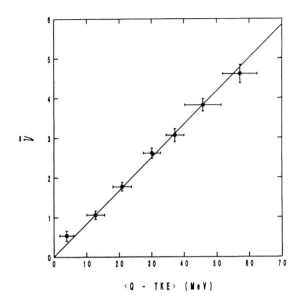

Fig. 4. A plot of neutron multiplicity, $\bar{\nu}$, vs Q–TKE (fragment-excitation energy) for the SF of ^{260}Md shows the linear relationship between available fragment-excitation energy and neutron emission.

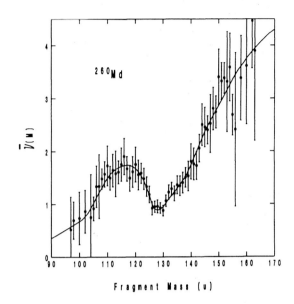

Fig. 5. The function $\bar{\nu}(M)$ vs. fragment mass for ^{260}Md SF, assuming our measured values for total neutron emission for a given mass division, partitioned between the fragments according to the calculation of Brosa.[3]

fission events and indicate fragments with higher excitation energies that emit more neutrons per fission. The direct linear relationship between excitation energy and neutron multiplicity is quite evident in Fig. 4; the line was force-fitted through the origin and has a slope corresponding to about 12 MeV per neutron emitted.

We can obtain from our data only the average sum of the neutrons emitted from the fragments for each mass division. We must assume in some way the contribution from each fragment of a given mass division in order to generate the function $\bar{\nu}(M)$ vs. fragment mass. To do this, we obtained a calculation of this function made specifically for ^{260}Md by Brosa[3] and used it to partition our measured neutron emission between the fragments. The resulting curve is shown in Fig. 5; the line drawn through the data points represents an "eyeball" fit to facilitate interpolation of the values for each mass division. The effect of correcting the mass and TKE distributions is quite small; the full width at half-maximum of the corrected mass distribtuion is about 4% less than that of the provisional mass distribution, and the average value for the corrected TKE increased by only 0.8%. It should be emphasized that the neutron-emission correction just described is only an estimate, and that a correct and precise determination of the $\bar{\nu}(M)$ curve is not likely to be attainable due to the improbability of producing sufficient ^{260}Md.

Conclusion

We have shown that the lower average neutron multiplicity from the SF of ^{260}Md indeed results from the lower average excitation energy of the fragments because the high TKE

fissions having nearly spherical fragments. We have extended the relationship between excitation energy and the number of neutrons emitted to a much lower range of excitation energies than previous experiments had revealed.

Work performed under the auspices of the U. S. Department of Energy by Lawrence Livermore National Laboratory under Contract W-7405-Eng. 48 and with the support of the FRG BMFT under Contract no. 06MR553.

*Philipps Universität, D-3550, Marburg/Lahn, FRG.

References

1. E. K. HULET *et al.*, Phys. Rev. Lett. <u>56</u>, 313 (1986).

2. R. R. SPENCER, R. GWIN, and R. INGLE, Nucl. Sci. Eng. <u>80</u>, 603 (1982).

3. U. BROSA, private communication, 1989.

CORRELATION CHARACTERISTICS OF TRITON AND LONG RANGE

ALPHA PARTICLE ACCOMPANIED FISSION OF Cf-252

HAN HONGYIN, HUANG SHENGNIAN, MENG JIANGCHEN,
and
BAO ZONGYU, YE ZONGYUAN
Institute of Atomic Energy
P. O. Box 275-46, Beijing, China

ABSTRACT

The multi-parameter technique was used to study detailed correlation characteristics of light charged particle (long range alpha (LRA) or triton) energy with the total kinetic energy (TKE) of fragments and with the average number of prompt neutrons $\bar{\nu}$ and with the average number of prompt γ-rays. For binary fission, triton- and LRA-accompanied fission the values of mean TKE are 184.3 MeV (used here as standard), 173.6±0.2 MeV and 171.9±0.1 MeV, while it was found that the average number of the prompt neutrons are 3.737±0.009, 2.95±0.05 and 3.13±0.02. It has been found that the value of prompt γ-ray yield in triton accompanied fission (TAF) is same as that in long range alpha accompanied fission (LRAF) and is equal to 84% of γ-ray yield in binary fission. The detailed correlation characteristics in both TAF and LRAF were obtained and compared.

INTRODUCTION

Investigation of characteristics in light charged particle (LCP) accompanied fission can provide information about nuclear scission configuration and the dynamic property in fission process. Because of much lower emission probability of tritons than that of LRA particles[1], the experimental investigation of triton accompanied fission is quite insurfficient, only Nardi[2] and Blocki[3] have given a little information about the mean TKE and the $\bar{\nu}$ for process. In this article, we present the detailed correlation characteristics in both triton- and LRA-accompanied fission of Cf-252 and a detailed comparion between two fission modes. In order to study the correlation characteristics in ternary fission the three separate experiments were completed.

KINETIC ENERGY EXPERIMENT

The Cf-252 source was a self-transfer one and its activity was equal to 1.6×10^4 fis/sec. A ΔE-E particle telescope consisted of a 55 μm thick full depleted silicon detector and a 3 mm thick Si(Li) drifted detector was employed to record the light charged particles. An Al-foil with thickness of 8.1 mg/cm² was placed in front of the telescope for preventing fragments and natural alphas from reaching ΔE detector. Two Au(Si) barriers detectors were adopted to detect fragment pair.

This four-parameter experiment lasted about 600 hours. In total about 5×10^4 LRA events and 3248 triton events were accumulated. Correlations for the energy loss in the backing and the Al-foil and for recoil effect of light charged particles were made during off-line analysis.

NEUTRON MULTIPLICITY EXPERIMENT

A platinum backing Cf source with an activity of 600 fis/sec was adopted. The telescope used in above experiment was set to face the back of the source and another surface barrier detector was set close to the source surface for detecting fragments. Because 9.8 mg/cm² platinum backing was not thick enough to stop natural alphas entering the ΔE detector, an Al-foil with thickness of 4.0 mg/cm² placed in front of the telescope. when light charged particles were not detected the signals from the fragment detector were used to veto the data acquisition sestem for eliminating binary fission neutron interference in determination of $\bar{\nu}$ and P(ν) of ternary fission. The source-telescope assemble was placed in a vacuum chamber located at the centre of a Ga-loaded liquid scintillation tank used as the neutron detector. A multievent analyzer was employed to analyze the pulse number from the tank. The output of analyzer, together with pulses from the telescope was sent to a four-parameter data acquisition system and recorded event by event. The experiment lasted 800 hours and in total about 4800 triton events and 7×10^4 LRA events were accumulated. Some corrections including dead time, background, effects from the source backing and the Al-foil, leakage of neutrons from the central channel of the tank, angular distributions of neutrons were made.

GAMMA-RAY CORRELATION EXPERIMENT

A Cf-252 source was prepared using electroplating technique on a platinum backing with thickness of 0.1 mm.The source spot was 6 mm in diameter and the its activity 1x10⁵ fis/sec.The telescope used in the above experiment was set to face the source surface.A Na(Tl) detector,its threshold value of detecting γ-rays was 80 KeV,can removed around the source on the measurement plane. The solid angles subtended by Na(Tl) detector and telescope were 5% and 3% of 4π space,respectively.The two-dimension multichannel computer system was used to measure the ΔE-E spectra in the case when prompt γ-rays were detected or not.From the measured ΔE-E spectra the LCP energy spectra can be obtained.For each of chosen energy windows of the light charged particles,ratio of count rate in the LCP spectrum with γ-ray detection to that without γ-ray detection was determined after corrections of prompt neutron emission,γ-ray angular distributions and accident coincidence.The value of ratio illustrates the dependence of relative γ-ray yield per fission on energy of light charged particles.In convenience sake,the above ratio value was normalized by the relative γ-ray yield in binary fission, which was got by detecting coincidence between prompt γ-rays and fragments in our experimental condition. All together about 6x10⁵ LRA events and 4.3x10⁴ triton events analyzed.

RESULTS AND DISCUSSION

1. The width of LRA particle spectrum as a function of fragment mass ratio R is given in the figure 1(a),here σ=FWHM/2.36. σ increases, when R decreases downwards from 1.3 to 1.0,may be caused by fragment shape fluctuations at symmetric mass splits.

2. The width of TKE distribution of fragment pair in LRA accompanied fission as a function of fragment mass ratio R is illustrated in figure 1(b). Here the fragment shape fluctuations are observed again in the case of R less than 1.3.

3. The values of mean TKE of fragments are 184.3 MeV for binary fission (used as standard) , 173.6±0.2 MeV for TAF events and 171.9±0.1 MeV for LRAF events,respectively.The mean TKE differences are equal to: $E_{Kb}-E_{K\alpha}$=12.4±0.3 MeV and $E_{Kt}-E_{K\alpha}$=1.7±0.2 MeV.The TKE of fragment pair as a function of mass ratio R for three fission modes is displayed in figure 2. It should be noted that the TKE-value for TAF events is systematically higher than that for LRAF events,though the difference is small.

4. After the average energy of LRA particles $\bar{E}_\alpha$ was calculated for data points of LRA particle energy greater than 12.0 MeV,we have the following main results.

(1). The correlation of $\bar{E}_\alpha$ with fragment mass ratio R for different windows of TKE-value of fragment pair is shown in figure 3. Two phenomena can be found: (a) As TKE of fragment pair increases,the correlation of $\bar{E}_\alpha$ with mass ratio R becomes

stronger and stronger; (b) In the case of TKE-value of fragments less than 166.0 MeV,the correlation is very weak in the region of mass ratio R greater than 1.4.

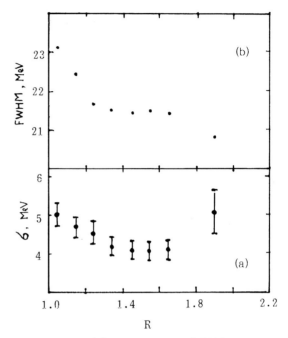

Figure 1 (a) the   width of LRA spectrum σ; (b)   the width of TKE of fragments FWHM as a function of mass ratio R.

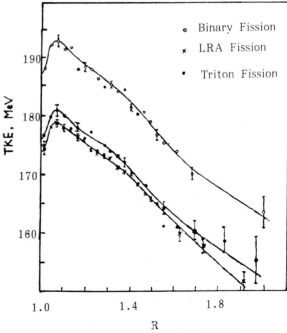

Figure 2   Variation of TKE with R.

(2). Figure 4 illustrates the correlation of $\bar{E}_\alpha$ with TKE of fragment pair for different windows of mass ratio R. Main features are as follows: (a)Correlation between $\bar{E}_\alpha$ and TKE of fragment pair becomes stronger and stronger with increasing R-value. when R changes from 1.4 to well above 2.0, $\bar{E}_\alpha$ decreases at a higher rate than that for R less than 1.4. (b) Each curve seems to have a critical value of TKE of fragment pair E_c, when TKE-value of fragments is less than E_c, correlation is very weak; if TKE of fragments varies upwards from E_c, $\bar{E}_\alpha$ decreases rapidly. It is worthwhile to note that the critical value drops off as mass ratio **R** increases, for example when R is between 1.0 and 1.2, the value of E_c is approximately equal to 170 MeV, if R lies between 1.6 and 1.7, E_c-value is already close to 160 MeV.

5. The average number of prompt neutrons per fission for binary fission is equal to 3.757±0.009 (used as standard), 3.13±0.02 for LRAF events and 2.95±0.05 for TAF events. Figure 5 gives the dependence of $\bar{\nu}$ on LRA energy E_α or triton energy E_t. The slope of fitting line for LRAF events is $d\bar{\nu}/dE_\alpha$ =-0.037±0.003 n/MeV and for TAF events the slope $d\bar{\nu}/dE_t$ =-0.039±0.008 n/MeV, respectively. The different $\bar{\nu}$-values in above three fission modes indicate that fragments in triton accompanied fission is much colder than those in both LRA accompanied fission and binary fission, while fragments in LRAF is also

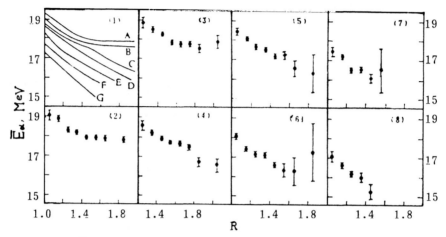

Figure 3 $\bar{E}_\alpha$ as a function of mass ratio R for different windows of TKE of fragments. The curves marked by A, B, C, D, E, F and G in (1) were obtained by fitting the data points in (2)-(8), TKE is in unit of MeV; (2)130 < TKE < 160; (3)160 < TKE < 166; (4)166 < TKE < 172; (5)172 < TKE < 178; (6)178 < TKE < 184; (7) 184 < TKE < 190; (8) 190 < TKE < 204;

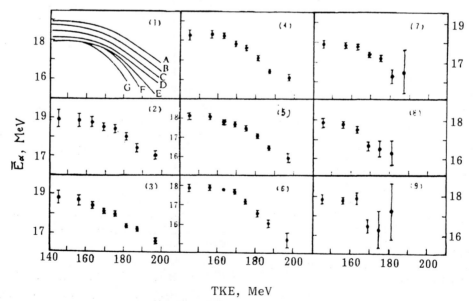

Figure 4   Variation of $\bar{E}_\alpha$ with TKE for different windows of mass ratio R. The curves labeled by A, B, C, D, E, F and G are obtained by fitting data points in (2)-(8); (2)1.0 < R < 1.1; (3)1.1 < R < 1.2; (4) 1.2 < R < 1.3; (5)1.3 < R < 1.4; (6)1.4 < R < 1.5; (7)1.5 < R < 1.6; (8) 1.6 < R < 1.7; (9)1.7 < R < 2.1.

much colder than those in binary fission. From the fact that TKE of fragments in LRAF is 1.7±0.2 MeV lower but the emitted neutron number from fragments in LRAF is 0.18±0.05 more than the values in TAF, it is concluded that the fragment shape deformation as well as the distance between main fragment pair in scission point of LRAF may be larger than those in TAF. According to the similar reason mentioned above, we also come to a conclution that the fragment shape deformation in ternary fission is larger than that in binary fission.

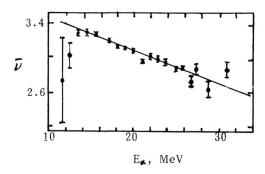

Figure 5(b) $\bar{\nu}$ versus E_α.

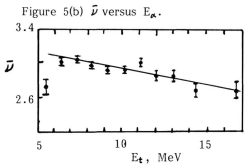

Figure 5(a) $\bar{\nu}$ versus E_t.

6. The value of ratio of the average number of prompt γ-ray yield per fission in TAF to that in binary fission R as a function of triton energy E_t is given in figure 6. The similar plot for LRAF also shown in figure 6. It has been found that the value of prompt γ-ray yield in TAF is same as that in LRAF and equal to 84% of prompt γ-ray yield in binary fission. It should be pointed that in figure 6 the anomalous correlations appear in the region of E_α less than 12.0 MeV or E_t less than 5.0 MeV. In figure 5, the anomalous correlations for prompt neutron emission also observed as E_α less 12.0 MeV or E_t less than 7.0 MeV. It is not clear whether these anomalous correlations, which seems not to be explained by traditional fission thoery, imply a new ternary fission mechanism. The detailed experimental study may be desirable.

7. Energy balance calculation: The mass formula of Myers was used to calculate the reaction Q-value differences between above three fission modes. The results are, $\Delta Q_{b\alpha}$=4.5 MeV and $\Delta Q_{\alpha t}$= 7.6 McV, here $\Delta Q_{b\alpha}$ refers to the energy difference between binary fission and LRA accompanied fission and $\Delta Q_{\alpha t}$ refers that between LRA events and triton

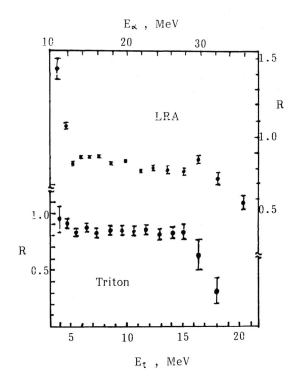

Figure 6 Variation of relative yield of prompt γ-rays with E_α or with E_t.

events. From our experimental data, the release energy differences are: $\Delta Q_{b\alpha}$(exp)=2.3±0.4 MeV and $\Delta Q_{\alpha t}$(exp)=8.5±0.9 MeV. Comparing the experimental values with the calculated ones, we find a good agreement if we take into account insufficient accuracy of mass formula in the regoin of nuclides far from beta-stability.

REFERENCES

1. S. W. COSPER, J. CERNY, and R. C. GATTI, "Long Range Particles in Z=1 to 4 Emitted during Fission of Cf-252", Phys. Rev., 154, 1193 (1967).

2. E. NARDI, Y. GAZIT, and S. KATCOFF, "Energetics and Mass Distribution of Fission Fragments in Triton- and Proton-Accompanied fission of Cf-252", Phys. ReV., 182, 1244 1969.

3. J. BLOCKI, J. CHWASZCZEWSKA, M. DAKOWSKI, T. KROGULSKI, E. PIASECKI, H. PIEKARZ, and J. TYS, "Correlation Emission of Light Nuclei and Neutrons in U-235 and Cf-Fission", Phys. and Chem. of Fiss., IAEA, Vienna, 1969, p. 115.

UNUSUAL FISSION-MASS DISTRIBUTIONS, A < 200, STUDIED USING 200 MeV PROTON AND ^{3}He INDUCED FISSION

F.D. Becchetti, P.M. Lister, J. Jänecke and A. Young
Department of Physics
University of Michigan, Ann Arbor, MI 48109

A. Nadasen
Department of Natural Sciences
University of Michigan-Dearborn, Dearborn, MI 48128

J. Brown
Department of Physics
Princeton University, Princeton, NJ 08544

H. Karwowski
Department of Physics
University of North Carolina, Chapel Hill, NC 27514

K. Kwiatowski
Indiana University Cyclotron Facility, Bloomington IN 47405

K. H. Hicks
Department of Physics
Ohio University, Athens, OH 45701-2979

ABSTRACT

The fission properties of nuclei 100 <A <240 (mass distributions, kinetic energy release, angular correlations, and cross sections) have been studied using 190 MeV proton- and 270 MeV ^{3}He-induced fission. Highly asymmetric fission mass distributions are often apparent near A=140 suggesting a new region of fission mass asymmetry.

INTRODUCTION

Recent studies[1,2,3] of proton-induced fission of targets 80 <A <200 have indicated unusual fission-mass distributions near A = 140 e.g. Ce → M=50 + M=80 + neutrons.[1,2] Although the LDM predicts a broadening of the fission mass distributions (Businaro-Gallone i.e. BG point)[4] fission into distinct, asymmetric groups is not *apriori* expected. Fission induced by energetic light ions explores a region of mass, energy, and angular momentum transfer quite different from spontaneous or heavy-ion induced fission.

Unlike HI-induced fission, light-particle induced fission involves compound systems which are along or near the limits of β-stability. Thus the nuclear levels, level densities, deformations, binding energies, etc. are well known for these nuclei. Also, the low angular momentum in LI fission facilities the interpretation of the TKE values in terms of simple coulomb and nuclear forces, even for fission of nuclei near A=100, which is near the maximum in fission barrier heights.[4] However, owing to the small fission probabilities A ~ 100 light-ion induced fission in this mass region has not been extensively explored. In addition, the theory for fission following pre-equilibrium light particle particle emission has recently been put on a quantitative footing and fission barriers can be deduced, in particular for A < 200.

EXPERIMENTS

We have made extensive measurements with protons,[2] E = 190 MeV, and recently ^{3}He, E = 270 MeV, at the Indiana University Cyclotron Facility (IUCF). The target nuclei included Nb, Ag, Te, La, Ce, Pr, Nd, Dy, and heavier targets made from ultrapure materials (Ames Laboratory) to minimize heavy contaminants. We utilized an ion-chamber Si-detector array (Fig. 1) for ΔE - E measurements (for Z identification) which combined with TOF information (relative to the cyclotron beam, Δt < 0.8 nsec) could be used to separate and identify coincident fission fragments, determine their angular correlations, angular distributions, deduce

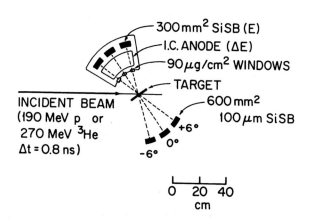

Fig. 1 EXPERIMENTAL SET UP USED AT IUCF.

approximate Z, M, and determine the total kinetic energy release (TKE). Plastic track detectors (CRONAR) were also used to determine more completely fission angular distribution for heavier nuclei. Both the SiSB detectors and the plastic-track detectors indicate rather isotropic fission angular distributions.

Typical ΔE - E and TOF spectra from targets A $\cong$ 140 are shown in Figures 2 and 3. Broad ΔE (hence ΔZ) distributions are observed in the case of Nb, Ag, Te, Ce, Pr, La, and other nuclei in this mass region. Often, two distinct groups are apparent (Z $\cong$ 15 to 30) at angles corresponding to the maximum in the angular correlation between fission fragments. The TKE and angular correlations of these groups correspond to those expected for binary fission with $\Delta p/p < 100$ percent (Fig. 4).

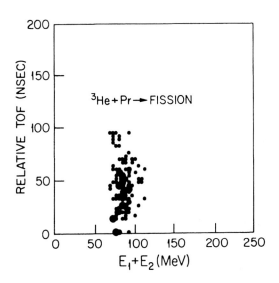

Fig. 3 TIME-OF-FLIGHT (TOF) SPECTRUM.

MASS SPECTRA

The $\Delta Z/Z$ distributions inferred from the ΔE-E and TOF data correspond to the approximate $\Delta M/M$ values deduced from measurements of $E_2/(E_1 + E_2) \cong [M_1/(M_1 + M_2)]$. Some of the latter are displayed in Figure 5. The $\times 3$ or greater increase in $\Delta M/M$ from A $\cong$ 200 ($Z^2/A \cong 34$) to A $\cong$ 100 ($Z^2/A \cong 24$) appears to qualitatively follow the behavior expected[4] from the LDM, i.e. the transition from simple binary fission to more asymmetric forms of fission (BG point).

Although the mass-division statistics are limited (due small fission probabilities for A $\leq$ 150) there appears (Fig. 5) to be a number of targets which indicate a preference for asymmetric fission, at least at some correlation angles. Often the mass division can be approximately correlated with magic Z and/or N i.e. Z,N = 20, 28, 40, 50 hence A $\doteq$ 40, 48, 68, and 90. Thus shell effects may be important for fission in this mass region and result in asymmetric fission.

THE MEASUREMENTS

Analysis of the total fission fragment kinetic energy release (TKE) yields the data and fits shown in Figure 6, viz. TKE = 0.126 $Z^2/A_{CN}^{1/3}$ + 1.1 MeV. This is compared with an expression for TKE recently derived by Viola et al. from fitting HI fission data[5] viz. TKE = 0.1189 $Z^2/A_{CN}^{1/3}$ + 7.3 MeV. Our data for A $\leq$ 150 yields a TKE somewhat (2-4 MeV) lower than the latter. This difference may be due to the extra KE provided by angular momentum in the HI fission TKEs, which is expected to be of this order of magnitude.

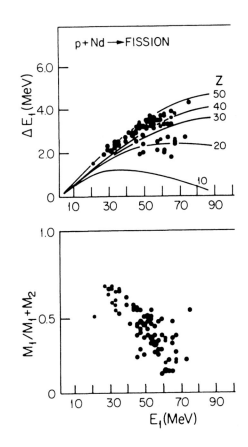

Fig. 2 Z IDENTIFICATION USING ΔE-E (see also Fig. 1).

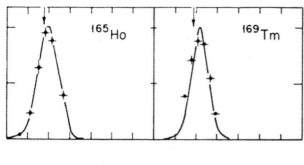

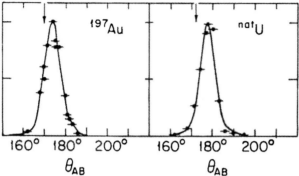

^{3}He FISSION

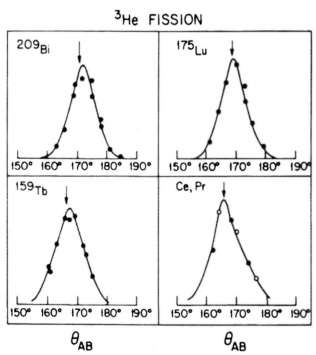

Fig. 4 TYPICAL FISSION ANGULAR CORRELATION DATA FOR 190 MeV PROTONS INCIDENT (TOP) AND 270 MeV ^{3}He INCIDENT (BOTTOM). THE ARROWS CORRESPOND TO $\theta_{AB}^{cm} = 180°$ I.E. FULL MOMENTUM TRANSFER TO THE CN SYSTEM.

CROSS SECTIONS AND FISSION BARRIERS

The measured fission probabilities i.e. cross sections are displayed in Figure 7. We have analyzed the fission cross section data using an advanced fission code[6] which includes precompound nucleon emission. We have found the latter necessary in earlier analyses of the 190 MeV proton fission data[2,7,8] and related, 45 MeV ^{3}He-induced fission data.[9] Fits to the data A<200 generally require a slight reduction ($\sim 20\%$) in E_B from E_B^{LDM} depending on a_F/a_N, the level density parameters. This reduction is comparable to that expected in finite-range nuclear-force models and yields a higher fission cross sections A $\doteq$ 100 than one would predict using conventional[4] LDM barriers.

CONCLUSIONS

The often apparent fission of nuclei A $\doteq$ 140 into distinct asymmetric mass groups may be a consequence of the known shell closures at Z, N $\doteq$ 20, 28, 40, and 50 which result in neutron-rich doubly-magic nuclei. In any case proton- and ^{3}He-induced fission data, A < 200, appear to display new and interesting aspects of the nuclear fission process in medium-mass nuclei.

ACKNOWLEDGEMENTS

This work was supported, in part, by the US National Science Foundation Grants PHY8308072 and PHY8605907 (UM), PHY8608227 (UM-D), and PHY8243334 (IUCF).

REFERENCES

1. H.-Å. GUSTAFSSON, G. HYLTÉN, B. SCHRØDER, and E. HAGEBØ, "Mass Distributions in the Fission of Medium-Heavy and Light Nuclei," *Phys. Rev. C24*, 769 (1981); G. ANDERSSON, M. ARESKOUG, H.-Å. GUSTAFSSON, G. HYLTÉN, B. SCHRØDER, AND E. HAGEBØ, "Medium Energy Proton Induced Fission in Tb, La and Ag," *Z. Physik A293*, 241 (1979).

2. F.D. BECCHETTI, J. JÄNECKE, P. LISTER, K. KWIATOWSKI, H. KARWOWSKI, and S. ZHOU, "190 MeV Proton-Induced Symmetric and Asymmetric Fission," *Phys. Rev. C28*, 276 (1983).

3. L.A. VAISHNENE, L.N. ANDRONENKO, G.G. KOVSHEVNY, A.A. KOTOV, G.E. SOLYAKIN, and W. NEUBERT, "Fission Cross Sections of Medium-Weight and Heavy Nuclei Induced by 1 GeV Protons," *Z. Physik A302*, 143 (1981); L.N. ANDRONENKO, A.A. KOTOV, M.M. NESTEROV, V.F. PETROV, N.A. TARASOV, L.A. VAISHNENE, and W. NEUBERT, "Fission Studies of Highly Excited Nuclei," *Z. Physik A318*, 97 (1984).

4. JAMES RAYFORD NIX, "Further Studies in the Liquid-Drop Theory of Nuclear Fission," *Nucl. Phys.* **A130**, 241 (1969).

5. V. VIOLA, K. KWIATKOWSKI, and M. WALKER, "Systematics of Fission Fragment Total Kinetic Energy Release," *Phys. Rev.* **C31**, 1550 (1985).

6. M. BLANN and T.T. KOMOTO, "Statistical Fission Parameters for Nuclei at High Excitation and Angular Momenta," *Phys. Rev.* **C26**, 472 (1982).

7. P.M. LISTER, F.D. BECCHETTI, J. JÄNECKE, A. NADASEN, J. BROWN, H. KARWOWSKI, K. KWIATOWSKI, and K.H. HICKS, "Further Studies of Unusual Fission-Mass Distributions, A < 200," *Proc. 4th International Conference on Clustering Aspects of Nuclear Structure and Nuclear Reactions*, Chester, England, p. 243 (1984).

8. F.D. BECCHETTI, P.M. LISTER, J. JÄNECKE, A. NADASEN, J. BROWN, H. KARWOWSKI, K. KWIATOWSKI, and K.H. HICKS, "Study of Unusual Fission-Mass Distributions, A < 200, Using ~200 MeV Proton and ^{3}He Fission," *Proc. Workshop on Nuclear Dynamics IV*, Copper Mountain, Colorado, Conf.-860270, UC-34C, p. 22 (1986).

9. F.D. BECCHETTI, K.H. HICKS, C.A. FIELDS, R.J. PETERSON, R.S. RAYMOND, R.A. RISTINEN, J.L. ULLMANN, and C.S. ZAIDINS, "^{3}He-Induced Fission of Nuclei 159<A<232," *Phys. Rev.* **C28**, 28 (1983).

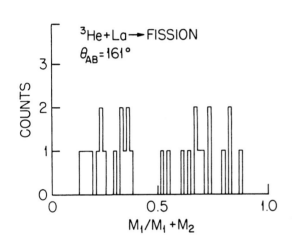

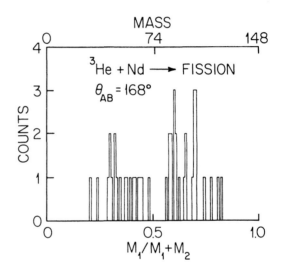

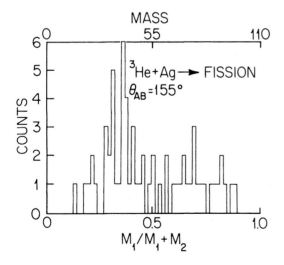

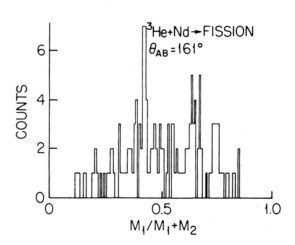

Fig. 5 DEDUCED FISSION MASS DISTRIBUTIONS FROM E_1, AND E_2 (GATED BY ΔE-E AND TOF, Figs. 2 and 3).

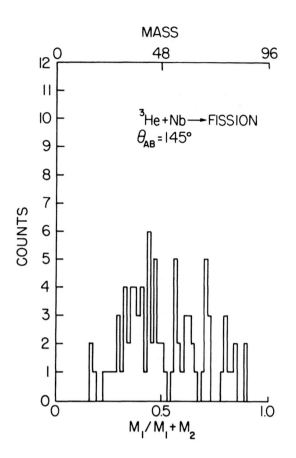

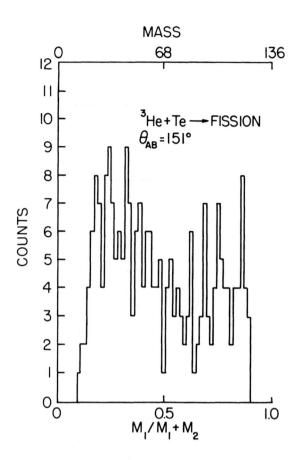

Fig.5 continued

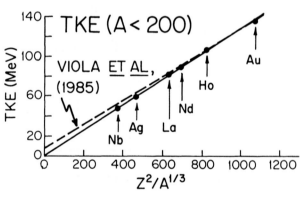

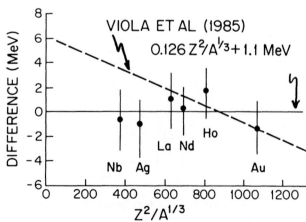

Fig. 6 FISSION TKE VALUES, $A \leq 200$, COMPARED WITH THE EXPRESSION DERIVED BY VIOLA *ET AL.*, (Ref. 5).

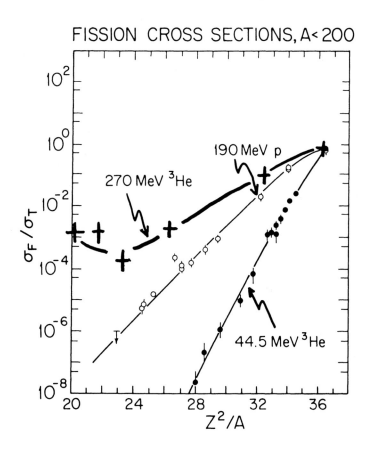

Fig. 7 MEASURED FISSION PROBABILITIES (this work and Refs. 2, 7, 8, and 9). THE QUANTITY $\sigma_{\equiv} \pi (1.35A_{CN}^{1/3})^2$ IS THE GEOMETRICAL NUCLEAR CROSS SECTION.

THE DISCOVERY AND SPONTANEOUS FISSION PROPERTIES OF ^{262}No

R. W. Lougheed, E. K. Hulet, J. F. Wild, K. J. Moody, and R. J. Dougan,
C. M. Gannett,* R. A. Henderson,* D. C. Hoffman,* and D. M. Lee*

University of California
Lawrence Livermore National Laboratory
Nuclear Chemistry Division
P. O. Box 808, L-232
Livermore, CA 94551

*University of California
Lawrence Berkeley Laboratory
One Cyclotron Road
Berkeley, CA 94720

ABSTRACT

We have discovered ^{262}No, as the electron capture daughter of ^{262}Lr ($t_{1/2} = 216$ m). This new isotope of nobelium decays by spontaneous fission with about a 5-ms half-life which is several orders of magnitude longer than recent theoretical estimates. We measured a sharply symmetric fission-fragment mass division and a bimodal total kinetic energy distribution; the high-energy symmetric-fission path was most abundant. ^{262}No is the first nuclide with 160 neutrons to be discovered and is the closest to the N=162 neutron subshell for which enhanced stability is predicted.

INTRODUCTION

The predicted spontaneous-fission (SF) half-lives and total kinetic-energy (TKE) distributions of the neutron-rich heavy actinide nuclides are extremely sensitive to calculations of the potential-energy surface and inertial mass. Recent theoretical calculations[1-3] allow two or more fission paths in the potential-energy surface leading to bimodal fission[4] (both high and low TKE symmetric fission from the decay of the same isotope), but fail to explain the observation of nearly equal branching ratios for the fission paths. Further, SF half-lives calculated from these new paths in the potential-energy surface are inconsistent with the newer measured half-lives. Our aim, in measuring the fission properties of the heavy, neutron-rich isotopes, is to confront theory with additional experimental information in the hope that the physics of the fission process will eventually be clarified.

From experiments conducted in 1985 and 1987, we discovered two long-lived isotopes of lawrencium, ^{261}Lr and ^{262}Lr, with half-lives of 39 m and 216 m, respectively.[5] The SF activities we observed did not necessarily arise from the lawrencium isotopes, but could have come from the decay of ^{261}No or ^{262}No formed by electron capture (EC) from the longer-lived lawrencium parents. Q-value predictions for the EC decay of ^{262}Lr are about 2 MeV,[6] making EC decay of the 216-m ^{262}Lr a strong possibility. In the experiments reported here, our goals were to determine if ^{262}Lr decayed by EC and to measure the half-life and SF decay properties of it or its daughter, ^{262}No, by measuring the time intervals between nobelium K x-rays and subsequent SF events in samples of chemically purified lawrencium.

EXPERIMENTAL

We bombarded a target containing 1.4×10^{17} atoms/cm^2 of ^{254}Es with 127-MeV ^{22}Ne ions at the Lawrence Berkeley Laboratory's 88-in cyclotron and collected the recoil products on molybdenum foils. We performed a series of bombardments ranging in time from 1.5 to 9 h. At the end of each bombardment, we dissolved the foil with HNO$_3$ and HCl in the presence of the rare earth tracers ^{171}Tm and ^{166m}Ho and passed the resultant solution through a Dowex 1 x 8 anion exchange column to remove the molybdenum and unwanted reaction products.

To remove interfering gamma activities, we then performed a cation-exchange chromatographic separation of the actinides from the lanthanides using a mixture of ethanol and water saturated with HCl.

We separated lawrencium from interfering actinides using solutions of ammonium α-hydroxyisobutyrate to elute the trivalent actinides from cation-exchange resin.[7,8] Actinides and holmium and thulium tracers were eluted from the column through a 0.8-mm-i.d. Teflon capillary tube that was placed directly against the face of an intrinsic germanium detector. Because lawrencium elutes between thulium and holmium, we were able to reliably collect a single lawrencium fraction by starting the collection as the thulium activity decreased as detected by the germanium detector. We stopped the collection at the first indication of holmium activity. Mendelevium elutes at almost exactly the same position as holmium, and hence is efficiently separated from lawrencium by this procedure. We evaporated the lawrencium fraction to dryness with additional [166m]Ho tracer, and then performed a second separation of lawrencium from trivalent actinides as above. This procedure reduced interfering actinide SF activities to undetectable levels.

We prepared the counting sample by electroplating the lawrencium onto 27 μg/cm² polyimide films that were overplated with 25 μg/cm² of gold. The chemically purified lawrencium fraction was first evaporated to dryness, fumed with perchloric acid to destroy organic residues, and then transferred to an electroplating cell using dilute HNO_3 and isopropyl alcohol.

We measured the energies of fission fragments and of photons in the nobelium K x-ray region using a specially built, high-geometry counting chamber.[9] The sample was inserted between two Si(Au) surface barrier detectors and two intrinsic Ge detectors to measure fission fragment and photon energies, respectively. The energies of SF events and photons with energies between 118 and 150 keV and the time intervals between the five preceding photons were recorded in list mode using computer-operated measurement and control (CAMAC) modules interfaced to an LSI-11/73 computer.

RESULTS AND DISCUSSION

The mean lifetime of [262]No and confirmation of [262]Lr EC decay to [262]No are derived from the distribution of logarithmic time intervals between photons having nobelium K x-ray energies and fission events as shown in Fig. 1. If [262]Lr decays by EC to [262]No, which in turn shortly decays by SF, we should observe a time correlation between x ray-SF event pairs that is different than that of a background photon followed by a SF event. Two distributions, which follow Poisson statistics, are resolved in Fig. 1. The larger peak, with a mean time of 1480 ms between a photon and a subsquent SF event, is due to background photons preceding a fission event. We attribute the smaller peak, with a

mean time of 6 ms before occurrence of a fission event, to nobelium K x rays and photons (60 net events) from the EC decay of [262]Lr and some tailing from background events (18 events). A similar plot with all photons in the 118- to 150-keV region has a background peak with a mean time of 883 ms and a smaller peak with a mean time of 11 ms. The mean time between correlated photon-SF event pairs is then the mean lifetime ($t_{1/2}/ln2$) of [262]No. From these distributions of time intervals, we calculate a weighted average of 5 ms for the half-life of [262]No.

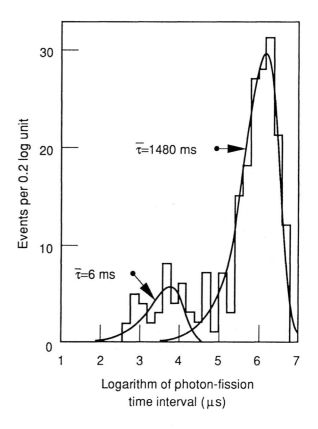

Fig. 1. The logarithmic distribution of time intervals between the last photon with nobelium K x-ray energies preceding a SF event. The smooth curves are exponential fits to the measured data shown by the histogram.

Considering the efficiency of the germanium detectors (34%) and the fraction of K x rays per EC decay, we expected to observe only one nobelium K x ray preceding every four fissions. However, we observed only about 65% of the nobelium K x rays that we expected. Because the decay scheme of [262]Lr is unknown, it is quite possible that the missing K x rays are due to losses by summing of the K x rays with gamma-ray transitions and/or L x rays arising from internal conversion in the [262]Lr decay scheme. This is especially probable because of the large counting efficiency of the germanium detectors and because [262]Lr is likely to have a 3+ ground state which would decay to excited levels in ^{262}No.

The energy distribution of photons in the 118- to 150-keV window for those events that are within 50 ms of a fission event is shown in Fig. 2. The distribution is about that expected for a nobelium K x-ray distribution, plus some background events, except that the ratio of $K_{\alpha2}/K_{\alpha1}$ events is about three times too high. We attribute the excess events in the 120-keV peak to a gamma ray in the ^{262}No decay scheme.

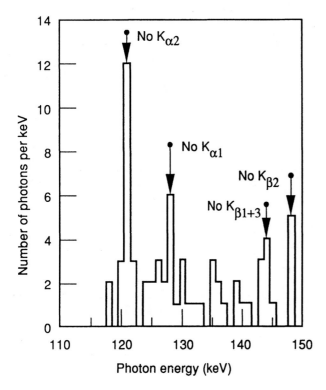

Fig. 2. The energy spectrum for photons preceding fission by 50 ms.

The fission-fragment mass and total-kinetic-energy distributions are shown in Fig. 3. The mass distribution is sharply symmetric (FWHM ≈12 amu) but the TKE distribution is asymmetric, peaking at 237 MeV, with a lower-energy component near 200 MeV. This distribution is similar to that of other nuclides in which we have observed bimodal fission. The fraction of high-energy symmetric fission in ^{262}No is greater than in ^{258}No, the other nobelium isotope for which we have made TKE measurements. This is consistent with our measurements of the fission properties of fermium and mendelevium isotopes, which show the fraction of the high-energy component increasing with neutron number.

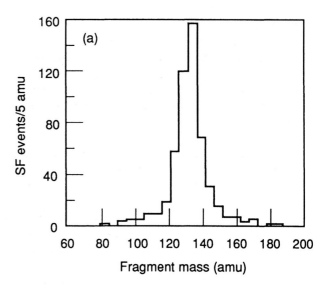

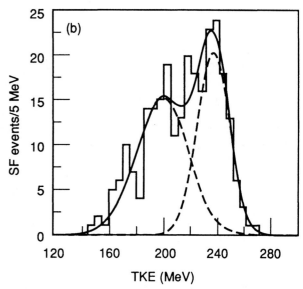

Fig. 3. The fission-fragment mass and energy distributions for ^{262}No: a) The fission-fragment mass distribution, and b) The TKE distribution. The higher-energy peak comprises 65% of the events.

SUMMARY

The presence of two almost equally populated fission paths in the neutron-rich fermium, mendelevium, and nobelium isotopes does not have a satisfactory explanation. Calculations by Möller et al.[1] indicate a lower inertial-mass path for very heavy nuclides as they approach ^{264}Fm, which can fission into two doubly magic ^{132}Sn nuclei. This low inertial-mass path for compact shapes produces much shorter half-lives than previous estimates. Möller explains the experimental observation of bimodal fission by a switchback path (also predicted by Brosa et al.)[2] in which the nucleus initially follows the new, lower-inertia path but then can go either into the new valley (high-energy symmetric fission) or the old valley (low-energy symmetric fission). This model qualitatively predicts bimodal fission, however, it does not predict the observation of nearly equal branching ratios for the two paths we find in so many isotopes.

Möller's calculated SF half-life[10] for ^{262}No is 10^{11} less for the lower inertia path vs the old path and is 10^2 shorter than our measured value. The half-life of an even-even nuclide like ^{262}No is one of the simplest to estimate, yet recent calculations from the same author[1,11] vary by a range of 10^5. Even the trend of estimated half-lives with neutron number for the even-even nobelium isotopes is incorrect. Möller overestimates the SF half-life of ^{256}No by several orders of magnitude, he is very close at ^{260}No, and he underestimates the ^{262}No half-life. Although it has been 50 years since the discovery of fission, half-life predictions still not accurate enough to dependably design experiments to search for new actinide nuclides.

Theory now provides qualitative explanations for bimodal fission, however, dependable quantitative predictions for both half-lives and fission paths are still not obtainable. Finally, we do not observe the predicted trend of increasing stability against SF upon approaching the 162 neutron subshell.[12-14] This may be due partially to the high-energy fission path observed in bimodal fission.

Work performed under the auspices of the U. S. Department of Energy by Lawrence Livermore National Laboratory under Contract W-7405-Eng. 48.

REFERENCES

1. P. MÖLLER, J. R. NIX, and W. J. SWIATECKI, *Nucl. Phys.* **A469,** 1 (1987).

2. U. BROSA, S. GROSSMANN, and A. MÜLLER, *Z. für Phys.* **A325,** 241 (1986).

3. V. V. PASHKEVICH, *Nucl. Phys.* **A477,** 1 (1988).

4. E. K. HULET, J. F. WILD, R. J. DOUGAN, R. W. LOUGHEED, J. H. LANDRUM, A. D. DOUGAN, M. SCHÄDEL, R. L. HAHN, P. A. BAISDEN, C. M. HENDERSON, R. J. DUPZYK, K. SÜMMERER, and G. R. BETHUNE, *Phys. Rev. Lett.* **56,** 313 (1986).

5. R. W. LOUGHEED, K. J. MOODY, R. J. DOUGAN, J. F. WILD, E. K. HULET, R. J. DUPZYK, C. M. HENDERSON, C. M. GANNET, R. A. HENDERSON, D. C. HOFFMAN, D. M. LEE, K. SÜMMERER, and R. L. HAHN, *Nuclear Chemistry Division FY 87 Annual Report*, Lawrence Livermore National Laboratory, LivermoreCalif., UCAR 10062/87 (1987) p. 4-2.

6. *Atomic Data and Nucl. Data Tables*, **39** No. 2, July, 1988.

7. G. R. CHOPPIN, B. G. HARVEY, and S. G. THOMPSON, *J. Inorg. Nucl. Chem.* **2**, 66 (1956).

8. H. L. SMITH and D. C. HOFFMAN, *J. Inorg. Nucl. Chem.* **3**, 243 (1956).

9. E. K. HULET, R. W. LOUGHEED, J. F. WILD, R. J. DOUGAN, K. J. MOODY, R. L. HAHN, C. M. HENDERSON, R. J. DUPZYK, and G. R. BETHUNE, *Phys. Rev. C* **34**, 1394 (1986).

10. P. MÖLLER, private communication, Lawrence Berkeley Laboratory, Berkeley, Calif. (July 1988).

11. P. MÖLLER, private communication, Lawrence Berkeley Laboratory, Berkeley, Calif. (May 1988).

12. P. MÖLLER, J. R. NIX, W. D. MEYERS, and W. D. SWIATECKI, *Proc. 4th Winter Workshop on Nuclear Dynamics, Copper Mt., Colorado, February 22–28, 1986.*

13. K. BÖNING, Z. PATYK, A. SOBIECZEWSKI, and S. CWIOK, *Z. Phys.* **A325**, 479 (1986).

14. S. CWOIK, V. V. PASHKEVICH, J. DUDEK, and W. NAZAREWICZ, *Nucl. Phys.* **A410**, 254 (1983).

NON-EQUILIBRIUM FISSION PROCESSES

IN INTERMEDIATE ENERGY NUCLEAR COLLISIONS

W. LOVELAND, C. CASEY, Z.XU
Oregon State University
Corvallis, OR 97331, USA
(503)-754-2341

G.T. SEABORG
Lawrence Berkeley Laboratory
Berkeley, CA 94720, USA
(415)-486-5661

K. ALEKLETT, L. SIHVER
Studsvik Neutron Research Lab.
S-611 82 Nyköping, Sweden
+46-155-21000

ABSTRACT

We have measured the target fragment yields, angular and energy distributions for the interaction of 12-16 MeV/A ^{32}S with ^{165}Ho and ^{197}Au and for the interaction of 32 and 44 MeV/A ^{40}Ar with ^{197}Au. The Au fission fragments associated with the peripheral collision peak in the folding angle distribution originate in a normal, "slow" fission process in which statistical equilibrium has been established. At the two lowest projectile energies, the Au fission fragments associated with the central collision peak in the folding angle distribution originate in part from "fast" ($\tau \sim 10^{-21}$s), non-equilibrium processes. Most of the Ho fission fragments originate in non-equilibrium processes. The fast, non-equilibrium process giving rise to these fragments has many of the characteristics of "fast fission", but the cross sections associated with these fragments are larger than one would expect from current theories of "fast fission."

INTRODUCTION

Due to the large scale collective motions involved, fission is generally thought of as a "slow" process. For heavy nuclei excited by the resonance capture of neutrons, fission lifetimes can be measured to be $\sim 10^{-15}$ - 10^{-14}s. When one increases the temperature of the fissioning system, the fission lifetimes are expected to decrease, due to the overall decrease in the lifetime of the excited nucleus and the vanishing of the fission barrier. More specifically, for a heavy nucleus like ^{208}Pb, the neutron decay lifetime at a temperature of 5 MeV is estimated[1] to be $\sim 10^{-22}$s. The fission barrier of ^{208}Pb is expected[2] to vanish at T=5 MeV even with l=0. Thus there are reasons to expect that in highly excited nuclei, fission will become a much faster process especially if it is to compete with particle emission as a decay path for highly excited nuclei.

In this paper we report studies of fission induced by intermediate energy heavy ions that are fairly massive (S,Ar). Using the symmetry of the moving frame fragment angular distributions as a clock, we report the observation of a fast, non-equilibrium fission process whose lifetime is of the order of a nuclear relaxation time. In the reactions induced by energetic S and Ar ions, the expected values of the nuclear temperatures are 4-6 MeV, possibly giving rise to an unusual setting for the fission process, i.e., a nonexistent fission barrier and competiting decay channels with short lifetimes.

EXPERIMENTAL

We have measured the target fragment yields, and angular distributions for the interaction of 12-16 MeV/nucleon ^{32}S with ^{165}Ho and ^{197}Au, 32 and 44 MeV/nucleon ^{40}Ar with ^{197}Au. Also the fragment energy spectra were measured for the interaction of 16 MeV/nucleon ^{32}S with ^{165}Ho. The experiments were performed at the LBL 88" cyclotron (^{32}S beam), the MSU National Superconducting Cyclotron (32 MeV/nucleon ^{40}Ar) and at GANIL (44 MeV/nucleon ^{40}Ar). The experimental apparatus, the methods used to acquire the data and to analyze it have been described previously [3,4]. The measurements were made using radioanalytical techniques. The corrections to the angular distributions for fragment scattering and the finite angular resolution of the detection apparatus are discussed in reference 4. The measurements of the target fragment production cross sections at LBL and MSU were made by a simple irradiation of a thick Ho or Au foil surrounded by ~15 mg/cm^2 carbon catcher foils. The radionuclide content of the irradiated foil stack was determined by off-line gamma ray spectroscopy. Production cross sections were calculated from end of bombardment activities [5]. (For the GANIL irradiation, the total nuclidic production cross sections were determined by integrating the measured fragment angular distributions.)

For the reaction of 16 MeV/nucleon ^{32}S with ^{197}Au, the angular distributions of 49 different target fragments were measured along with the production cross sections for 102 different nuclides. For the reaction of 32 MeV/nucleon ^{40}Ar with ^{197}Au, angular distributions were measured for 40 fragments while the yields of 83 fragments were measured. In the reaction of 44 MeV/nucleon ^{40}Ar with ^{197}Au, the angular distributions and yields of 78 different target fragments were measured. In the reaction of 12-16 MeV/nucleon ^{32}S with ^{165}Ho, the yields of 75 different radionuclides were measured along with the angular distributions of 82 different target fragments. From the measured target fragment production cross sections,

fragment mass yield distributions were deduced using techniques described previously [6].

EVIDENCE FOR UNUSUAL ASPECTS OF FISSION

In Figures 1 and 2, we show the deduced mass yield curves for the two reactions of 12-16 MeV/nucleon ^{32}S with ^{165}Ho and ^{197}Au. Also shown in these figures are the isobaric yield distributions from reactions induced by similar velocity ^{16}O ions (as well

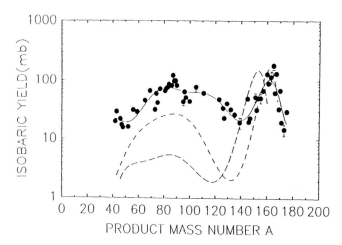

Figure 1. Isobaric yield distributions for the fragmentation of ^{165}Ho by (a) 12 MeV/nucleon ^{32}S, solid points, solid line (b) 17 MeV/nucleon ^{16}O, short dashed line (c) 442 MeV ^{12}C, long dashed line.

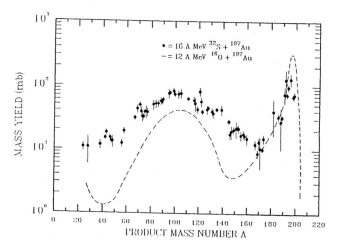

Figure 2. Comparison of isobaric yield distributions for the fragmentation of ^{197}Au by (a) 12 MeV/nucleon ^{16}O, dashed line and (b) 16 MeV/nucleon ^{32}S.

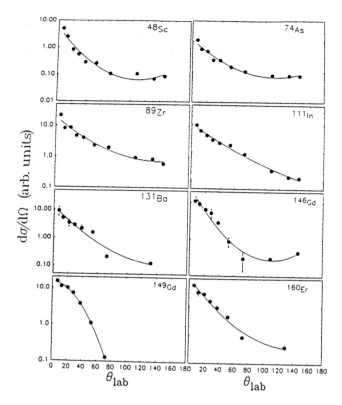

Figure 3. Laboratory frame angular distributions for representative fragments from the reaction of 16 MeV/nucleon ^{32}S with ^{165}Ho.

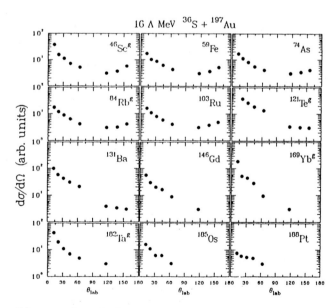

Figure 4. Laboratory frame angular distributions for representative fragments from the reaction of 16 MeV/nucleon ^{32}S with ^{197}Au.

as ^{12}C ions of similar total projectile kinetic energy interacting with ^{165}Ho). One notes two prominent peaks in the mass distribution, a fission peak (A~50-150) and a heavy residue peak(A>150). The fission cross section (σ_z(Ho)=2060 mb, σ_z(Au)=2600 mb). is enhanced for the ^{32}S induced reactions relative to the other (C,O) reactions. The yields of the heavier fission products are especially enhanced. The overall width of the fission mass distribution is unusually broad.

In Figures 3 and 4, we show the laboratory frame angular distributions for a series of typical fragments from the interaction of 16 MeV/nucleon ^{32}S with ^{165}Ho and ^{197}Au. (For lack of space, we omit a detailed discussion of the angular distributions for the two higher energy reactions although similar conclusions can be reached for these reactions[7].) The laboratory frame angular distributions are all strongly forward-peaked. For the reactions involving the Au target, the light mass fission fragments (A=40-106) have a similar "dipper" shape while the heavier members of this distribution (A=111-169) have a very different shape. This latter group of fragments exhibits more forward-peaked distributions similar to those observed for the heavy residues.

Each fragment angular distribution was integrated from 0 to $\pi/2$ and $\pi/2$ to π to obtain the ratio of fragments recoiling forward (F) to those recoiling backward (B). To extract further information from the data, the laboratory frame angular distributions were transformed into the moving frame of the target residue following the initial target-projectile encounter. To do this we have assumed that the final velocity of the fragment in the laboratory system can be written as $V_{lab} = V + v$, where the velocity v is the velocity of the moving frame and V is the velocity kick given the target fragment by particle emission or fission at an angle θ_{KF} with respect to the beam direction in the moving frame. The vector v has components of v_l and v_t, parallel and perpendicular to the beam direction.

In lieu of detailed information about v_t, the forward-peaked nature of the distributions and the difficulty of getting information about v_t, we have assumed $v_t=0$. We have used standard formulas[8] to make transformations for $d\sigma/d\Omega$ and θ.

For the value of η_1 ($=v_1/V$) needed to make such transformations, we have used values of η_1 derived from integrating the angular distributions. To get the value of η_1 from F and B, we assume the angular distributions of the fission fragments in the moving frame can be represented as $1 + \alpha \cos^2 \theta_{KT}$. In this case, it can be shown[8] that

$$F=\tfrac{1}{2}[1+(1+\eta^2\alpha/3)\eta/(1+\alpha/3)]$$

$$B=\tfrac{1}{2}[1-(1+\eta^2\alpha/3)\eta/(1+\alpha/3)]$$

These equations were solved numerically using a Levenberg – Marquardt method to give values of η and α. (The values of α range from 0 to 0.2 but were mostly ~0).

The values of η_1 obtained from this procedure for the reactions involving Au targets are shown in Figure 5. The values of η_1 change as a function of fragment mass number with high η_1 values being associated with the heavy fission fragments and low η_1 values being associated with the lighter fission fragments. The average values of η_1 for each fragment group agree well with previous measurements of η_1 for the same or similar reactions using the fission fragment folding angle technique[9-11]. Thus the heavy fission fragments for the two lower projectile energies appear to have η_1 values characteristic of central collisions (high momentum transfer) while the light mass fission fragments appear to have η_1 values characteristic of peripheral collisions(low momentum transfer). For the highest projectile energy (44 A MeV ^{40}Ar), where the fission mass distribution extends from A=70 to A=110) fission only occurs with η_1 values characteristic of peripheral collisions. The η_1 values associated with the Ho fission fragments are all large and characteristic of central collisions. That the Ho fission events are associated with high

linear momentum transfer events is not surprising given the small fissionability of Ho and the need to impart substantial amounts of

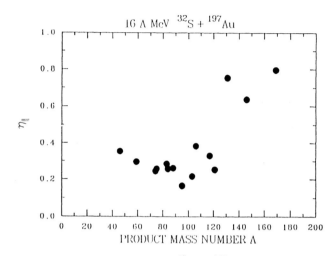

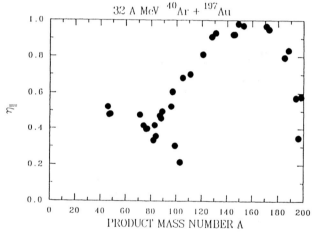

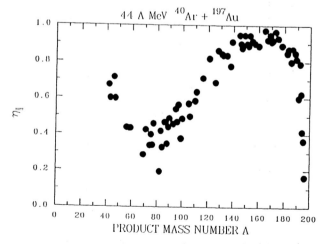

Figure 5. Values of η_1 as a function of product mass number for all the reactions involving Au targets.

701

angular momentum to cause fission[12]. It would be an oversimplification, however, to believe that for Au, the high linear momentum transfer events lead strictly to heavy mass fragments and low momentum transfer events lead to light mass fragments. The situation is probably more complicated as we shall discuss presently.

To gain further insight into what might be happening, we show (in Figures 6 and 7) the moving frame angular distributions corresponding to the data shown in Figures 3 and 4. All the events with high values of η_1 have angular distributions that are asymmetric with respect to 90° in the moving frame while the events with low values of η_1 have symmetric distributions. Symmetry in the moving frame implies a "slow" process in which statistical equilibrium has been achieved while the lack of symmetry implies a "fast" process in which statistical equilibrium has not been established. (The terms "slow" and "fast" are to be taken relative to the time required for the establishment of statistical equilibrium which has been estimated[13] to be 2-3 x 10^{-23}s.) Furthermore it can be shown that for many of the fragments no choice of a value (or a set of values) of η_1 will lead to a symmetric distribution in the moving frame. <u>We believe that this unique observation suggests the occurrence of a fast, non-equilibrium mode of fission for these fragments.</u>

As to the puzzling observation that the heavy mass Au fission fragments preferentially show this "fast" production mechanism, it can be argued that "normal, slow" fission will always occur to produce these fragments. But that these fragments are also produced by a fast, non-equilibrium process. The fast non-equilibrium process is assumed to have an unusually broad mass distribution, thus making its relative importance greater for the more asymmetric fission events. Using the 32 MeV/nucleon ^{40}Ar + ^{197}Au reaction as an example, this argument may be carried further. If we assume the distribution for the light mass fragment ^{87}Y is

representative of normal fission, we can normalize it to the distribution of a typical heavy mass fragment

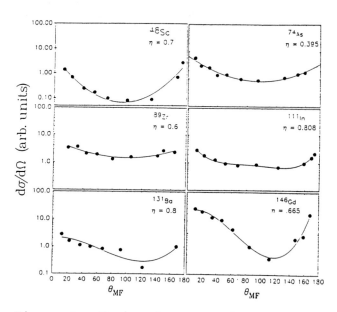

Figure 6. Moving frame angular distributions for representative fragments from the interaction of 16 MeV/nucleon ^{32}S with ^{165}Ho.

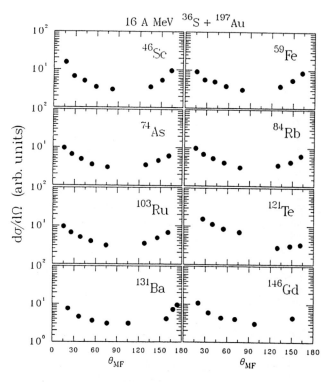

Figure 7. Moving frame angular distributions for representative fragments from the interaction of 16 MeV/nucleon ^{32}S with ^{197}Au.

702

(^{131}Ba) at backward angles (Figure 8a). The difference between the two distributions (Figure 8b) can be taken as the contribution of a "fast" direct fission mechanism to the production of ^{131}Ba and other heavy mass fragments.

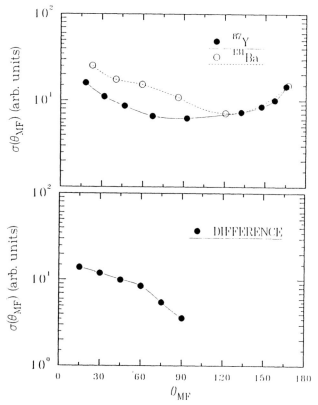

Figure 8. (a) The moving frame distributions of ^{87}Y and ^{131}Ba from the 32 MeV/nucleon ^{40}Ar + ^{197}Au reaction normalized at back angles. (b) The difference between the distributions in (a).

SPECULATIONS ABOUT THE REACTION MECHANISMS INVOLVED.

A known nuclear reaction mechanism[14] for low energy nuclear collisions, "fast fission" or "quasifission" is a possible candidate for the suggested non-equilibrium mechanism. In this mechanism, all partial waves between the l-wave at which the fission barrier vanishes, $l_{Bf=0}$, and the critical angular momentum, l_{crit} go via fast fission. In these events, the fusing system never reaches a configuration inside the fission saddle point and the resulting event is fast. Experimental signatures for such events are the lack of symmetry of the moving frame angular distributions and a broader than normal fission mass distribution. The principal difficulty with this explanation is the magnitude of the measured cross sections for the "fast" events. By using the difference technique described above, one estimates "fast" cross sections for the Au target reactions that are ~2.9x the expected[14] fast fission cross section. For the Ho target reaction, the measured "fast" cross section is about the twice the expected fast fission cross section.

ACKNOWLEDGMENTS

We wish to gratefully acknowledge the participation of D.J. Morrissey, J.O. Liljenzin and M. de Saint-Simon in these experiments. We wish to thank the operations staff of the accelerators involved for their assistance during the experiments. This work was supported in part by the U.S. Department of Energy under Grant No. DE-FG06-88ER40402 and Contract No. DE-AC03-76SF00098 and the Swedish Natural Sciences Research Council. One of us (WDL) wishes to thank the Studsvik Neutron Ressearch Laboratory for their hospitality during the time when this manuscript was being prepared.

REFERENCES

1. H. DELAGRANGE, C. GREGOIRE, F. SCHEUTER, and Y. ABE, "Dynamical Decay of Nuclei at High Temperature: Competition between Particle Emission and Fission Decay," Z. Phys. A323, 437 (1986).

2. X. CAMPI and S. STRINGARI, "Temperature Dependence of Nuclear Surface Properties," Z. Phys. A309, 239 (1983).

3. K. ALEKLETT, M. JOHANSSON, L. SIHVER, W. LOVELAND, H. GROENING, P.L. MCGAUGHEY, and G.T. SEABORG, "Heavy Residue Spectra in the Interaction of 85 A MeV ^{12}C with ^{197}Au," Nucl. Phys. A (in press).

4. R.H. KRAUS,JR.,W. LOVELAND, K. ALEKLETT, P.L. MCGAUGHEY, T.T. SUGIHARA, G.T. SEABORG, T. LUND, Y. MORITA, E. HAGEBO, AND I.R. HALDORSEN, "Target Fragment Angular Distributions for the Interaction of 86 MeV/A ^{12}C with ^{197}Au," Nucl. Phys. A432, 525 (1985).

5. D.J. MORRISSEY, D. LEE, R.J. OTTO, and G.T. SEABORG, "Measurement of the Product Mass Distributions from Heavy-Ion Induced Nuclear Reactions," Nucl. Inst. Meth. 158, 499 (1978)

6. D.J. MORRISSEY, W. LOVELAND, M. de SAINT-SIMON, and G.T. SEABORG, "Target residues from the reaction of 8 GeV ^{20}Ne with ^{181}Ta and ^{197}Au," Phys. Rev. C21, 1783 (1980).

7. K. ALEKLETT, W. LOVELAND, L. SIHVER, Z.XU, C. CASEY, D.J. MORRISSEY, J.O. LILJENZIN, M. de SAINT-SIMON, and G.T. SEABORG, "Changes in Target Fragmentation Mechanisms with Increasing Projectile Energies in Intermediate Energy Nuclear Collisions," Phys. Rev. C (submitted for publication).

8. J.M. ALEXANDER, in Nuclear Chemistry, Vol I, L. Yaffe, ed., (Academic, New York, 1968) pp273-357.

9. E.C. POLLACCO, M. CONJEAUD, S. HARAR, C. VOLANT, Y. CASSAGNOU, R. DAYRAS, R. LEGRAIN, M.S. NGUYEN, H. OESCHLER, and F. SAINT-LAURENT, "High Momentum and Energy Transfer induced by 1760 MeV ^{40}Ar on ^{197}Au and ^{232}Th Targets," Phys. Lett. 146B, 29 (1984).

10. Y. PATIN, S. LERAY, E. TOMASI, O. GRANIER, C. CERRUTI, J.L. CHARVET, S. CHIODELLI, A. DEMEYER, D. GUINET, C. HUMEAU, P. LHENORET, J.P. LOCHARD, R. LUCAS, C. MAZUR, M. MORJEAN, C. NGO, A. PEGHAIRE, M. RIBRAG, L. SINOPOLI, T. SUOMIJARVI, J. UZUREAU and L. VAGNERON, "Fission Fragment-Light Particle Coincidences and Linear Momentum Transfer," Nucl. Phys. A457, 146 (1986).

11. G. BIZARD, R. BROU, H. DOUBRE, A. DROUET, F. GUILBAULT, F. HANAPPE, J.M. HARASSE, J.L. LAVILLE, C. LEBRUN, A. OUBAHADOU, J.P. PATRY, J. PETER, G. PLOYART, J.C. STECKMEYER, and B. TAMAIN, "Reaction Mechanisms in the ^{40}Ar + ^{197}Au Collisions at 35 MeV/nucleon," Nucl. Phys. A456, 183 (1986)

12. C.CASEY, W. LOVELAND, Z.XU, L. SIHVER, K. ALEKLETT, and G.T. SEABORG, "Non-Equilibrium Fission and Heavy Residue Production in the Interaction of 12-16 MeV/nucleon ^{32}S with ^{165}Ho," Phys. Rev. C (submitted for publication)

13. K. ALEKLETT, W. LOVELAND, T. LUND, P.L. MCGAUGHEY, Y. MORITA, G.T. SEABORG, E. HAGEBO and I.R. HALDORSEN, "Fast and slow processes in the fragmentation of ^{238}U by 85 MeV/nucleon ^{12}C," Phys. Rev. C33, 885 (1986).

14. C. GREGOIRE, C. NGO, AND B. REMAUD, "Fast Fission Phenomenon, Deep Inelastic Reactions and Compound Nucleus Formation Described Within a Dynamical Macroscopic Model," Nucl. Phys.A383, 392 (1982).

A STUDY OF MONOENERGETIC, FAST NEUTRON-INDUCED TERNARY FISSION IN ^{238}U

K. RANDLE
School of Chemistry
University of Birmingham
PO Box 363, Birmingham B15 2TT, UK.
021 414 4420

H. AFARIDEH
School of Physics and Space Research
University of Birmingham
PO Box 363, Birmingham B15 2TT, UK.
021 414 4718

ABSTRACT

We have investigated the emission probabilities
of light charged particles (LCP) emitted on
ternary fission of ^{238}U induced by monoenergetic
neutrons. The particles detected were mainly
tritons and alpha particles. The detection
system comprised a ΔE-E telescope consisting
of two surface barrier detectors. Total fission
events were recorded by a separate surface
barrier detector. Events recorded in the
telescope detector were displayed as a 2-D
Mass v Energy spectrum. Monoenergetic neutrons
of energies 3.6 and 4.12 MeV were produced via
the D(d,n) ^{3}He reaction using the Dynamitron
accelerator. Fission was induced in a thin,
pure ^{238}U target located about 3 cm. from the
detector telescope.

INTRODUCTION

There has been virtually no experimental
work on ternary fission in ^{238}U induced by fast,
monoenergetic neutrons. In particular, there
is considerable uncertainty regarding the
emission probabilities of LCP and the ratio of
tritons or alpha particles to the number of
binary fission events.

The production of tritium by ternary
fission is of particular interest in the
nuclear power industry due to the potential
hazard of this radioactive gas. Until recently,
tritium yields for fast fission were estimated
by calculations using the yields obtained from
thermal fission. Now, however, experimental
results have indicated that the yield of tritium
from fast fission is considerably higher than
that from thermal fission. Few data, however,
are available at precise neutron energies and it
was one of the purposes of this work to determine
tritium yields at specific neutron energies
relevant to a fast reactor neutron spectrum.

The amount of tritium produced by ternary
fission is dependant firstly on the relative
emission of tritons compared to other LCP
(chiefly alpha particles) and secondly on the
rate of ternary fission compared to binary
fission. There is relatively little data on
fast-neutron-induced ternary fission in ^{238}U
but a radiochemical study suggested that the
triton and alpha particle were emitted with
almost equal probability[2]. This contrasts
sharply with most other nuclides which have been
investigated where in general the ratio of the
triton to alpha particle yield is of the order
of 0.1 to 0.2. Hence it was hoped to confirm
or refute the radiochemical data in the present
series of experiments.

EXPERIMENTAL PROCEDURES

The fission reactions and the detection of
LCP emitted in ternary fission were carried out
in a specially constructed vacuum-chamber, 40 cm
diameter shown in Fig 1. This chamber was
equipped with two independent rotating arms
pivoted about the centre of the chamber. Several
detectors could be mounted on each arm, with
reasonable separation between them. In practice,
a ΔE-E particle detector telescope was mounted
on one arm whilst the other carried a surface
barrier, total fission detector. The target
assembly for producing neutrons was located
inside the chamber at the end of an accelerator
beam line. The location of this target assembly
was adjustable in distance from the centre of
the chamber. A ^{238}U fission foil was aligned
on the axis of the chamber and adjusted to be
at the same height and in the same plane as the
neutron target, perpendicular to the chamber
axis and approximately 15 mm from the neutron
producing target (see Fig 1). This ^{238}U foil
was situated at the centre of the chamber and
the arms carrying the detectors were placed
either side of the fission foil and could be
rotated independently if required. In practice
they were placed at 30° to the beam direction.
The detectors themselves were very carefully
adjusted so that their centres were at the same
height as those of the neutron target and the
fission foil, and perpendicular to the arms. The
complete assembly is shown in Fig 1. Through-

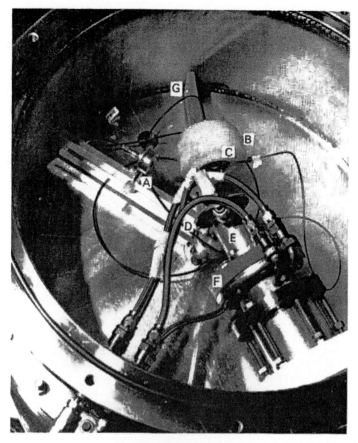

FIG 1 ARRANGEMENT OF EQUIPMENT INSIDE VACUUM CHAMBER
A. Fission Detector B. E Detector and
C. ΔE Detector (inside polythene shield)
D. ^{238}U Fission Foil E. Neutron-producing
Target F. Collimator G. Detector Arm

out the course of the experiments the chamber
was maintained at a pressure of about 10^{-5} torr.

A. Details of targets and detectors.

The neutron producing targets consisted of
a deuterated layer of titanium, 25 mm diameter on
a 31.7 mm diameter, 0.5 mm thick silver backing.
The disc was water-cooled to allow deuteron beam
currents of about 200 μa to be used. The beam
spot was collimated to 11 mm diameter and
scanned across the target.

The ^{238}U fission foil was prepared by the
sample preparation group of the Central Bureau
for Nuclear Measurements, Geel, Belgium. It was
prepared by electrospraying highly depleted
^{238}U (99.99% ^{238}U) to form a very uniform
deposit, 500 μg/cm^2 thick and 20 mm diameter
on a 7 μm thick gold-coated polymide foil. This
foil was then mounted on an annular aluminium
ring, with inside diameter of 30 mm. The thickness of the ^{238}U deposit was a compromise between
being thin enough not to seriously degrade the
energy of the LCP but thick enough to produce a

reasonable number of fission events.

The total fission detector was a surface
barrier detector of 100 μm thickness. This was
located 120 mm from the ^{238}U fission foil. The
ΔE detector was fully depleted with a thickness
of about 50 μm and active area of 75 mm^2. The E
detector had a thickness of 800 μm and an active
area of 400 mm^2. Its initial energy resolution
was approximately 36 keV for 6.05 MeV alpha
particles. The energy calibration for the
detectors was carried out with a series of alpha
sources covering the energy range 5.48 MeV
(^{241}Am) to 8.78 MeV (^{228}Th). The mean telescope
to fission foil distance varied from 25 to 50 mm
in these experiments.

A 12μm Al foil absorber was placed between
the fission foil and the ΔE detector in order to
prevent binary fission fragments reaching this
detector and so degrading its resolution. Alpha
particles from the decay of ^{238}U could pass
through the Al foil but were completely stopped
in the ΔE detector and were therefore not
recorded by the telescope.

B. Determination of the geometrical counting efficiency

Because the detector telescope and the total fission detector were at different distances from the ^{238}U fission foil the geometrical counting efficiency of these two sets of detectors were different. This counting efficiency factor was determined by placing mica track detectors adjacent to the ΔE detector and to the fission detector. The mica recorded the heavy fission fragments at each location and hence gave a measure of the total fission fragments that could theoretically interact with each detector system. From the track density in each mica sheet (determined after etching in 48% HF) and the known angular anisotropy for neutron-induced fission of ^{238}U[3], it was possible to calculate the geometrical counting efficiency at each detector.

C. Electronics and Data Acquisition

In the main, standard NIM electronic units were used with the detector telescope, and the system has been previously described[4]. These units gave rise to signals equivalent to the energy deposited in the ΔE and E detectors. The key to the mass determination of the LCP was a unit known as the Particle Identification Unit (PIU). The theory and operation of this unit have been discussed elsewhere[5], and only a brief summary is given here. The principle of operation of the PIU arises from the relationship between the type of charged particle and the rate of energy loss during its passage through matter. For non-relativistic particles this relationship can be expressed as a product, thus

$$\Delta E . E_T^{'} = \text{constant} \times M\,Z^2 \qquad (1)$$

where ΔE $(= dE/dX.t)$ is the energy deposited in a thin transmission detector of thickness, t, and $E_T^{'}$ is the energy deposited in a stopping detector (E detector). In other words the product of the signals from the ΔE and E detectors is proportional to MZ^2. Equation (1) is valid for a limited range only, and a better representation of MZ^2 is given by

$$MZ^2 \simeq (E_T^{'} + K_o - K_1 . \Delta E + K_2 . \Delta E^2 + \ldots) \qquad (2)$$

The constants K_o, K_1, K_2, etc. have been evaluated over a wide range of energies and it has been shown that only K_o and K_1 need be considered. Provision is made in the PIU to alter the constants K_o and K_1 to give output signals corresponding to the masses of the particles detected.

A two-dimensional display of the energy-mass distributions of the LCP was obtained using a multi-channel analyser system, with energy displayed along the X-axis, mass along the Y-axis and counts recorded on the Z-axis. This was achieved by operating two ADC's in multiparameter mode, one accepting effective mass signals, M, from the PIU and the other a signal representing the incident energy, E_T, of the LCP. Coincident $M-E_T$ data pairs were stored in a 128 x 64 channels matrix in the analyser.

D. Irradiations

Several days of irradiation were required to produce sufficient ternary fission events, using a deuteron beam current of about 200µA. A weak, annular alpha source of ^{241}Am, coated on a stainless steel disc, was permanently mounted between the ΔE and E detectors to allow continuous monitoring of the resolution of these detectors during the course of the irradiations. The annular design meant that the source did not interfere with the detection of the LCP in the telescope.

Neutron energies of 3.6 and 4.1 MeV were used in these experiments and were obtained by bombarding the deuterium target with either 900 KeV or 1.4 MeV deutrons, respectively.

RESULTS AND DISCUSSION

In fission involving fast neutrons, there is always the possibility of the production of low mass particles by processes other than that of ternary fission. In other words, from nuclear reactions in the structural materials or the detector materials themselves. These interfering reactions must be taken into consideration where they are energetically possible. In Table 1 are listed the more probable reactions based on the composition of the detectors and stopping materials.

For these cases which are energetically possible it was possible to prevent the induced charged particles from being counted without at the same time losing a significant number of particles from ternary events. This was done by adjusting the acceptance threshold of the electronics associated with the E detector. Chance coincidences were counted in a separate scaler.

There was a considerable background count recorded by the telescope close to the triton and alpha-particle regions of the spectrum. This is shown in the two-dimensional spectrum of energy vs mass of Fig 2. Shown here is the "raw" spectrum of the data collected in the 128 x 64 channel matrix, including the background counts. Figure 3 shows the same spectrum after removal of the background counts.

The spectrum was recorded continuously throughout an irradiation but was periodically stored. During the course of the irradiation the E detector suffered damage and loss of resolution. This became particularly noticeable towards the end of an irradiation period when

TABLE 1   POSSIBLE INTERFERING REACTIONS IN THE
DETERMINATION OF LCP FROM TERNARY FISSION

REACTION	Q VALUE (MeV)	THRESHOLD ENERGY (MeV)
$^{27}Al(n,p)^{27}Mg$	-1.827	1.89
$^{28}Si(n,p)^{28}Al$	-3.86	3.93
$^{29}Si(n,p)^{29}Al$	-2.90	3.93
$^{27}Al(n,\alpha)^{24}Na$	-3.13	3.24
$^{28}Si(n,\alpha)^{25}Mg$	-2.65	2.75
$^{29}Si(n,\alpha)^{26}Mg$	-0.034	0.036

the boundaries of the background and triton counts became blurred and merged into one another. In addition, the triton to alpha ratio, which remained fairly constant during the earlier parts of the irradiation began to increase, indicating a contribution from the background to the apparent triton counts.

Consequently, only the spectrum and counts prior to this point were used in the final results.

Table 2 shows the emitted number of LCP detected by the telescope, total fission events as recorded by the fission detector and the emission probability (yield) for alpha particles and tritons relative to the total binary fission events at each neutron energy.

The present data for ternary fission of ^{238}U do not enable us to provide any reliable information about the energy spectra of the particles owing to the very low counts obtained.

Tables 3 and 4 summarise the reported values for tritium and alpha yields for ^{238}U from fast neutron fission. It should be noted that for triton yields the data reported in this paper are the only experimental values for fission induced by monoenergetic neutrons. Indeed, for triton yields the data of Buzzelli et al[2] are the only other experimental data available. They measured the tritium yield after chemical separation and liquid scintillation counting. Their reported value for the yield of tritium (referred to the total fissions) is a factor of four greater than the theoretically calculated value[6]. This is in contrast to our results, shown in Table 3 which are broadly in agreement with the theoretical predictions. Buzzelli et al also quoted a very small error (2.9 to 3.3%) on their reported values which do not appear to take into account all the uncertainties in their method. Our results for the tritium yield indicate that the value reported by Buzzelli et al may not be due purely to ternary fission but may include a tritium contribution from other modes of production present in a fast reactor. These

TABLE 2   THE ALPHA AND TRITON YIELDS AND ALPHA/TRITON RATIO AS A FUNCTION OF INCIDENT NEUTRON ENERGY

NEUTRON ENERGY (MeV)	TRITON COUNTS (t)	ALPHA COUNTS (α)	FISSION COUNTS	GEOMETRY[a] CORRECTION	RATIO t/α	ALPHA[b] YIELD ($\times 10^{-3}$)	TRITON YIELD ($\times 10^{-4}$)
3.6	16	102	13400	6.73	0.157	1.13±0.11	1.8±0.4
4.1	16	78	2894	32.16	0.205	1.15±0.13	2.4±0.6

a   This correction takes into account the differences in distance of the telescope detector and fission detector from the ^{238}U foil. It is obtained from track counts in mica foils placed adjacent to each detector (see text for further explanation).

b   The alpha and triton yield values refer to the ratio of the number of these particles to the total fission events.

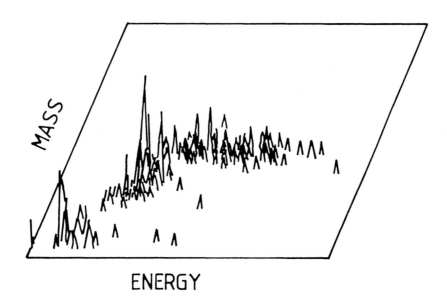

FIG 2 MASS vs ENERGY SPECTRUM FOR TERNARY FISSION
PRODUCTS FROM ^{238}U OBTAINED USING THE PIU (SEE
TEXT). RAW SPECTRUM, INCLUDING BACKGROUND COUNTS.

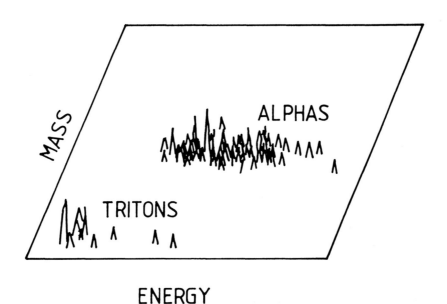

FIG 3 SAME SPECTRUM AS FIG 2 BUT BACKGROUND SUBTRACTED.

would include activation of boron and lithium
present in the reactor.

Our results indicate that the ratio of
tritons to alpha particles is about 0.16 to 0.18,
a factor of three greater than the same ratio in
thermal fission of ^{238}U. In other words, the
production of tritium will be some three times
greater in a fast reactor compared to that in a
current thermal one. This much higher value indicates the importance of tritium production by
ternary fission in fast reactors.

It is difficult to establish any neutron energy dependence of the tritium yield due to the paucity of current data. There is an indication from our results of a correlation of tritium yield with neutron energy but work at other neutron energies will be required before any more definite statement can be made.

For the yield of alpha particles in the ternary fission of ^{238}U, more data are available, as shown in Table 4. This table, however, also shows the wide divergence in the data previously published. Our results would appear to be in reasonable agreement with those of Nagy et al[8] and with the value predicted by Rider[7]. A least-squares fit of all of the data in Table 4 indicates a relatively constant value for this yield with increasing neutron energy.

These observations are in contrast with the observation of Fluss et al[2] for the monoenergetic-neutron-induced fission of ^{235}U. Both detector telescope and radiochemical techniques were used in this study and indicated an increase in the yield of tritium of greater than two from thermal energies to a neutron energy of 170 keV.

The weak correlation of the yield of LCP with neutron energy may be linked to the observation that there is no correlation between the average fragment kinetic energy and the initial excitation energy. In addition, Table 2 indicates that the triton to alpha yield ratio does not seem to be strongly neutron-energy dependant, although it does increase with neutron energy.

TABLE 3   PUBLISHED VALUES FOR THE RATIO OF BINARY FISSION TO TRITON EMISSION IN THE NEUTRON-INDUCED FISSION OF ^{238}U

NEUTRON ENERGY (MeV)	RATIO BINARY FISSION/ TRITON EMISSION	METHOD OF MEASUREMENT	REFERENCE
FAST NEUTRONS[a]	434.7±14	RADIOCHEMICALLY	BUZZELLI ET AL[2]
FAST NEUTRONS[b]	1000±29	"	"
FAST NEUTRONS	384		"
FAST NEUTRONS	3840	CALCULATION	ANL-7450[6]
FAST NEUTRONS	9000	"	RIDER[7]
3.6	5700±1400	DETECTOR TELESCOPE	THIS WORK
4.12	4200±1100	"	"

[a] Irradiation position 42 cm from core midplane
[b] Irradiation position 5 cm from core midplane

TABLE 4   PUBLISHED VALUES FOR THE RATIO OF BINARY FISSION TO LONG-RANGE ALPHA-PARTICLE
EMISSION IN THE NEUTRON-INDUCED FISSION OF ^{238}U

NEUTRON ENERGY (MeV)	RATIO BINARY FISSION/ ALPHA-PARTICLE EMISSION	METHOD OF MEASUREMENT	REFERENCE
FAST NEUTRONS	645	CALCULATION	RIDER[7]
2.5	1103±28	EXPERIMENTAL	NAGY ET AL[8]
2.5	600	"	SOLOVENA[9]
2.5	4550±350	"	DRAPCHINSKII ET AL[10]
14	795±35	"	NAGY ET AL[8]
14	3750±270	"	DRAPCHINSKII ET AL[10]
14	1050±100	"	PERFILOV ET AL[11]
3.6	880±90	DETECTOR TELESCOPE	THIS WORK
4.12	870±100	"	"

ACKNOWLEDGEMENTS

We would like to thank Mr J Harling for his invaluable help in the design and construction of the vacuum chamber. Thanks are also due to the Dynamitron operations team. One of us (HA) wishes to thank the Iranian Atomic Energy Authority for financial assistance during the course of this work.

REFERENCES

1. M.J. FLUSS, N.D. DUDEY, and R.L. MALEWICKI, "Tritium and Alpha-Particle Yields in Fast and Thermal Neutron Fission of ^{235}U," Phys. Rev., C6, 2252(1972).

2. G. BUZZELLI, S. LANGER, C. JONES, and B. GAINEY, "Tritium: Fast Fission Yields of ^{238}U and ^{232}Th," Trans. Am. Nucl. Soc., 24, 458(1976).

3. H. AFARIDEH, A Study of Fission in ^{238}U Induced by Monoenergetic Neutrons and Heavy Ions and of Light Particle Emission in ^{252}Cf Spontaneous Fission , Ph.D. Thesis, University of Birmingham, 1988 (unpub.).

4. H. AFARIDEH, K. RANDLE, and S.A. DURRANI, "An Investigation of Energy and Emission Probabilities of Tritons and α-Particles in the Spontaneous Fission of ^{252}Cf," Ann. Nucl. Energy, 15, 201(1988).

5. J.B.A. ENGLAND, "Fast Analog Particle Identification System," Nucl. Instr. Method, 106, 45(1973).

6. ARGONNE NATIONAL LAB. CHEMICAL ENGINEERING DIVISION, RESEARCH HIGHLIGHTS, May 1967-April 1968, ANL-7450, Argonne National Laboratory (1968).

7. B.F. RIDER, "Compilation of Fission Product Yields," NEDO-12154-3(B), Vallecitos Nuclear Center (1980).

8. L. NAGY, T. NAGY and I. VINNAY, "Measurement of Relative Probabilities of Triple Fission of ^{233}U, ^{235}U, ^{238}U and ^{232}Th," Sov. J. Nucl.

Phys., _8_, 257(1969).

9. Z.I. SOLOV'EVA, "Uranium Nuclei Complex
    Fission by 2.5 MeV Neutrons," At. Energ.
    (USSR), _8_, 137(1960).

10. L.V. DRAPCHINSKII, S.S. KOVALENKO, K.A.
    PETRZHAK, and I.I. TYTUGIN, "The Probability
    Ratio of the Ternary Fission of ^{235}U and
    ^{238}U by Neutrons of Various Energies," At.
    Energ. (USSR), _16_, 144(1964).

11. N.A. PERFILOV, Z.I. SOLOV'EVA, and R.A.
    FILOV, "The Ternary Fission of ^{235}U with
    14-MeV Neutrons," At. Energ. (USSR), _14_,
    7(1962).

K-EQUILIBRATION IN LIGHT- AND HEAVY-ION-INDUCED FISSION

R. P. SCHMITT, L. COOKE, H. DEJBAKHSH, D. R. HAENNI,
B. K. SRIVASTAVA, T. SHUTT, H. UTSUNOMIYA
Cyclotron Institute
Texas A&M University
College Station, Texas, 77843
(409)845-1411

ABSTRACT

Basic assumptions in statistical models of fission fragment angular distributions predict an angular variation of the fragment spins which is governed by the same parameters that control the angular distribution. This effect has been investigated in both light- and heavy-ion induced fission using γ-ray multiplicity techniques. While the multiplicities vary with angle, the effect is usually much weaker than expected. The disparity between theory and experiment is reduced significantly if the excitation of angular momentum bearing collective modes is included in the calculations. However, discrepancies still persist, suggesting a partial breakdown in the assumptions of the model.

INTRODUCTION

Much of the available information on nuclear saddle point shapes has been extracted from fission fragment angular distributions using a transition state model (TSM) analysis.[1] While the validity of this approach is supported by a large body of data from light ion fission studies, the situation is less clear in heavy-ion reactions.[2,3] Sometimes characteristics, such as asymmetric angular distributions and incompletely relaxed mass distributions, signal contributions from non-compound processes, i.e. fast fission. At other times, the data show no obvious signature of this process, making it hard to evaluate fast fission contributions and difficult to determine what, if any, shape information is conveyed by the angular distributions. Additional methods are needed to define the conditions under which one can reasonably extract nuclear shape information from the angular distributions.

Studies of the properties of the fragment spins can provide further insight into the problem. As discussed below, basic assumptions of the TSM predict an angular variation of the spins of the fission fragments. Because this variation is governed by the same parameters as the angular distributions, simultaneous measurements of the yields and spins of the fragment provide stringent tests of the applicability of the TSM. Using γ-multiplicity techniques we have investigated this effect in both light and heavy ion induced fission reactions. While the experimental results are in qualitative accord with the predictions of the TSM, it is difficult to account for the data quantitatively. The observations suggest at least a partial breakdown in the assumptions of the TSM.

THEORETICAL CONSIDERATIONS

Within the framework of the TSM, the angular distributions are determined by thermal fluctuations in the orientation of the fission axis with respect to the total spin, I. These fluctuations are assumed to be fixed at the saddle point, implying that the projection of I on the decay axis, K, is conserved during the descent from saddle to scission. On rather general grounds the K-distribution is expected to be a Gaussian. The width of this distribution is controlled by the parameter K_o, which is a function of the saddle point shape.[1]

In the semiclassical limit the angular distribution for a single

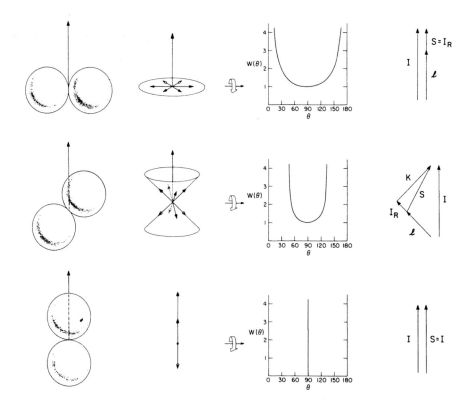

FIG. 1   SCHEMATIC DEPICTING THE GEOMETRICAL ORIGIN OF THE ANGULAR
          DISTRIBUTIONS AND THE FRAGMENT SPINS FOR A TRANSITION STATE
          CONSISTING OF TWO TOUCHING SPHERES.

partial wave is proportional to[4]

$$(2I+1)\exp(-\beta^2)I_0(\beta^2)/K_0\mathrm{erf}(\alpha),$$

where I_0 is the zeroth order modified Bessel function. The quantities α and β are defined by

$$\alpha = (I+1/2)/(2K_0^2)^{1/2}$$

and

$$\beta = \alpha \sin(\theta)/\sqrt{2}.$$

By analogy it is straightforward to derive a analytic expression for the mean square K-value as a function of angle.[5]   For a fixed total spin I, it is given by

$$(1/2)(I+1/2)^2\sin^2\theta[1-I_1(\beta^2)/I_0(\beta^2)]$$

where I_1 is the first order modified Bessel function. These equations show that the angular dependence of $\langle K^2 \rangle$ is governed by exactly the same parameters that control the angular distributions.

The connection between the tilting fluctuations and the angular distributions is most easily understood geometrically.   The geometry relevant to a fusion reaction is illustrated in fig. 1 for a hypothetical transition state consisting of touching, symmetric spheres.   The upper left hand corner of fig. 1 depicts the case in which there is no tilting, i.e. when the disintegration axis lies in a plane perpendicular to I.   Since there is no preferential emission direction for a fusion reaction, the fission fragments are emitted isotropically in this plane. Averaging over all possible orientations of I yields an angular distribution where the preponderance of the fission fragments appear at either small or large angles.   The resulting fragment spin tends to be small in this case, only $2I/7$ for the assumed shape.   The

714

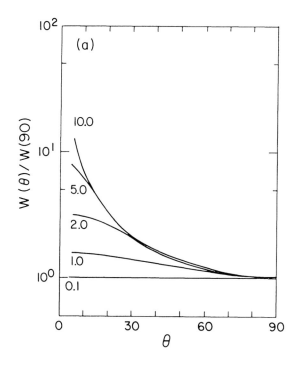 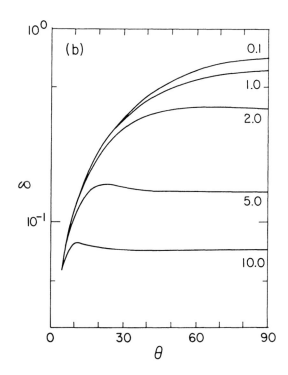

FIG. 2   CALCULATED YIELD (A) AND REDUCED K VALUES (B) OF FISSION
FRAGMENTS AS A FUNCTION OF ANGLE FOR SEVERAL VALUES OF α.

bulk of the initial angular momentum
ends up in orbital motion.

The middle row of fig. 1
illustrates the situation where there is
a 45° angle between I and the decay
axis. For this orientation the fission
fragments are emitted on conical
surfaces, leading to an angular
distribution which is confined to the
angular range 45°-135°. The fragment
spins are larger for this configuration.
Since there is no orbital angular
momentum associated with motion along
the fission coordinate, the entire
projection of I on the symmetry axis has
to be converted into fragment spin. The
extreme case of fission along the spin
direction is shown at the bottom of fig.
1. With the above picture in mind, one
expects the total fragment spin to be
largest in the vicinity of 90.° In
fig. 2 the yield and the quantity δ =
$K_{rms}/(I+1/2)$ are plotted as a function
of angle for selected values of α.

While the TSM predicts K^2 as a
function of angle, it does not specify
the spin components normal to the
disintegration axis. Probably the most
obvious approach is to postulate rigid
rotation. For rigid rotation the mean

square fragment spin for symmetric
fission is of the form

$$\langle S_T^2 \rangle = \langle f^2(I^2-K^2) + K^2 \rangle.$$

The quantity f, the fraction of the
angular momentum normal to the decay
axis that is converted into fragment
spin, depends on the shape and mass
asymmetry of the system.

Figure 3 shows the results of
calculations for the α + U system
assuming touching symmetric spheres and
a triangular ℓ-distribution. The rigid
rotor TSM predicts a substantial
variation of S_{rms}. As indicated in fig.
3, S_{rms} is expected to change by almost
$5\hbar$ over the angular range of the
measurements. Let us now turn to the
experimental results.

RESULTS AND DISCUSSION

In a series of experiments a
variety of targets were bombarded with
43 MeV ^{4}He, 120 MeV ^{16}O and 214 MeV ^{32}S
beams produced by the Texas A&M's 88
inch cyclotron. A schematic of one of
the experiments is shown in fig. 4.
Fission fragments were detected with
arrays of silicon detectors and silicon

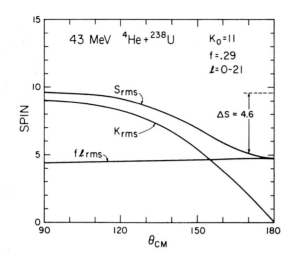

FIG. 3. CALCULATED FRAGMENT SPINS AS A
FUNCTION OF ANGLE FOR A RIGIDLY
ROTATING TRANSITION STATE. THE
R.M.S. ℓ- AND K-VALUES ARE ALSO
SHOWN AS A FUNCTION OF ANGLE.

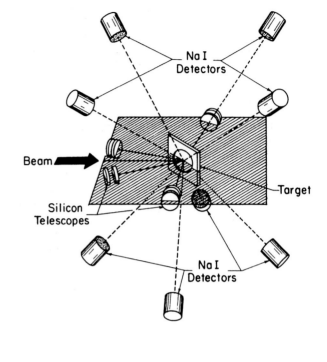

FIG. 4 SCHEMATIC OF THE EXPERIMENTAL
SETUP.

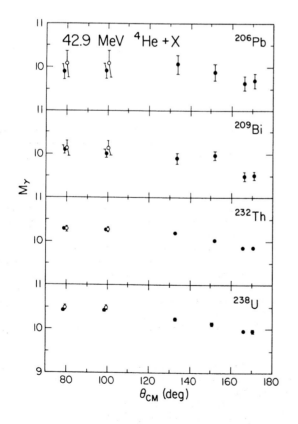

FIG. 5. M_γ AS A FUNCTION OF CENTER-OF-
MASS ANGLE FOR SEVERAL 43 MeV
α-INDUCED REACTIONS.

telescopes spanning the approximate angular range $\theta_{cm}=90^{0}$-$170.^{0}$ An array of eight 7.6x7.6 cm NaI detectors was employed to measure M_γ. Additional NaI counters provided information on the angular distribution of the γ rays. The details of the experiments can be found in the literature.[6,7]

The results for the α-induced reactions are shown in fig. 5. In qualitative agreement with TSM predictions, the M_γ data generally exhibit maxima in the vicinity of $\theta_{cm} = 90^{0}$. However, the change in M_γ over the angular range of the measurements (ΔM_γ) is relatively small (at most about 5%), and is consistently less than predicted by a rigid rotor transition state model. Since $2\Delta M_\gamma$ should be the upper bound on the change in fragment spin (ΔS), the predicted ΔS's are typically 2-4 times larger than the experimental values. The largest disparities are observed for systems with the highest K_0 values, where the greatest spin changes are expected. Similar disagreement is observed for the other reactions.

In large part, the gap between theory and experiment can be explained by the excitation of collective modes, such as bending wriggling and twisting.[8,9] These modes produce an angle-independent spin enhancement which attenuates the angular variation of the fragment spin. Convincing evidence for this effect is seen in the strong target dependence of M_γ for the ^{16}O-induced reactions. Even though the ℓ-distributions are similar in these reactions, M_γ varies by nearly 50% as the target mass changes from 174 to 238.

To understand this effect, let us consider a simple model in which the collective spin enhancement dominates over rigid rotation. Since the energy investment in collective modes should be on the order of the temperature, T, one expects that

$$T \propto I^2/J,$$

where I is the total spin and J is the appropriate moment of inertia. In many cases (spheroids or touching spheroids) one expects that $J \propto A_{cn}^{5/3}$, which implies

$$I \propto T^{1/2} A_{cn}^{5/6}.$$

In fig. 6 M_γ is plotted as a function of the above quantity. The estimated temperature at the saddle has been used, which is actually very similar for all

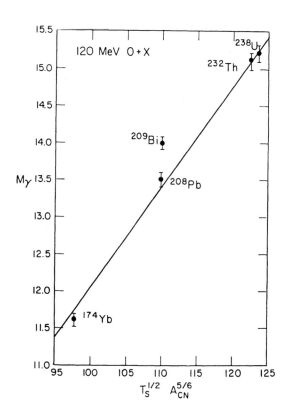

FIG. 6 M_γ AS A FUNCTION OF $A^{5/6}T^{1/2}$ FOR THE ^{16}O-INDUCED REACTIONS.

the systems. With the exception of the ^{209}Bi point, a linear dependence is observed, in agreement with the simple model.

It is interesting to note that there is a significant difference (half a unit) in the M_γ values for O + Pb and O + Bi even though the systems differ by just a single proton. This can be explained as a nuclear structure effect arising from the large ground state spin (9/2) of ^{209}Bi. Though this may seem to be a rather trivial effect, it provides evidence of sensitivity of M_γ to spin. It also suggests that S is in the range of 1 to 1.5M_γ.

With a collective spin enhancement, S_{cm}, the total fragment spin will be given by

$$\langle S_T \rangle = \langle \; f^2I^2+(1-f^2)K^2+S_{cm}^2 \; \rangle.$$

The results of a series of calculations

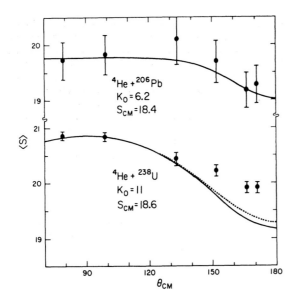

FIG. 7 COMPARISON BETWEEN THE
CALCULATED FRAGMENT SPIN AND
"MAXIMUM" FRAGMENT SPIN FOR TWO
α-INDUCED REACTIONS.

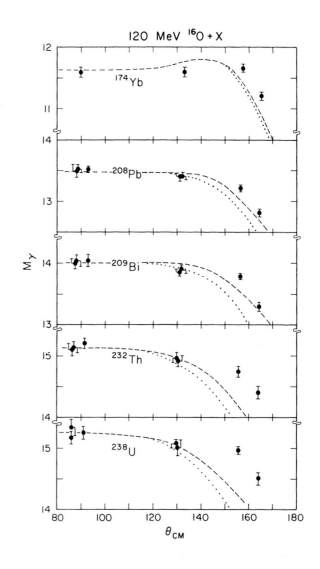

FIG. 8 COMPARISON BETWEEN THE
CALCULATED FRAGMENT SPIN AND
"MAXIMUM" FRAGMENT SPIN FOR THE
O-INDUCED REACTIONS.

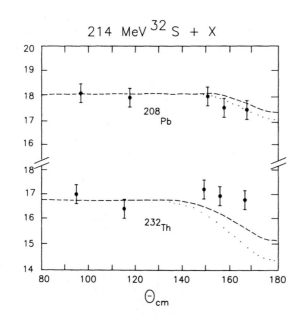

FIG. 9 COMPARISON BETWEEN THE
CALCULATED FRAGMENT SPIN AND
"MAXIMUM" FRAGMENT SPIN FOR THE
S-INDUCED REACTIONS.

are shown in figs. 7-9 for various reactions. In each case the upper curves show the predicted spins or M_γ values assuming that f is determined at the saddle. The lower curves assume that f is fixed at scission. In all the calculations, S_{cm} was determined by forcing agreement with the maximum expected fragment spin at $\theta_{cm} \simeq 90^\circ$, $2M_\gamma$. It is critical to note that lower values of S_{cm} *always* lead to a stronger angular dependence of the fragment spin, in poorer agreement with experiment.

Overall, the agreement between theory and experiment looks reasonable, but there is a systematic tendency in the calculations to overestimate the variation in the spin. Since the discrepancies are largest for the reactions with the heaviest targets, one might attribute this effect to sequential fission contributions. From multiplicity data obtained for correlated fragments with complete momentum transfer, one finds that only part of the discrepancies arises from sequential fission. Moreover, one should not lose sight of the fact that extreme assumptions have been made in the calculations. For example, using more reasonable relationships to convert M_γ to spin leads to greater disparities especially for the O-induced reactions.

CONCLUSION

In summary the γ-ray multiplicities of fission fragments from a number of reactions have been studied as a function of angle. As predicted by the statistical model, M_γ varies with angle. However, the angular dependence of M_γ is much weaker than expected from a rigid rotor TSM model. A significant part of the discrepancy can be explained by collective spin enhancement effects. However, even using what should be the maximum enhancement fails to explain all the data. Discrepancies still remain.

We cannot currently offer a unique explanation for this effect. It is our feeling that the discrepancies arise because the K-state distribution deviates from the assumed Gaussian form. This could be due to a K-dependence of the saddle point shape. However, calculations based on a flexible rotor model[10] do not provide a better description of the data. Another possibility is that the K-distribution is determined at scission rather than the saddle point as suggested by recent

models.[11,12] However, it can be shown[7] that statistical scission models yield essentially the same predictions as the TSM if the collective spin enhancement is included. A more likely explanation is that there are violations in K-conservation during the descent from saddle to scission which alter the form of the K-distribution. This seems especially likely in cases where the saddle and scission point shapes differ significantly.

ACKNOWLEDGEMENT

This work was supported by the U.S. Department of Energy and The Robert A. Welch Foundation.

REFERENCES

1. R. VANDENBOSCH and J. R. HUIZENGA, Nuclear Fission. Academic Press, New York, (1973).

2. P. GLÄSSEL, D. v. HARRACH, Y. CIVELEKOGLU, R. MÄNNER, H. J. SPECHT, and J. B. WILHELMY, "Three-Particle Exclusive Measurements of the Reactions U + U and U + Cm," Phys. Rev. Lett. 43, 1483 (1979).

3. B. B. BACK, "Complete Fusion and Quasifission in Reactions between Heavy Ions," Phys. Rev. C 32, 195 (1985).

4. J. R. HUIZENGA, A. N. BEHKAMI and L. G. MORETTO, " Note on the Interpretation of Fission-Fragment Angular Distributions at Moderate Excitation Energies," Phys. Rev. 177, 1826 (1969).

5. R. P. SCHMITT and M. TIRION, "Testing the Validity of Statistical Models of Fission Fragment Angular Distributions," Phys. Rev. C 31, 701 (1985).

6. R. P. SCHMITT, H. DEJBAKHSH, D. R. HAENNI, G. MOUCHATY, T. SHUTT, and M. TIRION, "Exploring the K-Distribution in Fission," Phys. Lett. 192B, 44 (1987).

7. R. P. SCHMITT, D. R. HAENNI, L. COOKE, H. DEJBAKHSH, G. MOUCHATY, T. SHUTT, AND H. UTSUNOMIYA, "Probing the Tilting Mode in Fission with γ-Ray Multiplicity Techniques," Nucl. Phys. A487, 370 (1988).

8. L. G. MORETTO and R. P. SCHMITT,

"Equilibrium Statistical Treatment
of Angular Momenta Associated with
Collective Modes in Fission and
Heavy-Ion Reactions," Phys. Rev. C
21, 204 (1980).

9. R. P. SCHMITT and A. J. PACHECO,
"Equilibrium Treatment of Spin-
Depolarizing Modes in Mass
Asymmetric Heavy-Ion Systems,"
Nucl. Phys. A379, 313 (1982).

10. M. PRAKASH, V. S. RAMAMURTHY, S. S.
KAPOOR and J. M. ALEXANDER,
"Transition-State Theory for
Fission Angular Distributions: A
Flexible-Rotor Model," Phys. Rev.
Lett. 52, 990 (1984).

11. H. ROSSNER, J. R. HUIZENGA and W.
U. SCHRÖDER, "Fission Fragment
Angular Distributions," Phys. Rev.
C 33, 560 (1986).

12. P. D. BOND, "Re-examination of
Fission Fragment Angular
Distributions and the Fission
Process: Formalism," Phys. Rev. C
32, 471 (1985)

LIGHT CHARGED PARTICLE EMISSION IN FISSION

H. IKEZOE, N. SHIKAZONO, Y. NAGAME,
Y. SUGIYAMA, Y. TOMITA, K. IDENO
Department of Physics, Japan Atomic
Energy Research Institute
Tokai-mura, Ibaraki-ken, 319-11
0292(82)5454

H. NAKAHARA, T. OHTSUKI, T. KOBAYASHI,
K. SUEKI
Department of Chemistry, Faculty of
Science, Tokyo Metropolitan University
Setagaya-ku, Tokyo, 158
03(717)0111

ABSTRACT

Light charged particles in the reaction ^{19}F + ^{197}Au with the bombarding energy range of 92 MeV to 138 MeV have been measured in coincidence with fission fragments. Most of ^{4}He measured at backward angles in coincidence with fission fragments were accounted for by evaporation from a compound nucleus before a fission process takes place. The observed pre-fission multiplicity of ^{4}He was enhanced at the low bombarding energies compared with the statistical model calculation assuming the level density parameter independent on the excitation energy. From the present measurement, the dependence of the level density parameter on the excitation energy was extracted.

INTRODUCTION

It is well known that the nuclear level density plays an important role in the statistical treatment of the probabilities of evaporation and fission of an excited nucleus. The dependence of the level density parameter on the excitation energy is especially important because most nuclei are produced in their excited states by the nuclear reactions. Up to now a few experimental data are available in connection with this point. At the low excitation energy below 10 MeV the neutron resonance data are available.[1,2]

In the present work, we investigated the dependence of the level density parameter on the excitation energies in the range of 45 MeV to 90 MeV. For the present purpose, the reaction ^{19}F + ^{197}Au was used to produce the compound nucleus ^{216}Ra. It was expected that ^{4}He may be likely emitted from the excited compound nucleus ^{216}Ra before fission, because the daughter nucleus ^{212}Rn has the neutron magic number N=126 and the Q-value for the ^{4}He emission has large positive value (9.5 MeV). It was also expected that the ^{4}He emission should depend on the excitation energy of the daughter nucleus ^{212}Rn and the shell correction energies of the excited states rapidly disappear[3] and then the level density approaches to the liquid drop value as the excitation energy increases. With these expectations, we tried to explore the excitation energy dependence of the level density paramater by measuring the pre-fission ^{4}He multiplicity as a function of the excitation energy of the compound nucleus.

EXPERIMENTS

A self-supported ^{197}Au target of a thickness of 1.2 mg/cm^2 was bombarded by ^{19}F beams from the JAERI tandem accelerator. The experiments were performed with the bombarding energies of the ^{19}F beams from 92 MeV (just above the Coulomb barrier between ^{19}F and ^{197}Au) to 138 MeV. Fission fragments were measured by an ionization chamber detector (IC) in the inclusive measurements and a large area solid state detector (LSSD, 900 mm^2) in the coincidence measurements. The ionization chamber detector is composed of an anode to measure the energy loss ΔE of reaction products in the 10 Torr isobutane gas filled in the chamber and a solid state detector (300 mm^2) to measure their residual energy E. These detectors were set up at the backward angles $\theta_{lab} > +120°$ with respect to the beams.

From the two dimensional display of E versus ΔE measued by the IC, it was found that almost all the reaction products detected at the backward angles were fission fragments and light ions like ^{4}He and proton at the bombarding energies larger than 100 MeV. The fission fragments and the light ions were also well separated in the energy spectrum measured by the LSSD. Based on this observation, the LSSD with a solid angle of 35.6 msr was used to detect the fission fragments in the coincidence measurements.

At the lower bombarding energies of 92 and 99 MeV, fission fragments and projectile-like products were partly overlapped in energy each other even at the backward angles, because of the large grazing angles of 112° for 99 MeV and ~180° for 92 MeV. In order to detect the fission fragments separately from the projectile-like products, a thin polyester foil of a thickness of 140 μg/cm^2 was put in front of the LSSD. The fission fragments were well separated from the projectile-like products in the energy spectrum due to the large difference of their energy losses in the thin foil.

Light particles (^{4}He and proton) were measured by solid state detector telescopes (30 μm and 2000μm thickness) at the inplane ($\varphi = 90°$) and the out-of-plane ($\varphi = 30°$), where the inplane is the plane defined by the directions of the beams and the fission fragments. The out-of-plane angle φ is the angle between the normal of the inplane and the direction of the detector telescope.

These telescopes were set up in the coincidence experiment at inplane negative angle $\theta_{lab} = -135°$ for all bombarding energies except 138 MeV, where the negative angle means the angle in the opposite side to the LSSD with respect to the beams. In the experiment with the bombarding energy of 138 MeV, the detector telescopes were set up at $\theta_{lab} = -95°$ and the fission fragments were measured at several inplane angles ($\theta_{lab} = 60°$, 75° and 90°) by the ionization chamber detector in coincidence with light charged particles.

RESULTS AND DISCUSSION

Inclusive spectra

In the present work, we maily concentrated our attention to the coincidence measurements between the fission fragments and the ⁴He particles, because it was difficult to identify the emission source of the proton measured in coincidence with the fission fragments, that is, the emission from the excited fission fragments or the pre−fission emission. This identification is relatively easy for ⁴He because of the large difference in the Coulomb barrier heights between two emitter (the fission fragments and the compound nucleus) and ⁴He.

A velocity contour map of the invariant coss section for the inclusive ⁴He emission is shown in Fig.1, where the measured velocity of ⁴He was decomposed to the parallel $V_{\parallel}$ and the perpendicular $V_{\perp}$ compoments with respect to the beam direction. The circular arcs centered on the c.m. velocity V_{cm} reproduce the backward data ($\theta_{lab} > 90°$) very well. This indicates that the ⁴He measured at the backward angles mainly originates from the evaporation of the compound nucleus.

The inclusive energy spectrum of ⁴He is shown in Fig.2 as the solid line. The ⁴He energy measured at $\theta_{lab} = 150°$ was transfered to the center of mass system assuming the evaporation of the compound nucleus. The result of the statistical model calculation is also shown by dashed line, where the statistical model code PACE[4] was used. The optical model potential parameters of ref.[5] were used for the ⁴He evaporation from the compound nucleus. It is obvious that the observed most probable energy is shifted to the lower energy by the amount of 2 MeV compared with the PACE calculation. This phenomenon has been commonly observed in the evaporation spectrum of ⁴He in the nuclear reaction as reported in ref.[6]. This suggests that the effective potential barrier height for the ⁴He emission decreases by about 2 MeV.

In order to verify this, the transmission coefficients for the ⁴He emission were artificially shifted to the low energy by the amount of 2 MeV. The PACE calculation with this modification is shown in Fig.2 with the dash−dotted line and reproduces the data very well. We also observed a shift of about 1 MeV of the most probable energy to the low energy in the proton energy spectrum. We took account of these shifts in the pre−fission multiplicity calculation by modifying the transmission coefficients of ⁴He and proton.

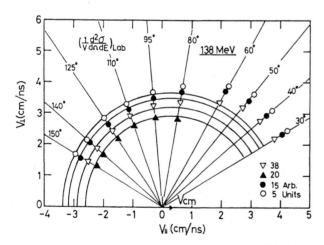

Fig.1 Velocity contour map of invariant cross section for inclusive ⁴He emission at the bombarding energy of 138 MeV. The measured velocity was decomposed of the parallel $V_{\parallel}$ and the perpendicular $V_{\perp}$ components with respect to the beam direction. V_{cm} is the c.m. velocity. The arcs are centered on V_{cm}. The straight lines from the origin represent the detection angles.

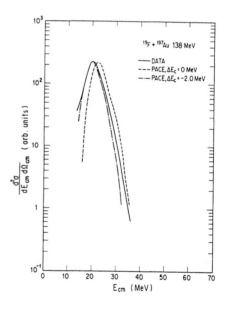

Fig.2 Inclusive c.m. energy spectrum of ⁴He (solid line) measured at the bombarding energy of 138 MeV. The dashed line is the result of the statistical model calculation using the code PACE with no shift in the transmission coefficients for ⁴He. The dash−dotted line is the result of the calculation assuming the 2 MeV shift to the low energy in the transmission coefficients.

Fission cross section.

The angular distributions of the inclusive fission fragments were measured maily at the backward angles ($\theta_{lab} \geq 90°$) by the ionization chamber detector. The fission cross sections were obtained by integrating the angular distribution transfered to the center–of–mass system assuming the total kinetic energy (TKE) of the fission fragments predicted by the Viola's systematics[7]. The fission cross sections are shown in Fig.3 as a function of the bombarding energy. The solid line represent the fusion cross section predicted by the Bass model[8]. The data are reproduced by the solid line very well. This indicates that in the present reaction system the fusion–fission process is dominant compared with the fusion–evaporation process. The statistical model calculation also predicts the same trend as the data indicate.

Coincidence spectra

In general, there are three different sources for the ⁴He emission, that is, the evaporations from fission fragments (FE), the compound nucleus emission (CE) and the pre–equilibrium process (PE). Since the ⁴He in the coincidence measurements was detected at the backward angles, the contribution from PE was negligible. The coincidence data were analysed by taking into account two emission sources of FE and CE.

The energy spectra of ⁴He in coincidence with the fission fragments are shown in Fig.4, where the ordinate is defined as

$$d^2M/dE_\alpha d\Omega_\alpha = (d^3\sigma/dE_\alpha d\Omega_\alpha d\Omega_{fiss})/(d\sigma/d\Omega_{fiss}),$$

where $d\sigma/d\Omega_{fiss}$ is the inclusive cross section of the fission fragments. The dotted and the dash–dotted lines represent the calculated energy spectra corresponding to the emission sources of CE and FE, respectively.

The energy spectra from FE were calculated by the code PACE assuming the following input parameters. The excitation energies of the fission fragments were estimated using the Q–value for the symmetic mass division and TKE predicted by the Viola's systematics. The angular momentum brought into the fission fragments was estimated by assuming the sticking limit for two touthing fragments. Transmission coefficients calculated using the optical model potential[6] were used. The ⁴He energy spectra from CE were calculated by assuming the effective potential barriers for ⁴He, where the transmission coefficients were shifted to the low energy by the amount of 2 MeV. In these calculations, the level density parameter a was assumed to be A/8, where A is the mass number of nucleus.

The calculated energy spectra for FE and CE were simultaneously fitted to the inplane and the out–of–plane data, where the angular distribution of the ⁴He emitted from FE was assumed to be isotropic. This assumption can be justified because of the small angular momentum brought into the fission fragments ($\sim 7\ \hbar$ at $E_{lab} = 138$ MeV). Since the low energy bumps seen in the spectra can be easily identified as originated from FE for all the bombarding energies except at 138 MeV, the components were unambiguously subtracted from the data to obtain

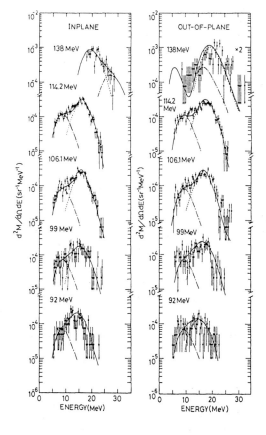

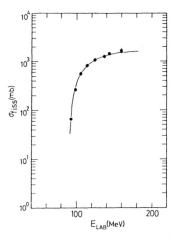

Fig.3 Fission cross section as a function of the bombarding energy. The prediction of the Bass model is shown as the solid line.

Fig.4 Energy spectra of ⁴He in coincidence with the fission fragments. The dotted and the dash–dotted lines represent the calculated spectra corresponding to the emission sources of CE and FE, respectively. The out–of–plane data were measured at $\varphi = 30°$

the components of CE. In the case of the 138 MeV data, the contribution from FE was estimated with a large error of ±20%, because the bump observed in the high energy tail in the inplane data was too small to fit the data acculately with the calculated energy spectrum of FE and the statistics of the out–of–plane data were poor.

Pre–fission multiplicity

The ^{4}He energy spectra, after the components of FE were subtracted from the data, were integrated to get the differential pre–fission multiplicity $dM/d\Omega\alpha$ which are shown in Fig.5 for the inplane and the out–of–plane measurements. The out–of–plane angular distributions were fitted by a function $C_1 \exp(C_2 \sin^2 \varphi)$ to estimate the pre–fission multiplicity M, where C_1 and C_2 are the fitting parameters[9].

The pre–fission multiplicity for ^{4}He obtained after the integration of the out–of–plane angular distribution are shown in Table I and are plotted in Fig.6 as a function of the excitation energy U. The upper scale $\tilde{U}$ is the excitation energy reckoned from the energy of the ground state as given by the liquid drop model ($\tilde{U} = U + \delta E_s$), where δE_s is the experimental value of the shell correction energy to the mass formula,

$$\delta E_s = M_{exp}(Z,A) - M_{ld}(Z,A). \qquad (1)$$

The experimental mass defect is denoted by $M_{exp}(Z,A)$ and the calculated mass defect from the liquid drop model of Myers–Swiatecki[10] by $M_{ld}(Z,A)$.

In order to compare the observed M with the results of the statistical model calculation, the code PACE was

Table I The pre–fission multiplicity of ^{4}He

E_{Lab}(MeV)	U(MeV)	M
92	48.0	0.016±0.002
99	54.4	0.024±0.003
106.1	60.8	0.026±0.003
114.2	68.2	0.028±0.003
138	90.0	0.055±0.008

used assuming the liquid drop masses for the excited parents and daughter nuclei and the level density parameter a = A/8. The results of this calculation are shown in Fig.6. The ratio a_f/a_n of the level density parameters at the saddle point and equilibrium deformations was varied to see the dependence of the calculated M on the excitation energy. It is obvious that the observed data are enhanced at the low excitation energy compared with the calculated results (the dotted, the dashed and the dash–dotted lines represent the results for $a_f/a_n = 0.95$, 1.00 and 1.02, respectively).

The observed enhancement may come from the shell effect in the daughter nucleus ^{212}Rn after ^{4}He is evaporated. The shell effect is revealed in the level density parameter a and the shell correction energy δE_s.

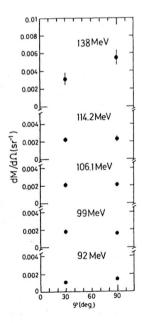

Fig.5 Differential pre–fission multiplicity of ^{4}He as a function of the out–of–plane angle.

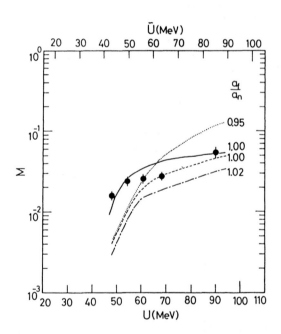

Fig.6 Pre–fission multiplicity of ^{4}He as a function of the excitation energy U. The upper scale $\tilde{U}$ is the excitation energy rekoned from the energy of the ground state as given by the liquid drop model. The results of the statistical model calculation assuming $a_f/a_n = 0.95$, 1.00 and 1.02 are shown in the dotted, the dashed and the dash–dotted lines, respectively. The solid line is the calculated result taking into account the excitation energy dependence of the level density parameter with $\gamma = 0.06$.

According to Ignatyuk[1], the level density parameter is expressed as

$$a(U) = \tilde{a} \, (1 + f(U)\delta E_s/U), \qquad (2a)$$

where

$$f(U) = 1 - \exp(-\gamma U). \qquad (2b)$$

The asymptotic value of a at high excitation energies is denoted by $\tilde{a}$ and γ is a parameter representing the degree of the shell smearing and to be fixed by the experimental data.

It is noted that the entropy $S(U) = 2\sqrt{a(U)U}$ is always larger than the asymptotic value $\tilde{S} = 2\sqrt{\tilde{a}U}$ at the fixed value of U if δE_s is negative. Since the level density is proportional to $\exp(S)$, the ^{4}He emission from the excited compound nucleus ^{216}Ra to the daughter nucleus ^{212}Rn with large negative value $\delta E_s = -8.5$ MeV is expected to be enhanced compared with the calculation using the liquid drop value $\tilde{S}$.

The statistical model calculation taking into account the excitation energy dependence of a(U) as written by eq.(2) was performed, where $\tilde{a}$ was assumed to be A/8 and the parameter γ was adjusted to fit the present data. The best fit is shown in Fig.6 with the solid line. The obtained value of γ was 0.06, which is close to the value 0.05 estimated by Ignatyuk from analysis of the neutron resonance data[1].

The sensitivity of M on γ was examined as shown in Fig.7(a) with the fixed ratio of $a_f/a_n = 1.00$. Although M is not so sensitive to γ, the allowed values of γ was in the range of 0.04 to 0.12. The ratio a_f/a_n was also varied to examine an effect on M. As shown in Fig.7(b), the allowed values of a_f/a_n was limitted in the small range of 1.00 to 1.02. This allowed range is consistent with the result obtained by Ward et al[11] in the measurements of the pre−fission neutron multiplicity.

SUMMARY

We measured the light charged particles in coincidence with the fission fragments in the the reaction ^{19}F + ^{197}Au. Most of the ^{4}He measured at backward angles in coincidence with the fission fragments were accounted for by evaporation from the compound nucleus before the fission process takes place. The obtained pre−fission multiplicity of ^{4}He as a function of the excitation energy show the enhancement at the low excitation energies (45 − 60 MeV) of the compound nucleus. This phenonenon was explained by taking into account the excitation energy dependence of the level density parameter. The parameter γ, which characterizes the shell smearing in the level density as a function of the excitation energy, was determined to be 0.06 from the present measurement and close to the value exstimated by Ignatyuk. The pre−fission multiplicity of ^{4}He was very sensitive to the ratio a_f/a_n of the level density parameters at the saddle point and the equilibrium deformations. The value of the ratio was also determined to be in the range of 1.00 to 1.02 from the present

measurement.

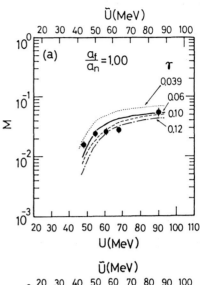

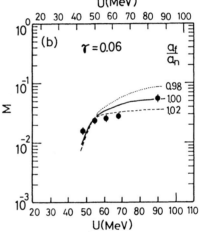

Fig.7 Results of the statistical model calculation are shown in (a) assuming various values of γ with the fixed value of $a_f/a_n = 1.00$ and (b) assuming various values of a_f/a_n with the fixed value of $\gamma = 0.06$.

REFERENCES

1. A. V. Ignatyuk, G. N. Smirenkin ,and A. S. Tishin, "Phenomenological Description of the Energy Dependence of the Level Density Parameter", SOV. J. NUCL. PHYS., 21, 255 (1975)

2. H. Baba, "A Shell−model Nuclear Level Density", NUCL. PHYS., A159, 625 (1970)

3. A. Bohr and B .R .Mottelson, Nuclear Structure, Vol. 2. V. A. Benjamin, Inc., Reading, Massachusetts, (1975)

4. A. Gavron, "Statistical Model Calculation in Heavy Ion Reactions", PHYS. REV. C21, 230 (1980)

5. J. R. Huizenga and G. Igo, "Theoretical
    Reaction Cross Sections for Alpha Particles
    with an Optical Model", <u>NUCL. PHYS. 29</u>, 462
    (1962)

6. J. M. Alexander, D. Guerreau and L. C. Vaz,
    "Evaporation Barriers for ^{4}He Indicate Very
    Extended Forms for Many Emitting Nuclei", <u>Z.
    PHYS. A305</u>, 313 (1982)

7. V. E. Viola, K. Kwiatkowski and M. Walker,
    "Systematics of Fission Fragment Total
    Kinetic Energy Release", <u>PHYS. REV. C31</u>, 1550
    (1985)

8. R. Bass, "Fusion of Heavy Nuclei in a
    Classical Model", <u>NUCL. PHYS. A231</u>, 45 (1974)

9. G. L. Catchen, M. Kaplan, J. M. Alexander and
    M. F. Rivet, "Semiempirical Methods for
    Estimating Fragment Spins from Studies of ^{4}He
    and ^{1}H Emission", <u>PHYS. REV. C21</u>, 940 (1980)

10. W. D. Myers and W. S. Swiatecki, "Anormalies
    in Nuclear Masses", <u>ARK. FYSIK. 36</u>, 593 (1967)

11. D. Ward, R. J. Charity, D. J. Hinde, J. R. Leigh
    and J. O. Newton, "Measurement of Pre-fission
    Neutron from ^{200}Pb; Further Limits to the
    Statistical Fission Parameters", <u>NUCL. PHYS.
    A403</u>, 189 (1983)

THE RELATION BETWEEN THE PROMPT GAMMA-RAY YIELDS FROM FISSION FRAGMENTS

AND THE CHARGE AND MASS DISTRIBUTION IN $^{235}U(n_{res},f)$ REACTION

A.A.BOGDZEL, N.A.GUNDORIN, A.DUKA-ZOLYOMI,[a] J.KLIMAN,[b] J.KRISTIAK[b]

Joint Institute for Nuclear Research,Dubna,
Head Post Office,P.O.Box 79,Moscow,U.S.S.R.

ABSTRACT

Prompt γ-ray yields of primary fission fragments of ^{235}U were measured. On the basis of γ-ray emission yields from all neutron resonances between 1 and 36eV independent yields of light and heavy fission fragments as a function of A and Z were determined. Good agreement between γ-rays yields and independent yields of fission fragments was observed The variance of the isobaric Z-distribution σ_z^2 was found to be (0.42 ± 0.02). The odd-even effect δ for protons and neutrons was determined to be equal to(35.7 ± 2.1)% and (6.8 ± 5.2)%, respectively. Both values depend on the nuclear charge and neutron number of fragments. Results make possible to use prompt γ-rays for the study of independent yields of fission fragments.

INTRODUCTION

In the present work the yields of promt γ-quanta emitted by nuclides in the light and heavy fragment group from resonance neutron fission of ^{235}U are reported.

Cheifetz et al.[1] have been starting an application of the discrete prompt γ-rays spectroscopy from fission fragments to determine the mass and charge distribution of fragments from the spontaneous fission of the ^{252}Cf nucleus.

The main aim of this work is to prove the suitability of the in-beam prompt γ-ray spectroscopy method for the deter-

[a] Department of Nuclear Physics,Comenius University,Bratislava,Czechoslovakia.
[b] Institute of Physics,EPRC,Slovak Acad. of Sciences,Bratislava,Czechoslovakia

mination of the fission fragment independent yield.

I. EXPERIMENT

The measurements were performed on the 57m flight path of the IBR-30 reactor operating in booster mode with LINAC. The reactor was kept in a power level of 6 kW with 100 Hz repetition rate and the neutron pulse width of 4 μs. The neutron flux was $\sim 5.10^3$ n/cm^2 s.eV .

The multilayer fission chamber was employed as a sample and a fast detector of fission fragments.[2] The total amount of ^{235}U isotope was 10.1 g. The used uranium was enriched with ^{235}U up to 90%.

For the registration of γ-rays fission fragments a coaxial Ge(Li) detector of ~ 30cm^3 (energy resolution ~ 2.8keV at 1332keV) was used . The absolute efficiency of the Ge(Li) detector was determined using standard calibration set.

A fast-slow coincidence scheme was used to set-up needed electronics for the detection of γ-rays in coincidence with fission.

The Ge(Li) system employed the amplitude rise-time compensation method to suppress Compton background.[3] The width of the time window for all experiments was equal to 33 nsec.A detailed description of hardware and software of this system can be found in ref.[4] After each measurement the data were sorted into an ordered matrix.From this matrix the γ-rays spectra have been obtained spectra by integrating over given intervals of neutron resonances or the time-of-flight spectra of incident neutrons over intervals of γ-rays spectrum.

II. RESULTS AND ANALYSIS

Three runs of measurements were performed in which $1.5 \cdot 10^9$ fissions and $2 \cdot 10^7$ coincidences were registered. The intensity of coincidences was ∿60 counts/sec from which ∿0.5 count/sec was a chance coincidence. The energy and intensity of all relevant peaks have been determined. After this the γ-ray intensities were normalized to the number of fissions in a relevant neutron resonance. The identification of fission fragment with a given atomic mass A and atomic number Z has been done on the basis of γ-ray energies E_γ as well as relative intensities I_γ of γ-ray lines.[5]

The data (E_γ, I_γ) on 143 γ-transitions have been determined of which 78 have been ascribed to 23 light and 27 heavy fragments. Part of this information is given in Tab.1.[6,7] The independent yield Y_χ has been corrected for the internal conversion if the type and multipolarity of relevant γ-transition are known. The Y_χ data are mean values of three runs. We did not take into account an anisotropy of γ-rays since it is small. The given errors of Y_χ are mainly statistical with small contribution from the efficiency calibration. The errors of E_γ are mostly smaller than ±0.5 keV.

The comparison of the independent yields of the isotope $_z A$ in the thermal vs. resonance neutron fission allows the following conclusions:
1) the yields Y_χ for even-even nuclei which correspond to γ-transition between 2^+-0^+ states are in very good agreement with the independent yields Y_z determined by other methods. But these are giving the yields of ground state or of a long-lived isomer.
2) the yields Y_χ of odd-A or odd-odd nuclei are smaller then the independent yield Y_T. It corresponds to the common knowledge concerning the feeding of excited nuclear states by neutrons and/or γ-rays cascade.
3) there is no systematic difference between "thermal" yields and the mean value of Y_γ over individual neutron resonances of ^{235}U isotope with spin 3^- and 4^-.

So, our results verify the basic assumption made in the paper of Cheifetz et al.[1] They assumed that total intensity of the 2^+-0^+ γ-transition observed in deexcitation of highly excited even-even fission fragment reflects the indepen-

dent yield of this one. We observe that the total intensity of transitions feeding the 0^+ ground state through the 2^+ excistated state is lower than 10%. This value is consistent with the zero if the estimated errors are taken in account. The feeding of y-rast band $(0^+$-2^+-4^+-6^+ levels sequence) in several even-even fragments can be also calculated from data of Tab.1. Mean transition intensities at the band normalized to Y_χ $(2\!-\!\!0)$ are equal to 0.72, 0.38 for $(4\!-\!\!2)$ and $(6\!-\!\!4)$ transitions, respectively. These values are in very good agreement with the results of Cheifetz et al(0.87,0.40) and theoretical statistical calculations (0.75, 0.45).[8] This agreement also suggests that the primary fission fragments from fission of $(3^-$ or $4^-)$ states of the compound nucleus ^{236}U have spins in the range of $(5\!-\!9)\hbar$. The yields of γ-transition Y_χ from the first excited state in light and heavy fission fragments are shown in Fig.1 and 2. Thick vertical lines are our experimental data with

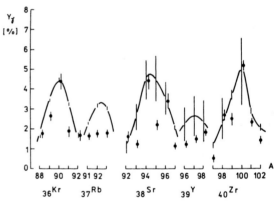

FIG.1 YIELD OF γ-TRANSITION Y_χ IN LIGHT FISSION FRAGMENTS. LIGHT VERTICAL LINES ARE THE Y_T.[7] THICK LINES ARE THE Y_γ.

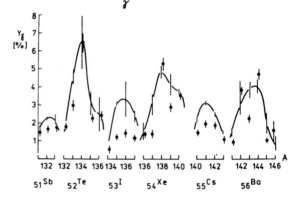

FIG.2 YIELD OF γ-TRANSITION Y_γ IN HEAVY FISSION FRAGMENTS

ELEMENT	MASS A	MULTIPLICITY OF NEUTRONS ν^{20}	INDEPENDENT YIELD THERMAL FISSION Y_T [%]	INDEPENDENT γ-RAY YIELD RESONANCE FISSION Y_γ [%]	ENERGY OF TRANSITION E[keV]	ΔZ
$_{36}$Kr	88	1.27	1.61±0.10	1.75±0.16	775.3	-0.79
	89	1.32	3.43±0.07	2.65±0.18	498.1	-0.38
	90	1.35	4.36±0.09	4.39±0.40	707.2	0.02
	91	1.38	3.22±0.06	1.88±0.17	953.1	0.42
	92	1.41	1.66±0.07	1.67±0.29	812.6	0.82
$_{37}$Rb	91	1.41	2.27±0.05	1.69±0.29	551.5	-0.42
	92	1.41	3.16±0.10	1.78±0.13	192.5	-0.02
	93	1.46	3.06±0.06	1.80±0.13	250.7	0.39
$_{38}$Sr	92	1.41	1.81±0.35	1.63±0.30	814.2	-1.01
	93	1.46	2.57±0.64	1.04±0.10	219.4	-0.60
	94	1.49	4.43±1.10	4.40±0.42	836.5	-0.20
	95	1.52	4.47±1.20	2.20±0.25	351.9	0.20
				3.78±0.15	204.0	
				2.22±0.18	682.7	
	96	1.54	3.56±0.90	3.40±0.36	814.8	0.60
				2.21±0.18	977.7	
	97	1.55	2.10±0.08	1.17±0.13	167.2	1.00
$_{39}$Y	96	1.56	2.22±0.89	1.18±0.14	931.8	-0.45
	97	1.55	2.65±1.06	1.52±0.20	697.3	-0.05
	98	1.56	2.40±1.08	1.83±0.12	170.2	0.34
$_{40}$Zr	97	1.55	1.14±0.13	0.50±0.06	1103.1	-1.09
	98	1.56	2.48±1.11	2.69±0.25	1221.8	-0.70
				1.56±0.23	824.2	
	99	1.56	3.65±0.22	2.47±0.34	121.8	-0.31
	100	1.56	4.99±2.00	5.18±0.20	212.7	0.08
				3.61±0.18	352.1	
				2.45±0.17	497.9	
	101	1.56	2.87±0.17	2.29±0.14	216.7	0.47
	102	1.57	2.02±0.16	1.95±0.43	151.6	-0.86
$_{51}$Sb	131	0.38	1.65±0.10	1.49±0.21	798.4	-0.50
				1.22±0.15	1143.3	
	132	0.49	2.22±0.13	1.67±0.17	898.9	-0.006
				1.11±0.10	247.3	
	133	0.65	2.18±0.32	1.74±0.24	962.3	0.39
$_{52}$Te	132	0.49	1.56±0.09	1.79±0.18	937.9	-0.86
				1.63±0.35	989.6	
	133	0.65	5.04±0.50	1.87±0.18	912.3	-0.41
				0.87±0.13	1704.2	
	134	0.85	6.51±1.95	5.91±0.50	1279.8	-0.06
				4.61±0.28	295.7	
	135	0.99	3.12±0.25	2.26±0.19	1131.5	0.50
	136	1.07	2.48±0.98	2.44±0.23	1178.4	0.92
				1.65±0.25	325.8	
$_{53}$I	134	0.85	0.87±0.05	0.55±0.20	180.1	-0.88
	135	0.99	3.09±0.10	1.20±0.15	603.7	-0.44
	136	1.07	3.32±1.00	1.81±0.28	333.9	0.02
	137	1.11	2.46±0.39	1.16±0.09	243.3	0.39

	A	υ^{20}	Y_T [%]	Y_γ [%]	E[keV]	ΔZ
$_{54}$Xe	136	1.07	1.51±0.60	1.38±0.14	1313.9	−0.97
				1.01±0.08	381.5	
	137	1.11	2.99±0.60	1.38±0.16	601.7	−0.56
				1.36±0.14	1218.6	
	138	1.14	4.80±0.48	5.30±0.40	588.8	−0.16
				4.62±0.30	484.3	
				1.50±0.20	431.1	
	139	1.17	4.15±0.33	2.86±0.21	571.2	0.24
				1.05±0.25	537.0	
	140	1.21	3.73±0.22	3.48±0.23	376.9	0.65
				2.73±0.31	457.6	
$_{55}$Cs	140	1.21	2.20±0.23	1.47±0.12	621.1	−0.56
	141	1.23	3.09±0.10	1.94±0.15	468.0	−0.16
				1.26±0.14	909.4	
	142	1.25	2.48±0.14	1.87±0.16	571.7	0.23
				1.08±0.13	250.7	
	143	1.27	1.45±0.09	1.09±0.13	232.4	0.63
$_{56}$Ba	141	1.23	1.50±0.30	0.94±0.11	561.5	−1.00
	142	1.25	3.42±1.02	3.79±0.28	359.3	−0.59
				2.53±0.22	473.4	
				1.83±0.19	632.0	
	143	1.27	3.80±0.40	2.20±0.24	306.2	−0.19
	144	1.29	4.02±0.36	4.72±0.33	199.1	0.21
				3.61±0.25	331.0	
				1.28±0.20	431.7	
	145	1.31	2.02±0.65	1.01±0.06	175.6	0.61
				1.14±0.08	297.8	
	146	1.33	0.86±0.50	1.69±0.64	180.9	1.00

$\Delta Z = Z_p - Z_c$, Z_p mean charge of isobaric distribution, Z_c - the most probable charge

errors, thin lines are the independent yields the of fragment ground state Y_T from the evaluation of Rider and Meek.[7] There are remarkable differences because of very complicated deexcitation pattern of excited states in odd-odd as well as odd-A fragments. But the sum of our Y_γ's in the case of ^{95}Sr, ^{137,139}Xe, ^{141,142}Cs nuclei gives correct independent yields if relevant level schemes are taken into account.

The ratio of Y_γ/Y_T as a function of number of neutrons N is shown in Fig.3. Here the behaviour of the derivative of the Fermi energy of neutrons $\Delta\lambda_N$ is also shown by a thin curve. This derivative is calculated from Fermi energy $\lambda_N = -1/2 S_{2n}$[9], where S_{2n} is the two-neutron separation energy calculated from the binding energies B.[10] As Bengston et al.[9] has shown, the inflexion point which appears on the $\lambda_N(N)$ curve is possible to identify with the transition from spherical to deformed shape of the nucleus.

There are several interesting trends:

1) Minima at the region of N ∿56 and 82, in which ∿60% of deexcitation of highly excited states are fragmented into many states.
2) The situation looks differently in the case of N ∿ 61 and 80. Apprroximately 80% of intensity ends at definite low lying state. It is noteworthy that ^{101}Zr nucleus with N=61 is very deformed ($\beta \sim 0.3-0.4$).[11]
3) Some correlation between the ratio Y_γ/Y_T and the derivate of λ_N can be observed. It points to larger fragmentation of the intensity of γ-ray transitions from high-excited states in the case of spherical fission fragments.

III. YIELDS AND ISOBARIC, ISOTOPIC DISTRIBUTION

Our data on the yields Y_γ have been used to study charge and mass division in the fission process. The isobaric distribution is the distribution of independent yields of fission fragments with mass A as a function of nuclear

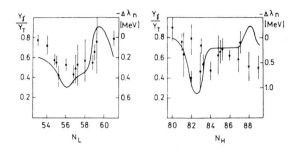

FIG.3 DEPENDENCE OF RATIO Y_γ/Y_T ON NUMBER OF NEUTRONS IN ODD-MASS FISSION FRAGMENTS

charge Z. In our work we assume that the constant charge ratio is valid. In this case it was assumed that the scission phase of compound nucleus fission is rapid. Therefore,both fragments have the same neutron to proton ratio as the compound nucleus A_f the most probable charge Z_c of primary fission fragment with mass A can be written as $Z_c = Z_f A(A_f -\upsilon)$ where A_f is the mass of compound nucleus and υ is the total number of prompt neutrons emitted in the fission. Then the experimental mean charge $Z_p = Z_f (\bar{A}_Z+\upsilon-)/A_f$,where $\bar{A}_Z$ is the mean atomic mass of isotopic chain Z and $\upsilon-$ is the mean number of neutrons emitted by nuclei from this isotopic chain. These mean values are calculated from the independent yields $Y(A_i)$ given in Tab.1. using the relation

$$\bar{A}_Z = (\Sigma_i A_i \cdot Y(A_i))/(\Sigma_i Y(A_i))$$

for $\bar{A}_Z$ and $\upsilon-$,respectively. The most probable charge $Z_c(A_i)$ of each isobaric chain can be determined as
$$Z_c(A_i) = Z_f(A_i+\upsilon_i)/A_f ,$$
where υ_i is the number of prompt neutrons emitted by a fragment $(A_i + \upsilon_i)$. So the charge distribution which we are looking for can be characterized by a difference ΔZ , between Z_p and Z_c . The values of ΔZ for light and heavy fragments are given in Tab.1. The used values of prompt neutrons υ_i ,the isobaric yields Y_T,Y_γ from the thermal or resonance neutron fission are also shown for completeness.

The yield Y_γ as a function of ΔZ is shown in Fig.4. The Y_γ distribution is separately given for 3 different groups of fragments (even-even, odd Z, and even-odd). It is noteworthy that all distributions are similar regardless of their absolute values. Such behaviour of Y_γ was preliminary published in Dubna.[13]

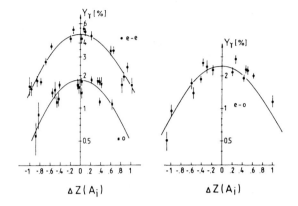

FIG.4 DEPENDENCE OF YIELD Y_γ ON A DIFFERENCE OF THE MEAN CHARGE Z_p AND THE MOST PROBABLE CHARGE Z_c

The dependence of Y_γ and Y_T on $\Delta Z(A)$ was described by the formula

$$Y_{\gamma,T}(A,Z)=Y_{0,\gamma T} \cdot \exp[-(\Delta Z)^2/(2(\sigma+1/12)^2)] ,$$

where σ^2 describes the width of the charge distribution and 1/12 is Shepard's correction for the discrete change of Z.The values of parameters Y_0,σ^2 as determined by the least square method are given in Tab.2. The coefficients K, the ratio $Y_{0\gamma}/Y_{0T}$,are also included. The value of K is very important. It indicates how much of γ-rays intensity omits the primary γ-transitions detected in these three groups of fragments. It is remarkable that there is no difference between odd-Z and even-odd fragments in spite of higher density of levels in odd Z nuclei. Our values of charge dispersion σ^2 are in mutual accord and agree with the value $\sigma^2 = 0.40\pm0.05$ determined by the mass-spectrometric measurement of light mass fragments.[6]

IV. ODD-EVEN EFFECT IN THE YIELD OF FISSION FRAGMENTS

In the last several years it was shown that the yield Y of fragments with even or odd number of nucloens is sensitive to the dynamics of fission. As several authors before us we have been trying to understand the fission dynamics using the so-called odd-even effect δ the in yield of fission fragments.This effect is defined separately for neutrons δ_N, and protons, δ_Z,as

$$\delta_K(i) = \frac{Y_\gamma(i-even) - Y_\gamma(i+1)}{Y_\gamma(i) + Y_\gamma(i+1)} ,$$

where K=N or Z. The experimental values of $Y_\gamma(i)$ have been calculated from the Y_γ values of Tab.1 using the coefficient K as the correction. Such corrected values have been summed over A with a constant number of protons Z or neutrons N, respectively. The dependence of Y_γ on the atomic number Z of light and heavy fission fragments is shown in Fig.5. The similar dependence of Y_γ on the number of neutrons N in fragments is displayed in Fig.6. The comparison of these figures reveals the fact that $Y_\gamma(Z)$ dependence is very strong.

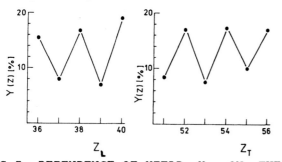

FIG.5 DEPENDENCE OF YIELD Y_γ ON THE NUMBER OF Z OF FISSION FRAGMENTS

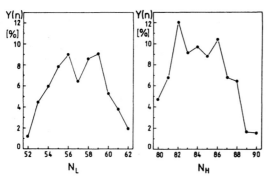

FIG.6 DEPENDENCE OF YIELD Y_γ ON THE NUMBER OF N OF FISSION FRAGMENTS

The best way to study the dependence of the odd-even effect on the relevant number of nucleons (Z or N) is to calculate the quantity $\delta_K(i)$ introduced by Tracy et al.[14] It is defined as the mean odd-even effect averaged over the interval j centered at $(i+3/2)$. Explicitly,

$$\delta_K(i) = (-i)^{i+1}[(S_3-S_0)-3(S_2-S_1)]/8,$$

where $S_j = \ln[Y_\gamma(i+j)]$, $j = 0...3$, K=N,Z. Our data show that δ_z depends on Z strongly e.g. δ_z changes by 15% when Z decreases from 38.5 to 37.5, but δ_z increases by 29% decreasing Z from 54.5 to 53.5. The mean value of δ_z for the group

of light and heavy fragments is (37.1±3.4)% and (34.2±1.9)%, respectively. So our proton odd-even effect δ_z determined by the γ-ray spectroscopy of primary fragments is equal to (35.7±2.1)%. Our mean value of δ_z for light fragments differs from the mean value $\delta_z = (23.7±0.7)\%$ obtained using the mass spectrometer "Lohengrin".[6] But our δ_z is in good agreement with higher kinetic energy (see fig.20 of ref 6).

The determination of the neutron odd-even effect δ_N is much more complicated because this is influenced by the emission of neutrons from the primary $(A+\upsilon)$ fission fragment. The mean value of δ_N calculated from our data is equal to (6.8±5.2)%. But there is a big difference between $\delta_N = (2.6±2.1)\%$ for the light fragments and $\delta_N = (11.0±1.9)\%$ calculated for the heavy fragments. The value of $\delta_N = (5.4±0.7)\%$ was deduced from the "Lohengrin" data for the light fragments but an earlier value of Siegert et al.[15] is (9±1)%.

The dependence of the odd-even effect δ_N on the neutron number N of light as well as heavy fragments is shown in Fig.7. Our data show that this odd-even effect is heavily affected by N. The general behaviour of δ_N vs.N for the light fragments is similar to the one published by Lang et.al.[6] The complementary trend in δ_N for heavy fragments was at originally published in our preprint.[16]

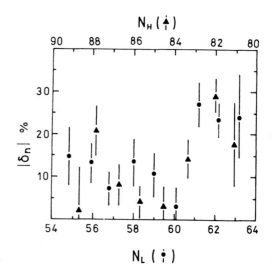

FIG.7 DEPENDENCE OF NEUTRON ODD-EVEN EFFECT δ_N ON NUMBER OF NEUTRONS OF LIGHT (L) AND HEAVY (H) FRAGMENTS

TABLE 2   PARAMETERS OF CHARGE DISTRIBUTION
OF FISSION FRAGMENTS

Parameter	Fragments (Z,N)		
	Even-even	Even-odd	Z-odd
$Y_{0\gamma}$	4.90±0.14	2.44±0.13	1.82±0.10
σ^2_{z}	0.42±0.02	0.45±0.05	0.37±0.06
Y_{0T}	4.96	4.07	3.00
σ^2_{T}	0.39	0.53	0.33
ratio K	1.00	1.67	1.65

Meaning of symbols: γ-data from yields of γ-transition in fission fragments from resonance neutron induced fission; T-data from independent yields of fission fragments from thermal neutron induced fission.[6,7,19]

V.   CONCLUSION

The present paper deals with the determination of the intensity of γ-transitions in primary fragments from the resonance neutron fission of the [235]U isotope. It was shown that this new experimental procedure for the study of fission dynamics is complementary to more common techniques (the mass spectrometer, the multiwire ionization chamber). The mean values of γ-ray yields Y_γ from all neutron resonances between 1 and 36 eV are in good agreement with the independent yield of relevant isotopes from the thermal neutron fission.[7] In this way the basic assumption of the pioneering work of Cheifetz et al.[1] on a possibility to use γ-ray spectroscopy for the study of [252]Cf spontaneous fission has been verified.

The isobaric variance $\sigma^2 = (0.42±0.02)$ has been calculated using values of Y_γ. The detailed knowledge of the γ-ray yields Y_γ has revealed interesting features of the proton and the neutron odd-even effect in the yield. The magnitudes of this effect are (35.7±2.1)% and (6.8±5.2)% for proton and neutron, respectively.

The experimental value of the charge dispersion σ^2 may be interpreted by three different models, namely the scission-point model, the isovector giant dipole resonance model (IGDR), and the asymmetric two-center model.[17] In the case of IGDR[18] description the magnitude of σ^2 is caused by the general phenomenon of quantum-mechanical zero-point fluctuation. Then the radius of the neck at a moment of its disruption is 2.1 fm.

The creation of the charge distribution in fission fragments lasts longer than $1.7.10^{-21}$ s.

The odd-even effects may be consistently interpreted by several models. There is one common outcome that the magnitude of odd-even effects can be used as an indicator for the intrinsic excitation of the system during its descent from saddle to scission. The "average" intrinsic excitation energy that the [236]U nucleus has obtained along a fission path is (6.8±1.4)MeV. It may be understood if the dissipation energy is due to two-body dissipation mechanism with a viscosity coefficient μ = 0.01 TP. The deformation energy of both fragments at the moment of neck rupture $E_D \sim 15$ MeV.

REFERENCES

1. E.CHEIFETZ, J.B.WILHELMY,R.C.JARED, S.G.THOMPSON,"Determination of the Charge and Mass Distribution in the Fission of [252]Cf", Phys.Rev.C4 (1971)1913

2. A.A.BOGDZEL,A.DUKA-ZOLYOMI,J.KLIMAN, V.PRESPERIN, S.P.AVDEEV, V.D.KUZNE-TSOV,Z.DLOUHY,"Fast ionization Chamber for Fission Fragment Detection with a Large Amount of U-235",Nucl. Meth.200(1982)407

3. A.DUKA-ZOLYOMI,J.KLIMAN,J.KRISTIAK, "A Rise-Time Discriminator for Background Supression in the Ge(Li) Detector Sp[ectrum","Low-Level Counting and Spectrometry",Bratislava: Veda,1987,p.165.

4. S.A.ANTONOV,A.A.BOGDZEL,N.A.GUNDO-
    RIN,A.DUKA-ZOLYOMI,J.KLIMAN,D.KRI-
    STEK,A.I.OSTROVNOJ,T.M.OSTROVNAJA,
    A.B.POPOV,V.PRESPERIN,V.G.TISHIN,
    N.J.SHIRIKOVA,"Techniques of Mul-
    tidimentional Measurements and Ana-
    lysis of Yields of Nuclear Products
    Fission by Resonance Neutrons",(in
    Russian), Comm.JINR,13-85-71,Dubna,
    (1985)

5. C.M.LEDERER, V.S.SHIRLEY, Table of
    Isotopes,7-th edit.,Wileg-Intersci-
    ence Publ.(1978),
    U.REUS,W.WESTMEIER,"Gamma-Ray Cata-
    logue",Atomic Data and Nucl.Data
    Tables 29(1983),
    J.BLACHOT,C.FICHE,"Tableau des iso-
    topes radioaktifs et des principaux
    rayonnements emis",Anales de Physi-
    que,Suppl.6,(1981)

6. W.LANG, H.G.CLERC, H.WOHLFART,
    H.SCHRABER, K.H.SCHMIDT, "Nuclear
    Charge and Mass Yields for ^{235}U(n,
    f) as a function of the Kinetic
    Energy of the Fission Products",
    Nucl.Phys.A345(1980)34

7. B.F.RIDER,M.E.MEEK, Fission Yields,
    NEDO 292,IAEA,Vienna,(1981)

8. J.B.WILHELMY,E.CHEIFETZ,R.C.JARED,
    S.G.THOMPSON,H.R.BOWMAN,J.R.RASMU-
    SEN,"Angular Momentum of Primary
    Products Formed in the Spontaneous
    Fission ^{252}Cf",Phys.Rev.C5(1972)2141

9. R.BENGTSSON,P.MOLLER,J.R.NIX,YING-
    YE-ZHANG, "Nuclear Shapes and Shape
    Transitions",Phys.Scripta 29(1984)

10. J.K.TULI, Nuclear Wallet Cards,U.S.
    Nuclear Data Center,New York,(1985)

11. J.H.HAMILTON,P.G.HANSEN,E.F.ZGANJAR,
    "New vistas from nuclei far from
    stability",Rep.Prog.Phys.48(1985)631

12. J.P.GANGRSKIJ,B.DALCHAUREN,B.M.MAR-
    KOV,Fragments of Nuclear Fission,
    (in Russian), Energoizdat, Moscow,
    (1986)61

13. A.A.BOGDZEL, N.A.GUNDORIN, A.DUKA-
    ZOLYOMI,J.KLIMAN,J.KRISTIAK,"Inves-
    tigation of Prompt Gamma-Ray Yields
    as a Function of Mass and Charge of
    ^{236}U Fission Fragments"(in Russ.)
    Comm.JINR R3-87-862,Dubna,(1987)

14. B.L.TRACY, J.CHAUMONT, R.KLAPISCH,
    J.M.NITSCHKE, A.M.POSKANZER,
    E.ROECKL,C.THIBAULT,"Rb and Cs Iso-
    topic Cross Section from 40-60 MeV
    Proton Fission of ^{238}U,^{232}Th and
    ^{235}U", Phys.Rev.C5(1972)222

15. G.SIGERT,B.PFEIFFER, "Nuclear Char-
    ge Distribution of Fission Products
    from ^{233}U(n$_{th}$,f) of the Mass 79 to
    100", Phys.Rev.C14(1976)1864

16. A.A.BOGDZEL, N.A.GUNDORIN, A.DUKA-
    ZOLYOMI, J.KLIMAN, J.KRISTIAK, "The
    Study of Fragment Charge and Mass
    Fragmentation under ^{235}U Fission
    with Resonance Neutrons"(in Russian)
    Comm.JINR P15-88-385,Dubna, (1988)

17. N.A.GUNDORIN,A.DUKA-ZOLYOMI,J.KLI-
    MAN,J.KRISTIAK,"Analysis of Dyna-
    mic Characteristics of ^{235}U Fission
    with Resonances Neutrons on the Ba-
    sis of Data on Fission Fragment
    Charge and Mass Fragmentation"(in
    Russian), Comm. JINR P15-88-386,
    Dubna, (1988)

18. M.ASGHAR, "Charge distribution in
    Fission - a Quantum Mechanical
    Phenomenon",Zeit.Phys.A296(1980)79

19. H.G.CLERC, W.LANG, M.MUTTERER,
    C.SCHMITT, J.P.THEOBALD, V.QUADE,
    K.RUDOLPH,P.AMBRUSTER,F.GONNENWEIN,
    H.SCHRABER,D.ENGELHARDT,"Cold Frag-
    mentation in Thermal-Neutron-Indu-
    ced Fission ^{233}U and ^{235}U",
    Nucl.Phys.A452(1986)277

PRODUCTION OF ^{242}Am AND THE

FISSION ISOMER ^{242f}Am IN THE REACTION ^{7}Li + ^{238}U

L. P. SOMERVILLE[a]
Engineering and Physics Department
Oral Roberts University
Tulsa, Oklahoma 74171
1989 phone: (415) 486-6471

R. WADA
Cyclotron Institute
Texas A&M University
College Station, Texas
77843-3366
(409) 845-1411

J. P. DONAHUE[b]
Chemistry Department
Oral Roberts University
Tulsa, Oklahoma 74171
1989 phone: (303) 399-6947

K. L. WOLF
Cyclotron Institute
Texas A&M University
College Station, Texas
77843-3366
(409) 845-1411

ABSTRACT

After bombarding a stacked foil arrangement we detected the α particles from ^{242}Cm following β^--decay of ^{242}Am, to determine an excitation function for the reaction ^{238}U(^{7}Li,3n)^{242}Am(16 hr). In a separate experiment transporting recoils past mica we recorded fission tracks from the 14-ms isomer ^{242f}Am. Our peak cross section of 0.26±0.06 mb for the ground state is x12 lower than estimated using experimental $< \Gamma_n/\Gamma_f >$,[1] masses,[2] and fission barriers,[1] and assuming both a constant nuclear temperature of 0.95 MeV and a fusion cross section equal to the prompt fission cross section of Freiesleben *et al.*[3] Part of this discrepancy is undoubtedly due to the production of the 141-yr[4] isomer ^{242m}Am, which we did not measure; the rest is within the experimental uncertainty in $< \Gamma_n/\Gamma_f >$.[1] We speculate that similar long-lived isomers might exist in some of the isotopes ^{238}Am, $^{242-245}$Bk, and ^{246}Es, and partly explain the reduced production cross sections for the ground states measured by Williams and Seaborg[5,6] and Thomas.[7]

I. INTRODUCTION

Most of the peak cross sections for fusion evaporation residues of heavy elements produced with heavy ions up to neon are reproduced to wtihin a factor of three by the neutron evaporation code JORPLE.[8] In this code the cross section σ_{xn}(E) at laboratory bombarding energy E for production of the compound nucleus product with x neutrons evaporated is given by[9]

$$\sigma_{xn}(E) = \sigma_{fus}(E, r_o, D) P_{xn}(E^*, T) \prod_{i=1}^{x} \left(\frac{\frac{\Gamma_n}{\Gamma_f}}{\frac{\Gamma_n}{\Gamma_f} + 1} \right)_i . \tag{1}$$

This code utilizes a fusion cross section σ_{fus} calculated using the optical model with a Wood-Saxon nuclear potential;[8] the Jackson model[10] for neutron evaporation probability $P_{xn}(E^*, T)$ using fission barriers and neutron binding energies calculated with the aid of a semiempirical mass formula of Myers and Swiatecki;[11] the empirical systematics of Sikkeland *et al.*[12] for Γ_n/Γ_f, independent of excitation energy E^*; and parameters such as the constant nuclear temperature T, along with the nuclear radius parameter r_o and diffuseness D from the Wood-Saxon potential which have been adjusted to fit experimental cross sections for the heavy-element region. There are a number of experimental cross sections measured by Williams and Seaborg,[5,6] and Thomas,[7] however, which are overpredicted using the JORPLE code by large factors of 10 to 60. But more importantly, in some of the cases where the values of $< \Gamma_n/\Gamma_f >$, averaged over a neutron evaporation chain, or $(\Gamma_n/\Gamma_f)_i$ de-

---

[a]Present address: Department of Physics and Astronomy, San Francisco State University, San Francisco, California 94132

[b]Present address: 880 Cherry Street, Apt. 407, Denver, Colorado 80220

termined from one- and two-neutron transfer reactions, along with the masses[2] and fission barriers[1] are all experimentally known, the percent discrepancies are larger than the uncertainties that the most recent measurements of $(\Gamma_n/\Gamma_f)_i^{13,14}$ and fission probabilities[15] will allow.

The maximum production cross section we report here for the reaction $^{238}\text{U}(^7\text{Li,3n})^{242g}\text{Am}$ is also significantly lower than both an estimation from equation 1 using others' experimental data[1-3] and a calculation using the JORPLE code. Prior to our study of this reaction Freiesleben et al.[3] commented that the data of Fleury[16] "show that the (^{7}Li,3n) cross section is small compared with the fission cross section," but the (^{7}Li,3n) cross section cross section was not published. Although there have been many studies of direct or transfer reactions with ^{6,7}Li projectiles there are relatively few measurements of fusion cross sections with them, particularly with heavy targets. Bemis et al.[17] have reported a production cross section of 1.8 ± 0.1 μb for the fission isomer $^{240f}\text{Am}(0.9$ ms) in the reaction $^{238}\text{U}(^7\text{Li,5n})^{240f}\text{Am}$ with 49-MeV ^{7}Li ions. In one study of the reactions $^{6,7}\text{Li}+^{209}\text{Bi}$ Freiesleben et al.[18,19] reported that near the Coulomb barrier the sum of the cross sections for (^{6,7}Li,αxn) and (^{6,7}Li,d or t xn) transfer products was even larger than the total fusion cross section. This dominance of transfer products has been attributed to the loosely bound α-d or α-t structures of these projectiles, as discussed in, for example, Refs. 18, 20, and 21. This idea is supported by the facts that the prompt fission cross sections with a ^{238}U target[3] and the transfer cross sections with a ^{209}Bi target[18] and a ^{232}Th target[16,22] are in general all larger for the more weakly bound ^{6}Li than for the ^{7}Li projectile near the Coulomb barriers.

We report here an excitation function for the reaction $^{238}\text{U}(^7\text{Li,3n})^{242g}\text{Am}$ producing the 16-hour ground state (g) of ^{242}Am as well as a single production cross section for the 14-ms fission isomer ^{242f}Am. We then attempt to understand why our production cross sections for ^{242g,f}Am in the reaction ^{7}Li+^{238}U are much lower than expected from equation 1, in which the relevant information on $<\Gamma_n/\Gamma_f>^1$, masses[2], and fission barriers[1] together with the prompt fission data of Freiesleben et al.[3] for our reaction have all been measured. A few comments on the shortcomings of the JORPLE code will then be in order. Finally, we will speculate that our explanation might contribute to the low production cross sections for some of the transuranium nuclei measured by Williams and Seaborg[5,6] and Thomas.[7] But first, in the next section we discuss exactly how our production cross sections were measured.

II. EXPERIMENTAL

A. Alpha Particle Detection

A beam of 62-MeV ^{7}Li extracted from the Texas A&M Variable Energy Cyclotron struck a stack of aluminum degrader foils, six uranium oxide targets with thicknesses of 134- to 668-μg/cm^2 $^{238}\text{U}_3\text{O}_8$ and six $\approx$2-mg/cm^2 gold catcher foils, as illustrated in Fig. 1, in order to measure an excitation function for the reaction $^{238}\text{U}(^7\text{Li,3n})^{242}\text{Am}(16\ \text{hr})$. The ^{7}Li energies at the targets ranged from 29 to 55 MeV. The stacked-foil assembly was part of a deep Faraday cup which was electrically insulated from the collimator. A horseshoe magnet caused secondary electrons to spiral back into the target and Faraday cup walls to insure proper measurement of the beam intensity. The ^{7}Li energies through the stack and the compound-nucleus recoil ranges for both the spontaneous-fission and α-particle experiments were

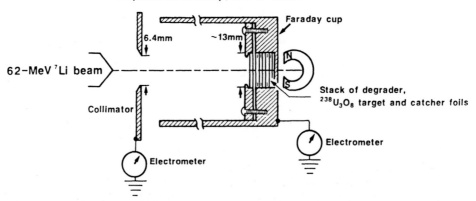

Experimental setup, not to scale

FIGURE 1. EXPERIMENTAL SETUP FOR THE MAY, 1987 EXPERIMENT TO MEASURE THE EXCITATION FUNCTION FOR THE REACTION $^{238}\text{U}(^7\text{Li,3n})^{242g}\text{Am}(16\ \text{hr}).$

calculated using the tables of Northcliffe and Schilling.[23]

At the end of the bombardment the α activity in the gold catcher foils was measured using solid-state detectors with areas 100-900 mm^2. The measurements used in determining the cross sections of Fig. 2 were all made with a 900-mm^2 area detector at 26±4% of 4π geometry. In such a high geometry we were concerned that α particles with up to 62 degrees from normal incidence might not be detected as full-energy α particles. But using an ^{241}Am calibration source we found no measurable loss in detection efficiency within the 2% uncertainty of

measurement at 9.3 mm compared to 29.4 mm from a 900-mm^2 detector. The detected α pulses were amplified and pulse-height analyzed by either a multichannel analyzer or an IBM personal computer interfaced to operate as a pulse-height analyzer. During spectra accumulation with the IBM personal computer we continously checked for amplifier gain drifts using a pulser. In separate test experiments we checked the pulse height analysis with a pulser over the energy range 1.8-9.0 MeV. In the high-geometry detector configuration with thick gold catcher foils the detected α paricles could be emitted from a range of depths and angles, limiting our resolution to no better than ±180 keV for 6.1-MeV α particles.

Figure 3a shows that shortly after bombardment the dominant α peaks were 5.866-MeV ^{211}At(7.2 hr) and 7.45-MeV ^{211}Po(0.516 s). We verified these assignments on the basis of their correct α particle energies, determined from ^{241}Am and ^{228}Th calibration sources, the ≈7-hour half-life for decay of each of these peaks, and from

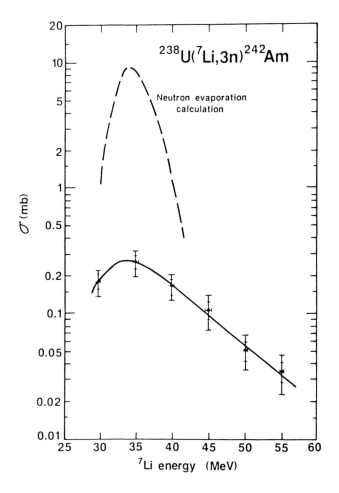

FIGURE 2. EXPERIMENTAL EXCITATION FUNCTION FOR PRODUCTION OF THE 16-HR GROUND STATE ^{242g}Am IN THE REACTION ^{238}U(^{7}Li,3n)^{242}Am. BOTH THE ABSOLUTE, AND SMALLER, RELATIVE ERROR BARS ARE SHOWN. THE SOLID LINE IS MEANT TO GUIDE THE EYE THROUGH THE POINTS WITH THEIR ERROR BARS. THE DASHED CURVE IS THE EXCITATION FUNCTION CALCULATED USING THE NEUTRON-EVAPORATION CODE JORPLE.[8]

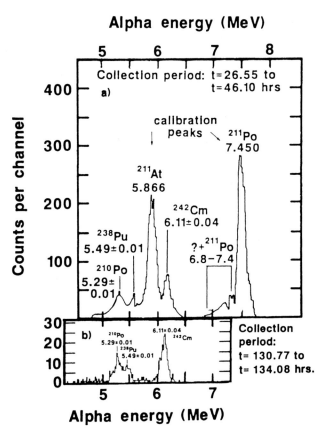

FIGURE 3. ALPHA-PARTICLE SPECTRA FROM A GOLD CATCHER FOIL FOR THE REACTION 34.7-MeV ^{7}Li + ^{238}U RECORDED (a) BETWEEN 26.55 AND 46.10 HOURS AND (b) BETWEEN 130.77 AND 134.08 HOURS AFTER THE END OF THE MAY, 1987 BOMBARDMENT.

the approximate agreement in the intensity ratio for the peaks, I(5.866 MeV)/I(7.45 MeV)≈0.73, calculated from decay scheme in Ref. 24. Clearly [211]At is the source of both peaks, probably made from [207,208]Pb impurities in the target. As early as 1971 Nurmia[25] noted that in the molecular plating process used in the production of our uranium targets "it is quite difficult to reduce the lead content of these targets below a few nanograms."

We determined the production rates of [242g]Am from the measured 6.10-MeV α activities of [242]Cm, the β^--decay daughter of [242g]Am. Taking advantage of the difference in half-lives of the 7-hour peaks of [211]At and [211]Po compared to the 163-day [242]Cm, we simply waited 5.4 days after the end of the bombardment before measuring the [242]Cm α activity. As shown by the α-particle spectrum in Fig. 3b the interference of 5.866-MeV [211]At is then almost eliminated and the [242]Cm peak is the dominant peak in the spectrum.

Because of possible confusion of 6.10-MeV [242]Cm with 6.11-MeV [252]Cf and 5.69- to 6.29-MeV [228]Th together with the low detected [242]Cm α activities of 0.1-1.5 α particles/min. extreme care was taken to keep the background to 0.2-2.0 α particles/hr, or not more than a 4% background for any [7]Li energy by cleaning the contaminated detecting chamber, lining it with clean aluminum foil, and by occasionally blowing dry nitrogen over the detector surface.

The 163-day [242]Cm was identified by α energy and roughly by half-life with intermittent measurements over one year. Our measurement for the α energy of 6.11±0.04 MeV agrees with the centroid of all α particle energies, 6.10±0.04 MeV, in the decay of [242]Cm.[24] In computing the cross sections we included the 82.7% β^--branch and the growth and decay of [242]Cm α particles with time following β^--decay of [242]Am.[26]

B. Spontaneous Fission Detection

To detect the 14-ms fission isomer [242f]Am with 35.6-MeV [7]Li ions we used the recoil tape transport system[27,28] shown in Fig. 4 to transport recoil nuclei at a speed of 0.71 m/s past fixed mica track detectors. We could associate a definite decay time after production with a given track distance from the point where the recoils were deposited in the tape. From the event-time distribution we could determine both the half-life and the production cross section for [242f]Am after correcting for the scanning efficiency for deep tracks. The scanning efficiency of 83±8% was determined by comparing the detected spontaneous fission rates from a [252]Cf source using both mica track detectors and a gas proportional counter with 2π-geometry.[27] For [242]Am recoils with a calculated recoil energy of 1 MeV that we produced here the calculated deposition depth[23] in the tape was so shallow that the emissivity of fragments from the tape should be 100%, based upon earlier measurements.[27] In this exper-

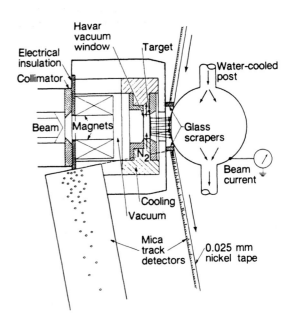

FIGURE 4. RECOIL-TAPE TRANSPORT SYSTEM[28] WE USED TO MEASURE BOTH THE PRODUCTION CROSS SECTION AND HALF-LIFE OF 14-MS [242f]Am IN THE REACTION [238]U([7]Li,3n)[242f]Am. SEE THE TEXT. SPONTANEOUS FISSION FRAGMENTS OF [242f]Am PRODUCED THE DIAMOND-SHAPED TRACKS IN THE MICA, WHICH BECAME VISIBLE UNDER A MICROSCOPE AFTER ETCHING IN HYDROFLUORIC ACID.

iment the beam was not turned off as in Refs. 27-28 during the tape direction reversals after one tape reel filled up with tape. But we estimated that on the average only 0.7 of the 63 tracks we observed could have occured during the slow down and speeding up of the tape while the direction was reversing.

In separate experiments we replaced the mica track detectors with four Si(Au) surface-barrier detectors, each with 400-mm^2 active area. But because we had only four Si(Au) detectors compared to an area of ≈1.9 x 64 cm^2 of mica, we detected many more spontaneous fissions per unit beam flux in the experiment using mica compared to one using surface barrier detectors.

III. RESULTS AND DISCUSSION

Figure 2 shows the excitation function we measured for 16-hr [242g]Am from our May, 1987 bombardment. An earlier March, 1987 bombardment with a slightly different experimental setup gave consistent results, but with poorer statistics. The cross sections we determined from both of these experiments are tabulated in Table 1.

TABLE 1

FORMATION CROSS SECTIONS IN MICROBARNS FOR 16-HR ^{242g}Am IN THE REACTION ^{7}Li + ^{238}U, DETERMINED FROM TWO SEPARATE BOMBARDMENTS WITH THE STATED BEAM FLUXES.

^{7}Li energy (MeV)	May, 1987 bbdt. (4.47x10^{16} ^{7}Li^{+2}) $\sigma(^{242g}$Am) (μb)	March, 1987 bbdt. (1.24x10^{16} ^{7}Li^{+2}) $\sigma(^{242g}$Am) (μb)
29.3	–	130±100
29.6±0.4	180±40	–
34.5	–	250±180
34.7±0.3	260±60	–
39.7±0.3	165±40	225±160
44.8±0.3	110±35	–
50.1±0.2	52±15	–
55.0±0.2	35±12	≤39

The production cross section at the peak of 0.26±0.06 mb is 36 times lower than the maximum cross section calculated with our evaporation code JORPLE.[8] But more importantly it is 12 times lower than an estimate σ_{3n}=3.0±2.6 mb we obtained using equation 1 with the following other experimental data. First,

$$\prod_{i=1}^{3}\left(\frac{\frac{\Gamma_n}{\Gamma_f}}{\frac{\Gamma_n}{\Gamma_f}+1}\right)_i = \left(\frac{<\Gamma_n/\Gamma_f>}{<\Gamma_n/\Gamma_f>+1}\right)^3 \qquad (2)$$

was substituted in equation 1 with $<\Gamma_n/\Gamma_f>$=0.9±0.5, determined by Britt et al.[1] as an average over the neutron evaporation chain from ^{245}Am to ^{242}Am. Secondly, the prompt fission cross section, σ_{fis}=307±31 mb interpolated from the data of Freiesleben et al.,[3] was substituted for the fusion cross section $\sigma_{fus}(E,r_o,D)$, neglecting at first the transfer fission process. Thirdly, the Jackson model[10] for the neutron evaporation probability $P_{3n}(E^*,T)$, modified by Sikkeland et al.[9,12] to include fission, experimental masses[2] and fission barriers[1] were used along with the constant nuclear temperature

T=0.95 MeV, appropriate for heavy element excitation functions. A 5% reduction in excitation energy was assumed due to rotational energy as is done in the JORPLE code.

Part of the discrepancy is undoubtedly due to production of the 141-yr,[4] 5$^-$ isomer of ^{242}Am, which we did not measure due to the long half-life. But for the system ^{133}Cs(^{7}Li,3n)^{137m,g}Ce with a similar spin difference of 4 between the isomeric and ground states the isomer-to-ground-state production ratio is 2.4, measured by Kiefer and Street[29] at the same maximum angular momentum corresponding to our reaction 34.7-MeV ^{7}Li + ^{238}U. Assuming this same production ratio for ^{242m}Am to ^{242}Am(16hr) our cross section for all ^{242}Am nuclei would be estimated as 0.9 mb, which is now well within the uncertainty of our estimate from other data of 3.0±2.6 mb, with most of this uncertainty in the $<\Gamma_n/\Gamma_f>$ measurement.[1]

There could also be some transfer fission, which we assumed to be zero in the estimate of the cross section above and which Freiesleben et al.[3] claimed to be small. But including transfer fission would decrease the estimated cross section to even closer to our result, corrected for ^{242m}Am production. For the reactions ^{7}Li + ^{209}Bi[18] and ^{7}Li + ^{159}Tb[30] it is noteworthy that transfer reactions amount to ≈57% of the total reaction cross sections slightly above the respective Bass barriers.[31]

We now analyze the JORPLE code in overpredicting our cross section by a factor of 36 by comparing the calculation of the important factors of the cross section in equation 1 against the best estimates from experimental data. We should first mention that the code does not include the isomer production in the product ^{242}Am, which we already estimated could lower the ground state production by a factor of ≈3.4. The empirical formula of Sikkeland et al.[12] leads to a total survival probability against fission through the chain ^{245}Am→^{242g}Am which is 2.2 times the value we derived from the measurement of $<\Gamma_n/\Gamma_f>$ by Britt et al.[1] and slightly outside the large uncertainty in the derivation from the measurement. The fusion cross section calculated in JORPLE is nearly identical to the experimental prompt fission cross section of 307±31 mb, interpolated from the data of Freiesleben et al.[3] for 34.7-MeV ^{7}Li ions; for 38-MeV ^{7}Li ions the JORPLE code overpredicts the fusion cross section by at least 28%, depending upon the percentage of transfer fission in the prompt fission measurement of Freiesleben et al.[3] Because the JORPLE code uses fission barriers and neutron binding energies for the heavy nuclei which are calculated with the aid of a semiempirical mass formula[11] instead of using experimental values, the probability to evaporate three neutrons is calculated x1.4 higher than if experimental barriers and neutron binding energies had been used. Altogether then x11 of the x36 overprediction using the JORPLE code can be accounted for without assuming any transfer fission, as well as we can estimate the factors of equation of 1 from various experimental data of other groups.

For the fission isomer ^{242f}Am we measured a production cross section of 160±70 nb with 35.6-MeV ^{7}Li ions using mica track detectors. We obtained a compatible result with the mica track detectors replaced by four Si(Au) surface barrier detectors, but with much poorer statistics. Our ratio of this cross section to that of the 16-hr ground state is $(6\pm4)\times10^{-4}$, a value consistent with $(1.5\text{-}5)\times10^{-4}$ measured in many other heavy ion reactions,[32–38] except for the reactions ^{238}U + ^{238}U[39] or with single-neutron transfers.[40]

Similar low production cross sections have also been measured by Thomas[7] for ^{238}Am and Williams and Seaborg[5,6] for $^{242-245}$Bk and ^{246}Es produced in ^{10,11}B- and ^{15}N-induced reactions. Williams and Seaborg[6] stated the low cross sections were consistent with the uncertainties in the $(\Gamma_n/\Gamma_f)_i$ measurements of Gavron et al.[13] But now more complete measurements of fission probabilities[15] or $(\Gamma_n/\Gamma_f)_i$[14] for other Bk and Am isotopes are incompatible with the $<\Gamma_n/\Gamma_f>$ values we derived from the cross-section measurements in Refs. 5 and 6 using the JORPLE code to compute the fusion cross sections and neutron evaporation probabilities. Further study is required to check whether the JORPLE code computes the latter two quantities in agreement with experiment. There may be a number of reasons for the low cross sections. But our study suggests that the cross section to produce a low-spin ground state in a transuranium isotope may be low when a long-lived, high-spin isomer is present. Such an effect was noted in ^{149m,g}Tb by Alexander and Simonoff.[41] Long-lived isomers are not uncommon among the transuranium nuclei, especially among odd-odd nuclei.[42] We note that in many of the cross section discrepancies in Refs. 5 and 6 odd-odd final products are produced. Therefore, we speculate that in some of the nuclei ^{238}Am, $^{242-245}$Bk, and ^{246}Es isomers with half-lives longer than the chemical separation times of 12 minutes or more[5] may exist and contribute to the depletion of the cross sections to produce some of the ground states.

IV. ACKNOWLEDGEMENTS

Two of us (LPS and JPD) cheerfully acknowledge the financial support of the Oral Roberts University Faculty Research Committee, the assistance of the Word Processing Department staff at Oral Roberts University, and the kind hospitality and financial assistance of the Texas A&M Cyclotron Institute for making this research possible. We also want to thank Dr. Albert Ghiorso for the loan of the tape system and uranium targets and G. Hartley for the gold foil. Special thanks are due to J. Leyba for assistance with α-particle detection; to K. Robinson, L. Cooke, H. Kent, J. Symon, and Dr. A. Faruq for assistance in the experiments; and to M. G. Mustafa, M. Blann, J. Gilat, M. J. Nurmia, and P. Möller for fruitful discussions.

V. BIBLIOGRAPHY

1. H. C. BRITT, M. BOLSTERLI, J. R. NIX, and J. L. NORTON, "Fission Barriers Deduced from the Analysis of Fission Isomer Results," *Phys. Rev. C* **7**, 801 (1973).

2. J. K. TULI, *Nuclear Wallet Cards*, National Nuclear Data Center, Brookhaven National Laboratory, Upton, New York (1985).

3. H. FREIESLEBEN, G. T. RIZZO, and J. R. HUIZENGA, "^{6}Li and ^{7}Li Induced Fission of ^{232}Th and ^{238}U," *Phys. Rev. C 12*, 42 (1975).

4. A. G. ZELENKOV, V. A. PCHELIN, YU. F. RODIONOV, L. V. CHISTYAKOV, and V. M. SHUBKO, "New Measurements of the Partial Half-Lives of an Isomeric State of ^{242m}Am," *At. Energ.* **47**, 405 (1979) [*Sov. J. Atomic Energy 47*, 1024 (1979)].

5. K. E. WILLIAMS, "Radiochemical Studies of Neutron Deficient Actinide Isotopes," Ph. D. thesis, Lawrence Berkeley Laboratory Report LBL-7714 (1978).

6. K. E. WILLIAMS and G. T. SEABORG, "New Isotope ^{242}Bk," *Phys. Rev. C 19*, 1794 (1979).

7. K. E. THOMAS, III, unpublished data quoted in Ref. 5.

8. J. R. ALONSO, "Synthesis of Transuranic Elements in Charged Particle Reactions," *Gmelin Handbuch der Anorganischen Chemie* (Springer, Berlin, 1974), Band (Vol.) 7b, *Transurane*, Teil (part) A 1, II: *Die Elemente*, p. 104.

9. T. SIKKELAND, J. MALY, and D. F. LEBECK, "Evaporation of 3 to 8 Neutrons in Reactions between ^{12}C and Various Uranium Nuclides," *Phys. Rev. 169*, 1000, (1968).

10. J. D. JACKSON, "A Schematic Model for (p,xn) Cross Sections in Heavy Elements," *Can J. Phys. 34*, 767 (1956).

11. W. D. MYERS and W. SWIATECKI, "Nuclear Masses and Deformations," University of California Lawrence Radiation Laboratory Report UCRL-11980, Lawrence Berkeley Laboratory, Berkeley, California (1965).

12. T. SIKKELAND, A. GHIORSO, and M. NUR-MIA, "Analysis of Excitation Functions in Cm(C,xn)No Reactions," *Phys. Rev.* *172*, 1232, (1968).

13. A. GAVRON, H. C. BRITT, E. KONECNY, J. WEBER, and J. B. WILHELMY, "Γ_n/Γ_f for Actinide Nuclei Using (^{3}He,df) and (^{3}He,tf) Reactions," *Phys. Rev. C 13*, 2374 (1976).

14. A. GAVRON, H. C. BRITT, P. D. GOLDSTONE, R. SCHOENMACKERS, J. WEBER, and J. B. WILHELMY, "Γ_n/Γ_f in Heavy Nuclides," *Phys. Rev. C 15*, 2238 (1977).

15. B. B. BACK, H. C. BRITT, O. HANSEN, B. LER-OUX, and J. D. GARRETT, "Fission of Odd-A and Doubly Odd Actinide Nuclei Induced by Direct Reactions," *Phys. Rev. C 10*, 1948 (1974).

16. A. FLEURY, "Aspects Radiochimiques des Inter-action entre les Ions Li et B et les Cibles de ^{232}Th et d'^{238}U," Ph. D. thesis, University of Bordeaux, Bordeaux, France (1969).

17. C. E. BEMIS, JR., J. R. BEENE, J. P. YOUNG, and S. D. KRAMER, "Optical Isomer Shift for the Spontaneous-Fission Isomer ^{240}Am^m," *Phys. Rev. Lett. 43*, 1854 (1979).

18. H. FREIESLEBEN, H. C. BRITT, J. BIRKE-LUND, and J. R. HUIZENGA, "^{6}Li, ^{7}Li Induced Reactions on ^{209}Bi," *Phys. Rev. C 10*, 245 (1974).

19. H. FREIESLEBEN, H. C. BRITT, and J. R. HUIZENGA, in "Energy Dependence of Γ_f/Γ_n for the Nucleus ^{216}Rn", *Proceedings of the Third International Atomic Energy Symposium on the Physics and Chemistry of Fission*, Rochester, New York, August 13-17, 1973, paper IAEA-SM-174/56. International Atomic Energy Agency, Vienna, (1974), p. 447.

20. K. IOANNIDES, P. ASSIMAKOPOULOS, A. PAKOU, and S. KOSSIONIDES, "Reaction Mechanisms in the ^{7}Li + ^{51}V Reaction," *Z. Phys. A 321*, 225 (1985).

21. Y. SAKURAGI, "Energy and Target Dependence of Projectile Breakup Effect in Elastic Scattering of ^{6}Li," *Phys. Rev. C 35*, 2161 (1987).

22. A. FLEURY and F. HUBERT, "Mécanisme du Noyau Composé Dans les Interactions des Ions ^{11}B et ^{10}B avec des Cibles de Thorium et d'Uranium," *Journal de Physique 31*, 855 (1970).

23. L. C. NORTHCLIFFE and R. F. SCHILLING, "Range and Stopping-Power Tables for Heavy Ions," *Nuclear Data Tables 7*, 233 (1970).

24. E. BROWNE, J. M. DAIRIKI, R. E. DOEBLER, A. A. SHIHAB-ELDIN, L. J. JARDINE, J. K. TULI, and A. B. BUYRN, *Table of Isotopes*, 7th edition, C. M. LEDERER and V. S. SHIRLEY, Eds. Wiley-Interscience, New York, (1978).

25. M. J. Nurmia, "Heavy-Element Research at the Berkeley HILAC," *Nuclear Science Division Annual Report*, Report No. LBL-666, Lawrence Berkeley Laboratory, Berkeley, California, (1971), p. 42.

26. G. FRIEDLANDER, J. W. KENNEDY, E. S. MA-CIAS, and J. M. MILLER, *Nuclear and Radio-chemistry*, 3rd edition. Wiley Interscience, New York, (1981).

27. L. P. SOMERVILLE, "Observation of New Sponta-neous Fission Activities from Elements 100 to 105," Ph. D. thesis, University of California, Berkeley, Lawrence Berkeley Laboratory Report LBL-14050 (1982).

28. L. P. SOMERVILLE, M. J. NURMIA, J. M. NITSCHKE, A. GHIORSO, R. W. LOUGHEED, and E. K. HULET, "Spontaneous Fission of Rutherfordium Isotopes," *Phys. Rev C 31*, 1801, (1985).

29. R. L. KIEFER and K. STREET, JR., "Isomer Ratio of Ce^{137m} to Ce^{137g} Produced in Several Charged-Particle Reactions," *Phys. Rev. 173*, 1202 (1968).

30. R. BRODA, M. ISHIHARA, B. HERSKIND, H. OESCHLER, S. OGAZA, and H. RYDE, "Heavy-Ion Fusion Cross Sections," *Nucl. Phys. A 248*, 356 (1975).

31. R. BASS, "Fusion Reactions: Successes and Limi-tations of a One-Dimensional Description," in *Proceedings of the Symposium on Deep Inelastic and Fusion Reactions with Heavy Ions, Lecture Notes in Physics 117*, 281 (1980).

32. G. N. FLEROV, N. MARTALOGU, A. A. PLEVE, S. M. POLIKANOV, D. POENARU, and N. VÎLCOV, "Reactions with Protons Leading to the Formation of Spontaneously Fissioning Isomers," *Rev. Roum. Phys. 12*, 109 (1967).

33. G. N. FLEROV, A. A. PLEVE, S. M. PO-LIKANOV, E. IVANOV, N. MARTALOGU, D. POENARU, and N. VÎLCOV, "The Excitation Function and Isomeric Yield Ratio for the 14 msec Fissioning Isomer from Deuteron Irradiation of Plutonium," *Rev. Roum. Phys.* **10**, 217 (1965).

34. A. F. LINEV, B. N. MARKOV, A. A. PLEVE, and S. M. POLIKANOV, "The Formation of a Spontaneously Fissioning Isomer in the Capture of Neutron by Am," *Nucl. Phys.* **63**, 173 (1965).

35. YU. P. GANGRSKIĬ, B. N. MARKOV, S. M. PO-LIKANOV, and KH. YUNGKLAUSSEN, "Investigations of the Reaction $U^{238} + B^{11}$, which leads to the Spontaneously-fissioning Isomer Am^{242}," *Yad. Fiz.* **5**, 22 (1967) [*Sov. J. Nucl. Phys.* **5**, 16 (1967)].

36. G. N. FLEROV, YU. P. GANGRSKIĬ, B. N. MARKOV, A. A. PLEVE, S. M. POLIKANOV, and KH. YUNGKLAUSSEN, "Isomeric Ratio in Nuclear Reactions Leading to the Isotopes Ir^{190}, Au^{196}, Am^{242}," *Yad. Fiz.* **6**, 17 (1967) [*Sov. J. Nucl. Phys.* **6**, 12 (1968)].

37. S. M. POLIKANOV, "Spontaneously Fissioning Isomers," *Usp. Fiz, Nauk* **94**, 43 (1968) [*Sov. Phys. Uspeckhi* **11**, 22 (1968)].

38. YU. TS. OGANESSIAN, YU. V. LOBANOV, M. HUSSONNOIS, YU. P. KHARITONOV, B. GORSKI, O. CONSTANTINESCU, A. G. POPE-KO, H. BRUCHERTSEIFER, R. N. SAGAIDAK, S. P. TRETYAKOVA, G. V. BUKLANOV, A. V. RYKHLYUK, G. G. GULBEKYAN, A. A. PLEVE, G. N. IVANOV, and V. M. PLOTKO, "The Experiments Aimed to Synthesize Element 110," Joint Institute for Nuclear Research Report No. D7-87-392, Dubna, U.S.S.R., (1987); also submitted to *International School on Physics "Enrico Fermi,"* Varenna, Italy, 23 June- 3 July, 1987.

39. H. GÄGGELER, E. SCHIMPF, W. WEBER, and G. WIRTH, "Search for Superheavy Elements with Half-Lives Down to 1 msec in ^{238}U on ^{238}U Collisions," GSI Scientific Report 1979, Report GSI-80-3, Gesellschaft für Schwerionenforschung mbH, Darmstadt, West Germany, p. 62.

40. YU. P. GANGRSKIĬ, B. A. GVOZDEV, B. N. MARKOV, S. M. POLIKANOV, and H. JUNG-CLAUSSEN, "Production of the Spontaneously Fissile Isomers Am^{240} and Am^{242} in Neutron-transfer Reactions," *Yad. Fiz.* **5**, 535 (1967) [*Sov. J. Nucl. Phys.* **5**, 380 (1967)].

41. J. M. ALEXANDER and G. N. SIMONOFF, "Excitation Functions for Tb^{149g} from Reactions between Complex Nuclei," *Phys. Rev.* **130**, 2383 (1963).

42. E. BROWNE and R. B. FIRESTONE, *Table of Radioactive Isotopes*, V. S. SHIRLEY, Ed., Wiley Interscience, New York, (1986).

STATISTICAL MODEL APPROACH TO FISSION NEUTRON EMISSION

H. Märten, A. Ruben, and D. Seeliger
Technische Universität Dresden, Sektion Physik
Mommsenstrasse 13, DDR-8027 Dresden
German Democratic Republic

ABSTRACT

Based on a general theoretical concept for the description of fission neutron emission as a fragment de-excitation process, two statistical model approaches (SMA) are presented and applied to calculate multiplicities, energy and angular distributions of prompt fission neutrons (PFN): (i) cascade evaporation model (CEM); (ii) temperature distribution model (FINESSE — FIssion NEutronS' Statistical Emission). In conjunction with a scission point model (TSM - Two-Spheroid Model) or the prediction of energy partition in fission as function of mass asymmetry, the SMA are used to describe PFN data for any fission reaction in the Th-Cf region in a physically consistent manner.

1. INTRODUCTION

On the basis of the assumption that PFN are evaporated from fully accelerated fragments several models for describing PFN spectra have been proposed.[1-7] They can be classified with respect to

(i) the spectrum ansatz in the centre-of-mass system (CMS) including CMS anisotropy,

(ii) the degree of consideration of the fragment occurrence probability P as function of a fragment parameter set $\{p_f\}$ = {A,Z,TKE,E*,J, ...}, i.e., mass and charge number, total kinetic energy, excitation energy, angular momentum, respectively.

The CMS emission distribution depending on energy and emission angle with reference to fragment direction, i.e., $\phi(\varepsilon,\delta:\{p_f\})$, can be described using either Hauser-Feshbach theory (applied to level continuum)[3] with consideration of angular momentum effects or Weisskopf-Ewing approach[1,2,5] or any approximations.[4,6] Recently, statistical multi-step compound (SMC) theory has been modified to account for equilibrium and pre-equilibrium PFN emission in closed form.[7] However, the prediction of the intricate fragment distribution $P\{p_f\}$ is one of the outstanding problems in fission theory as well as PFN theory. Most of the PFN calculations have been performed on the basis of experimental data or rough empirical approaches for describing P to a certain extent. Note that P is often reduced drastically to a fragment group approach, i.e., use of group averages of fragment parameters. Starting with a brief description of a general SMA (paragraph 2.1), two recent SMA versions are presented in this work. The complex CEM (paragraph 2.2) as well as FINESSE (paragraph 2.3) are applied to the standard PFN spectrum from ^{252}Cf(sf). Compared to the Generalized Madland-Nix Model,[6] FINESSE is a more realistic temperature distribution model considering the A dependence of fragment energies. Further, the scission point model TSM including semi-empirical, temperature-dependent shell correction energies (chapter 3) provides essential input data for SMA applications to any fission reaction.

2. PFN THEORY

2.1. General Concept

Applying standard evaporation theory to cascade particle emission by steps (i) (including γ-ray emission) from a fragment for a given initial distribution $P_0(E*,J)$, i.e., A, Z, and TKE fixed, we get the CMS spectrum of particle π as

$$\phi_\pi(\varepsilon_\pi) = \sum_i \int dE* \sum_J P_i(E*,J)$$

$$\times \frac{\Gamma_\pi(\varepsilon_\pi,E*,J)}{\sum_{\pi'} \Gamma_{\pi'}^{tot}(E*,J) + \Gamma_\gamma^{tot}(E*,J)} \quad (1)$$

$$\Gamma_\pi(\varepsilon_\pi,E*,J) = (2\pi\,\rho(E*,J))^{-1}$$

$$\times \sum_{J'} \rho^\pi(U_\pi,J') \sum_{l_\pi,s_\pi} T_l^\pi(\varepsilon_\pi) \quad (2)$$

$$U_\pi = E^* - B_\pi - \epsilon_\pi \quad , \quad \vec{J} = \vec{J}' + \vec{1}_\pi + \vec{s}_\pi \quad (3)$$

(Γ - emission width, Γ^{tot} - total decay width, ϵ_π - CMS emission energy of particle π, $\rho(E^*,J)$ - nuclear level density, separation energy, B_π - separation energy, U_π, J' - rest-nucleus excitation energy and angular momentum, respectively, 1_π - orbital momentum, s_π - spin of particle π, T_1^π - transmission coefficient for particle π with orbital momentum 1_π to be calculated in the framework of the optical model).

Note that the fragment occurrence probability $P_i(E^X,J)$ for i>1 has to be deduced from $P_{i-1}(E^X,J)$ considering the spectra of emission step i-1. Further, the quantities as ρ, T_1, and B have to be taken for relevant A values, which are diminished by steps 1 during cascade emission of neutrons n. In particular, B_n rises within a n cascade. Transformation of eq. (1) into the laboratory system (LS)[1,5,8] taking into account CMS anisotropy due to fragment spin[10] yields the LS distribution $N_\pi(E,\theta:A,Z,TKE)$. Thus, the total distribution is given by

$$N_\pi(E,\theta) = \sum_{A,Z} \int dTKE \; N_\pi(E,\theta:A,Z,TKE) \; P(A,Z,TKE) \quad (4)$$

As summarized in ref. 8, a complex SMA is based on the fragment distribution $P(A,Z,E^*,TKE, J, ...)$ considered as an "asymptotic" one, i.e., after dissipation of fragment deformation energy and fragment acceleration, but before de-excitation. However, calculations are limited due to the lack of knowledge of this distribution. In the promising case of ^{252}Cf(sf), it can be deduced from experimental data with more or less accuracy in the following form[5,8,9]

$$P(A,TKE,E^X), \; P(Z:A), \; P(J:A) \quad . \quad (5)$$

In the present work, recent experimental data[11] on neutron multiplicities depending on A and TKE have been used to deduce average excitation energies $\bar{E}^*(A,TKE)$ (cf. ref. 5, e.g., concerning the widths of distributions in E^*).

Note that fission theory fails to reproduce the intricate probability function P with sufficient accuracy and completeness.

2.2. Cascade Evaporation Model (CEM)

Full-scale calculations have been performed for a simplified evaporation ansatz:

$$\Gamma_\pi(\epsilon_\pi, E^*, \bar{J}) = (2\pi\rho(E^*, J=0))^{-1} \epsilon_\pi \; \sigma_{inv}(\epsilon_\pi)$$
$$\times \rho(E^*, J'=0) \; C(E^*, \bar{J}) \quad (6)$$

(σ_{inv}-inverse cross section of compound-nucleus formation to be calculated in the framework of the optical model) with a correction factor

$$C(E^X,J) \sim (1 - \exp(-C_1(E^X - B_\pi)^{C_2})) \quad (7)$$

to account for neutron-γ-competition in respect of eq. (1). (C_1, C_2 - parameters depending on $\bar{J}$).

Optical model calculations have been performed using SCAT-2 (ref. 12). The approach by Schmidt et al.[13] was taken to deduce $\rho(U)$.

2.3. Temperature Distribution Model (FINESSE)

Following the ideas of Madland and Nix,[4] the so-called Generalized Madland-Nix Model (GMNM) has been proposed in ref. 6. The CMS spectrum is given by

$$\phi(\epsilon:A) = \int_{T_0}^{T_m(A)} P(T) \; K(T) \; \sigma_{inv}(\epsilon:A) \; \epsilon \; \exp(-\frac{\epsilon}{T})dT \quad (8)$$

including the temperature distribution P(T). K is a normalization constant given by

$$K(T) = \left[\int_0^\infty \sigma_{inv}(\epsilon:A) \; \epsilon \; \exp(-\frac{\epsilon}{T}) \; d\epsilon \right]^{-1} \quad . \quad (9)$$

Equation (8) describes the PFN spectrum for a distribution in rest-nucleus temperature T corresponding to a distribution in E^* for all cascade emission steps i>1. It can be well reproduced by the relation

$$P(U) = \sum_{i>1} P_i(E^*) = \frac{1}{1 + \exp((U-\hat{U})/d)} \quad (10)$$

$\hat{U}$ is the edge parameter of the distribution P(U) given by

$$U(A) = \bar{E}^*(A) - \frac{1}{2}(B_n(A) + \bar{\epsilon}(A)) \quad (11)$$

where

$$\bar{\epsilon}(A) = \frac{4}{3}\sqrt{\bar{E}^*(A)/a(A)} \quad (12)$$

is the average CMS emission energy of neutrons.[4]

The parameter d denotes the "diffuseness" of the distribution P(U). Based on the approximation for the variance of $P_0(E^*:A)$, i.e.

$$\sigma_{E^*}^2(A) \cong 3.3 \; \text{MeV} \; \bar{E}^*(A) \quad , \quad (13)$$

one gets

$$d(A) \cong \sqrt{\bar{E}^*(A) \; \text{MeV}} \quad . \quad (14)$$

744

Finally, P(U) is transformed into the temperature distribution P(T) using the Fermi gas model expression $U = a T^2$ with the level density parameter $a(A)$. Effective values $a(A)$ have been derived from CEM calculations based on eq. (11). Note that T_0 accounts for neutron-γ-competition of fragment de-excitation as well as pairing effects in level density.

Compared with GMNM, the present temperature distribution model is a more realistic one reproducing the distribution in U (or T) as function of A "exactly". The GMNM had been based on an idealized triangular shape of P(T) as in ref. 4.

2.4. Results

Both CEM and FINESSE have been used to describe the well-known standard neutron spectrum from spontaneous fission of ^{252}Cf. Calculations have been performed on the basis of several optical potentials.[14-18] Results are shown in figs. 1-4 in comparison with Mannhart's evaluation. In the case of CEM, neither a parameter fit nor an arbitrary normalization has been done. FINESSE includes one free parameter T_0. It has been adjusted on the basis of the Cf standard spectrum. For the optical potentials considered one gets T_0 in the limits 0.30 - 0.38 MeV. Simultaneously, the angular distributions of PFN are well reproduced. Calculated double-differential emission probabilities $N(E,\theta)$ have been presented in ref. 7 in comparison with experimental data. It has been shown that CEM is successful in describing energy and angular distributions of PFN indicating that the mechanism assumed is the predominant one.

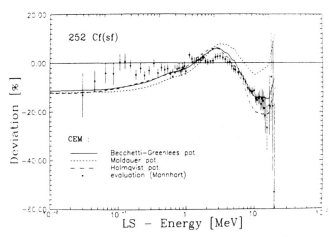

Fig. 2 The same as for fig. 1, but CEM results for the global optical potentials according to refs. 15-17.

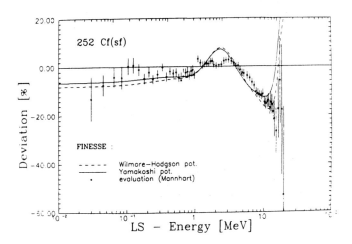

Fig. 3 The same as for fig. 1, but FINESSE results for the global optical potentials according to refs. 14, 18.

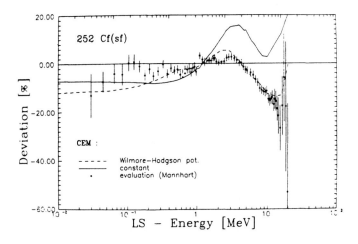

Fig. 1 The Cf standard spectrum represented as percentage deviation from a Maxwellian with a 1.42 MeV "temperature" parameter: CEM calculations for a constant inverse cross section of compound-nucleus forma-tion as well as a global optical poten-tial (ref. 14) in comparison with the recent evaluation, ref. 19.

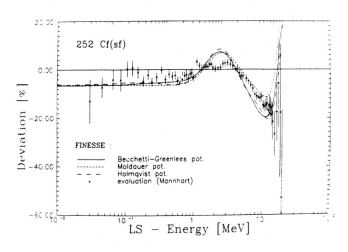

Fig. 4 The same as for fig. 1, but FINESSE results for the global optical potentials according to refs. 15-17.

$$\overline{Q}\left[\frac{A_1}{A_2}\right] + E_c = \underbrace{E_{pre} + E_{coul}}_{\overline{TKE}\left[\frac{A_1}{A_2}\right]} + \overbrace{E_{def}^{(1)} + E_{def}^{(2)}}^{F} + \underbrace{\overbrace{E_{def}^{(1)} + E_{def}^{(2)}}^{} + E_{dis} + E_h}_{\overline{E}^*\left[\frac{A_1}{A_2}\right]} \qquad (15)$$

Above equation with braces labelled:

F spans $E_{def}^{(1)} + E_{def}^{(2)}$

$E_{int}^{(1)} + E_{int}^{(2)}$ spans $E_{dis} + E_h$

$\overline{TKE}\left[\frac{A_1}{A_2}\right]$ spans $E_{pre} + E_{coul}$

$\overline{E}^*\left[\frac{A_1}{A_2}\right]$ spans $E_{def}^{(1)} + E_{def}^{(2)} + E_{dis} + E_h$

E_{pre} — pre-scission kinetic energy,

E_{coul} — Coulomb potential energy at scission,

$E_{def}^{(i)}$ — deformation energy of fragment i at scission,

E_{dis} — intrinsic excitation energy at scission due to dissipation between second-saddle point of fission barrier and scission point,

$E_{int}^{(i)}$ — intrinsic excitation of fragment i at scission,

E_h — intrinsic excitation energy ("heat") at the second-saddle point,

F — potential energy at scission for given mass asymmetry.

---

3. SCISSION POINT MODEL OF ENERGY PARTITION IN FISSION

A essential problem in predicting the fragment occurrence probability is the question, how the total available energy, i.e., the sum of energy release $\overline{Q}(A_1/A_2)$ and the excitation energy of the compound nucleus E_c is distributed on both complementary fragments. The kinds of fragment energies are the kinetic energies $\overline{E}_{k\,i}(A)$, which can be measured directly, and the excitation energies $\overline{E}_i^*(A)$, which can be deduced from experimental data on $\overline{\nu}(A)$ as well as average total γ-ray energy $\overline{E}_\gamma(A)$ (i.e., in an asymptotic manner). The TSM, which has firstly been described in ref. 20 (preliminary version), is a simple scission point model bsed on a general energy balance (see eq. (15) above).

According to Terrell[21] we describe the fissioning system by two spheroidically shaped fragments nearly touching at the scission point. The nuclear forces between the fragments cause a small distance d ~ 1.4 fm at the place of contact (cf. ref. 22). The deformation energy $E_{def}^{(i)}$ is assumed to be quadratic in radius change with reference to a spherical nucleus with radius $R^{(i)}$:

$$E_{def}^{(i)} = \alpha^{(i)} (D^{(i)} - R^{(i)})^2 \qquad (16)$$

($D^{(i)}$ - major semi-axis of spheroid i). $\alpha^{(i)}$ is the deformability parameter related to the stiffness parameter $C_2^{(i)}$ as[23]

$$C_2^{(i)} = \frac{5}{2\pi} \alpha^{(i)} R^{(i)2} \qquad (17)$$

V_{coul} is assumed to be the Coulomb interaction energy of two charges $Z^{(i)}e$ effectively located at the centres of the fragments, i.e.

$$V_{coul} = Z^{(1)}Z^{(2)}e^2/(D^{(1)} + D^{(2)} + d) \qquad (18)$$

Minimizing F, i.e., $\partial F/\partial D^{(i)} = 0$, one gets a set of equations:

$$E_{def}^{(i)} = \frac{V_{coul}^4}{4\,\alpha^{(i)}\,Z^{(1)2}\,Z^{(2)2}\,e^2} \qquad (19)$$

$$E_{def}^{(1)}/E_{def}^{(2)} = \alpha^{(2)}/\alpha^{(1)} \qquad (20)$$

The energy parts E_{pre} and E_{dis} are taken from the systematic study by Gönnenwein.[24] Both energies increase with increasing fissility Z^2/A. Finally, the "heat" energy at the second saddle is assumed to be

$$E_h = E_c - E_{f,B} - \Delta_p \qquad (21)$$

with the constraint $E_h > 0$. E_h vanishes in the case of spontaneous and threshold fission. The dependence of the pairing energy Δ_p on excitation energy is described by the approach of

Kristiak[25]. In principle, the deformability parameter α can be described in the framework of the liquid-drop model (LDM). However, nuclear stiffness is strongly influenced by shell effects. In order to deduce effective shell correction energies $\delta W(A)$ for fragments with typical deformations at scission the equations given above have been applied to well-known fission reactions (^{252}Cf (sf), ^{235}U(n_{th},f) a.o.) to determine the deformability parameter $\alpha(A)$. Based on the semi-empirical equation[23]

$$\alpha(A) = \alpha_{LMD}(A) \frac{K-\delta W(A)}{K+\delta W(A)} \quad (22)$$

with $K = 8$ MeV the parameter α is related to the corresponding LDM value. Equation (22) has been used to derive sets of semi-empirical shell correction energies $\delta W(A)$. Both E_h and E_{dis} determine the temperature τ at scission. Assuming $\tau^{(1)} = \tau^{(2)}$, the intrinsic excitation energies $E_{int}^{(i)}$ of the complementary fragments can be calculated on the basis of the Fermi-gas model approach, namely:

$$E_{int}^{(i)}(A) = a^{(i)}(A) \, \tau^{(i)2} \quad (23)$$

Due to the temperature τ at scission, the shell effects are diminished. Taking into account the relations[26]

$$\delta W(A,\tau) = \delta W(A,\tau=0) \frac{t^2 \, \sinh^2 t}{\cosh t} \quad (24)$$

$$t = 2\pi^2\tau/\omega \quad , \quad \omega \sim A^{-1/3}, \quad (25)$$

shell correction energies at zero temperature can be obtained. As shown in fig. 5, the shell correction energies for fragments in very different fission reactions are quite similar. Therefore, it seems to be justified to use even these parameter sets for the application of the TSM to any fission reaction (including interpolation).

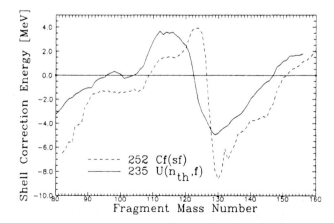

Fig. 5 Zero-temperature shell correction energies as deduced within the TSM for the fission reactions specified (cf. ref. 22).

The fragment energies of interest are $E^*(A)$ and $\overline{TKE}(A_1/A_2)$. They are obtained using

$$\bar{E}^{*(i)}(A) = E_{def}^{(i)}(A) + E_{int}^{(i)}(A), \quad (26)$$

$$\overline{TKE}(A_1/A_2) = E_{coul} + E_{pre} \, . \quad (27)$$

According to energy balance of fragment de-excitation due to the evaporation of neutrons (multiplicity $\bar{\nu}$) and γ-ray emission (average total energy $\bar{E}_\gamma$), we have

$$\bar{E}^*(A) = \bar{\nu}(A) \, (\bar{B}_n(A) + \bar{\epsilon}(A)) + \bar{E}_\gamma \, , \quad (28)$$

where $\bar{B}_n(A)$ is the neutron binding energy averaged over the neutron cascade and the distribution in charge number Z. The average γ-ray emission energy is given by

$$\bar{E}_\gamma = (6.6867 - 0.15578 \, Z_{FN}^2/A_{FN}) \, \bar{\nu}$$
$$+ (0.11127 \, Z_{FN}^2/A_{FN} - 2.2408) \, , \quad (29)$$

where Z_{FN} and A_{FN} are mass and charge number of the fissioning nucleus, respectively (cf. ref. 27).

The temperature dependence of $\delta W(A)$ and its influence on fission characteristics is summarized as follows:

i) As lower δW, in particular with negative sign, as higher α, i.e., as lower E_{def}. Therefore, E^* rises strongly with increasing E_c (or incidence energy) in regions with very low δW, in particular around $A = 132$ (double-magic fragment). The excitation energy of complementary fragment do not change remarkably. In general, the well-known saw-tooth curve $\nu(A)$ becomes less pronounced with increasing E_c.

ii) The value $\tilde{\alpha} = (1/\alpha^{(1)} + 1/\alpha^{(2)})^{-1}$ can be interpreted as total deformability of the fissioning system at scission. Changes of $\tilde{\alpha}$ with E_c cause corresponding changes in $\overline{TKE}$. Hence, $\overline{TKE}$ is diminished (enhanced) with increasing E_c for fragment pairs with (negative-) positive-sign $\tilde{\alpha}$.

iii) The change of τ increasing incidence energy is also influenced by the second-barrier height in relation to the first one as well as pairing effects. If we consider total energy parameter changes, i.e., values averaged over A taking into account the fragment yield $P(A)$, the dependence $P(A, E_c)$ may be important.

Total kinetic energies $\overline{TKE}$ averaged over fragment mass are shown in fig. 6 for different fission reactions induced by fast neutrons. In particular, the opposite behaviour of $\overline{TKE}$ as function of E_i for the cases ^{232}Th, ^{235}U, and ^{239}Pu fission can be explained (cf. experimental data from refs. 28-30). Even here, the height of the second saddle in relation to the total barrier height, which corresponds to the fission threshold, is of high importance for the influence of pairing effects.

The main part of incidence energy is transformed into excitation energy of the fission fragments resulting in an increase of $\bar{\nu}$ with incidence energy. However, certain changes of TKE must result in opposite influences on $\bar{\nu}$ (energy balance, cf. eq. 15). A typical example of neutron multiplicities is shown in fig. 7.

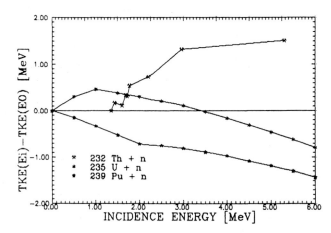

Fig. 6 Total kinetic energies of fragments from neutron-induced fission reactions as indicated. TSM results are represented as differences with reference to the low-limit incidence energy.

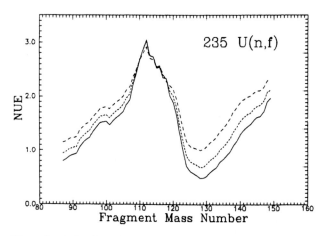

Fig. 7 Calculated neutron multiplicity as function of fragment mass number for three selected neutron incidence energies (thermal neutrons - continuous line, 3 MeV, 6 MeV)

4. CONCLUSIONS

PFN emission can be well described by complex SMA based on the assumption that all neutrons are evaporated by fully accelerated fragments. The possible role of non-equilibrium neutron emission in fission has been discussed in ref. 7. Both CEM and FINESSE are suitable to describe PFN spectra in a wide energy range. The neglection of optical potential in SMA calculations yields wrong results (cf. fig. 1). The energy region between about 1 and 4 MeV is a crucial one. Obviously, the present SMA overestimates the evaluated Cf standard spectrum. However, some of the experimental data considered in the evaluation confirm the theoretical results (cf. ref. 19 and references therein). A further precision measurement covering the energy range discussed is strongly recommended.

The TSM as a scission point model with semi-empirical, temperature-dependent shell correction energies for deformed fragments at scission is successful in describing the main features of energy partition in fission as function of mass asymmetry. The diminution of shell effects due to scission point temperature, which depends on the dissipated energy as well as incidence energy (influenced by pairing effects), causes considerable changes of fragment energies as function of E_C (or E_i). It is emphasized, that the _average_ features of energy partition in fission as function of mass asymmetry are described. Channel effects appearing at fission threshold especially are not taken into account. However, they could be considered approximatively by using effective values for the fission barrier and, thus, simulating collective transition states.

The results of TSM calculations are the necessary precondition for the application of complex statistical fission neutron theories for calculations of energy and angular distributions.

REFERENCES

1. J. Terrell, Phys. Rev. 113 (1959) 527.

2. E. Nardi et al., Phys. Rev. C8 (1973) 2293.

3. J.C. Browne and F.S. Dietrich, Phys. Rev. C10 (1974) 2545.

4. D.G. Madland and J.R. Nix, Nucl. Sci. Eng. 81 (1982) 213.

5. H. Märten and D. Seeliger, J. Phys. G: Nucl. Phys. 14 (1984) 349.

6. H. Märten and D. Seeliger, Nucl. Sci. Eng. 93 (1986). 370

7. K. Arnold et al., Proc. Int. Conf. on Fifty Years Research in Nuclear Fission, Berlin (West), April 3-7, 1989, in print.

8. H. Märten, Proc. IAEA Advisory Group Meeting on Nuclear Theory for Fast Neutron Nuclear Data Evaluation, Beijing, 12-16 Oct. 1987, IAEA-TECDOC-483 (1988) 148.

9. J.B. Wilhelmy et al., Phys. Rev. C5 (1972) 2041.

10. T. Ericson and Strutinski, Nucl. Phys. 8 (1958) L84 (Errata: Nucl. Phys. 9 (1959) 689).

11. C. Budtz-Jorgenson and H.-H. Knitter, Proc. IAEA Consultants' Meeting on the Physics of Neutron Emission in Fission, Mito (Japan), 24 - 27 May 1988, in print.

12. O. Bersillon, Report CEA-N-2227, CE Bruyeres-le-Chatel (1981).

13. K.H. Schmidt et al., Z. Phys. A308 (1982) 215.

14. D. Wilmore and P.E. Hodgson, Nucl. Phys. 55 (1964) 673.

15. F.D. Becchetti and G.W. Greenlees, Phys. Rev. 182 (1969) 1190.

16. P.A. Moldauer, Nucl. Phys. 47 (1963) 65.

17. B. Holmqvist, Arkiv Fysik 38 (1968) 403.

18. H. Yamakoshi, Proc. Int. Conf. on Nuclear Data for Science and Technology, Mito (Japan), 1988, ed. by S. Igarasi (JAERI) (1988).

19. W. Mannhart, Proc. IAEA Advisory Group Meeting on the Properties of Neutron Sources, Leningrad, 1986, IAEA-TECDOC-410 (1987) 158.

20. H. Märten et al., ibid., p. 153.

21. J. Terrell, Proc. IAEA Symp. on Physics and Chemistry of Fission, Salzburg, 1965 (Vienna, 1965) Vol. II, p. 3.

22. B.D. Wilkins et al., Phys. Rev. C14 (1976) 1832.

23. M. Kildir, N.K. Aras, Phys. Rev. C25 (1982) 365.

24. F. Gönnenwein et al., Proc. XVIIth Int. Symp. on Nucl. Phys. - Nuclear Reactions Gaussig (GDR), 1987, ZfK-646 (1988) 129.

25. J. Kristiak, Proc. 5th Int. Symp. on Neutron Induced Reactions, Smolenice, 1988, in print.

26. A. Bohr and B.R. Mottelson, Nuclear Structure (Benjamin, New York, 1975) Vol. II.

27. H. Nifenecker, C. Signarbiex, R. Babinat, and J. Poitou, Proc. IAEA Symp. on Physics and Chemistry of Fission, Rochester, New York, 13-17 Aug. 1973 (IAEA, Vienna, 1974), Vol. II, 117.

28. C.A. Straede, Thesis, CBNM Geel, 1985.

29. J. Trochon et al., Nucl. Phys. A318 (1979) 63.

30. V.G. Vorobeva et al., INDC-128/G+Sp (1979).

A SYSTEMATIC STUDY OF MASS YIELD CURVES
IN LOW ENERGY FISSION OF ACTINIDES

T. OHTSUKI, K. SUEKI, Y. HAMAJIMA,
H. NAKAHARA
Department of Chemistry, Faculty of
Science, Tokyo Metropolitan
University, Setagaya 158, Tokyo,
Japan, 03(717)0111

Y. NAGAME, N. SHINOHARA,
H. IKEZOE
Department of Radioisotopes,
Japan Atomic Energy Research
Institute, Tokai, Ibaraki 319-11,
Japan, 0292(82)5796

ABSTRACT

Mass yield curves in low energy proton induced fission of ^{232}Th, ^{233}U, ^{235}U, ^{237}Np, ^{238}U, ^{239}Pu, ^{241}Am, ^{242}Pu, ^{243}Am, and ^{244}Pu were measured. The excitation energy dependence of the mass yield curves were investigated, and the existence of symmetric fission mode and asymmetric one has been shown. The peak-to-valley ratios as a function of proton energy and mass of the fissioning nucleus (A_f) have shown that the variation can be quantitatively explained on the basis of different fission barrier heights, one for symmetric and the other for asymmetric. The full width at half maximum (FWHM) of the heavier asymmetric peak of the mass yield curve has shown a sudden dip in the region of $A_f = 240 \sim 245$. The relation between FWHM and the influence of nuclear stability is discussed in terms of the deformation energy surface of a fissioning nucleus and fragment shells.

INTRODUCTION

Since the discovery of nuclear fission in 1939,[1] many experiments and theoretical calculations have been reported, and possible mechanisms have been proposed on the mass division process of the fissioning nucleus toward fission, namely, "saddle or scission" or "the dynamics from saddle to scission". To advance these experimental and theoretical studies, careful systematic studies of mass yield cures are further needed from the light to the heavy actinide regions as a function of excitation energy.

In the present paper, some mass yield curves obtained in the proton induced fissions of ^{232}Th, ^{233}U, ^{235}U, ^{238}U, ^{237}Np, ^{239}Pu, ^{242}Pu, ^{244}Pu, ^{241}Am, and ^{243}Am are reported. They have been discussed from the following four aspects: 1) incident energy dependence of the mass yield curve, 2) peak-to-valley ratio (P/V ratio), 3) symmetric and asymmetric

fission barriers in terms of the P/V ratio, and 4) FWHM of the asymmetric peak. The proton energy range covered was from 8 to 22 MeV for ^{232}Th+p, 8 to 32 MeV for ^{237}Np+p, 9 to 16 MeV for ^{233}U+p, and ^{239}Pu+p, 9 to 25 MeV for ^{238}U+p, 12 MeV and 18 MeV for ^{235}U+p, ^{242}Pu+p, ^{244}Pu+p, ^{241}Am+p, and ^{243}Am+p. The so-called stacked-foil method was used for the excitation function studies. Details of the experimental procedure are published elsewhere. Finally, three kinds of existing theories on the mass division in fission are discussed.

INCIDENT ENERGY DEPENDENCE OF MASS YIELD CURVES

Incident energy dependence of mass yield curves is shown in Figs.1(a) and 1(b), as some examples, for the proton induced fissions of ^{237}Np and ^{233}U, ^{239}Pu. Mass yield curves for 12 MeV proton induced fission of ^{235}U, ^{242}Pu, ^{244}Pu and ^{243}Am are shown in Fig.1(c). They were obtained from the observed cross section (mb) of each fission product to which the correction was applied, if necessary, for the charge distribution by assuming a Gaussian with the most probable charge Z_p of the unchanged charge distribution model.[2] All the mass yield curves are asymmetric as expected. The shape of the curve varies strongly in the valley region and the outer sides of the asymmetric peaks in comparison with the peak region. The valley width, in general, becomes narrower as the fissioning mass A_f becomes larger as is pointed for thermal-neutron induced fissions and spontaneous fissions by Gunten.[3] The mean mass numbers of the lighter and heavier asymmetric peaks are plotted in Fig.2 for 12 MeV proton induced fissions in which those for thermal-neutron induced fissions are also shown by broken lines for comparison. The mean mass numbers of the heavier asymmetric peaks stay constant for all A_f except for the ase of ^{232}Th+p, but they are smaller than those for thermal-neutron induced fissions by a few mass units.

For a clear depiction of the incident energy dependence, cross section ratios of several fission products are shown in Figs.3(a), 3(b), and 3(c) with respect to the cross section of a typical asymmetric product ^{97}Nb for ^{237}Np+p, ^{233}U+p and ^{239}Pu+p, respectively. The yield ratios of the asymmetric division products themselves and symmetric division products themselves are both rather independent of incident proton energy, while the yield ratios of the symmetric division products to ^{97}Nb vary with incident proton energy. This observation is in agreement with the report by Kudo et al.[4] However, it is to be noted that some exceptions from the above statement are observed especially for the ^{239}Pu+p fission products such as ^{85m}Kr ^{105}Rh, and ^{149}Nd. The excitation function studies strongly suggest the existence of two distinctly different threshold energies, one related to the so-called symmetric fission and the other to the asymmetric fission.

PEAK-TO-VALLEY RATIOS

For all nuclei studied it has been found that the peak-to-valley ratio decreases rapidly and eventually

approaches to the value 1.5~3 as shown in Fig.4 within the incident energy range studied. However, its energy dependence is very much characteristic of the reaction system.

The P/V ratios as a function of the mass number of the compound nucleus (A_f) with a fixed excitation energy above the saddle point are shown in Fig.5, in which the outer barrier heights reported by Back et al.[5] are used for the saddle point energy. Filled circles show the P/V ratios for the excitation energy of 9.5 MeV and filled triangles for 11.5 MeV. Also shown are the values taken from the work of Konecny et al.[9] (open circles) and Itkis et

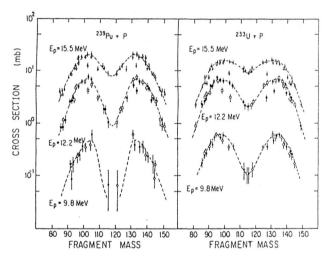

Fig.1(b) Mass yield curves of the proton induced fission of ^{233}U and ^{239}Pu targets in the proton energy range for 9~16 MeV. Filled symbols indicate the observed chain yields and open symbols, the reflected points.

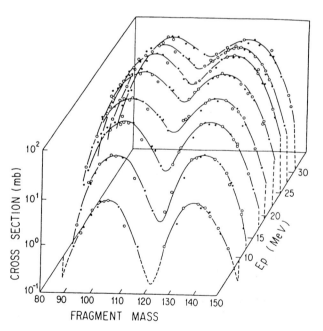

Fig.1(a) Mass yield curves of the the proton induced fission of ^{237}Np target in the proton energy range of 9~32 MeV. Filled circles indicate the observed chain yields and open circles, the reflected points.

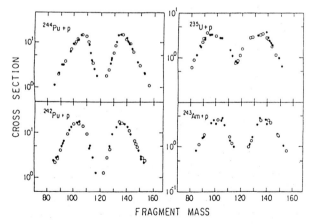

Fig.1(c) Mass yield curves of 12 MeV proton induced fission of ^{235}U, ^{242}Pu, ^{244}Pu and ^{243}Am.

al.[15](open triangles). From this figure, it is found that yields of the symmetric mass division become more favored as the compound mass increases at least up to 245 or to the neutron number of the compound nucleus N=150. It is interesting to note that the P/V ratios seem to vary smoothly from the actinide region (filled circles) to the distinctly triple-humped Ra region[6] and even down to the Z=84~ 85 region.[15] This smooth variation of the P/V ratio as a function of A_f indicates that some unknown cause of the asymmetric mass division, the shell effect at the saddle or at scission or the dynamics from the saddle to scission, gradually becomes more effective as A_f increases up to the actinide region.

SYMMETRIC AND ASYMMETRIC FISSION BARRIER HEIGHTS

The incident energy dependence of cross section ratios shown in Fig.3(a), 3(b), and 3(c) and the systematic study of the P/V ratio discussed above strongly suggest the existence of two independent fission paths with different fission barriers: one leading preferentially to the symmetric mass division and the other to the asymmetric mass division. If the fission barrier is of the nature of a static potential and the probability of

taking a certain path is determined by the level density at the barrier, it leads to the hypothesis of "two independent modes" first proposed by Turkevich and Niday.[7] This hypothesis has been experimentally supported by many works such as Britt et al.[8], Konecny et al.[9], Kudo et al.[10], and others.[11,12] The relative contribution of the asymmetric and symmetric mass division is then expressed by the following equation[13] for the asymmetric and symmetric fission barrier heights E_a and E_s.

$$\frac{\Gamma_a}{\Gamma_s} = C * \frac{e^{(2\sqrt{a_a(E_T-E_a)})}}{e^{(2\sqrt{a_s(E_T-E_s)})}},$$

where Γ_a and Γ_s are the decay widths through the symmetric and asymmetric channel, respectively, E_T is the excitation energy, a_s and a_a are the level-density parameters for the symmetric and asymmetric barriers respectively. The above two independent fission channels were incorporated into the conventional statistical calculation for fission and evaporation,[14] and the observed excitation functions and the P/V ratios were fitted by varying E_a, E_s and (a_a/a_s)as free parameters. The level density parameter a_n for neutron emission was assumed to be A/8 and a_a was fixed to 1.02 a_n. The difference in the two barrier heights (E_s-E_a) for the first chance fission obtained by the analysis is shown in Fig.6 as a function of the neutron number of the fissioning nucleus. Also shown are the values reported by Konecny et al.[9], and shown for Ra and Ac those for Po and At by Itkis et al.[15] The (E_s-E_a) value changes from a large positive value for N~ 150 to

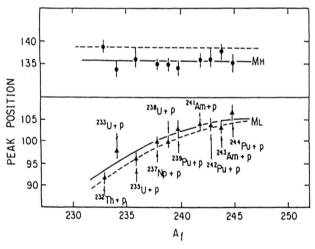

Fig.2 Weighted mean peak position of light and heavy groups in the fission of various nuclides. Filled circles are the peak positions of the heavy group, and filled triangles are those of the light group. Solid lines show the case of proton induced fissions, and dashed lines the case of thermal-neutron induced fissions. The lines are drawn to guide eyes.

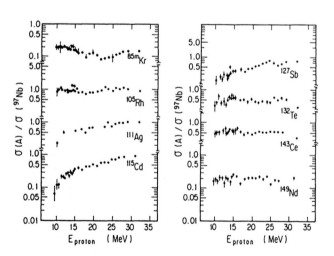

Fig.3(a) Cross section ratios σ (A)/σ (^{97}Nb) as a function of the incident proton energy for the ^{237}Np+p system.

a large negative value for N~ 126, although only a little increase is observed in the N=144~ 150 region. The values for Ac isotopes and ^{233}Pa seem to follow somewhat different trend from those for Ra isotopes and other actinides. The two barrier heights become comparable at N=136~ 137. It has been predicted by the macroscopic-microscopic theory[16,17] that the asymmetric outer barrier becomes more favored in energy at N=134~ 135, and it is rather insensitive to the proton number. The present result in height is of a qualitative agreement with this theoretical prediction. It is to be added that Pashkevich predicts both symmetric and asymmetric saddles by using the shape parameterization of Cassinian ovaloid for a deforming nucleus.[18]

FWHM OF ASYMMETRIC PEAK

Recently, we re-examined the reported mass yield curves of thermal-neutron induced fissions and spontaneous fissions of actinides, and have found that the full width at half maximum height (FWHM) of the heavier asymmetric peak produced by thermal neutron induced fissions exhibits a sudden dip in the region of A_f=240~ 245 while the FWTM (full width at tenth maximum height) monotonously increases with the increase of the mass number of the fissioning nucleus (A_f).[3] In the case of spontaneous fissions, however, this dip is not clear because of scarcity of data.

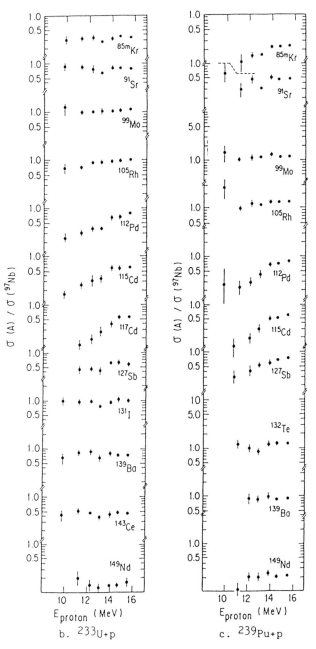

Fig.3(b),(c) Cross section ratios σ (A)/σ (^{97}Nb) as a function of the incident proton energy for ^{233}U+p and ^{239}Pu+p systems.

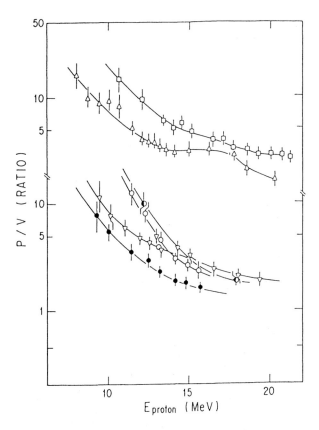

Fig.4 Variation of the P/V ratio as a function of the proton energy for ^{238}U($\square$), ^{232}Th($\triangle$), ^{239}Pu($\bigcirc$), ^{237}Np($\triangledown$) and ^{233}U($\bullet$) targets.

For the better understanding of this trend, the FWHM of the heavier asymmetric mass yield peak observed in 12 MeV proton induced fissions in this work are shown by closed squares in Fig.7. The open circles are the values for thermal-neutron induced fissions and the open triangles for spontaneous fissions. The FWHM is larger for proton induced fissions than those for thermal-neutron induced and spontaneous fissions. The dip around A_f=240∼ 245 is more pronounced for proton induced fissions. For further investigation of the cause of the difference in the FWHM between thermal-neutron induced fissions and proton induced fissions, the relation of the FWHM to the P/V ratios are plotted in Fig.8. The figure shows that the FWHM increases as the P/V ratio decreases. With a closer examination of the observed mass yield curves, it is found that the increase of FWHM is mostly caused by the increased yields of the fragments at the lighter side of the **asymmetric heavy peak** (the inner side of the peak, see Fig.2).

As the FWHM approaches to a constant value for P/V>10, the values at P/V=10 are plotted in Fig.7 by closed hexagonal symbols. They fall close to the open circles and the dip still remains in proton induced fissions. This decreasing trend at A_f=240∼ 245 is hardly understood by the liquid drop model which predicts a smoothly increasing trend with an increase of the fissioning mass. Therefore, it must be related to some characteristics of the mass yield curve caused by some shell effects.

For more quantitative comparison, it may be convenient if the shape variation of the mass yield curve can be expressed by parameters of some functional form that gives the best fit to the experimental data points. After having tried several functional forms, we found that a large number of observed mass yield curves could well be represented by the sum of two Gaussians. Six parameters of the two Gaussians, namely, height, peak position, and width were varied and the best fitting was obtained by the criterion of the χ^2 value. The parameters thus obtained for the heavier asymmetric peak of thermal-neutron induced fissions and spontaneous fissions are plotted in Fig.9, 10. Surprisingly, the peak positions of the two Gaussian stay constant in the wide range of the fissioning mass, one centering around A=134 (first Gaussian) and the other around A=140 (second Gaussian) with a slight increase to A=144 for A_f=250∼ 255. The width σ for the first Gaussian is very narrow and only

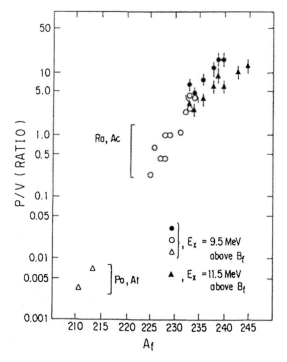

Fig.5 P/V ratios as a function of fissioning nuclides. Closed circles, open circles and open triangles indicate the excitation energy E_x=9.5 MeV above asymmetric fission barriers. Closed triangles are for E_x=11.5 MeV. Closed symbols are the results obtained in this work, open circles are from ref.9, open triangles from ref.15.

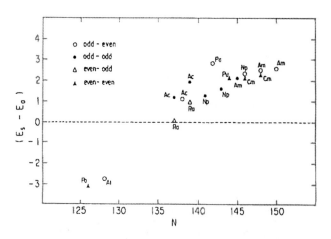

Fig.6 Difference in barrier heights (MeV), (E_s-E_a), as a function of neutron number. The value for Ra and Ac isotopes are from ref.9, and those for Po and At isotopes are from ref. 15.

2~3 units for all A_f while that for the second Gaussian is wider and varies from 4 to 7 as A_f increases from 230 to 255. The ratio of the peak heights (2nd/1st) is in the range of 1~3 and assumes a minimum value in the A_f=240~245. That is, the relative height of the 1st Gaussian becomes maximum in the A_f=240~245 and the larger contribution of this narrow 1st Gaussian to the total mass yield causes the dip in FWHM described above. The rather small variation of those Gaussian parameters throughout the range of A_f=230~255 may simply mean that the shape of the asymmetric peak of the mass yield curve for low energy fission of actinides is appallingly the same. Then, the invariant nature of the shape of the asymmetric peak must be related with the effects of nuclear shell structure either on the static potential or on the mass inertia, or on both.

The dynamical calculation by Pauli and Ledergerber[19] shows that the asymmetric dynamical barrier favors the production of the fragment mass A=140~142 while the static asymmetric saddle calculated by Moller and Nix[16,17] favors the production of the fragment mass A=130~132. The high yields at the two mass regions (A~134, 141) which are persistent phenomena for actinide fissions can not explained by either one of the two

theories. According to Wilkins et al,[20] fragment shell structures favor the production of fragments with A=142~144 which have a deformed neutron shell of N=88, and those with A=132~134 which have a spherical shell of N=82. Their model can explain the high yields at the two mass regions, but it should be pointed out that the variation of the relative heights of two Gaussians as a function of A_f (see Fig.10) is contrary to their prediction (see Fig.10 of ref.20 where they show the difference between the potential energy minima associated with two particular mass splits, (142+complement) and (134+complement), as a function of A_f). Brosa et al.[21] claim that there are two deformation paths in the static potential surface, as calculated by Pashkevich that lead to asymmetric mass divisions, standard I and standard II. Their standard I path corresponds to the 1st Gaussian and the standard II path to the 2nd Gaussian. Their prediction can explain the present results well, but further experimental studies and theoretical studies will be required to make any conclusion.

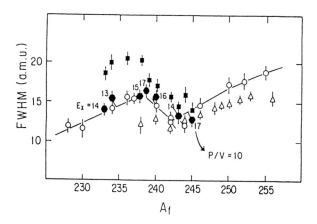

Fig.7 Full width at half maximum (FWHM) values as a function of the fissioning nuclide. Filled squares are the FWHM values of proton induced fissions observed in this work. Open circles are those of thermal-neutron induced fissions, open triangles those of spontaneous fissions, and filled hexagonal symbols those of proton induced fissions that give P/V=10. The number attached to the hexagonal symbol shows the excitation energy of the compound nucleus.

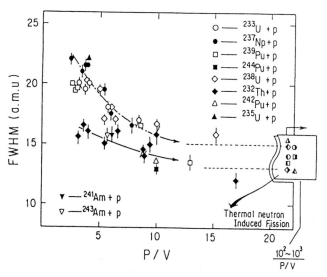

Fig.8 A relation between the FWHM value and P/V ratio. The symbols used for thermal-neutron induced fissions are: ◑ , ^{233}U+n; ◐ , ^{239}Pu+n; ◨ , ^{241}Pu+n; ◧ , ^{241}Am+n; ◆ , ^{236}Np+n; ◇ , ^{229}Th+n; ▲ , ^{243}Am+n; △ , ^{235}U+n.

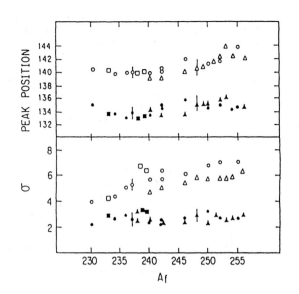

Fig.9 parameters obtained by Gaussian fit to the mass distribution of fission versus the mass number of fissioning nucleus(A_f): the width(σ) and the peak positions for the heavier fragments (open symbols) and the lighter fragments (closed symbols). ■ ,□ reflects for proton induced fission, ▲ ,△ for spontaneous fission, ● , ○ for thermal-neutron induced fission.

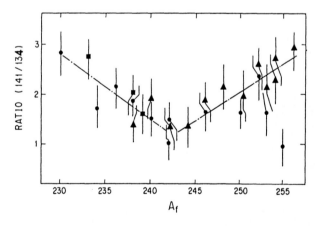

Fig.10 Peak height ratios of the heavier-side Gaussian(A∼ 141) to the lighter-side Gaussian(A∼ 134) as a function of fissioning nuclide. ■ reflects for proton induced fission obtained in this work; ▲ , for spontaneous fission; ● , for thermal-neutron induced fission.

REFERENCES

1 O. Hahn and F. Strassman, Naturwissenschaften 27, 11(1939).

2 J. A. MuHugh and M. C. Michel, "Fission Fragment Mass and Charge Distribution for the Moderately Excited ^{236}U Compound Nucleus", Phys. Rev. 172, 1160(1968).

3 H. R. Von Gunten, "Distribution of Mass in Spontaneous and Neutron-Induced Fission", Actinides Rev. 1, 275(1969).

4 H. Kudo, H. Muramatsu, H. Nakahara, K. Miyano, and I. Kohno, "Fission Fragment Yields in the Fission of ^{232}Th by Protons of Energies 8 to 22 MeV", Phys. Rev. C25, 3011(1982).

5 B. B. Back, O. Hansen, H. C. Britt, J. D. Garrett, and P. Leroux, "Experimental Fission Barrier for Actinide Nuclei", Physics and Chemistry of Fission, Proceedings of a Symposium at Rochester (IAEA, Vienna), Vol.I, 3(1974).

6 Specht, "The Shape of the Fission Barrier" Nucleonika 20, 717(1975).

7 A. Turkevich and J. B. Niday, "Radiochemical Studies on the Fission of ^{232}Th with Pile Neutron", Phys. Rev. 84, 52(1951).

8 H. C. Britt, H. E. Wegner, and J. C. Gursky, "Energetics of Charged Particle-Induced Fission Reactions", Phys. Rev. 129, 2239(1963).

9 E. Konecny, H. J. Specht, J. Weber, "Symmetric and Asymmetric Fission of Ra-and Ac-Isotopes", Physics and Chemistry of Fission, Proceedings of a Symposium at Rochester (IAEA, Vienna) Vol.II, 1(1974).

10 H. Kudo, Y. Nagame, H. Nakahara, K. Miyano, and I. Kohno, "Correlation between Angular Anisotropy and Fragment Mass in 15 MeV Proton-Induced Fission of ^{232}Th", Phys. Rev. C25, 909(1981).

11 S. Baba, K. Umezawa, H. Baba, "Mass Distribution and the Total Fission Cross Section in the Fission of ^{238}U with Protons of Energies Ranging between 13 and 55 MeV" Nucl. Phys. A175, 177(1971).

12 R. C. Jenson, and A. W. Fairhall, "Fission of 226Ra by 11-MeV Protons" Phys. Rev. 109, 942(1958).

13 C. F. Tsang, and J. B. Wilhelmy, "Interpretation of Mass Asymmetry in Fission Based on Deformation Energy Surface", Nucl. Phys. A184, 417(1972).

14 F. Plasil, Oak Ridge National Laboratory Report TM-6054, 1977(unpublished).

15 M. G. Itkis, V. N. Okolovich, A. Ya. Rusanov. and G. N. Smirenkin, "Experimental Investigation of the Region of Existence of Asymmetric Fission in Light Nuclei", Sov. J. Nucl. Phys. 41, 544(1985).

16 P. Moller, "Odd-Multipole Shape Distributions and The Fission Barriers of Elements in the Region $84 \leqq Z \leqq 120$", Nucl. Phys. A192, 529(1972).

17 P. Moller and J. R. Nix, "Calculation of Fission Barriers with the Droplet Model and Fold Yukawa Single-Particle Potential", Nucl. Phys. A229, 269(1974).

18 V. V. Pashkevich, "On the Asymmetric Deformation of Fissioning Nuclei", Nucl. Phys. A169, 275(1971).

19 H. C. Pauli, and T. Ledergerber, "The Dynamics of Fission in the Subbarrier Region of Deformation", Physics and Chemistry of Fission, Proceedings of a Symposium at Rochester, (IAEA, Vienna), Vol.I, 463(1974).

20 B. D. Wilkins, E. P. Steinberg, and R. R. Chasman, "Scission-Point Model of Nuclear Fission Based on Deformed-Shell Effects", Phys. Rev. C14, 1832(1976).

21 U. Brosa, and S. Grossmann, "In the Exit Channel of Nuclear Fission", Z. Phys. A310, 177(1983).

POSTER SESSION:
REACTORS AND SAFEGUARDS

FEASIBILITY OF BREEDING U-233 USING (D+D) "EXYDER" FUSION NEUTRON SOURCE

B. Maglich, C. Powell, J. Nering and A. Wilmerding
Advanced Physics Corp.,
14 Washington Rd., Bldg. 1,
Princeton Jct., NJ 08550
(609) 275-7337

M. Srinivasan and P.K. Iyengar
Bhabha Atomic Research Centre,
Trombay, Bombay, INDIA

ABSTRACT

The Indian Nuclear Power Programme plans for Th-233 to be converted into U-233 in LMFBRs for use in Th/U-233 reactors. We examine a near-term solution of using an alternate fusion system as the neutron source: a newly invented self-colliding beam device known as EXYDER (strong focusing migma), operating at $Q < 5$ and consuming net electrical energy; since it can store MeV ions, the D-D reaction will be used, circumventing tritium problems. A simulation with deuterons of 1.5 MeV, 1.6 A (beam power 2.4 MW), and stored ion density of 5×10^{14} cm^{-3} shows an n production rate of 1.1×10^{19} s^{-1} (in 4π) and energy cost of neutron production of 5 MeV per n. The net U-233 production rate from one 10 m^3 EXYDER is estimated to be 100 g/day of U-233 (35 kg/year).

I. INTRODUCTION

India has more than 360,000 tons of thorium reserves against only 45,000 tons of economically recoverable natural uranium. In order to use these resources in the most effective manner, Homi Bhabha first conceived of a three stage strategy for the Indian nuclear program with the first stage comprising of natural uranium fueled Pressurized Heavy Water Reactors (PHWRs). The entire natural uranium reserves available will be utilized in these first generation PHWRs over a period of 40 to 50 years leaving behind 100 tons of plutonium and a large quantity of depleted uranium. This plutonium is to provide the initial fissile inventory in the second stage for Fast Breeder Reactors (FBRs). In the third stage, the program envisages use of ^{233}U fuel in reactors optimized to operate on the Th/^{233}U fuel cycle.

Availability of non-fission methods of converting thorium into fissile ^{233}U could add an entirely new dimension to the Indian nuclear program. Exploitation of India's vast thorium reserves which is now relegated to the background may become a feasible proposition in a much earlier time frame than currently envisaged. It may even open up the prospects of operating the present CANDU type PHWRs on the Th/^{233}U cycle in the so called near breeder regime. Not many are aware that in a CANDU type reactor operating on the Th/^{233}U cycle as much as 95% of the energy comes from direct burning of fertile thorium (following in situ breeding-fissioning processes) and only about 5% of the fission energy arises from consumption of the initially loaded fissile ^{233}U. Consequently the annual fissile fuel make-up requirement is hardly 1 or 2% of the initial ^{233}U loading. These features make the CANDU-thorium near breeder reactor as an ideal partner for fusion breeders generating ^{233}U.

A detailed study[1,2] was recently carried out on the potential impact that fusion breeders can make on the growth of nuclear power in India. The study showed that even "sub-engineering breakeven" fusion systems having a Q of less than 3, which essentially consume a net amount of electrical energy to generate fissile ^{233}U, can play a crucial role. In Ref. (1) it is shown that even if up to 5% of the total electric power generated in the country is directed for fissile fuel production, net growth of electrical generation capacity is still possible using either fast breeders or advanced converters. The energy cost of ^{233}U used in that study was nearly 50 MeV/atom, which is well below the 200 MeV/atom limitation. The above study considered mainly large (d-t) fueled magnetically confined fusion systems such as tokamaks. The present paper examines the feasibility of adopting an alternate fusion confinement scheme, namely a colliding beam device operating with pure deuterium fuel, as a neutron source.

II. GENESIS OF FUSION DEVICE BASED ON SELF-COLLIDING ORBITS

It was in 1969, that Macek and Maglich first introduced the concept of "self-colliding orbits" and presented the theory of a weak-focusing precession based high-luminosity storage and collision device ("precetron") for high energy uncollimated particles.[3] This was the beginning of the "Migma" (Greek for mixture) system of precessing intersecting ion orbits, all passing through the axis of an axis symmetric magnetic mirror field. Migma is a mixture of large gyroradius ions in an axisymmetric "simple mirror" magnetic field whose precessing orbits pass through the field's axis. The magnetic field intensity decreases quadratically with radius, r, and increases with the distance from the mid-plane.

Migma is formed by collisional dissociation of molecular ions (e.g. D_2^+) that traps atomic ions in the Migma orbits. In the recent Migma experiments the space charge of the ions was neutralized by co-mingling electrons coherently oscillating along the axis. The oscillation frequency was controlled by applying voltage to end plates located a few Migma thicknesses to either side of the mid-plane. The electrons were maintained off-resonance with the axial ion betatron oscillations. The resultant Migma is a synthetic plasma representing a hybrid between colliding beams and plasma. In this way 700 KeV deuteron Migmas with average density n of 3×10^9 cm^{-3} and peak density 3×10^{10} cm^{-3} were routinely produced.[11] The Migma plasma here formed a 20 cm dia $\times$ 1 cm thick disc having 300 cm^3 volume. The energy confinement time was 20 s, during which energy loss was $\leq 5\%$.

The Migma device is thus far the only fusion system in which stable storage and collision of MeV ions has been experimentally demonstrated. In the four experimental versions of the Migma self-collider built between 1973 and 1982 the product of density and containment time was increased by 8 orders of magnitude. The maximum value of triple product of $E_i n T_E$ achieved to date is 3×10^{14} keV/cm^3-s, which is higher than the best obtained in conventional thermal or two component plasma confinement machines.

III. EXYDER-Z: PROPOSED STRONG FOCUSSING SELF-COLLIDER

Blewett pointed out in 1988 that the substitution of ring dipoles produced by two pairs of current loops for the simple mirror field of the Migma device would transform the weak-focusing system into an alternating-gradient strong-focusing field. The ion orbits in such a device, christened "EXYDER" by Maglich et al. are considered in the simple model.[1]

It has been shown that by property tailoring the radial field gradients, the band of focused (and hence trapped) particle energies in the exyder can be broadened to 100%. Further, it has been also shown that for fields of the type specified in eq. 2.3, a particle moving parallel to but outside of the median plane will be acted upon by the "magnetic lens" of the ring dipole field.

All the reactions products whose kinetic energies are much less than those of primary particles will be ejected axially and collected. This natural extraction of low-energy reaction products is especially suited for operation of the exyder as a particle factory (for, say, tritons, ^{3}He, antiprotons, etc.).

A. Space Charge Neutralization

The ion number density, n, in a storage ring is typically limited by space charge to 10^8 cm^{-3}. In the Migma IV experiment, however, as noted earlier, space charge limit in the central zone was exceeded by more than two orders of magnitude through dynamic charge neutralization by means of oscillating electrons.[6]

The Migma radial density in exyder falls off as $1/r$ from an on-axis peak density some ten times the average Migma density. In a large exyder the on-axis density will be 10 times larger than the average. We assume that the stored ions in an exyder would be typically neutralized as in the Migma IV experiment.[6] Thus the enhancement of the space charge limit due to strong focusing

(10^2), coupled to the dynamic neutralization factor augmented by biased electrostatic end plug (10^3) and the factor by which the core region density exceeds the average (10^2), leads us to expect — barring catastrophic collective instabilities — an average number density of 10^{13} to 10^{14} cm^{-3} with a core density of 10^{15} to 10^{16} cm^{-3} with a core density of 10^{-3}. Because of this density increase, the exyder luminosity, which is proportional to n^2, will be 10^{10} times larger than that achieved in storage rings operating at the space charge limit.

B. Luminosity

If the ions are totally neutralized by electrons so that space charge considerations vanish, the upper limit to the Migma density in the exyder is determined by the tolerable level of diamagnetism. To calculate the density limit for a realistic magnetic field profile and the effect of diamagnetism upon focusing properties requires a detailed computer simulation. Assuming a 10% tolerable diamagnetic effect Maglich et al. have estimated yield limiting density comparable to or slightly higher than earlier estimates on the basis of dynamic neutralization of space charge. They also find that the luminosity of the weak-focusing Migma scales linearly with magnetic field, while the strong-focusing exyder luminosity benefits from high particle energies. Consequently a high energy ion disc in an exyder need only neutralized in the central zone.

A method of closing the loss cone of an exyder has recently been proposed by Maglich.[7] For this on each side of the exyder will be placed a "magnetic funnel" whose magnetic field on the z axis is very strong and whose sign is opposite that of the field in the central region of the exyder. Each of the two funnels is formed by the addition of a simple coil of small radius to each side of the main exyder magnet. The central field at $r = z = 0$ can be approximately zero, so that the ratio of the magnetic field strength to that under the outer coils to that on axis at midplane, known as the mirror ratio R_M in adiabatic plasmas, will be very large, of the order of 1,000.

This value of R_M is orders of magnitude greater than that achievable in a simple mirror field. Hover, it must be noted that the concept of the mirror ratio does not apply to very large ion orbits. Unlike ordinary plasmas, the large-radius Migma ion orbits do not follow a flux surface (constant rA_0) but rather have their turning points on surfaces of constant A_0 on account of the constancy of ion canonical angular momentum. Containment of the ions is therefore a twofold problem. First, the focusing at the periphery of the exyder must be adequate; this depends on the tailoring of the B_z profile in the neighborhood of the midplane. Second, particles that undergo large-angle scattering from the high-density region near the axis will have their turning points on a critical A_0 surface that must not intersect the wall prematurely.

Magnetic moment is not even approximately conserved by Migma orbits. There is an adiabatic invariant, however, corresponding to the periodic transverse ion motion.

The confinement mechanism is quite similar to ordinary plasm in a spindle cusp except that there is always a one-gyroradius hole for ordinary plasmas that causes large loss, whereas the Migma ions will be effectively contained.

Figure 1. shows contours of constant A in the r, z plane. The A-surfaces have a smaller "loss cone" than flux surfaces. The B_z profile characterizes the "bandwidth" focusing properties.

In conclusion, the z-funneled exyder provides adequate axial confinement owing to the fact that the A-surfaces that define the turning points subtend a small loss cone that is available only to a beam of particles with very little perpendicular momentum.

IV. NEUTRON PRODUCTION RATE OF EXYDER

Since the ion confinement characteristics of the Exyder Migma is better at MeV energies, the (d-t) reaction does not hold any special advantages over the (d-d) reaction in terms of neutron production. This follows from the fact that for a 1 MeV temperature maxwellian plasma the (d-d) fusion reactivity is only a third of that of a (d-t) plasma at 40 keV. However the (d-d) system avoids the need to breed tritium in the neutronics blanket, besides elimination of the radiological hazards associated with handling the tritium itself. Hence for the Exyder neutron source we consider only the (d-d) reaction with D_2^+ beam injection at 1.5 MeV, corresponding to a circulating ion energy of 0.75 MeV.

An elaborate zero-dimensional ion collision and leakage computations backed up by more detailed 2D code simulations, have predicted a set of performance characteristics given in Table 1.

(a) On an average 1 neutron would be emitted for approximately 5 injected deuterons. Note that for 100% burn up one would expect 1 neutron for every 4 deuterons since each of the two branches of the (d-d) reaction have approximately equal probability. If the tritium released is also assumed to be fully confined

and burnt-up the number of deuterons required per neutron released would decrease to 2. In practice however on account of particle leakages through the loss cone and consumption of d^+ in (d-^{3}He) and (d-t) reactions, the number of deuterons consumed per neutron emitted becomes 5. This leads to a neutron energy cost of $t \times 0.75 \simeq 3.8$ MeV/n. If a mains-to-beam power conversion efficiency of 70% is assumed the net energy cost of neutron production becomes $(3.8/0.7) \simeq 5.5.$ MeV/n.

(b) The generated neutrons form two broad energy groups: 2/3 being produced in (d-d) reactions having a spectrum centered around 3 MeV, while the balance 1/3 are 14.5 MeV neutrons arising from (d-t) reactions. The angular distribution of the (d-d) neutrons at a center of mass energy of 0.75 MeV, equivalent to a beam on target energy of 1.5 MeV is somewhat peaked at a 0° angle. This means that a larger proportion of the neutrons would be emitted along the equatorial plane. However, on account of the disc type shape of the exyder Migma the neutron flux immediately outside the vacuum chamber i.e. in the blanket region is expected to be approximately uniform.

(c) The breakdown of the fusion power output is as follows (d-^{3}He) 42%; (d-t) = 30%; (d-d) = 25%; (^{3}He-t) $\simeq$ 3%; Total 100%

Note that although the primary fuel 15 d^+, (d-d) reactions account for only 25% of the energy output. The balance 75% is from secondary and tertiary reactions. The power generated in the secondary reactions 15 higher mainly because the q of these reactions is roughly 5 times that of the (d-d) reaction.

(d) The overall power gain of the system referred to as (total fusion power output plus injected beam power) divided by injected power, is estimated to be in the region of 5 to 6. However this is of no consequence to the application of the exyder as a neutron source since it is not considered worth while to extract this energy and recirculate it to the beam injection system.

(e) The charged particle leakage probability is typically in the region of 2 to 8% per second; the low value of 2% for tritium results from the fact that it has a high fusioning cross section while the high value of 8% is for particles.

(f) The overall efficiency of the injected deuterons is estimated to be as high as 60%. It is this feature that contributes to the very attractive features of the exyder.

(g) The absolute neutron yield and resultant fissile fuel production however depends on the scaling properties of the Exyder. The overall Migma dimensions and particle content are governed by parameters such as injection beam current (and power), Migma density and volume which in turn are limited by the vacuum chamber size as well as the magnitude of the magnetic field generated by ring dipole magnets — The following table summarizes the typical performance characteristics of a single disc exyder breeding.

V. PRELIMINARY NEUTRONICS ANALYSIS OF THE ^{233}U BREEDING BLANKET

The neutrons released in the central reacting zone of the Exyder chamber would be captured in a surrounding thorium bearing blanket to generate ^{233}U . The breeding ratio is defined here as the number of neutrons captured in thorium per fusion neutron produced. As in the case of other magnetically confined fusion reactor designs, the blanket would be located in the region between the first wall and magnetic field coils. For convenience spherical geometry was used in the present preliminary analysis. The neutronics computations were carried out using the one dimensional neutron transport code DTF-IV. The neutron source is considered to be an isotropic point source at the center of a large void region representing the Exyder Migma. This is followed by an inner moderator zone for partially slowing down the neutrons before they enter the breeding region, beyond which is located the outer neutron reflector. 16-group Hansen & Roach (HR) cross section set was employed, with the 3 MeV (d-d) source neutrons and 14.5 MeV (d-t) neutrons being emitted into the top group which encompasses all neutrons having energy ¿ 3 MeV.

The main objective of the parametric analysis was to maximize the neutron captures in thorium while keeping the overall blanket thickness within practicable limits. Neither the decrement in breeding ratio due to parasitic captures in the intermediate nuclide ^{233}Pa (27 d half life) or the in situ fissioning of ^{233}U was considered in these survey type calculations. Likewise the effects of first wall and structural materials also were neglected. Both H_2O and D_2O were studied as possible moderator-coolants. Two categories of blanket designs were kept in view while carrying out the optimization studies. In the first type thorium was considered to be composed of rods arranged parallel to the axis to form lattice in an annular vessel in which H_2O or D_2O flows axially. It has to be ensured that the volume available for coolant flow is adequate, without resulting in unduly large parasitic captures in the coolant. This type of blanket was simulated in the spherical geometry calculations by increasing the coolant volume fraction from zero until the breeding ratio began to decrease.

The second type of blanket design is a circulating fluid system wherein the thorium is carried either as a nitrate solution (as in the Homogenous Reactor Experiment HRE) or in the form of a colloidal suspension (as in the case of the Heavy Water Suspension Reactor concept and KSTR Experimental Reactor). The advantage of salt solution concepts is that one can possibly remove the ^{233}Pa and ^{233}U on-line as they are formed. In both these fluid fuel concepts however the effective thorium concentration should be kept below 600 g/l from flow and pumping considerations; this corresponds to an upper limit on the thorium volume fraction of 6%.

The atomic densities of H, D, O and Th per cm^3 used were 0.067, 0.067, 0.0335 and 0.0304 respectively in units of 10^{24}. Mixture densities were obtained by appropriate volumetric weighing while homogenizing each region.

The main conclusions of the neutronics computations are as follows:

(a) When thorium is considered to be in the form of rods, H_2O of 40% vol. fraction is found to be optimum. An overall blanket thickness of 27 cm inclusive of a 2 cm initial H_2O region is found to give a fissile breeding ratio of 0.87. Addition of either a H_2O or D_2O or graphite reflector does not improve the breeding ratio significantly.

(b) In the case of a homogeneous suspension or solution design since the thorium volume fraction cannot exceed 6%, D_2O is the preferable moderator. For example, a 40 cm thick D_2O solution blanket followed by a 20 cm thick D_2O reflector gives a breeding ratio of 0.80, for a thorium volume fraction of 4%.

(c) Parasitic captures in structural materials and loss of ^{233}U due to in situ fissioning, etc. and neutron leakage through vacuum feed through and other engineering perturbations will result in a decrement of the breeding ratio. (n12n) reactions in D_2O and Th have not been considered in the above calculations and these would somewhat improve the breeding performance. On the whole a breeding ratio of 0.6 appears reasonable and achievable in practice.

VI. SUMMARY AND CONCLUSIONS

Significant improvements in our understanding of the physics of self-colliding orbits or Migma as a fusion device has enabled conceptual design of a compact fusion neutron source based on the (d-d) reaction. The Exyder-z as it is called, is a strong focussing self-collider employing an alternate gradient ring magnetic filed in conjunction with magnetic funnel type axial end plugs and appears capable of steady state operation generating neutrons in the 10^{17} to 2×10^{18} n/s range with injected d_2^+ (1.5 MeV) beam powers of 50 kW to 1MW. The corresponding beam currents in the 0.1 to 1 A regime appear well within the realm of present day technology. The main uncertainty, if any, in the Exyder concept, which requires experimental confirmation is whether at the required ion densities of 5×10^{14} cm^{-3}, the Migma will remain stable as predicted.

The Exyder neutron source can be developed into a "mini-fusion breeder" to convert fertile thorium into fissile ^{233}U. Availability of such mini fissile fuel factories can have a significant impact on India's plans to harness its, vast thorium resources without having to resort to plutonium fueled short doubling time fast breeder reactors. Each of the 235 MWe CANDU type reactors of the type standardized in India today, if operated on the Th/^{233}U cycle would require hardly 10 kg or 15 kg of fissile ^{233}U annually. Thus installing one or two Exyder type mini breeders

with one or more Migma disc modules each to serve each nuclear power plant site would essentially render the power station self sufficient as far as its fissile fuel requirements is concerned. It is believed that some of the advanced high conversion tight lattice LWRs studied in detail in recent years, if designed with Th/^{233}U fuel can also lead to very efficient fuel cycle characteristics. Thus, coupling of exyder breeders with APWRs operating on the thorium cycle could also lead to fuel self sufficient nuclear power plant complexes. In view of its significant potentialities for the future, development of Exyder type colliding beam mini fissile fuel breeders merits serious attention.

It may not be out of place to point out here that (a) Th/^{233}U based fuel cycles are proliferation resistant to a great extent in view of the hard gamma radiation emanating from the daughter products of the smaller (levis to hundreds of ppm) amounts, of ^{232}U invariably present with ^{233}U and (b) The long lived actinide waste problem is practically non-existent in this fuel cycle.

[1]Blewett, NIM A271,

Table 1. Parameters of a D+D neutron source 10 m^3 exyder with injection of 5×10^{19} d cm^{-3} s^{-1} of d of 0.75 MeV energy closed to all particles except the loss cone.

1.	Mode of operation	D+D; all momenta confined
2.	Exyder volume	10 m^3
3.	Electric power input, P_{in}	6 MWe/(0.65)* = 9.2 MWe
4.	Charged particles electric power input	2.32 MWe
5.	Neutron production rate	1.1×10^{19}s^{-1} = 66 mg/h
6.	Gross energy cost per neutron	3.48 MeV/(0.65)/n = 5.36 MeV/n
7.	Gross energy cost per gram of n (dollar cost)	140 MWh/g; \$8,360/g
8.	Net cost of energy per neutron per g of n (#6 minus #7)	4.5 MeV/n = 119 MWh/g; \$7,140/g
9.	Overall sci. power gain $Q = P_{tot}/P_{in}$	4.8
10.	Neutronicism $N = P_{in}/P_{tot}$	0.42

*Acceleration efficiency of 65% assumed

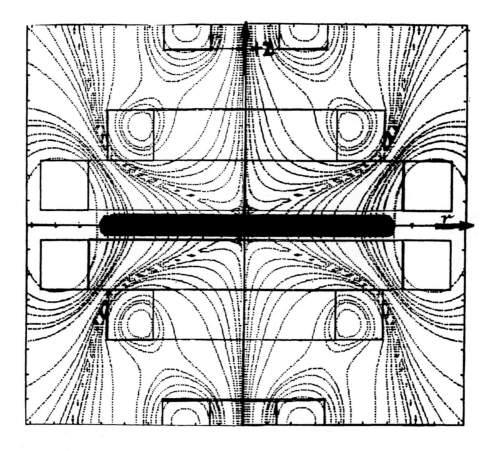

Figure 1. Profiles of constant vector potential A in r vs. z plane for Exyder-z consisting of three pairs of coils. Side view of the migma disc is shown in black.

SYSTEM DESIGN FOR THE LOW ENRICHED URANIUM CONVERSION/POWER UPGRADE OF

A NATURAL CONVECTION COOLED RESEARCH REACTOR

T. Aldemir, J. W. Talnagi and D. W. Miller
The Ohio State University
206 West 18th Avenue, Columbus, Ohio 43210 U.S.A.
(614) 292-4627

ABSTRACT

The 10 kW, highly enriched uranium fueled Ohio State University Research Reactor (OSURR) is being upgraded to operate at 500 kW with the recently developed low enriched uranium, high density U_3Si_2 fuel. The OSURR will be the first domestically licensed reactor to use the U_3Si_2 fuel for a full core conversion. The upgrade will take place with natural convection core cooling and a system configuration which minimizes pool top ^{16}N activity while maximizing the primary inlet temperature to the pool heat removal system to improve the heat exchanger efficiency. The computational/experimental studies for the conversion/upgrade are summarized and put into perspective with regard to the design objectives. The physical changes to the existing system are also described.

INTRODUCTION

The Ohio State University Research Reactor (OSURR) is a 10 kW, natural-convection-cooled reactor fueled with 14.0 g ^{235}U per 2.74 mm thick, flat-plate, highly enriched uranium (HEU) UAl-alloy MTR-type elements (Fig.1). To meet the research demand for increased thermal flux level, the OSURR is being upgraded to operate at 500 kW. In view of the 1986 U. S. Nuclear Regulatory Commission (NRC) ruling,[1] the conversion/upgrade will take place using "standardized"[2] low enriched uranium (LEU), 1.27 mm thick U_3Si_2-Al plates which have a nominal loading of 12.5 g ^{235}U. Natural convection core cooling mode will be maintained in the power upgrade and a pool heat removal system (PHRS) will be installed. Computational/experimental studies addressing specific neutronic and thermal-hydraulic aspects of the project have been reported previously[3-11]. This paper: a) summarizes these studies and puts them into perspective with regard to the design objectives, and b) describes the planned physical changes to the existing system.

COMPUTATIONAL/EXPERIMENTAL STUDIES

Design Objectives

The computational/experimental studies had the following five design objectives: 1) provide sufficient excess reactivity to compensate for experiment worth (0.7% $\Delta k/k$), temperature and equilibrium xenon feedback at full power (i.e. 500 kW) and other burnup effects (>0.5% $\Delta k/k$) while maintaining a minimum 1% $\Delta k/k$ cold, clean shutdown margin with the highest worth rod stuck out, 2) allow a minimum 20% margin to onset of nucleate boiling (ONB) in the hot channel at full power, 3) maximize the thermal neutron flux at the central irradiation facility (CIF) and the beam tube positions under the constraint imposed by objective #2, 4) minimize the pool top ^{16}N activity (PTNA), and, 5) maximize primary inlet temperature to the PHRS to enhance heat exchanger efficiency.

The LEU fuel element geometry was fixed as 16 and 10 standardized plates per standard element (SE) and control element (CE), respectively, with 3 mm coolant channel thickness (Fig.2). Each SE and CE also contains two unfueled plates. The function of the unfueled plates in SEs is to reduce core loading without a substantial reduction in core size, increase in local power peaking or increase in channel thickness (which reduces the ONB margin under natural convection[5,7,10]). The unfueled plates in CEs serve as control rod (CR) guides.

Neutronic Studies

In the first phase of the neutronic studies, the computational core model for diffusion calculations with 2DB[12] and UMDIF (a three-dimensional version of 2DB) was benchmarked by comparing the predicted excess reactivity, CR worths and thermal neutron flux distribution for the HEU OSURR core against measured values. The core model used a 67 X 72 mesh for 2DB and a 67 X 72 X 39 mesh for UMDIF

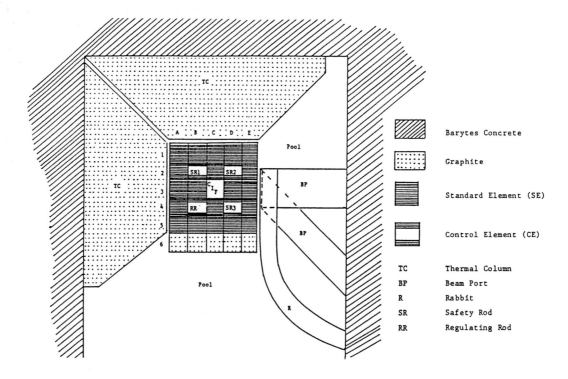

Fig.1: The HEU OSURR core and designation of grid plate locations

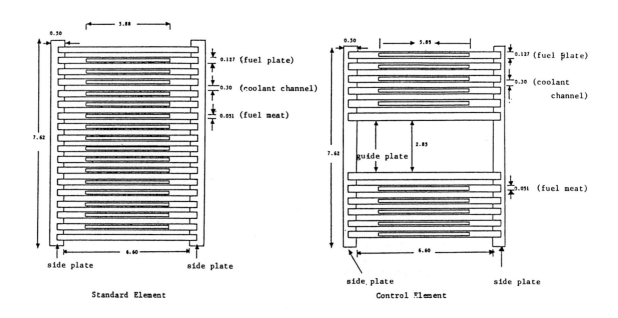

Fig.2 The LEU standard and control elements to be used in the conversion/upgrade of OSURR. All dimensions are in centimeters

runs. Fig.3 shows how the material zones are defined for the diffusion calculations. Zones 1 and 3 are the fuelled portions of the SEs and CEs, respectively, with zone 4 representing a highly loaded element. Zone 2 denotes the water-aluminum mixture of the CR slots when the rods are out. Zone 16 corresponds to the slot composition with the CR in. Zones 8 and 9 are graphite and water reflectors, respectively. The remainder of the material zones represent the structural material such as side plates (zone 7), end boxes (zones 13, 14 and 15), thermal column liner (zones 10 and 11), the CIF (zones 5 and 6) and the transition from the water reflector to thermal column (zone 12). The 4-group parameters for each zone (except for zone 16) were obtained by LEOPARD.[13] Effective absorption cross sections for zone 16 were found by matching the absorption rates predicted by VIM[14] and 2DB on a supercell containing the CR, as proposed in Ref.15. Comparison of the computed and experimentally determined data showed excellent agreement[4], with 0.18% $\Delta k/k$ difference in excess reactivity and a maximum difference of 0.25% $\Delta k/k$ in individual CR worth.

Next, 15 LEU core configurations were analyzed[6] using 2DB to determine the core which satisfies design objectives #1-#3. The core homogenization scheme is similar to the one shown in Fig.3, except that: a) zone 1 and zone 3 number densities correspond to the fueled portion of the LEU elements, b) zone 4 in Fig.3

is replaced by zone 1, c) the presence of the unfueled plates in the SEs is accounted for by an additional material zone and with appropriate reduction in zone 1 volume, and, d) zone 9 data (i.e. water reflector cross sections) is used for the empty positions on the grid plate. In these analyses, the mesh spacings and axial bucklings were identical to those used for the HEU core. The temperature effects on reactivity were determined by whole core calculations using: a) the temperature dependent cross section sets for zones 1 and 3 obtained from LEOPARD (in the range $23^\circ C$ to $60^\circ C$ for the moderator and $23^\circ C$ to $100^\circ C$ for fuel), and, b) the average fuel and coolant temperatures obtained from a single-channel thermal hydraulic model. The equilibrium xenon effect on reactivity was estimated by a first-order perturbation approximation[6], accounting for the spatial variations in the power density.

Three core configurations were identified as possible options for the conversion/upgrade of OSURR (Fig.4 and Table I). Comparison of the diffusion calculation results for excess reactivities and rod worths for cores G and I to the corresponding results of full core VIM simulations again showed excellent agreement. Transient analyses using PARET[16] indicate that all three cores can accomodate step reactivity insertions of up to $1.00 with a minimum burnout ratio (i.e. burnout heat flux/maximum heat flux during the transient) of 4.02, assuming no scram

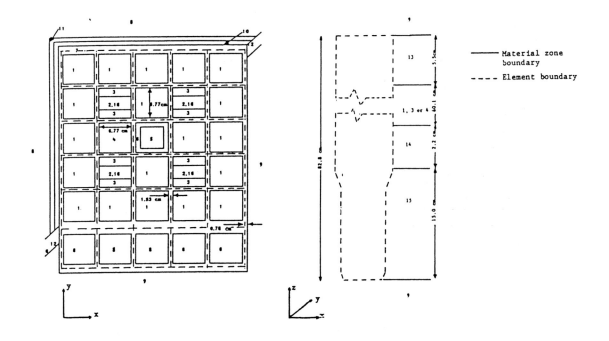

Fig.3: The OSURR core homogenization scheme for diffusion calculations

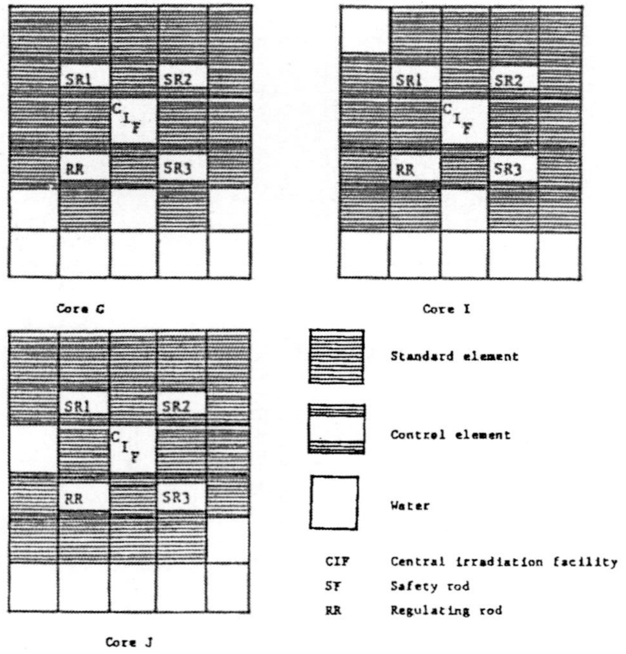
SR1
SR2
CIF
RR
SR3
Core G
Core I
Core J
Standard element
Control element
Water
CIF Central irradiation facility
SF Safety rod
RR Regulating rod

Fig.4: Potential LEU OSURR core configurations

Table I Some Characteristics of Cores G, I and J

	Core G	Core I	Core J
Cold, clean excess reactivity (%Δk/k)	3.01	2.71	3.29
Rod worths (%Δk/k)			
SR1+SR2+SR3	8.23	7.14	7.94
SR2+SR3	5.02	5.20	5.12
SR1+SR3	4.92	4.60	4.86
SR1+SR2	5.99	4.97	5.42
Thermal flux (10^{13} neutrons/cm^{2}s)			
CIF	1.28	1.27	1.29
Beam tubes	0.73	0.68	0.68
Temperature[a] and xenon feedback			
at 500 kW (%Δk/k)	-1.20	-1.13	-1.11
Radial power peaking factor[b]	1.44	1.41	1.39

[a] Based on 80^{0}C average fuel temperature and 40^{0}C average coolant temperature as determined by a single-channel, one-dimensional force balance model

[b] Defined as maximum plate power/average plate power

occurs.

Thermal-Hydraulic Studies

The thermal-hydraulic studies involved both computational and experimental work. The three-dimensional steady-state velocity and temperature distributions in the OSURR pool were simulated using the COMMIX-1A code[17], considering various pool arrangements to meet the design objectives #4 and #5 [Refs.5,8]. All the major pool components were explicitly described in the simulations and three different flow models were used to assess the effects of local turbulence on global pool dynamics. The simulations showed that a sufficiently deep stagnant water layer could be created below the pool surface by the conventional measure for limiting PTNA in natural-convection-cooled research reactors (i.e. plume dispersion by a flat water jet directed across the top of the core such as in TRIGA reactors, with the PHRS inlet away from the core) to yield an estimated ^{16}N dose rate of <1 mrem/hr at the pool surface[9]. However, the simulations also showed that this conventional measure is infeasible in view of objective #5. A better option was found to be to contain the core outflow in a shroud (a 75 cm tall open box) and to place the PHRS inlet within the shroud at the core outlet. There is no appreciable change in the PTNA compared to the conventional measure, but the coolant temperature at the PHRS inlet increases from $25^{\circ}C$ to $38^{\circ}C$.

Experimental studies were undertaken to investigate the validity of the currently used correlations for predicting the ONB heat flux in plate-type fuel element channels[18] under low-velocity, upward-flow conditions, and thereby to reduce the uncertainty in the determination of the ONB margin towards objective #2. Channel surface roughness, height, width and heat source distribution along the channel for the experiments simulated expected operating conditions[5,7]. The results for 2 to 4 mm channels and upward flow velocities in the range of 2 to 15 cm/second showed that the currently used correlations can over- or underestimate the ONB heat flux by as much as a factor of 10. A new correlation was obtained which predicts the experimental results within 13% and which is valid in the local pressure range of 1.40 to 1.46 atmospheres[10]. The ONB margins for the possible OSURR LEU core configurations were found to be in the range of 50 to 60 percent.

PHYSICAL SYSTEM MODIFICATIONS

The PHRS was designed using the following criteria: 1) it must not lead to upward forced convection (since then a new construction permit is required), 2) it must be capable of removing the full core heat load under a variety of environmental conditions, 3) the design should

be simple and reliable, 4) the instrumentation for operation and monitoring must interface with the reactor safety system, and, 5) cost should be minimized while satisfying criteria #2-#4.

Figure 5 schematically describes the PHRS and also shows the shroud/disperser arrangement to limit the PTNA. In view of criterion #5, a forced-draft 8-fan drycooler and two plate-and-frame heat exchangers are used rather than a conventional cooling tower and tube-in-shell heat exchangers. The working fluid through the drycooler is a mixture of ethylene and glycol to allow system operation under very low outdoor temperatures. The auxiliary heat exchanger (using once-through city water as heat sink) provides additional cooling capacity if the outdoor temperature exceeds $23^{\circ}C$. The heat removal capacity can be also adjusted by varying the number of fans operated at a time (4 or 8), by using the bypass leg, changing the flow rate through the secondary coolant pump and also by the modulating valve (in view of criteria #1 and #2). The following reactor trip functions are incorporated into the system in view of criterion #4: a) low pool water (<610 cm from the bottom of the pool), b) high core inlet temperature (>$35^{\circ}C$) and c) loss of flow in the primary or secondary coolant loops if the reactor power is above 120 kW. Also warning alarms are activated on changes in: a) flow rates in the primary and secondary loops, b) temperatures at various locations around the PHRS, c) pressure drops across certain system components, d) outdoor air temperature, and e) the status of pumps and fans. Other planned changes to the system include: a) extending the range of the startup power range monitoring channel, b) installing a solid-state digital electrometer in the linear power monitoring channel, c) installing of a second gaseous effluent monitor to measure ^{41}Ar concentration in the exhaust stream of the pneumatic transfer system and d) adding one or more area radiation monitor (ARM) channels to the existing ARM system.

CONCLUSION, STATUS AND FUTURE PLANS

The OSURR will be the first reactor to use the U_3Si_2 fuel for a full core conversion. The studies described above have identified three possible cores and a system configuration which allow operation at 500 kW while maintaining natural convection mode core cooling. The computational/experimental studies have also provided: a) a quantitative understanding of natural-convection-cooled research reactor pool dynamics with plume dispersion, resolving the difference in opinion regarding the feasibility of power upgrades under natural convection,[19] b) a new technique for simultaneously minimizing the PTNA and maximizing primary inlet temperature to the PHRS to reduce cooling system costs, and, c) an improved correlation for

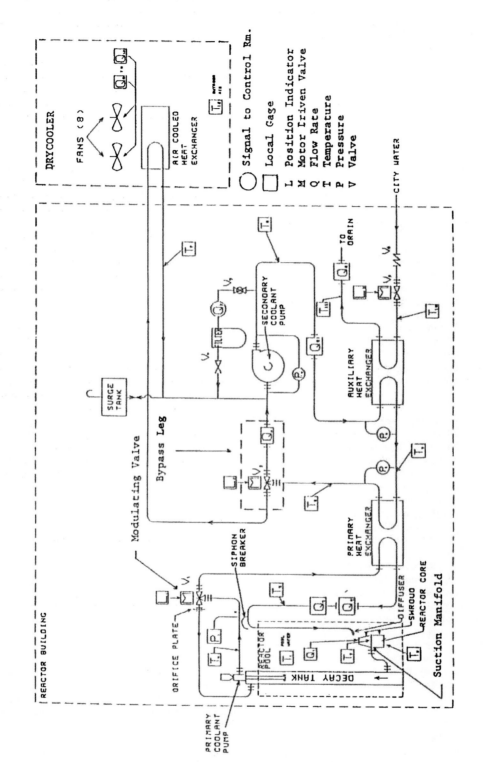

Fig.5: Schematic diagram of the future OSURR pool configuration and the heat removal system

772

predicting the ONB heat flux in plate-type natural-convection-cooled research reactors.

The conversion/upgrade of OSURR will take place in two steps: a) conversion to LEU fuel at 10 kW using a core configuration which has a maximum of 1.5 % $\Delta k/k$ excess reactivity (technical specification for the current HEU core), and, b) power increase to 500 kW as a license amendment. The OSURR went critical with a 16 SE LEU core configuration on December 15, 1988 at 2:34 p.m.. Comparison of the computed and measured values for several core parameters (Table II) shows excellent agreement. License application for the power increase has been submitted to NRC. The project is expected to be completed by January 1990.

ACKNOWLEDGEMENT

The authors would like to acknowledge Dr. J. E. Matos (ANL) and the RERTR Program staff for their cooperation since the inception of the OSURR conversion/upgrade project and their contribution to neutronic studies. The contribution of The Ohio State University Nuclear Engineering Program students (M. Belhadj, J.-J. Ha, M. D. Seshadri, H. S. Aybar) and faculty (Drs. R. N. Christensen and D. Richards) is recognised through the cited references. In addition, the authors would like to thank Dr. M. Caner (SOREQ, Israel) for installing LEOPARD, 2DB-UM and UMDIF on the OSU computer system, A. P. Clark (Assurance Technical Services) for his assistance in cooling system specification and design, and R. D. Myser (OSURR) for his assistance in drafting the revised technical specifications. The study was partly supported by the U.S. Department of Energy Grant No. DE-FG02-85ER75201.A000.

REFERENCES

1. U. S. NUCLEAR REGULATORY COMMISSION, "Limiting the Use of Highly Enriched Uranium in Domestically Licensed Research and Test Reactors", Federal Register, 51 (Feb. 25, 1986).

2. H. H. YOUNG, K. R. BROWN, J. E. MATOS, "Conversion and Standardization of University Reactor Fuels Using Low-Enriched Uranium - Plans and Schedules", ANL/RERTR/TM-9, 31-41, Argonne National Laboratory (1988).

3. M. CANER, T. ALDEMIR, "Preliminary Neutronics Calculations For the OSURR LEU Conversion/Upgrade Program", Reduced Enrichment For Research and Test Reactors, D. Reidel Publishing Co., 273-285 (1986)

4. M. D. SESHADRI, H. S. AYBAR, T. ALDEMIR, "Neutronic Design of An LEU Core for The Ohio State University Research Reactor", to appear in the Proceedings of the 1987 International RERTR Meeting, Buenos Aires, Argentina (Sept. 28-Oct. 2, 1987).

5. J.J. HA, M. BELHADJ, T. ALDEMIR, R.N. CHRISTENSEN, "Feasibility of Maintaining Natural Convection Mode Core Cooling in Research Reactor Power Upgrades", to appear in the Proceedings of the 1987 International RERTR Meeting, Buenos Aires, Argentina (Sept. 28-Oct. 2, 1987)

6. M. D. SESHADRI, T. ALDEMIR, "Neutronic Scoping Calculations for OSURR Core Design With Standardized U_3Si_2 Fuel Plates", ANL/RERTR/TM-9, 410-421, Argonne National

Table II Calculated and Measured Data for the 16 SE LEU OSURR Core

Core Parameter	Measured Value (% $\Delta k/k$)	Calculated Value[a] (% $\Delta k/k$)
Excess Reactivity	1.49	1.54
Rod Worths[b]		
SR1	2.60	2.70
SR2	2.47	2.40
SR3	1.85	2.16

[a]Using 2DB and the homogenization scheme in Fig.3

[b]See Fig.1 for locations

Laboratory (1988).

7. M. BELHADJ, R.N. CHRISTENSEN, T. ALDEMIR, "Experimental Investigation of Onset of Nuclear Boiling in Thin, Rectangular Channels", Proceedings of the 1986 International RERTR Meeting, ANL/RERTR/TM-9, 461-472, Argonne National Laboratory (1988).

8. J.-J. HA, T. ALDEMIR, "Thermal-Hydraulic Analysis of the OSURR Pool for Power Upgrade With Natural Convection Core Cooling", Proceedings of the 1986 International RERTR Meeting, ANL/RERTR/TM-9, 473-487, Argonne National Laboratory (1988).

9. J.-J. HA, T. ALDEMIR, "Pool Dynamics of Natural Convection-Cooled Research Reactors", Nucl. Technol., 79, 297-310 (1987).

10. M. BELHADJ, T. ALDEMIR, R. N. CHRISTENSEN, "Onset of Nucleate Boiling in Thin, Rectangular Channels Under Low-Velocity, Upward-Flow Conditions", Nucl. Technol. 82, 330-340 (1988).

11. T. ALDEMIR, "Neutronic/Thermal-Hydraulic Studies for the LEU Conversion/Upgrade of OSURR", Trans. Am. Nucl. Soc. 56, 572-573 (1988).

12. W. W. LITTLE, JR., R. W. HARDIE, "2DB User's Manual - Revision 1", BNWL-831, REV1 (1969).

13. R. F. BARRY, "LEOPARD - A Spectrum-Dependent Non-Spatial Depletion Code for the IBM-7094", WCAP-3269-26 (1963).

14. M. M. BRETSCHER, "Blackness Coefficients, Effective Diffusion Parameters, and Control Rod Worths for Thermal Reactors", ANL/RERTR/TM-5, Argonne National Laboratory (1984).

15. E. M. GELBARD, R. E. PRAEL, "Monte Carlo Work at the Argonne National Laboratory", ANL-75-2, p. 201, Argonne National Laboratory (1975).

16. W. L. WOODRUFF, "A Kinetics and Thermal-Hydraulics Capability for the Analysis of Research Reactors", Nucl. Technol, 64, 196-206 (1984).

17. H. M. DOMANUS, R. C. SCHMITT, W. T. SHA, V. L. SHAH, "COMMIX-1A: A Three-Dimensional Transient Single-Phase Computer Program For Thermal-Hydraulic Analysis of Single and Multicomponent Systems, Volume I: User's Manual", NUREG/CR-2896 Vol. I (1983).

18. "Research Reactor Core Conversion from the Use of Highly Enriched Uranium to the Use of Low Enriched Uranium Fuels - Guidebook", IAEA-TECDOC-233, 96, 368, International Atomic Energy Agency, Vienna, Austria (1980).

19. F. MERCHIE (CEN/Grenoble-France), H. WINKLER (EIR-Switzerland), A. F. DIMEGLIO (RINSC-USA), Private Communication (Nov. 5, 1986).

THIRTY YEARS OF NUCLEAR FISSION IN YUGOSLAVIA

M.PEŠIĆ, D.STEFANOVIĆ
Boris Kidrić Institute of Nuclear Sciences - Vinča
Nuclear Engineering Laboratory, P.O.Box 522
11001 Beograd, Yugoslavia
(011) 45 82 22

ABSTRACT

Experimental nuclear reactor 'RB' in 'Boris Kidrić' Institute in Vinča is the first nuclear facility built in Yugoslavia in which the first Yugoslav controlled nuclear fission is achieved thirty years ago, on April 26, 1958.

Designed by Yugoslav scientist as a bare, natural uranium - heavy water critical assembly, the 'RB' reactor has survived a series of modifications trying to follow directions of contemporary nuclear research.

The actual 'RB' reactor technical characteristics and experimental possibilities are described. The modifications are underlined, the experience gained and plans for future are presented. A brief review of reactor operation and experiments performed is shown.

INTRODUCTION

Thirty years of nuclear fission in Yugoslavia was passed on April 26, 1958. In meantime, beside the first zero power reactor 'RB' in 'Boris Kidrić' Institute of nuclear sciences ('IBK') in Vinca, two another research reactors ('RA', HWR 10 MW, IBK - Vinča, 1959, and 'TRIGA Mark II', pool LWR 250 kW, 'Jozef Štefan' Institute - Ljubljana, 1966) and only one NPP 'KRŠKO' (PWR/Westinghouse 632 MWe Krško, 1982) were built.

But history of the 'RB' reactor in IBK - Vinca represents actually history of nuclear fission in Yugoslavia. The 'RB' reactor operated a certain period each of 30 years passed. Only during serious modifications in 1959 the 'RB' reactor was shutdown.

HISTORY - THE FIRST TWENTY YEARS

A bare natural uranium - heavy water zero power critical assembly 'RB' was the first critical fission assembly designed completely by Yugoslav scientists[1]. Heavy water moderator and natural uranium fuel were bought in Soviet Union. No forced cooling system, nor radiation shielding was provided. The reactor core was formed from 208 natural uranium rods in 12 cm square lattice pitch inside cylindrical aluminum tank (2.3 m height and 2.0 m diameter). Two cadmium safety rods were designed at the top cover of the reactor. A criticality was achieved by increasing the heavy water level in the reactor tank.

The first chain reaction was reached on April 26, 1958, but the official date of operation is considered on May 17, 1958.

Determination of the critical parameters of U-D$_2$O systems and staff training, necessary for the 'RA' reactor operation (which was under building) were the main reasons of the 'RB' construction.

Measurements of the heavy water critical level, reactivity of safety rods, reactor buckling determination and measurement of neutron leakage from the reactor core were the first experiments performed at the 'RB' critical assembly.

Unfortunately, a serious accident in which 6 people of the reactor and experimental staff were heavily irradiated, one of them fatally, happened on October 15, 1958[2]. The irradiated personnel were in the reactor hall performing a subcritical experiment in aim to determine the magnitude of the spontaneous neutron source in the reactor.

Lack of the administrative and operation rules and inexperience together with breaking of the technical thresholds were the main causes of the accident. It was conclusion after a specially performed join experiment by Yugoslav and IAEA experts at the 'RB' reactor in April 1960[3]. There were no significant damages of the fuel. The total energy developed during accident was estimated to be about 80 MJ[2], and only a very small parts of the aluminum cladding of few 'RB' fuel elements were swollen.

The reactor control, safety and dosimetry systems were, after the accident, modified in 1959/1960, improving operational and safety characteristics. The modifications of the control system included addition of 2 linear and 2 logarithmic neutron DC channels, beside existing 2 start-up channels, a new heavy water on-line levelmeter and new control rod for the automatic power control. The dosimetry system included neutron and gamma doze monitoring in the reactor hall and certain points in the reactor building. A new safety system was designed with 12 trips and acts upon logic ONE of TWO. The new reactor interlock system was designed.

A 2% enriched uranium metal fuel of Soviet origin was obtained in 1959, because the same fuel elements were used for the 'RA', Vinca second research 10 MW reactor. The fuel elements are designed as 2 mm thick annulus of fuel covered with 1 mm aluminum cladding. Inside diameter of the fuel layer is 31 mm and outside diameter is 35 mm. The length of the fuel layer is 96 mm, and the length of the fuel element is 112.5 mm.

The 'RB' reactor core was modified for using of this low enriched fuel so the various lattice pitches, from 7, 8, 9, 12, and 13 cm can be formed inside the reactor tank. Also, a multiples of the basic lattice pitches with square root of 2 can be formed easily. The first safety report and regulatory rules were written in 1961/62.

These modification converted the 'RB' critical assembly to an experimental reactor with 1 W nominal power, operating usually at powers from only 10 mW up to 50 W, and in the special occasions at 'very high' (thermal) power up to 10 kW, only short time.

The 'RB' reactor operated safely using 2% enriched and natural uranium fuel in period 1962/1975. Over 300 different reactor cores were examined. The reactor reached criticality almost 3000 times.

Determination of the thermal and epithermal neutron flux space distributions in cell lattices or in the reactor, determination of the reactor static parameters (bukclings determination, substitution experiments, etc.), performing the kinetic experiments (reactivity determination, transfer function determination), irradiation experiments in the mixed thermal neutrons/gamma fields, training and determination of operation parameters were the main experiments realized at the reactor. The experiments performed helped in development of the new computer codes for the different reactor

aspects calculation in Nuclear Engineering Laboratory – NET of the 'Boris Kidric' Institute of nuclear sciences. The thermal reactor's lattice and core calculation computer codes, reactor shielding and thermal reactor safety codes are developed during first 20 years of the 'RB' reactor operation.

HISTORY – THE LAST TEN YEARS

New 80% enriched uranium dioxide fuel of Soviet origin is obtained in 1975, and the safety report was updated in 1978. The new fuel elements have the same shape and the mass of uranium isotope 235 (7.7 g) as the 2% enriched elements used at the Vinca reactors from 1959. A very wide spectrum of reactor experiments, mainly with thermal and epithermal neutrons using high enriched fuel, was performed at the 'RB' reactor until the end of 1978, when the 'RA" reactor was loaded with the first mixed fuel core.

A research in the fast neutron field design at the 'RB' reactor, which was started at the end of 1975, had resulted in development of the External Neutron Converter – ENC (1976[4]), the Experimental Fuel Channel – EFC (1982[5]) and modification of the 'RB' reactor for a Coupled Fast Thermal System (the first stage CFTS – 1, 1983[6]). The new computer codes for reactor lattice and core calculations were developed and the appropriate experimental methods were provided simultaneously. The very detail safety analyses were performed for the realized reactor modifications.

The ENC transforms the 'RB' thermal neutron core leakage flux into a fast, near to fission spectrum, neutron flux. It is designed as an aluminum big box (dimensions 1116 mm x 1120 mm x 76 mm) beside reactor core filled with 560 segments of 80% enriched uranium fuel (total mass of 4.3 kg ^{235}U). A special 'RB' core is designed to optimize the ENC flux output dependent of the 'RB' power.

The large experimental space and possibility of down-shifting of the ENC output fast neutron spectrum using screens of different materials are the principal advantages of the ENC. The shortcoming of the ENC is the low intensity of the fast neutron flux (approximately 2 10^5 n/cm^2/s, with neutron energy E > 0.1 MeV, at 1 W of the 'RB' power).

Due to its position outside of the 'RB' core and its very low effective multiplication factor, the ENC has no effects on safety and operational characteristics. It has been shown that ENC – 'RB' coupling can be controlled by existing 'RB' control system in the same way as in the case without the ENC.

The EFC was constructed of 10 modified 80% enriched uranium dioxide fuel segments in a standard fuel channel of the 'RB' core, but without moderator around fuel. The intensity of the fast neutron flux inside the EFC was upgraded on account smaller available experimental space (diameter 25 mm, height 1200 mm) and softer neutron spectrum than in the case of the ENC. A new 'RB' core was designed in order to increase epithermal neutron flux around the EFC which was positioned in central axis of the reactor core, surrounded with radial thermal zone filled with high enriched fuel elements without moderator inside fuel channels.

A feasibility study of coupled fast thermal system at the 'RB' reactor using existing nuclear fuel and required minimum reactor modification started in 1981 and resulted (at the end of 1983) in realization of the first version: the CFTS-1, which acts as in-core neutron converter. The main reason for the CFTS-1 realization was testing of the applied theoretical methods and developed and used computer codes.

The CFTS-1 fast zone (without moderator) was designed as an 80% enriched fuel elements annulus (inner/outer diameter 200/300 mm) surrounded with blanket made of two layers of the natural uranium fuel elements in separate aluminum tanks. A central air hole (with diameter 200 mm and height 1250 mm) is designed for irradiation purpose. The CFTS-1 thermal zone is the 'RB' thermal core of 2% and 80% enriched fuel elements in square lattice pitch of 120 mm (inner/outer diameter 540/1220 mm) surrounded with heavy water reflector.

Safety analyses performed showed that the 'RB' reactor can operate safely with developed fast neutron converters without any modification of the existing control and safety systems. There were no need for additional safety rods acting upon the fast zone, but for safety precautions the moderator filling detector is placed in external CFTS-1 tank and connected to the existing safety system of the 'RB' reactor.

Determination of the fast neutron spectra and other relevant characteristics of the realized fast neutron fields were the main experiments performed at the RB reactor in the last 10 years. A long bibliography is at disposal[7]. A great number of new computer programs for the reactor calculations and experimental data evaluations were developed in NET Laboratory at the 'Boris Kidric' Institute of nuclear sciences in Vinca.

ACTUAL REACTOR CHARACTERISTICS

After the accident happened in 1958, the 'RB' reactor operated safely the last 29 years without any bigger problems.

The start-up channels were replaced in 1978 with the new ones and included in the reactor interlock system. The two new linear and logarithmic power control DC neutron channels were added to control system in 1981 covering reactor power range from 10 mW up to 10 kW, the dosimetry system was upgraded in 1988 with 3 new gamma monitoring channels. The new 3 logarithmic DC neutron channels will be connected in the reactor control system with aim to replace the old DC channels designed in electronic tube technology.

The experimental possibilities of the reactor were upgraded with designed fast neutron fields: ENC, EFC and CFTS-1.

The main characteristics of all Yugoslav nuclear reactors are shown in Table 1, and the main experimental characteristics of the 'RB' reactor are shown in Table 2.

FUTURE PLANS

It is expected that new power control and dosimetry channels will be installed, connected to the safety system and examined until the end of 1989. The channels will be connected to the DEC VAX - 8250 computer for on-line monitoring, data acquisition and evaluation of the reactor operation and experiments performed data. The new automatic power control system using a computer will be designed and examined in the next years.

New analyzes of a real coupled fast thermal system at 'RB' reactor are under progress now[8]. This modification of the 'RB' reactor represents a natural continuation of examination and realization of the fast neutron fields at the 'RB' reactor, which was started in 1976. The new coupled system will has a central fast core designed with the existing 'RB' fuel with real asymptotic fast neutron spectrum. It is expected that it will start operation in beginning of 1990.

CONCLUSION

The history of nuclear fission in Yugoslavia is began with 'RB' reactor. During 30 years of operation a great experience in reactor operation, safety and dosimetry is accumulated[7,9]. Over 450 different reactor cores were investigated, and reactor reached criticality more than 3600 times. The reactor systems were modified few times, converting the old critical assembly to a real experimental low power reactor with great flexibility.

With modifications mentioned above and ones expected in near future it is expected that the 'RB' reactor will continue its safe operation until the end of century.

REFERENCES

1. D.POPOVIĆ, "The Bare Critical Assembly of Natural Uranium and Heavy Water", Proc. 2nd UN Inter. Conf. PUAE Geneva, paper no. 15/P/491, 12, 392 (1958)

2. P. SAVIĆ. "Sur l'accident avec le reacteur de puissance zero du 15 octobre 1958", Bull. "Boris Kidrić" Inst., Vinča, 9, No.167, 1, (1959)

3. "The Vinča Dosimetry Experiment", IAEA Technical Report Series No. 6, Vienna (1962)

4. P. STRUGAR, O.ŠOTIĆ, M. NINKOVIĆ, M.PEŠIĆ, D. ALTIPARMAKOV "Conversion of the 'RB' Reactor Neutrons by High-Enriched Uranium Fuel and Lithium Deuteride", Kernenergie, 24, Hf.3, 101 (1981)

5. M. PEŠIĆ, H.MARKOVIĆ, M.ŠOKČIĆ, I.MIRIĆ, M.PROKIĆ, P.STRUGAR, "Experimental Fuel Channel for Samples Irradiation at the 'RB' Reactor", Kernenergie, 27, Hf.11-12, 461 (1984)

6. M. PEŠIĆ, "Coupled Fast – Thermal System at the 'RB' Nuclear Reactor", Kernenergie, 30, Hf.4, 142 (1987)

7. M. PEŠIĆ, D. STEFANOVIĆ, "Nuclear 'RB' Research Reactor – Thirty Years Anniversary", Proc. of XXXII Conf. of ETAN, Sarajevo, 9, 11 (1988) (in Serbocroatian)

8. M.PEŠIĆ, P.MARINKOVIĆ, "The Preliminary Design Characteristics of the 'RB' Fast – Thermal Core", Conference "30 Years with Nuclear Fission", Gaithersburg, MD, April 25-28 (1989) U.S.A.

9. M.PEŠIĆ, S.CUPAĆ, D.STEFANOVIĆ, "Nuclear Safety Experience of the Research Reactors of 'Boris Kidric' Institute", Proc. of "International ENS/ANS Conf. on Thermal Reactor Safety – NUCSAFE-88", Avignon, 1, 33 (1988)

TABLE 1   YUGOSLAV NUCLEAR REACTORS

REACTOR	'RB'	'RA'	'TRIGA-MARK II'	'KRŠKO'
Location	IBK – Vinća	IBK – Vinča	IJS – Ljubljana	Krško
Type	experimental	research	research	NPP – PWR
Design	Yugoslav	USSR	USA/GA	USA/Westinghouse
Nominal power	1 W	6.5 MW	250 kW	632 MWe
Maximal power	10 kW	10 MW	300 kW	2000 MWt
Start of operation	1958	1959	1966	1982
Moderator	heavy water	heavy water	zirconium hydride	water
Coolant type	heavy water	heavy water	water	water
Heat transfer	natural convection	forced convection	natural convection	forced convection
Fuel type	natural uranium 2% enriched U 80% enriched uranium dioxide	2% enriched metal U 80% enriched uranium dioxide	20% enriched U 70% enriched U alloy with zirconium hydride	uranium dioxide: 2.1% enriched 2.6% enriched 3.1% enriched

NEUTRON FLUX AND FLUENCE

MONITORING IN A RESEARCH REACTOR

B. OŠMERA, O. ERBEN, F. TOMÁŠEK
Nuclear Research Institute
250 68 Řež
Czechoslovakia

ABSTRACT

In the article, the main characteristics
of the WWR-S research reactor situated
in the N.R.I. Řež are briefly described.
The reactor is of a multipurpose use and
the main types of experiments carried
out at the reactor and the experimental
devices installed are mentioned. The main
attention is paid to the experiments concerning the determination of radiation
field parameters in the reactor core. The
experiments are shortly described and
particular results concerning the following problems are presented:
intercomparison and intercalibration of
multicomponent activation detectors,
self- powered detectors (SPD) with different emitters and reactor calorimeters
with different bodies; longterm measurement of neutron flux distribution in the
core of the reactor; neutron and gamma
field monitoring at the irradiation channel of reactor water loop; neutron spectrum measurement and monitoring.

The WWR-S research reactor is being
reconstructed, new and special start-up
experiments connected with the new re -
constructed reactor dosimetry and monitoring systems are mentioned at the end of
the article.

INTRODUCTION

The WWR-S research reactor was put
into operation in N.R.I. in 1956. Since
this time it has been several times reconstructed in such a way that its power
has been increased from 2 MW (thermal)
up to 10 MW. The core of this multi-purpose research reactor is composed of
IRTM type fuel elements, Be reflector
elements and structural components made
from a standardized aluminium based alloy.
The IRTM fuel elements consist of three
or four concentric tubes of quadratic
form. The fuel itself is a U-Al metalic
dispersion (80 % U 235 enrichment)
thickness of 0.4 mm (more details as
well as core operational configuration
could be found in /1/). During the new
reconstruction, started in 1988, the power of the new LVR-15 should be increased up to 15 MW and the low enriched
(36 % U 235) element (the same geometry
as the IRTM) will be gradualy introduced.
The typical operational configuration
of the LVR-15 core is in Fig. 1.

The horizontal channels of the
WWR-S (LVR-15) reactor as well as the
thermal column are used for solid state
physics research (neutron difraction,
etc.), nuclear reaction studies, neutron
capture therapy studies, neutronography
and other applied research. Various irradiation equipment is installed, or
could be used, in the core. The parameters of the reactor water loop correspond
to the VVER-1000 type power reactor.
Other equipment is used for the irradiation of the silicon crystals, a special irradiation rig is used for the
material research (for the steel radiation damage studies especially). The
reactor is also equipped by pneumatic
rabbit connected with several laboratories.

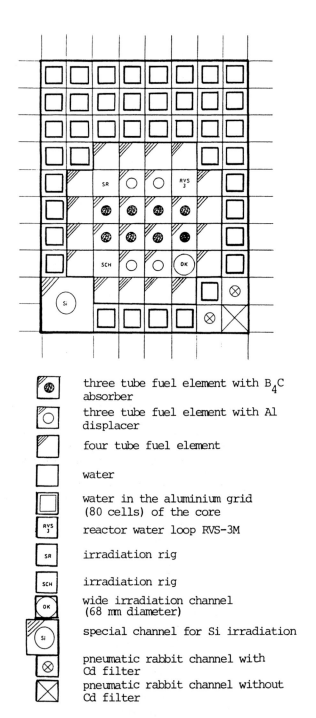

| three tube fuel element with B_4C absorber |
| three tube fuel element with Al displacer |
| four tube fuel element |
| water |
| water in the aluminium grid (80 cells) of the core |
| reactor water loop RVS-3M |
| irradiation rig (SR) |
| irradiation rig (SCH) |
| wide irradiation channel (68 mm diameter) (OK) |
| special channel for Si irradiation |
| pneumatic rabbit channel with Cd filter |
| pneumatic rabbit channel without Cd filter |

FIG. 1   DIAGRAM OF A TYPICAL CONFIGURATION
OF LVR-15 CORE

NEUTRON FIELD PARAMETERS

The typical reactor core neutron spectrum is shown in Fig. 2, the spectral indexes of the typical irradiation channels are summarized in Table 1.

TAB. 1   SPECTRAL INDEXES IN TYPICAL CORE
IRRADIATION CHANNELS
(RELATIVE ABUNDANCE)

Energy interval /MeV/	Water channel	Dry channel
(E-10, E-7)	17.3 %	8.9 %
(E-7 , E-1)	53.0 %	55.4 %
(E-1 , 18)	29.7 %	35.7 %
(0.5 , 18)	17.0 %	21.2 %
(1.0 , 18)	8.8 %	10.5 %

The progress in irradiation equip - ments should be accompanied byt the progress in the monitoring of the neutron- -photon radiation field parameters. Several measuring methods have been developed to cover the whole spectrum of the demands for the monitoring of the experiments and irradiations in the multipurpose operation of the reactor. To unify and standardize the monitoring methods several intercomparison and intercalibration experiments have been performed including the international intercomparison with the institutes in USSR, Poland, GDR. The following in core sensors like multicomponent activation detectors, SPD with rhodium, vanadium, platinum, cobalt and lead emitters and reactor calorimeters with bodies made of UO_2, lead, tungsten, aluminium, graphite and stainless steel have been studied. A set of long-term measurements with the continuous and activation methods including the monitoring of neutron spectrum in WWR-S reactor has been performed too /3/. A significant contribution to the improvement of the method of interpretation of the VVER NPP in-core control system signals was brought about by the measurement in the LR-0 experimental reactor /2/ physical mock-up of the VVER NPP reactor core. The maximum neutron flux density in the LR-0 core (about $10^{13} m^{-2} s^{-1}$) corresponds to the rhodium SPN detector signal of a few pA /3/. For these conditions the measuring channel with rhodium SPN detector has been developed together with the data recording and processing system.

The neutron spectrum measurements /1/ are based on the progress in reactor neutron spectrometry reached in the frame of the activity of the Czechoslovak Working Group on Reactor Dosimetry /2/. The multicomponent activation detector

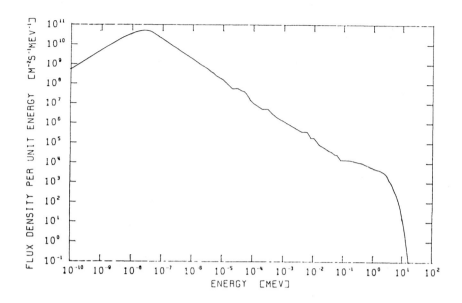

FIG. 2   NEUTRON SPECTRUM IN THE WWR-S REACTOR
IRRADIATION CHANNEL

or set of activation foils are used for the neutron flux density and spectrum monitoring in various points during the reactor operation.

The individual irradiation points and apparatures are equipped with the monitors according to the purpose of the experiment. For example the irradiation channel of the water loop is equipped with the 7 SPD and 5 tungsten calorimeters to provide the local and derived mean and integral values of the neutron flux and photon densities in the channel. The thermal neutron flux densities monitored by SPD during one week irradiation

TAB. 2   MEAN VALUES OF THERMAL NEUTRON FLUENCE AND THE
GAMMA RADIATION DOSE FOR EACH IRRADIATION WEEK

Irradiation week	$(\emptyset_{th} \cdot t)$ $/10^{23} \, m^{-2}/$	$(q \cdot t)$ $/10^9 \, Gy \, /$
17-18	1.450	2.691
19	0.787	1.474
20	0.807	1.519
21	0.844	1.539
total 17-21	3.888	7.223
35-36	1.110	1.996
37	0.757	1.300
38	0.701	1.286
39	0.698	1.272
total 35-39	3.266	5.854

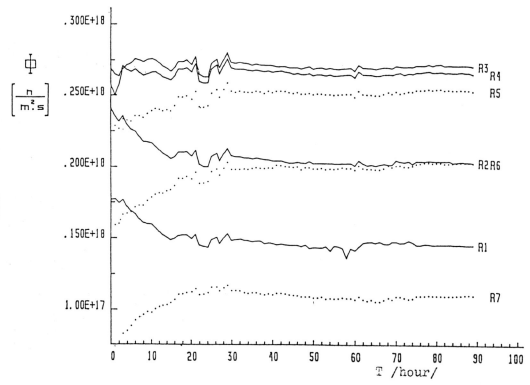

FIG. 3   THERMAL NEUTRON FLUX MONITORED BY 7 SPD (THE DETECTORS
ARE SITUATED ONE ABOVE THE OTHER WITH THE DETECTOR R 1
LOCATED AT THE BOTTOM)

are illustrated in Fig. 3. The reactor power was 5.3 - 5.5 MW. As a further example, the numerical data of mean values of thermal neutron fluence and the gamma radiation dose along the irradiation channel are presented in Table 2 for experiments carried out in 1987 (in the week 17 and 35 including Saturday and Sunday; the reactor power was 5.9 - 6.5 MW).

The 90 % response intervals of the activation monitors in the irradiation rig for the material radiation studies are shown in Table 3.

TAB. 3   90 % RESPONSE INTERVAL OF ACTIVATION DETECTORS IN IRRADIATION RIG FOR MATERIAL TESTING

detector	90 % response interval /MeV/
^{58}Ni (n , p)	(2.2 , 7.8)
^{54}Fe (n , p)	(2.4 , 7.9)
^{59}Co (n , γ)	(0.8 E-9 , 1.35 E-4)
^{63}Cu (n, α)	(4.8 , 11.3)
DPA	(0.135 , 6.1)

During the last four years the (axially) averaged thermal (below 0.1 eV) and fast (above 0.1 MeV) flux monitored by activation detectors varied in the interval $(3.1 - 6.6)10^{16}$ n/MW.m².s and $(10.6 - 15.5).10^{16}$ n/MW.m².s respectively in the dry irradiation channel from March 1984 to October 1987. The averaged values during this period were $5.8.10^{16}$ n/m².s.MW and $5.9.10^{16}$ n/m².s.MW for thermal and fast neutron flux density with standard deviation 28.3 % and 15.1 % respectively. The target accuracy 20 % in the fast neutron fluence monitoring for the steel radiation damage studies was reached for the relatively short interval (several months of reactor operation). The perturbations of the neutron field caused by the considerable changes in the core configuration should be better monitored in the years to come. A special experiment has been performed to study the perturbation caused by the steel specimen in the irradiation rig. The measurements were done in full scale model placed in core at low power level. Further effort would be concentrated on the neutron spectrum monitoring.

782

FUTURE PROGRAMME

To improve the monitoring in the reconstructed reactor a special set of reactor dosimetry experiments will be performed during the start up of the reactor.

The neutron spectra will be measured in the typical irradiation environment - dry and water irradiation channels, pneumatic rabbit channel with Cd filter, the neutron leakage spectrum falling into the thermal collum, etc. For this measurement a special set of ultra thin resonance activation detectors like in /2/ will be used. The activity measurement of several detectors will be performed by three independent laboratories.

If the reactor vessel and all other core structural elements of the reactor will have been replaced during the reconstruction, the physical start up with new fresh fuel elements is the convenient period for the use of neutron differential spectrometers because of low gamma background. The neutron flux density energy distribution measured by proton recoil method (hydrogen filled spherical proportional counters, stilbene scintilator) and 6Li sandwich detector at defined points will be used as the input spectrum in the adjustment of the activation measurement. The neutron spectra measured during the start up operation will create the base for the evaluation of all neutron dosimetry measurement in LVR-15 reactor. The error propagation for the monitored values is summarized in /4/.

The neutron flux density distribution in the LVR-15 reactor will be measured by threshold and multicomponent threshold - resonance activation foils. The axial and radial power distribution measurements will be performed by means of gold foils.

New systems for neutron and gamma fields monitoring of main irradiation devices and channels installed at the reactor are also being developed. The system for pneumatic rabbit installation should give automatically the value of the neutron flux density in the irradiation position and necessary time of irradiation according to the prescribed exposure. The system for the silicon radiation dopping devices should measure the neutron flux density distributions along the irradiation channels, choose the positions of irradiations and determine the irradiation time. The system should also provide the history of irradiation including the alarm signals in abnormal situation.

REFERENCES

1. B. OŠMERA et al.: "Neutron Spectra Measurements in WWR-S Reactor". Proceedings of the Fourth ASTM-Euratom Symposium Reactor Dosimetry, Vol.1, 587 (1982)

2. B. OŠMERA et al.: "The Activity of the Czechoslovak Working Group on Reactor Dosimetry in the Period from 1980 to 1983". Proceedings of the Fifth ASTM-Euratom Symposium on Reactor Dosimetry, Vol. 2, 967 (1984)

3. K. DACH, O. ERBEN, V. KRETT, B. OŠMERA, F. TOMÁŠEK: "On the Activity of the Nuclear Research Institute Řež in the Field of In-Core Measurement". OECD Specialists' Meeting on In-Core Instrumentation and Reactor Core Assessment. Cadarache, 7th - 10th June 1988

4. B. OŠMERA, V. ŠTĚPÁNEK: "The Determination of the Error in Monitoring the Neutron Flux and Fluence in a Nuclear Reactor". Jaderná energie, Vol. 33, No. 8-9, p. 304 (1987)

PRELIMINARY DESIGN CHARACTERISTICS OF THE RB FAST-THERMAL CORE 'HERBE'

M.PEŠIĆ
Boris Kidric Institute - Vinča
Nuclear Engineering Laboratory, P.O.Box 522
11001 Beograd, Yugoslavia
(011) 45 82 22

P.MARINKOVIĆ
Faculty of Electrical Engineering
Nuclear Engineering Department
B.Revolucije 73, 11000 Beograd, Yugoslavia
(011) 32 18 22

ABSTRACT

The 'RB' is zero power heavy water critical assembly designed in 1958. in Yugoslavia. The reactor operated using natural metal uranium, 2% enriched metal uranium, and 80% enriched UO_2 fuel of Soviet origin. A study of design of fast neutron fields began in 1976 and three fast neutron fields were designed up to 1983: the external neutron converter, the experimental fuel channel and the internal neutron converter, as the first step to fast-thermal coupled system. The preliminary design characteristics of the HERBE - a new fast - thermal core at the RB reactor are shown in this paper.

INTRODUCTION

The RB reactor[1] was designed in 1958 as an unreflected zero power heavy water - natural uranium critical assembly. Nuclear material was bought in Soviet Union, but complete design of the reactor was done in Yugoslavia. During last 30 years of the reactor operation, the 2% enriched metal uranium fuel and 80% UO_2 fuel of Soviet origin were obtained and used in the reactor core.

Modifications of the reactor control, safety and dosimetry systems (done in 1959-1960, 1976, 1986 and 1988) converted the RB critical assembly to the experimental reactor with 1 W nominal power, normally operated up to 50 W and in special occasions up to 10 kW.

A study of the fast neutron fields of the RB reactor began in 1975 when new fuel, 80% enriched UO_2 dispersed in aluminum, become available. The external neutron converter[2] (ENC) was designed in 1976, the experimental fuel channel[3] (EFC) was made in 1982 and the first version of coupled fast-thermal system[4] (CFTS-1) acting really as an internal neutron converter was designed in 1983.

New computer codes were developed and application of the adequate experimental methods was adopted at the designed fast neutrons fields.

THE CFTS-1, THE FIRST VERSION

The 80% enriched uranium dioxide fuel of Soviet origin is obtained in 1975. The new fuel elements have the same geometrical shape and the mass of uranium isotope 235 (7.7 g) as the 2% enriched uranium fuel elements used at the RA and RB reactors in Vinca from 1959. The fuel elements are designed as cylindrical segments of 2 mm thick annulus of fuel material covered with 1 mm aluminum cladding. Inside diameter of the fuel layer is 31 mm and the fuel outside diameter is 35 mm. The length of the fuel layer is 96 mm, and the length of the fuel element is 112.5 mm.

A very wide spectrum of cell and reactor experiments, mainly with thermal and epithermal neutrons using high enriched fuel, was performed at the RB reactor until the end of 1978, when the RA reactor was loaded with the first mixed fuel core. At the same period the ENC was designed and examined at the RB reactor. The EFC was designed and examined in 1982-1983.

A feasibility study of coupled fast thermal system at the RB reactor using existing nuclear fuel and required minimum reactor modification started in 1981 and resulted (at the end of 1983) in realization of the first version: the CFTS-1, which acts as in-core neutron converter. The main reason for the CFTS-1 realization was testing of the applied theoretical methods and developed and used computer codes.

All calculation for the CFTS-1 design were performed using numerical codes developed in Nuclear Engineering Laboratory. The well-known coupled fast thermal reactors, as ZPR - V[5], STEK[6] and STARK[7], were thorough studied before the CFTS-1 design at the RB reactor has been initiated.

The basic requirements for the CFTS-1 design were set as following:
a. the CFTS-1 must be formed using existing RB fuel elements with minimum possible modifications of the RB reactor systems;
b. the RB operation with CFTS-1 must be safely with existing control and safety systems of the

reactor;

c. the CFTS-1 fast core should have the highest possible ratio of the fast to the thermal fissions, and

d. the thermal core kinetics parameters of the CFTS-1 should be dominate and determine kinetics behavior of the whole CFTS-1 at the RB reactor.

The CFTS-1 fast zone (without moderator) was designed as an 80% enriched fuel elements annulus (inner/outer diameter 200/300 mm) surrounded with blanket made of two layers of the natural uranium fuel elements in separate aluminum tanks. A central air hole (with diameter 200 mm and height 1250 mm) is designed for irradiation purpose.

The CFTS-1 thermal zone is the RB thermal core of 2% and 80% enriched fuel elements in square lattice pitch of 120 mm (inner/outer diameter 540/1220 mm) surrounded with heavy water reflector.

Safety analyses performed showed that the RB reactor can operate safely with developed CFTS-1 as fast neutron converter without any modification of the existing control and safety systems. There were no need for additional safety rods acting upon the fast zone, but for safety precautions the moderator leaking detector is placed in external CFTS-1 tank and connected to the existing safety system of the RB reactor. Its purpose is to shutdown the reactor in case of leaking heavy water into fast zone.

All requirements, a. - d., except c. were satisfied. A central air hole had to be designed due to insufficient number of highly enriched fuel elements at the RB reactor. So designed the CFTS-1 acts as fast neutron converter inside the RB reactor. There were no asymptotic neutron spectra in fuel in fast zone. Calculation showed that only 2.51% of total fissions are occurred in the fast neutron core, and 78.19% in the thermal core.

Determination of the fast neutron spectra and other relevant characteristics of the realized CFTS-1 were the main experiments performed at the RB reactor in last few years. Parallel, the new computer programs for the reactor calculations and experimental data evaluations were developed in Nuclear Engineering Laboratory in Vinca.

HERBE - NEW COUPLED FAST THERMAL CORE

New analyzes of a real coupled fast thermal system at RB reactor are under progress now. This modification of the RB reactor represents a continuation of the examinations and realizations of the fast neutron fields at the RB reactor, especially CFTS-1. The new coupled system should has a central fast core designed from the existing RB fuel elements with real asymptotic fast neutron spectrum inside center of the fast core. It is expected that it will start operation during 1990.

A first study of the HERBE at the RB reactor has began in beginning of 1988. The HERBE should has a fast core designed of natural uranium or 80% UO_2 fuel in the RB reactor center surrounded with a neutron filter and a neutron converter. A thermal neutron core will surround the fast zone as a driver. This new design conception was adopted from Soviet's coupled system BTS-4[8].

A design demands were set as for previously designed CFTS-1, except that demand c. was modified in requirement to achieve a fast neutron asymptotic spectrum in the center of the fast core. Although the optimal core composition should demand the fast core with almost 40 cm radius, the requirements for minimum RB reactor modifications were fundamental for decision.

Any modifications at the RB reactor with a diameter of 80 cm wide fast zone in the reactor's tank (diameter 200 cm) would demand completely reconstruction of the RB reactor's top cover at which two safety rods, one control rod and on-line automatic heavy water levelmeter should be displaced to the edges of the reactor tank. The new fuel supporters in the reactor tank should be designed too.

These were the reasons that lead to try to meet demands for the HERBE using experience and available three aluminum tanks from the CFTS-1 fast core design. At the same time, due to possibility to use additional 80% enriched fuel segments, the two version of the HERBE are analyzed.

The HERBE-1 fast core should be designed from natural uranium fuel elements of the RB reactor placed in the cylindrical aluminum tank (diameter 20 cm), as tight as possible. The HERBE-2 fast core should be formed in the same aluminum tank as HERBE-1, but with 80% enriched UO_2 fuel elements of the RB reactor.

The HERBE fast core will be surrounded with neutron filter designed from thermal neutron absorbing material in a narrow zone and natural uranium buffer zone. The BISCO Co. (U.S.A.) RADSTOP material and a few materials with B_4C were examined in calculations as possible materials for the neutron filter. The exact composition and with of the neutron filter zone depends of desired neutron spectrum in the fast zone. The neutron filter zone and natural uranium buffer zone are designed in the same separate cylindrical aluminum tank (inner/outer diameter 20.2/30.2 cm).

The RB 80% enriched UO_2 fuel elements are used as the neutron converter surrounding the neutron filter zone in the separate cylindrical aluminum tank in which the HERBE fast zone is placed (inner/outer diameter 30.2/40.6 cm). There is no heavy water in the fast zone.

The HERBE thermal core is based on the RB reactor core with square lattice pitch of 12 cm with 80% UO_2 fuel elements moderated and reflected with heavy water. The inner moderator of heavy water, width 7 cm, surrounds the fast core.

The RB reactor thermal core and HERBE fast core cell parameters were calculated using VESNA[9] computer code. The HERBE reactor criticality calculation are done using modified 2D RZ diffusion TWENTY GRAND[10] computer code, and one-dimensional, a multigroup, collision probability computer code AVERY[11], based at Avery model[12] of coupled systems.

It was shown that criticality of the alone fast core is far away from 1 and that the fast and thermal core are strongly coupled according to of Avery's parameters. Heavy water critical level in thermal zone is determined as 1050 mm + 50 mm by calculation with numerical codes mentioned above. The safety calculations are under progress and it is expected that they will certificate demands for safe operation of the HERBE without modification of the RB control and safety systems.

In any case a new safety trip is designed with a detector of heavy water leaking in the external Al tank of the fast zone.

A horizontal cross section of the HERBE fast zone (version #1 and #2) and horizontal cross section of the HERBE system at the RB reactor are shown in the Figure 1. Preliminary designed characteristics of the HERBE-1 core, compared with reactor STARK and previously designed CFTS-1 characteristics, are shown in Table 1.

CONCLUSION

The HERBE-1 fast-thermal coupled system is designed using existing nuclear fuel at the RB reactor. All design demands were fulfilled. The actual operation of the HERBE-1 will began in 1990, after the safety analyses were completed.

The further improvement in the HERBE system is plan to design the fast core from square UO_2 fuel elements to avoid high dilution in the fast core. It will open new field of the RB operation as coupled fast-thermal system.

REFERENCES

1. D.POPOVIĆ, "The Bare Critical Assembly of Natural Uranium and Heavy Water", Proc. 2nd UN Inter. Conf. PUAE Geneva, paper no. 15/P/491, 12, 392 (1958)

2. P. STRUGAR, O.ŚOTIĆ, M. NINKOVIĆ, M.PEŠIĆ, D. ALTIPARMAKOV, "Conversion of the 'RB' Reactor Neutrons by High-Enriched Uranium Fuel and Lithium Deuteride", Kernenergie, 24, Hf.3, 101 (1981)

3. M. PEŠIĆ, H.MARKOVIĆ, M.ŚOKČIĆ, I.MIRIĆ, M.PROKIĆ, P.STRUGAR, "Experimental Fuel Channel for Samples Irradiation at the 'RB' Reactor", Kernenergie, 27, Hf.11-12, 461 (1984)

4. M. PEŠIĆ, "Coupled Fast-Thermal System at the RB Nuclear Reactor", Kernenergie, 30, Hf. 4, 142 (1987)

5. H.H.HUMMEL, C.E.COHN, C.J.FISCHER, W.Y.KATO, F.H.MARTENS, D.MENEGHETTI, B.J.TOPPEL, "Experimental and Theoretical Studies of the Coupled Fast-Thermal System ZPR-V", Proc. 2nd UN Inter. Conf. PUAE Geneva, paper no. P/599, 12, 166 (1958)

6. M.BUSTRAAN, J.COEHOORN, J.J. VEENEMA, "STEK, the Fast-Thermal Coupled Critical Facility of RCN at Patten", Proc. Soviet-Belgian-Holand Symposium on Fast Reactor Physics Problems", 2, (1970)

7. H.MEISTNER, K.BECKURTZ, W.HAFELE, W.H.KOHLER, K.OTT, "The Karlsruhe Fast-Thermal Argonaut Reactor Concept", KFK-217, KfK G.m.b.h. (1964)

8. M. V. BICHOV, I.V.ZHUK, V.M.LOMONOSOVA, O.I.YAROSHEVICH, "Experimental Determination of Neutron Spectra in Fast-Thermal Critical Assembly", Academy of Science of SSR Belorusia, Nuclear Energy Institute, Minsk (1987) (in Russian)

9. M. MILOŠEVIĆ, "Reactor Cell Code VESNA and Group Constants Library NEDA", IBK-NET Code Library, Vinča (1983)

10. M.L.TOBIAS, T.B.FOWLER, "The TWENTY GRAND Program for the Numerical Solution of Few Group Neutron Diffusion Equations in Two Dimensions", ORNL-3200, (1962)

11. M.MILOŠEVIĆ, M.PEŠIĆ, "AVERY - a Reactor Coupled Cores Code", IBK-NET Code Library, Vinča (1982)

12. R.AVERY, "Theory of Coupled Systems", Proc. 2nd UN Inter. Conf. PUAE Geneva, paper no. P/1858, 12, 182 (1958)

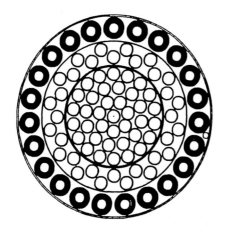

HERBE-1 FAST CORE   HERBE-2 FAST CORE

O RB NATURAL URANIUM FUEL ELEMENT

⬤ RB ENRICHED URANIUM FUEL ELEMENT

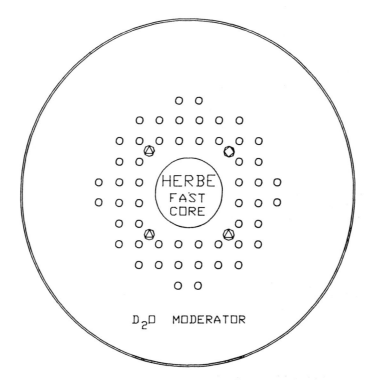

⊿ SAFETY RODS IN THERMAL CORE   ⬡ CONTROL ROD IN THERMAL CORE

FIG.1. HERBE HORIZONTAL CROSS-SECTION

TABLE 1. HERBE-1 PRELIMINARY DESIGNED PARAMETERS

PARAMETER	SNEAK[7]	SBTS-1[4]	HERBE-1
1. Fast Core			
1.1. outer radius (cm)	18.9	15.0	10.0
1.2. volume fraction (%)	7.57 ^{235}U	9.3 UO_2 (enr.=80%)	50.5 U (natural)
	65.53 ^{238}U	23.8 Al	10.4 Al
	26.90 Al_2O_3	66.9 air	39.1 air
2. Fast Core Blanket (Neutron Filter & Converter)			
2.1 outer radius (cm)	23.9	20.3	B – filter: 11.5
			U – filter: 15.1
			U – converter: 20.3
2.2. volume fraction (%)	0.72 ^{235}U	62.5 U (enr.=0.72%)	B – filter: B_4C 100
	99.28 ^{238}U	10.4 Al	U – filter: U 41.0
		27.1 air	(enr.=nat.) Al 9.3
			air 49.7
			U-converter: UO_2 8.3
			(enr.=80%) Al 24.3
			air 67.4
3. Fast Zone Nuclear Characteristics			
k_{FZ}	?	0.1571	0.1936
k_{11}	0.7610	0.4523	0.271
k_{12}	0.1316	0.1526	0.154
l_{12} (ms)	0.06755	0.209	0.064
l_{11} (ms)	0.00793	0.0796	0.032
l_1 (ms)	0.02147	0.149	0.0551
$alpha_1$	0.411	0.214	0.123
4. Thermal Core			
4.1 inner radius (cm)	30.5	27.0	27.0
4.2. outer radius (cm)	46.0	60.6	55.8
4.3. material composition	15.40 %(vol.) U_3O_8 (enr.=20%)	28 RB fuel elements UO_2 (enr.=80%)	52 RB fuel elements UO_2 (enr.=80%)
	35.96 %(vol.) H_2O	36 RB fuel elements metal U (enr.=2%)	
	48.64 %(vol.) graphit	moderator D_2O (0.76% mol H_2O) lattice pitch 12 cm	moderator D_2O (1.55% mol H_2O) lattice pitch 12 cm
4.4 reflector			
radial central	d = 6.6 cm	d = 6.4 cm	d = 6.4 cm
radial outer	d = 40 cm	d = 39.6 cm	d = 44.2 cm
axial bottom	–	d = 10 cm	d = 10 cm
5. Thermal Zone Nuclear Characteristics			
k_{22}	0.8330	0.8505	0.8981
k_{21}	0.3023	0.5363	0.5014
l_{21} (ms)	0.1012	0.171	0.469
l_{22} (ms)	0.1226	0.525	0.521
l_2 (ms)	0.1190	0.517	0.515
$alpha_2$	0.589	0.7856	0.877
6. System			
critical height (cm)	70.0	122.0	105.0
neutron lifetime (ms)	0.0789	0.365	0.341

NEUTRON SPECTRUM IN FISSION REACTORS,

CALCULATIONS, UNFOLDING AND NEUTRON CROSS SECTIONS

RADIATION DAMAGE, UNCERTAINTIES AND FUTURE

C. ERTEK

International Atomic Energy Agency

Wagramerstrasse 5 P.O.Box 2oo,A-14oo,Vienna

Austria

ABSTRACT

In this work, I would like to present an overview of fission neutron spectrum calculation and experiments,unfolding techniques related cross section data, REAL-8o(Reaction rate estimates,evaluated by adjustment and analysis in Leading Laboratories) and REAL-84 Projects, Neutron Damage in LWR reactors and uncertainties with future suggestions. This study will reflect my personnal ideas and conclusions. Special emphasis are given to the unforseen difficulties on the way to calculate or measure neutron flux spectrum in fission reactors and to their uncertainties. Light Water Reactor Pressure Vessel (LWR-PV) Surveillance Dosimetry Improvement Program end results are summarized in a very concise way. Important sources of errors, neutron flux spectrum unfolding, input spectrum, cross sections and reaction rates with their covariance matrices are discussed. Damage cross section uncertainties are also included. Improvements and suggestions for future activities including new raw data generation for standardization and better data adjustment and uncertainty assessment of radiation damage are discussed.

INTRODUCTION

In this work, an overview of fission reactor neutron flux density spectrum calculations and experiments, unfolding techniques related neutron foil activation cross sections, displacement cross sections, REAL-8o, REAL-84 and REAL-88 projects, the results of light water pressure vessel surveillance dosimetry improvement program, recent improvements in fission cross section calculations, new cross section measurements needs and their reasons in connection with neutron spectrum measurements, self shielding and self absorption corrections, new

dosimeters and future suggestions are presented. In section 1, aims and goals are presented. In section 2, the end results of light water reactor pressure vessel surveillance dosimetry improvement program is summarized. In section 3, REAL-8o, 84 and 88 projects are presented. In section 4, important sourses of errors in dosimetry and metallurgy for pressure vessel end of life determination are briefly summarized. In section 5, other neutron spectrum measurement techniques are very briefly stated. In section 6, way to standardization will be discussed. In section 7, neutron spectrum unfolding, measurements for nuclear material safeguards application are briefly stated, and in section 8, conclusions, future needs and some recommendations are presented.

SECTION 1

Remembering the historical wonderful neutron spectrometer build by Enrico Fermi at CP-5 Reactor, Chicago in early forties, advanced neutron spectrometers and double differential difractometers build for cross section measurements, cristallography and material research. Resonance parameters for neutron reactions using single level and multi-level Breit-Wigner formalisms are established. Then the time of flight spectrometers played and playing an important role in neutron physics and material cross section determinations. The data for neutron and gamma induced changes in embrittlement parameters of reactor components including pressure vessels contained large scatter 1 resulting from a number of sources of uncertainties. What were these sources of uncertainties?

1. Existing data base uncertainties

2. Dosimetry uncertainties

3. Irradiation temperature uncertainties

4. Flux, fluence and spectra uncertainties

5. Metallurgical uncertainties pretreatment

6. Impurity uncertainties in the construction materials(S,P,Cu..)

7. Welding uncertainties

The general objective of the following works is to develop a methodology that will reduce the uncertainty in estimates of the flux and fluence affecting the pressure vessel of Light Water Reactors. A large uncertainty in the fluence estimate may result in reactors having to be shut down much earlier than necessary. Reducing the uncertainty from about 40% down to 15 to 20% can be equivalent to extending the effective full-power lifetime of a reactor vessel by several years.

For the 1979 data base, dosimetry uncertainties were found to contribute 20-40%; irradiation temperature 30-40%; and the metallurgical variables 50-90%; with an over-all transition temperature uncertainty of 60-160%[1]. At that time improper correlation procedures led to large prediction errors. These experimental scatter in the data base were coming from errors in measuring embrittlement parameters; imprecise specification of damage variables like irradiation temperature, damaging neutron exposure and the gross metallurgical variables as characterized by alloy type and thermo-mechanical treatment (i.e. composition and microstructure); and lack of specification of potential damage variables including flux, time-at-temperature, microstructure and microchemistry.

SECTION 2

The US Nuclear Regulatory Commission(NRC) established the Light Water Reactor Pressure Vessel (LWR-PV) Surveillance Dosimetry Improvement Program in 1977 to improve, standardize and maintain dosimetry, damage correlation and the associated reactor analysis procedures used for predicting the integrated effects of neutron exposure to LWR-PV s[2]. In this program metallurgical test specimens and dosimetry sensors are placed in surveillance capsules at or near the reactor PV inner wall. They are then irradiated in a temperature and neutron flux spectrum environment as similar as possible to the PV itself for periods of time of about 1.5 to 15 effective full power years(EFPY), with removal of the last capsule at afluence corresponding to 30 year plant end-of-life(EOL) fluence.

The resulting ASTM standards are to be used for:

. Calculating neutron flux spectra and exposure parameters

. Performing and analyzing neutron dosimetry

. Evaluating and correlating the neutron-induced radiation damage measured in surveillance capsule metallurgical specimens

. Applying the results to current and EOL projections of the condition of LWR-PV and support structure steel materials and components.

Strong cooperative links between the NRC supported activities at HEDL, ORNL, NBS and NRL and those supported by CEN-SCK(Mol, Belgium), EPRI(Palo Alto, USA), KFA(Julich, Germany) and several UK laboratories have been extended to a number of other countries[3]. For routine LWR power plant calculations using transport methods, the Pool Critical Assembly(PCA) at ORNL results validate the statement that "results can be obtained as accurate as $\mp 15\%$ (1σ) for flux and fluence greater than 1 Mev if the calculations are properly modelled and subjected to benchmark neutron field verification. Otherwise errors can be much higher". The detailed comparisons in terms of the C/E ratios for the Ni^{58}(n,p) and other reactions at different locations are done[1]. It was concluded that, in general, values of these exposure parameters can be derived with accuracies in the range of 5% to 15%(1σ) for the PCA and similar benchmark neutron fields. The accuracy, howevever, will be less in applications to actual power plants due to greater uncertainty in defining core boundary source distributions, greater complexity of geometric modeling, and a reduced degree of benchmark referencing of both dosimetry and neutron transport calculations. Discrepancies due to inadequacies in the iron non-elastic scattering cross section data above 4-5 Mev subject to resolution. There is evidence from dosimetry experiments in LWR-PV environments that corrections of up to about 35% for photo fission in U^{238} are necessary to explain experimental results. Also there is an important work on the uncertainties of the ENDF/B-V U^{238} unresolved resonance parameters in the range 4 kev to 45 kev[4]. Work stresses the arbitrariness in the uncertainty assignment.

An important work performed in Argonne National Laboratory for irradiation damage calculations.[5,6] The computer code SPECTER is based on the displacement code DISCS[7]. All of the data in the files has been calculated using the cross section data in ENDF/B-V. The displacement damage cross section predicted by SPECTER is far higher than extrapolation from the high energy code VNMTC. The reasons for this difference are not well understood. The SPECTER predicts both damage rate and total demage for a specified length of irradiation. The code agrees very well with other programs, such as NJOY [8]; however, SPECTER is not intended to be as conprehensive in its scope. One advantage of SPECTER is that it is completely self-contained and requires no access to ENDF/B-V. Furthermore, since SPECTER contains complete recoil atom energy distributions, users can in principle use these distributions directly to test other damage models if desired. There are other neutronic, mechanical, chemistry, temperature, stress,.. uncertainties that involves in-vessel embrittlement and crack propagation assessments.

SECTION 3

In REAL-8o project which is executed in 1981 in a very short time among the leading laboratories under the auspices of International Atomic Energy Agency[9], two different neutron spectra are investigated and 68 different solutions from 13 laboratories were obtained. Individual participant's data on R_{Ni} results showed deviations from the measured value which are between +4 and -4 per cent for orr, and between -1 and -23 per cent for YAYOI. In REAL-84 project which was a follow-up of the REAL-8o project, the main aim was to improve the assesment of accuracies in radiation damage predictions by various laboratories by using good quality input data and proper calculation methods. 7 different neutron spectra are investigated. 39 different solutions from 1o laboratories were obtained. The following main conclusions can be stated. The situation with respect to consistency and quality of input data was disappointing.[10] Sometimes large inconsistencies in the input data set were found(PSI,PR2,CFR), detected by χ^2 value or by deviating reaction rates. The participants had different actions for the solution of this problem. They changed the weight (variance) of some reaction rates in the calculations, deleted reactions from the adjustment, or modified the input spectrum. The REAL-88 projects results are under evaluation.

In the REAL-84 project the characteristic damage was calculated for a specified steel type. The uncertainty in the damage parameters was determined by two contributions, i.e. damage or gas production cross section uncertainty and output spectrum uncertainty. Artificial uncertainty data were made available in the input information for the displacement and gas production cross sections.

The intention of the REAL-88 is to eliminate inconsistencies in the input data. This can be checked with a simplified damage characterization. For this reason the damage characterization of REAL-88 should be done for pure iron. The damage and gas production cross sections of the IRDF-85 can be used (MAT 8000, ST-ASTM as the displacement cross section). The uncertainty data of the damage and gas production values should be determined only by the uncertainty of the output spectrum.

SECTION 4

The fluence is determined by combining direct neutron transport calculations with experimental data from surveillance capsules. There are uncertainties due to; simplifications in the transport theory calculations ;uncertainties in nuclear data and dosimetry cross sections; reactor core representation; interpretation of the surveillance capsule data methodology used combining the measured data with calculated fluxes.

The capability of a simultaneous determination of fluxes in a number of fields, including benchmark fields and fields in a reactor, allows for the information gained from the benchmark fields to be utilized in the reactor field. This feature is effective when using the PCA results since this experiment includes measurements both at a surveillance point location, as well as at various locations within the pressure vessel mock-up. Flux information provided by the EPRI, LEPRICON LSQ procedure is not limited to the surveillance location (as in FERRET or STAYSL) but includes any desired locations within or outside the pressure vessel.[11] However, a potential disadvantage for the method may be due to the effort required in obtaining realistic estimates for the a priori uncertainties in the direct neutron transport calculation due to the numerical modeling and nuclear data. The systematic approach of going from simple benchmarks to more realistic fields permits to develop a solid nuclear data base . This may not be the case for the very complex geometries in a scattering, streaming, absorbing and the slowing down media.[12,13]

In the EOL and Life extention[14] cases e.g. in the case of Chooz A, it is found that the extent of the embrittlement of the specimens was somewhat greater than had been estimated using the empherical formulae established for more recent reactors. The discrepancy was attributed to the difference in irradiation temperatures (288°C assumed in the formula, 265°C for Chooz A). On the other hand, in 1987 it was found that the rate of embrittlement was nevertheless rather more rapid than first forecast. In addition to that the consistancy between the measured and the calculated value was quite good, with the exception of the U and Np dosimeters, which still diverged more than 10 per cent from the activation dosimeters.

SECTION 5

In this section, other neutron spectrum measurement techniques are very briefly discussed. NE-213 device is commonly used to find the neutron spectrum in mainly research reactors and some relatively low powered reactors. It needs a large calculational back-up and it has a difficulty of beeing sensitive to noise.

A differential spectrum can be obtained using a crystal spectrometer or by the time-of-flight method.[15] Although many careful investigations have been carried out with crystal spectrometers, this method has not prevailed over the time-of-flight method, chiefly because of the difficulty of calculating the energy dependence of the spectrometer's sensitivity. The common problem to all differential methods is the extraction of a representative neutron beam from the power reactor surveillance capsule positions in and around the pressure vessel, we are left with indirect neutron activation foil detectors and unfolding technique.

For the sake of completeness we can also add proton recoil counters, He-3 counters and nuclear emulsions. Proton recoil counters use the recoil protons as a measurement of neutron energies between 200 keV to 2MeV as in the case of He(n,p)H reaction. For nuclear emulsions, both internal and external recoil proton source are used, i.e., either the protons originate in a special foil outside the emulsion, or they are produced in the photoplate itself. 16

There are other works estimating the neutron spectra by unfolding the measured data of the multi-moderator neutron detector. In spectra unfolding, a correct detector response function and a highly accurate initial spectrum are essential requirements. How we will know the accurate initial spectrum and its uncertainties? Initial spectrum uncertainty variance and covariances in transport calculations are not yet available for reactor fields. Very good agreement between the neutron dose rate data obtained by the neutron rem(sievert) counter and the multi-moderator neutron detector is achieved. On the other hand ray effect of the two-dimensional discrete ordinates method disturbs the flux distribution in the void region. In the fast neutron components above 1MeV, there is a great disagreement between measurement and calculation.[16]

In France, Champion[17] obtained the reaction rates of neutron dosimeters around the reactor vessel and at an operating floor in a PWR. They used a transport calculation code based on S_n method, ANISN (one-dimensional) and DOT(two-dimensional), and the Monte Carlo code, TRIPOLI-2. They compared the results with measured values and obtained an agreement within a factor of 1.5. Aldrich applied a[18] Bonner-ball-type spectrometer and a tissue equivalent proportional counter (Rossi counter) to measure the neutron field (measured values only no comparison with calculations). Gamma ray measurements and n/γ ratios are also important from the nuclear material safeguards point of view, the measured values of gamma ray dose around the steam generator of a BWR after reactor shut-down were reported by Atakan in [19] the Federal Republic of Germany. Such[58] data for fast reactors are scarce. [20-21] Ohtani and Kawakita calculated radiation distribution around the reactor vessel of the fast reactor JOYO by using a two-dimentional S_n transport code, DOT 3.5, and compared the results with the measured values of fission chambers, thermo luminescent dosimeters, and activation foil neutron detectors. They obtained an agreement of a factor of 6 on dose rates on top of the reactor vessel. Improvements are needed. A comprehensive compilation of reaction rates and neutron spectra is performed by the author.[22-24]

On the other hand, an important initiative called "The IAEA Cross Section Processing Code Verification Project as it applies to Shielding Data" is started.[25] The objectives of this project are: (a) to test the accuracy of processing codes, (b) to understand and eliminate the sources of discrepancies, (c) to arrive at the point where we have a number of cross section processing codes which can be used as "black boxes".

The multicomponent activation detectors(MAD) has shown as a feasible technique for fission and as well as fusion neutron measurements [26] [59-61]

Further uncertainty sources is discussed very broadly in Ref [27].

SECTION 6

In this section standardization and dissemination of information will be briefly discussed. The intercomparison of the results for the damage parameters of the REAL-84 exercise showed that the participants values have a few percent spread. Differences might be due to:

a. The application of incorrect physical information

b. Algorithm(modelling)shortcomings

c. Computer accuracies

d. Real mistakes

Especially large spread(sometimes a factor greater than 3)in the uncertainty values of integral parameters was observed. This indicates that they are very sensitive to the data treatment and calculations procedures. This circumstance underlines the importance of this exercise(REAL-84) in the improvement of uncertainty predictions for damage parameters. furthermore it indicates the necessity of some kind of standardization for the adjustment. data treatment and uncertainty assessment of radiation damage data.

IRDF-85 uncertainty data converted to required group structure by UNC33 computer program in FORTRAN77 also FORTRANIV and it is available to participants in The IAEA,NDS.

Computer codes FITOCO. GROUPIE, LINEAR and utility programs to read the cross section and uncertainty libraries IRDF-85 and CS640 are ready on the way to standardization.

Zsolnay and Nolthenius[10] recommended to distribute a simple reactor physics code which neutron metrologists can use to calculate neutron self shielding factors and cover attenuation factors, required when in irradiation experiments covers and relatively thick activation detectors(foils and wires) are used. Ertek[12] presented neutron activation foil cover effects, neutron flux density depression and self shielding correction factors covering 114 references on the subject including streeming factors. Unfortunately these factors are not easy to establish for a composite activation and fission detector set due to complexity of the phenomena.

For example,the use of cadmium can effect the results of the microscopic reactor physics parameter measurements in five main ways.[28] First, if the bare foils are not placed enough far away from the cadmium pill-box, their activities will be decreased by the depression of the thermal flux caused by the cadmium. Second, the depression of the thermal flux will decrease the flux, because there will be fewer fast neutrons from thermal fission and as a result the activity induced by fast neutrons in the cadmium covered foils will be decreased. Thirdly, the effect of the decrease in the thermal flux may persist into the resonance flux; and in addition, the resonance flux may be perturbed by the displacement of moderator by the cadmium sleeve and by the higher resonances of cadmium. Fourthly, there is resonance scattering due to cadmium and finally there is moderation change because of cadmium pill-box. [27]

A comprehensive work by Ertek on reaction rate measurements, neutron spectrum unfolding, fluence, radiation damage, embrittlement for fission and fusion reactors, their [49] short comings and uncertainties presented with 203 references.

Ultra pure activation foils are in manifacture by Geel Laboratory, Belgium and reaction rates obtained by them will make a new impact to the neutron spectrum measurements.

The long term aim of the projects under consideration was to strive towards establishing standardized metrology procedures and recommended nuclear data for use in spectrum adjustment and damage parameter calculations.

An IAEA Specialists'Meeting on the results of the REAL-84 exercise was held in May 1987 in Jackson Hole (Wyoming, USA).

ASTM standards e.g. E-262-E266; E523,E526;E343. E393. E481 and E482 for reaction rate measurements; E693 for Characterizing Neutron Exposures in Ferritic Steels in Terms of Displacements Per Atom (DPA); E704, E705 E706 1E Master Matrix for LWR Pressure Vessel Surveillance Standards, E706 (1G), Guide E900, E944 and Method E646 and related others are very useful to follow and they are in continious progress.

A very useful tool for accommodating the new information is the method of correlated linear least

squares (CLLS). This provides considerable motivation for finding
approaches that avoid the inversion
of the large, joint covariance matrix of the old and new measurements.[57]

SECTION 7

MR. G. R. Keepin(LASL) will present his invited paper on "Nuclear Fission and Nuclear Safeguards: Common
Technologies and Challenges" in this
Conference. Therefore the author of
this work, would like to add few minor
thoughts along this line.

Neutron based assay systems have
found extensive use for nuclear material measurements for the purpose of
safeguards, process control and criticality safety. For samples with significant plutonium content, the assay
is complicated by the neutron multiplication and induced fission reactions
inside the sample. This multiplication
is dependent on sample size and density
as well as mass. It will be very challenging to develop methods to determine
the sample multiplication independently
and more accurate determination of Pu
content. More investigations are
needed concerning multiplication and
multiplication correction factors,
parametric studies, using Monte-Carlo
and/or reactor physics disciplins for
existing kinds of nuclear material including MOX.[29] The high level neutron
coincidence device is successful but
sensitive to the background, normali-
zations, sample size, quantity, shape,
spatial dependence, moderation, absorption, scattering and kinetic effects,[33]
under or over moderation, moisture content, density, matrix effects, impurities and multiplication. Simultaneous
density and moisture measuring devices
for bulk but up to now non nuclear
material have also been tested by[30-32]
neutron or gamma source active inter-
rogation. Active neutron assay systems
for Pu and U assay use a neutron source,
like accelerator, seal tube generator
Or radioactive source such as [252]Cf, [241]Am Li
and SbBe; moderator shield and a detector to measure induced signal.
The detectors required for an active
assay system often are the same as
would be used for passive assay.[29]
This active-passive combination makes
it possible to determine both components of materials such as U[235],U[238]
and U Pu in MOX. Physical phenomena
are spontaneous fissions, induced
fissions, (α,n) reactions and multiplication.

In addition to the advanced

HLNC device special detector heads
have been built for small samples[34]
(INVS), fast critical assembly fuel[35]
MOX fuel canisters,[36] Pu nitrate bott-
les,[37] fast breeder assemblies,[38] ship-
ping bird cages,[39] LWR MOX assemblies,[40]
barrels and fuel pin trays.[41] Shift-
register circuit may be replaced by[42]
J. Lightfoot's computer chip memory.
Basic problem remains however only
two measured parameters(R and T) for
three unknown variables (plutonium
mass, multiplication and (α,n) rate)
additional measurements and calculations performed to address this
problem such as higher moments in
the neutron distribution Cf-add-a-
source Monte Carlo calculations of
the multiplication, moisture measurements,not point but spatial source
calculations.   [43-45]

Looking for a relatively simple
and non-intrusive attribute test
method for safeguards purposes, a
novel ND method for assaying spent
fuel using neutron and gamma activation of indium has been developed
and is in the course of testing at
various type of reactors. Indium
activation detectors can provide
information on actinide content
and burnup of spent fuel assemblies. Indium foils can be used for
monitoring thermal neutrons by counting γ rays of [113]In, at the same time,
for monitoring fission product γ's
of energies above 1.08 MeV, by
counting γ-rays of [115]In produced by
isomer excitation via (γ,γ') process.
The neutron signature of the assem-
bilies obtained by bare In foils is
mainly due to [242,244]Cm content in
LWR's also Pu isotopes in HWR's.
However, use of In foils in plastic
moderator and Cd wrapping(i.e. monitoring epithermal and fast neutrons) is preferable in order to
eliminate the direct activation
by stray thermal neutrons resulting
from various sources in spent fuel
storage. The γ-signature of short
cooled (10-40 d)assemblies is due
to [140]Ba[140]La content, enabling power
distribution to be taken which was
existing just before reactor shutdown.

Indium foils covered by Be or
D converter can be used for monitoring fission product hard γ-s of
energies above 1.67 or 2.22 MeV,
detecting photoneutrons released
from Be or D, respectively. The
photoneutron γ-signature of medium
cooled (100-1000d) assemblies taken
by these Be-covered foils is due
to [144]Ce[144]Pr content, enabling
burnup monitoring. The [106]Ru-[106]Rh

794

content (being correlated with Pu content) can also be assayed above 200 d cooling using photoneutrons from D converter. These are additional measures to the existing methods such as Cherenkov, fork and Cd-Te devices. All have neighbour effect difficulties.

Cf-252 neutron source is extensively used in nuclear material safeguards for normalization purposes. Cf spontaneous prompt fission neutron spectrum extensively disscussed in Ref 54-55. and it includes experimental techniques like photo-emulsion, TOF, plastic scintillator, integral(Bramblett counter) Li-6 glass, liquid scintillator, integral (Mn bath), He-3 spectrometer, proportional counter, organic scintillator, integral(age), single crystal spectrometer, activation detector(threshold reactions), Li-6 I crystal, U-235 chamber, amplitude, Li(α,n) reaction, U-235 fission chamber, anthracene crystal NE213 PSD, proton recoil, gas counter and proton recoil stilbene crystal. A great effort in 70's and 80's.

In Ref.55,H. Maerten, A. Ruben and D. Seeliger used an extended version of the generalized Madland Nix model to calculate the energy spectrum of fission neutrons as well as multi-differential emission probabilities (energy and angular distributions for different fragment mass numbers A). This treatment can be used to deduce necessary fragment data for any [56] fission reaction semi-empirically. This new fission neutron spectrum model is also applied to the spontaneous fission of Cf-252.

It will also be very interesting to use,if possible,the burnup validation measurement point of the operator in the spend fuel pond to verify the burnup and nuclear material quantities.

SECTION 8
As a conclusion, more attention must be paid in the future for economic utilization of fission reactors as far as the nuclear poissons such as Gd are concerned[46,47] because it has a reactor kinetics effect to the neighbouring neutron measuring devices and to their performance with time. Important advances have been achieved in dosimetry, metallurgy, safeguards and in the simulation of the transient response of ionization chambers to bias voltage perturbations[48] for monitoring neutron flux levels and these type works must be promoted to find pure neutron flux

and possibly spectrum measuring devices in addition to the advancements in neutron buble devices, fission counters, CIC's, NE213's, and CR39 detectors. Neutron buble devices may find, together with the CR39's, applications in nuclear material safeguards, including foil activation techniques. The lowleakage loading patterns by Gd poissons result in reduced radial neutron losses relative to conventional out-in fueling schemes, leading to reduced enrichment and/or reload requirements, increased discharge burnup and, as a side effect, reduced pressure vessel fluence.[46]

Much of the prior attention to nil ductility transition temperature has been directed to reactor vessels themselves. Stuructural steel may receive less radiation, but could still undergo NDT rises from other causes and this must be inspected.[53]

The results of the coordinated research programs on irradiation effects on advanced pressure vessel steels are summarized by Steele L,E. et. al.[51] . The influence of chemical composition and neutron irradiation on embrittlement of RPV's summarized by J. P. Highton[52] and it is concluded that techniques presented rely on just one type of defect being predominant and as the number of defect types increases it becomes progressively more difficult to deconvolute the results. The study of near surface effects must continue. Reactor pressure vessel aging and countermeasures are summarized by[50] Ch. Leitz for KWU.

In spide of the lack of theoretical justification on of uniqueness of the parametric representation an attempt to specify uncertainties in the unresolved resonance parameters is done for ENDF/B-V U-238 (4keV-45keV).[4] Such uncertainties are necessary for the treatment of several reactor theory problems involving self-shielding factors.

Dissemination of information gathered on the subject presented here to the other laboratories and establishing a infrastructure of standard proceedures is very challenging.

ACKNOWLEDGEMENT

I would like to express my sincere gratitude to the distinguihed contributors, O. Ozer, A. Fabry, W. N. McElroy, C. M. Eisenhauer, C. z. Serpan, E. D. McGarry, F. W. Stallmann, R. E. MacFarlane, D. W. Muir, D. Cullen, J. A. Grundl, F. Schmittroth, L. R. Greenwood, F. B. K. Kam from USA; W. Zijp and H. J. Nolthenius from Nederlands; E. M. Zsolnay, E. Szondi and J. Csikai from Hungary; M. Petilli and V. Sangiust from Italy; R. Dierckx from EURATOM; A. Michaudon, P. Mas, P. Genthon and H. Derrien from France; M. Nakazawa, N. Ueda, A. Sekiguchi, T. Iguchi, T. Kosako and I. Kimura from Japan; W. Schneider, L. Weise, G. Nagel, W. Mannhartt, K. Kussmaul, M. Matzke, A. Fischer and K. H. Czock from GDR; D. Seeliger from DDR; H. Rauch, F. Bench, H. Boeck, H. W. Weber and H. Vonach, from Austria; M. Vlasov, H. Bondars, V. Chernyshev and A. Sinev from USSR; M. Brumowsky and B. Osmera from Czechoslovakia; S. B. Wright, J. L. Rowlands, A. K. McCracken, M. Austin from UK; J. T. Routti and J. V. Sandberg from Finland; M. Najzer from Yugoslavia; and finally to H. Hottermans, J. J. Schmidt, H. Lemmel, A. Lorenz, T. Biro, K. Okamoto, N. Kocherov, N. Bychkov, R. D. Arlt and B. Cross from IAEA.

REFERENCES

1. G.R. ODETTE, "A quantitative analysis of the implications of the accuracy of dosimetry to embrittlement predictions past, present and future" 3rd ASTM-EURATOM Reactor Dosimetry Sym., Oct. 1979, Ispra Italy
2. LWR Pressure Vessel Surveillance Dosimetry Improvement Program: PCA Experiments and Blind Test, Hanford Eng. Dev. Lab, Edited by W.N. Mc Elroy, NUREG CR-1861 HEDL-TME 80-87 R5. July 1981.
3. Proceedings of the 4th ASTM-EURATOM Symp. on Reactor Dosimetry, Gaithersburg, 22-26 March 1982.
4. G. de SAUSSURE and J.H. MARABLE, "Uncertainties of the ENDF/B-V U-238 Unresolved Resonance Parameters in the Range 4-45 keV", Nucl. Sci. Eng., 101, 285-292 (1989).
5. L.R. GREENWOOD and R.K. SMITHER, SPECTER: Neutron Damage Calculations for Materials Irradiations, ANL/FPP-TM TM-197, Argonne National Laboratory, January 1985.
6. L.R. GREENWOOD, "Specter Computer Code for Radiation Damage Calculations Proc. IAEA Consultants' Meeting on Nuclear Data for Radiation Damage Estimates for Reactor Structural Materials" May 20-22, 1985 Santa Fe, NM, USA
7. G. R. ODETTE and D.R. DORION, Nucl. Technol. 29, p.346 (1976).
8. R. E. Mac Farlane Proc. of Ref6.
9. W. L. ZIJP, E. M. ZSOLNAY, H. J. NOLTHENIUS, E. J. SZONDI, G. C. H. M. M. VERHAAG, D. E. CULLEN, and C. ERTEK "Final Report on the REAL-80 Exercise", ECN-128, Netherlands Energy Research Foundation (1983).
10. E. M. ZSOLNAY and H. J. NOLTHENIUS Proc. of the IAEA Consultants' Meeting on The Assessment of the Results of the REAL-84 Exercise Edited by V. PIKSAIKIN, March 1987, IAEA INDC(NDS)-190/G+F+R.
11. R. E. MAERKER, J.J. WAGSCHAL, B. L. BROADHEAD "Development and Demonstration of an Advanced Methodology for LWR Dosimetry Applications" NP-2188 Dec. 1981.
12. C. ERTEK, "Neutron Activation Foil Cover Effects, Neutron Flux Density Depression and Self Shielding Correction Factors" International Atomic Energy Agency, IAEA/RL/57 Feb. 1979.
13. C. ERTEK, "On the Penetration of Mono Energetic Neutrons Inside the Detector Foils" International Atomic Energy Agency Agency, IAEA/RL/44, Feb. 1977
14. J.C. GUILLERET, "Re-examining Reactor Vessel Embrittlement at Chooz A" Nuclear Engineering International Nov. 1988.
15. K. H. BECKURTS, K. WIRTZ Neutron Physics, Berlin: Springer 1964.
16. T. KOSAKO, J. MATSUMOTO, A. SEKIGUCHI, N. OHTANI, S. SUZUKI, S. TAKEDA and O. SATO, "Measurements and Evaluations of Neutron Dose and Spectra at the Reactor Top of the Liquid-Metal Fast Breeder Type Reactor, JOYO, Nuclear Technology Vol 77 June, 1987.
17. G. CHAMPION ET. AL., "Shielding Design for PWR in France,"Proc. 6th Int. Conf. Radiation Shielding, Tokyo, May 16-20,1983, Vol.I, p.546, Japan Atomic Energy Research Institute (1983).
18. J. M. ALDRICH, "Neutron Spectra and Dose Equivalent Inside Nuclear Power Reactor Containment,"NUREG/ CR-1714, PNL-3531, Pasific Northwest Laboratory (1981).
19. Y. ATAKAN, "Evaluation of Dose Rate Data for Use in Nuclear Power Plant Design," Nucl. Safety, 24, 66 (1983).
20. N. OHTANI and T. KAWAKITA, "Radiation Shielding Analysis of JOYO,"J. At. Energy Soc. Jpn., 25, 520(1983)(in Japanese).
21. N. OHTANI and T. KAWAKITA, "Radiation Shielding Analysis of JOYO,"Proc. 6th Int. Conf. Radiation Shielding, May 16-20,1983, VolII, p. 948, Japan Atomic Energy Research Institute (1983).
22. C. ERTEK, Compilation of Neutron Flux Density Spectra and Reaction Rates in Different Neutron Fields, Vol. I, IAEA/RL/61, June

1979.319 pages.
23.   C. ERTEK, ibid. Vol II,
IAEA/RL/63, July 1979, 251 pages.
24.   C. ERTEK, ibid. Vol III,
EAEA/RL/68, April, 1980, 381pages.
25.   D. E. CULLEN et. al."The IAEA
Cross Section Processing Code Verification Project as it Applies to
Shielding Data" INDC(NDS) 146/G,
April 1983.
26.   J. V. SANDBERG, "On the Feasi-
bilty of Multicomponent Activation
Detectors for Fusion Reactor Neutronics Measurements" Nucl. Inst. and
Methods 206(1983), 227-234.
27.   C. ERTEK, "Reaction Rate
Measurements, Neutron Spectrum Unfolding, Fluence, Radiation Damage,
Embrittlement and Safety for Fission
and Fusion Reactors Their Shortcomings
and Uncertainties"EAEA/RL/72 Oct. 1980.
28.   C. ERTEK, A. YALCIN, and Y.
INEL, Nucl. Sci. Eng., 36,209-221
1969.
29.   H. O. MENLOVE "Role of Neutrons in Safeguards" JNMM, July 1987
p. 83-86.
30.   C. ERTEK and N. HASELBERGER
"Measurement of Density and Water
Content of Soil Using Photon Multiple Scattering" Nucl. Inst. and
Methods 227(1984)182-185.
31.   O. CIFTCIOGLU and D. TAYLOR
Soil Sci.,113(1972) No.1.
32.   K. LIN, E. PIRIE and D. TAYLOR
Nucl. Inst. and Meth. 72 (1969) 325.
33.   N. ENSSLIN"A Simple Self Multiplication Correction for In Plant Use"
7thESARDA Annual Symp. on Safeguards
and Nuclear Materia Management 19,
(Liege,Belgium, 1985), L. Stanchi,
Ed., Joint Research Center, ISPRA,
Italy,pp.223-238.
34.   H. O. MENLOVE, O. R. HOLBROOKS
and A. RAMALHO, "Inventory Sample
Coincidence Counter Manuel" Los
Alomos National Laboratory, LA-9544M,
(ISPO-181) Nov. 1982.
35.   M. S. KRICK, H. O. MENLOVE
"Channel Coincidence Counter Ver-
sion I" Los Alamos Nationa Laboratory
LA-8404-MS(ISPO-97), June 1980.
36.   H. O. MENLOVE, E. L. ADAMS,
E. DAHN and A. RAMALHO"Plutonium Ca-
nister Counter Operations and Pro-
cedures" Los Alamos National Lab.
LA-10615-M(ISPO-216) Feb. 1986.
37.   H. O. MENLOVE, E. I. ADAMS and
O. R. HOLBROOKS,"Plutonium Nitrate
Bottle Counter Manual" Los Alamos Nat.
Lab.,LA-10009-M(ISPO-203) March, 1984.
38.   H. O. MENLOVE, G. W. ECCLESTON,
J. E. SWANSEN, P. GORIS, R. ABEDIN-
ZADEH, and A. RAMALHO, "Universal
Fast Breeder Reactor Subassembly

Counter Manual" Los Alamos Nat.
Lab. LA-10226-M(ISPO-215) Aug.1984.
39.   M. S. KRICK. H. O. MENLOVE and
A. RAMALHO "Bird Cage Neutron Coin-
cidence Counter Manual" Los Alamos
Nat. Lab. LA-10430-M July 1985.
40.   T. W. CRANE,"Detectability Li-
mits and Precision for Shufflers"
Los Alamos Nat. Lab.,LA-10158-MS
AUG. 1984.
41.   L. R. COWDER. H. O. MENLOVE
"Neutron Coincidence Counter for MOX
Fuel Pins in Storage Trays Manual"
Los Alamos Nat. Lab. LA-9493-M(ISPO
178) Aug. 1982.
42.   J. LIGHTFOOT, "W6 325 Neutron
Coincidence Electronics" British
Nuclear Fuels, plc. informal report
March 1985.
43.L. LAKOSI, A> VERES, I. PAVLI-
CSEK and ZS. NEMETH " Gamma and
Neutron Activation for ND Assay
of Irradiated fuel Assemblies,
Proc. 7th ESARDA Symp., Liege,
Belgium,1985,p.265-270.
44.L. LAKOSI, A. VERES, Zs. NEMETH
and I. PAVLICSEK "Photo and Neut-
ron Activation Studies on Spent
Reactor Fuel Assemblies, Proc. 4th
Working Group Meeting on Rad. Interaction, Leipzig, GDR, 1987,p.691-695.
45.A. VESES, L. LAKOSI, I. ALMASI, Zs.
NEMETH and I. PAVLICSEK "Photo-
activation of Nuclear Isomers for
Assaying Irradiated Reactor Fuel,
Proc. Int. Conf. on Nuclear Data
for Nuclear Science and Technology,
1988. MITO. Japan, pp 959-961.
46.   W. BOEHM, H. D. KIEHLMANN, A.
NEUFERT, and M. PEEHS, "Gd_2O_3 up to
9%, an established burnable poison
for advanced fuel management in
pressurized water reactors"Kerntechnik 50(1987)No.4.
47.   H. MAERKL and R. HOLZER
"Advanced Core and Fuel Design for
Light Water Reactors", Kerntechnik
50(1987)No. 4.
48.   T. ALDEMIR, S. A. ARNDT, and
DON. W. MILLER,"Simulation of the
transient responce of ionization
chambers" Nuclear Technology Vol.76
Feb. 1987.
49.   M. NAKAZAWA, T. IGUCHI and A.
SEKIGUCHI, Development of DT Neutron
Dosimetry Technique by Activation
Method, Journal of the Faculty of
Engineering, Univ. of Tokyo VolXXXIX
No.1.(1987).
50. CH. LEITZ "Reactor Pressure
Vessel Aging and Countermeasures"
Kerntechnik 51 (1987)No.4.
51. L.E. STEELE, et. al. "Results of the
IAEA co ordinated research programs on
irradiation effects on advanced PV,

Proc. of 12th Int. Sym. Effects of Radiation on Materials(eds. F. A. Garner and J. S. Perrin), American Society for Testing and Materials, Philadelphia, 1985, ASTM STP 870, 863-899.

52. J. P. HIGHTON, "Influence of Chemical Composition and Neutron Irradiation on Embrittlement of Reactor Pressure Vessel Steels" N. Nucl. Energy.1988, 27, No. 1, Feb. 15-19

53. NUCLEAR NEWS/Feb. 1988. p.28.

54. M. V. BLINOV Proc. IAEA Consultants' Meeting Neutron Properties, Debrecen, March,1980, IAEA Report INDC(NDS)-114/GT p.79.

55. IAEA-TECDOC-410, Properties of neutron sources Proc. of an Advisory Group Meeting by IAEA, Leningrad, USSR, 9-13 June 1986 paper presented by J. W. Boldeman p.125.H. Maerten et. al. p. 153.

56. M. LAMMER "Nuclear Data for Safeguards, IAEA, INDC(NDS)-187 Nov. 1986.

57. D. W. MUIR, "Evaluation of Correlated Data Using Partitioned Least Squares: A Minimum-Variance Derivation", Nucl. Sci. and Eng. 101, 88-93(1989).

58. S. IIJIMA, M. OBU, T. HAYASE, A. OHNO, T. NEMOTO, S. OKAJIMA, "Experimental Study of the Large-Scale Axially Heterogeneous Liquid Metal Fast Breeder Reactor at the Fast Critical Assembly" Nucl. Sci. Eng. 100, 496-506(1988).

59. C.ERTEK, "The REAL-80 Project Related Preliminary Results Argonne Seibersdorf Intercomparison Proc. 4th Sym.on Neutron Dosimetry p.251 Commission of the European Communities, Radiation Protection Munich-Neuherberg 1-5 June 1981. EUR 7448 EN Vol.II.

60. C.ERTEK, "Seibersdorf-Helsinki Intercomparison of Neutron Flux Density Spectra by Using the SAND-II and LOUHI Unfolding Programmes p.261.

61. C. ERTEK, M.F. VLASOV, B. CROSS, P. M. SMITH "Influence of Cross Section Structure on Unfolded Neutron Spectra" pp.654, Proc. Int. Conf. Nuclear Data for Science and Technology, Antwerp, Belgium, Sept. 6-10, 1982, CONF-820906, p.654. D. Reidel Publishing Company (1982).

SPECIAL ACTINIDE NUCLIDES : FUEL OR WASTE?

M. Srinivasan K. Subba Rao and M.V. Dingankar@
Neutron Physics Division
@Health Physics Division
Bhabha Atomic Research Centre
Trombay, Bombay 400 085, India

ABSTRACT

The special actinide nuclides such as Np, Cm etc which are produced as byproducts during the operation of fission reactors are presently looked upon as "nuclear waste" and are proposed to be disposed of as part of high level waste in deep geological repositories. The potential hazard posed to future generations over periods of thousands of years by these long lived nuclides has been a persistent source of concern to critics of nuclear power. However the authors have recently shown that each and every one of the special actinide nuclides is a better nuclear fuel than the isotopes of plutonium. This finding suggests that one does not have to resort to exotic neutron sources for transmuting/incinerating them as proposed by some researchers. Recovery of the special actinide elements from the waste stream and recycling them back into conventional fission reactors would eliminate one of the stigmas attached to nuclear energy.

INTRODUCTION

The term Special Actinides refers to all the "minor" transactinium elements such as protactinium, neptunium, americium, curium etc, distinguished from the "major" nuclear fuel actinides of uranium, plutonium and thorium. Significant quantities of special (or byproduct) actinide elements have accumulated in the spent fuels of nuclear fission reactors over the last four decades since the first production, research and power reactors began operation. Inspite of the fact that some of these special actinide nuclides are known to have specific applications, such as ^{238}Pu for thermionic power generators, ^{242m}Am for rocket propulsion etc, the minor actinides have generally been looked upon as "nuclear waste" and are proposed to be disposed off along with high level wastes (HLW) in deep geological repositories. The HLW which is compacted and fixed into some chemically inert matrix form such as borosilicate glass (or synroc) would thus comprise of the following four components:(i) Short lived fission products dominated by ~30 year half life ^{90}Sr and ^{137}Cs; (ii) A few very long half life fission products such as ^{99}Tc $(2x10^5y)$, ^{129}I $(1.6x10^7y)$ and ^{135}Cs $(2x10^6y)$; (iii) A small quantity (typically ~ 0.5%) of the fuel actinides of Pu and U contained in spent fuel and lastly (iv) All the byproduct actinide elements (Np,Am, Cm etc).

In assessing the hazards posed to future generations by HLW[1] entombed in subterranian repositories two approaches are being followed : The sophisticated—absolute approach[2,3] attempts to compute numerically in a detailed manner the radiation dose likely to be received by a "maximally exposed individual" at any time in the future upto millions of years. Such computer programs, model release of active nuclides through leaching, its subsequent dissolution by ground water, followed by transport, dispersion, migration etc and finally intake of the radionuclides through ingestion by humans via the biocycle. The results and conclusions of such studies are however highly sensitive to the various input data used, as pointed out by Cohen[4]. The crucial aspects of such codes are therefore sought to be validated by comparing with natural analogs such as the Alligator rivers basin[5], Oklo mine site[6] etc.

The other approach used may be characterised as a simplistic—relative one wherein we compare the potential hazards of the HLW buried underground with that posed either by a large uranium ore deposit occupying the same overall area, depth and volume as the underground waste repository[7] or by the parent uranium ore mined originally from the ground for fabricating the fuel elements[8]. If it can be shown that the hazards of HLW are not more than that of the equivalent uranium ore, it would contribute significantly towards public acceptability of nuclear power[9]. The ore rather than uranium metal is used for such comparisons since the ore contains its daughter products as well. In each of these approaches it is also of interest to find out which of the four components of HLW listed earlier is important and in particular amongst the three long lived components what is the relative contribution of the special actinides. It is the very long half lives of the alpha active nuclides and their daughters that has prompted both some concerned scientists as well as opponents of nuclear power to raise such socio—philosophic questions as to the moral right of the present "tenants of this planet" to contaminate the earth with "highly hazardous" radioactive substances, "endangering" future generations of humankind[10,11].

FORMATION ROUTES AND QUANTITIES GENERATED

Fig. 1 depicts the well known formation routes of the higher mass actinide nuclides following multiple neutron capture (n,r) events starting from the initial fuel components of ^{235}U and ^{238}U. Whenever the neutron to proton ratio drifts sufficiently away from the stability line there is a horizontal shift to the next higher element following a short half life beta decay transition, resulting in upper mass cut-off limits for each of the high Z actinide elements as follows: ^{239}U (23.5 m), ^{239}Np (2.35 d), ^{243}Pu (4.98 hr), ^{244}Am (10.1 hr) and ^{249}Cm (~1 hr) where the numbers in brackets are the half lives. The higher mass nuclides would in general be formed in exponentially decreasing quantities as the mass number increases, since the probability for capturing n successive neutrons decreases as p^n where p is the average neutron capture probability. Fig. 2 which is a semi-log plot of the mass spectrum of the nuclides formed in a Th-^{233}U fueled CANDU type reactor as calculated by ORIGEN code, brings out the near exponential feature elegantly. As may be expected the slope of this line is

increases. The mass spectrum of higher mass nuclides formed in uranium fueled reactors is somewhat

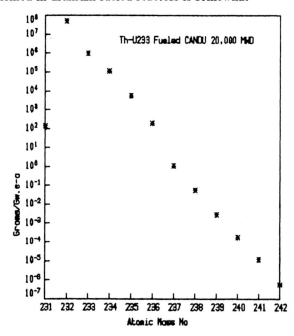

Fig.2   Mass Spectrum of New Actinides Formed in a Th-U233 Fuelled CANDU Reactor

complicated on account of the larger difference in atomic mass numbers between the two initiating isotopes, namely ^{235}U and ^{238}U.

Table I, reproduced from Ref[12] summarizes the quantities of byproduct actinides formed in normal operation as well as those built up while recycling. It is seen that the byproduct actinide (BPA) content in the discharged fuel varies in the region of 0.6 to 6 Kg per ton and constitutes somewhere between 2 to 20% of the new actinides formed, depending on whether the reactor involved is a PWR or FBR and also whether it

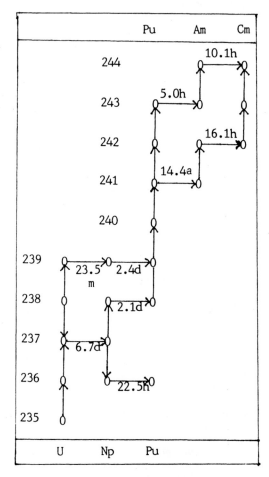

Fig.1   Formation Routes of Higher Mass Actinides

TABLE I: QUANTUM BPA FORMED IN PWR AND LMFBR BUILD-UP DUE TO RECYCLING (GRAMS PER TON OF HM-REF 12)

Nuclide	PWR-U N	PWR-U R	PWR-Pu N	PWR-Pu R	FBR N	FBR R
^{237}Np	345	716	309	584	396	950
^{241}Am	26	32	87	106	563	1350
^{243}Am	164	254	883	1130	324	993
^{244}Am	61	574	714	3670	46	689
^{245}Cm	2	27	38	219	4	209

N: Normal discharge;
R: Equilibrium recyled values

found   to   decrease   as   the   discharge   burn-up

is with or without recycling of BPA. In this context a point that is not commonly appreciated is that ^{241}Pu with a half life of 14.4 years is a potentially greater source of ^{241}Am than what is directly generated during reactor operation since there is often several years of delay between fuel discharge and subsequent recycle of Pu back into a reactor.

DECAY SERIES CONSIDERATIONS AND HAZARD POTENTIAL

All the higher mass actinide nuclides decay following well known chains referred to as the four main decay series as illustrated in Fig.3. Of these, three are the naturally occurring series, namely (i) Uranium series (4n−2) originating from ^{238}U (ii) Actinium series (4n−1) originating from ^{235}U and (iii) Thorium series (4n) originating from ^{232}Th. The fourth series referred to as Neptunium series (4n+1) comprises entirely of artificially produced isotopes, starting with ^{245}Cm.

The objective of bringing in decay series considerations here is mainly to point out the fact that conversion of uranium nuclei into one of the higher atomic number/mass nuclides in a nuclear reactor essentially tantamounts to jacking it up to a higher position in one of the four decay chains.

URANIUM	ACTINIUM	THORIUM	NEPTUNIUM
Cm-242	Cm-243	Cm-244	Cm-245
or	or		
Pu-242	Am-243	Pu-240	Pu-241
Pu-238	Pu-239	U -236	Am-241
or			
U -238	U -235	Th-232	Np-237
Th-234	Pa-231	U -232	U -233
U -234	Ac-227	Ra-228	Th-229
Th-230	Ra-223	Th-228	Ra-225
Ra-226		Ra-224	Bi-209
Pb-210	Pb-207	Pb-208	

Fig.3 Simplified Model of Four Actinide Decay Chains

As mentioned earlier ground water is the only source which is postulated to transport the radioactive materials from the deep geological repositories to the biosphere and "ingestion" of this contaminated water

by human populations in the future constitutes the potential hazard under discussion in this paper. The potential biological hazard of HLW may therefore be measured in terms of the volume of water that should notionally be added to the waste in order to render the resultant diluted water fit enough for drinking purposes by people. This hazard index, referred to in literature variously as Water Dilution Volume (WDV), "Untreated Dilution Index" (UDI), Toxicity Index etc, may be computed as follows:

$$\text{WDV (in m}^3) = \frac{g * (Bq/g)}{ALI}$$

Here g is the mass of the nuclide , Bq/g is its Sp.Activity and ALI, the Annual Limit of Intake in units of Bq/m^3. The International Commission of Radiological Protection(ICRP) published revised ALI values in their ICRP−30[13] document in 1979/80. In the context of the fission waste hazard problem, three important changes introduced in ICRP−30 are : (i) The hazard of ^{90}Sr, a key fission product, has been decreased; (ii) The hazard of three important long lived special actinide nuclides mentioned earlier, namely ^{237}Np, ^{241}Am and ^{243}Am, has been increased; (iii) The hazard of ^{226}Ra, an important daughter product of the ^{238}U decay chain, has been decreased. The consequence of all these changes has been to reduce the overall hazard potential of the original uranium ore containing the two main uranium isotopes along with their non−gaseous daughter products , while at the same time increasing the long term hazard potential of the actinide component of HLW.

Fig.4 shows plots of the variation with decay time

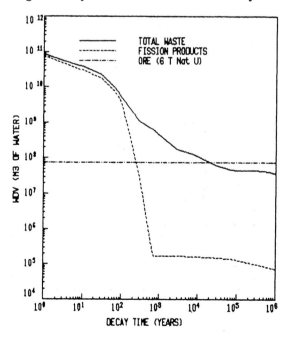

Fig.4 Comparison of WDV of HLW From One Ton of Discharged PWR Fuel With that of ParentORE

of the WDV of High Level Waste from a standard PWR. The WDV data are normalized to one ton of heavy metal in the spent fuel. Also shown for comparison in the same figure is the WDV corresponding to the original uranium ore from which the one ton of uranium was produced. In addition the figure presents the WDV of the fission products and actinides separately. It has earlier been shown[7] and we have also confirmed, that the WDV of the actinides is primarily due to the byproduct actinide component, the contribution of the U and Pu being much smaller in comparison. It is seen from the figure that the WDV of the actinide component begins to dominate over the fission products after a few hundred years. More importantly the WDV of HLW is seen to attain the uranium ore level only after about 20,000 years. Note that the ore line here corresponds to ~3500 tons of ore required to produce 6 tons of natural uranium or ~1 ton of 3.3% enriched uranium[8] . The long decay time of the WDV of HLW comes about mainly because of the use of the new ICRP–30 data. Fig 4–7 of Ref[2] also leads to the same conclusion. The new results derived using ICRP–30 data have thus rendered the comparison of the WDV of HLW and parent uranium ore unfavourable to HLW. This explains why since 1980 no new papers have appeared in literature claiming that HLW is less hazardous than its parent uranium ore.

It is worth remembering at this stage that a standard PWR burns barely 0.6% of the uranium contained in the mined ore. This low level of uranium utilization is a matter of deep concern to the nuclear industry since the available uranium supplies in the world would become exhausted some time by the second quarter of the 21st century, more or less around the same time when global supplies of oil are also expected to run out. To meet this alarming contingency, while simultaneously avoiding the CO_2 caused green house effect and acid rain problems, it is envisaged (atleast by nuclear energy enthusiasts) that fission reactors with improved fuel utilization would have to be introduced early in the next century.

The relevance of all this discussion however is only to point out that in the years to come the utilization of the mined uranium could jump from the present 0.6% level to values approaching 60%, so that in Fig.4 the WDV values corresponding to reactor produced wastes would have to be multiplied by a factor of ~ 100, while leaving the uranium ore line untouched. This point has to be taken into account while making a realistic comparison of the water dilution volumes of the HLW envisaged to be generated by a given quantity of mined uranium ore and that of the original ore itself. Fig.5 which shows such a curve, clearly brings out the big gap between the WDV of the long lived actinide component of the HLW produced by advanced converters having good fuel utilization (for example APWRs with high conversion tight lattices) and that pertaining to the original uranium ore. Interestingly Fig.5 is very similar to the WDV of unprocessed spent fuel.(See Fig. 13.4 of Ref[14]). It is now seen that WDV of the actinides entering HLW will not reach the original ore levels even after a million years.

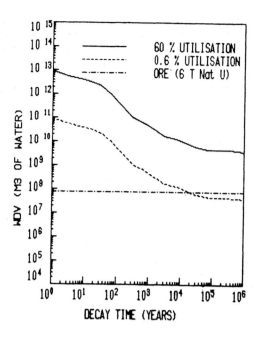

Fig.5 Effect of Fuel Utilisation on WDV of HLW from PWR

SYSTEMATICS OF CRITICALITY DATA OF ACTINIDE NUCLIDES

The authors recently carried out a systematic analysis of the criticality properties of approximately twenty nuclides belonging to seven trans–thorium elements[15]. Majority of the odd neutron actinide nuclides are known to be fissile with K_∞ values increasing systematically with the "fissility parameter" (Z^2/A). However it is not commonly known that the even neutron actinides which are fissionable only by fast neutrons having energies above their fission thresholds are surprisingly also capable of independently sustaining a fission chain reaction. In other words one can quote a critical mass for such nuclides also. The new term "fissible" to refer to these nuclides[16]. We have computed afresh the criticality parameters of a number of actinide nuclides starting from basic point neutron cross section files such as ENDL–82 and ENDF/B–IV using standard multigroup transport theory codes. The details of the methodology used and results obtained are discussed in Ref[16]. We present here only the essential results and conclusions of our study. Table II summarizes the criticality data pertaining to fast assemblies of a number of fissile and fissible nuclides.

In quest of systematics, the fast system K_∞ values of the fissile nuclides of Table II were plotted against their fissility parameter (Z^2/A). As evident from Fig.6 remarkable linear correlation is found with the data points fitting the relation

$$K_\infty = 0.662 \left[(Z^2/A) - 32.625 \right] \qquad (1)$$

Eq.(1) suggests that a (Z^2/A) value of atleast 34.1 is required to sustain a fission chain in an unmoderated fissile assembly. Note that at the upper end K_∞ becomes almost 4 for the fissile californium isotopes. K_∞ values of the fast fissible assemblies are in general lower for a given (Z^2/A) on account of their fission thresholds.

Column 7 of Table II gives $\sigma_c{}^b$, the surface mass density of the critical spheres, given by the quantity $(\rho R_c{}^b/3)$. $\sigma_c{}^b$ is a more basic parameter in criticality physics than critical mass or critical radius as it is independent of system density. The $\sigma_c{}^b$ values of the fissile nuclides are seen to lie in the region of 20 to 37 g/cm^2 (except for ^{235}U which is anomalously high). The $\sigma_c{}^b$ values of the fissible nuclides are in general higher on account of their lower K_∞ values. From a careful analysis of the data of Table II we find that the $\sigma_c{}^b$ values (in units of g/cm^2) of both fissile and fissible nuclides can be deduced directly from their (Z^2/A) values using the relation:

$$\sigma_c{}^b = \frac{94}{(Z^2/A) - (Z^2/A)_{th}} \qquad (2)$$

where $(Z^2/A)_{th}$ is 34.1 for fissile nuclides and 34.9 for fissible nuclides. This behaviour is brought out in Fig.7 which shows a plot of $(1/\sigma_c{}^b)$ against the quantity $[(Z^2/A) - (Z^2/A)_{th}]$. Once $\sigma_c{}^b$ is known the bare critical mass $M_c{}^b$ at density ρ can be computed using the relation

$$M_c{}^b = \frac{36\Pi\,(\sigma_c{}^b)^3}{\rho^2} \qquad (3)$$

Thus our study shows that the K_∞ values of both fissile and fissible special actinides are systematically higher than that of the commonly accepted fuel materials, namely uranium and plutonium, clearly indicating that the special actinide nuclides have high fuel value and as such should not be referred to as "waste" anymore. If reactor grade plutonium along with its higher mass isotopes of ^{240}Pu, ^{241}Pu and ^{242}Pu can be treated as valuable fuel material for both fast and thermal reactors inclusive of LWRs, then it is obvious that based on reactor physics considerations alone there is no justification to treat the special actinides as "nuclear waste".

BRIEF REVIEW OF EARLIER NEUTRON TRANSMUTATION STUDIES

During the seventies many studies were carried out on the feasibility of chemical separation of the special actinide elements and "transmuting" or "incinerating" them through neutron bombardment into short half life fission products. It was Claiborne[17] of ORNL who first pointed out in 1972 that the long lived actinide waste problem could be mitigated through neutron transmutation even in a Light Water Reactor. It was however generally believed in those days that most of the byproduct actinides could be fissioned only by fast neutrons, with the transmutation efficiency being larger at higher neutron energies. It was this that led to all kinds of "exotic" hard neutron spectrum devices such as fusion reactor

blankets, spallation neutron sources, impact fusion concepts, superconducting cyclotrons and in the present conference even a EXYDER colliding beam neutron source[18] being examined. However the more down–to–earth schemes considered only conventional fission reactors such as LWRs and LMFBRs. But in all these investigations an overriding consideration seems to have been that in the process of destroying these "highly hazardous" substances more byproduct actinides should not be generated. The final conclusion of majority of these studies was that although partitioning–transmutation (P–T) was technically feasible, the penalty to be paid in terms of cost, complexity and man–rem expenditure was not commensurate with the benefits that would accrue[12],[19]. An IAEA sponsored coordinated research programme[12] which was conducted during 1976–80 surmised that "All in all the implementation of P–T would be an immense undertaking involving a large proportion of a country's nuclear power programme but providing at best a rather small reduction in potential long term radiological hazards". Thus after the first world conference on Neutron Transmutation[20] held in 1980 much of the research funding for P–T programmes seem to have dried up.

One positive outcome of the "P–T era" however was that the neutron cross section data of many of the transactinium isotopes were compiled and evaluated with greater care and in a more systematic manner[21]. This contributed significantly towards a growing realization that the special actinide nuclides had more favourable fissionability properties than believed hitherto. Even though many of the western countries had given up on P–T , the Japanese picked up from where the earlier researchers had left off and began investigating the feasibility of constructing an Actinide Burning Fast Reactor (ABFR)[22] specifically devoted to the concept of neutron induced "incineration" of the byproduct actinides.They are presently carrying out a conceptual design study of a 150 MWth He cooled fast reactor unit to serve as a single module of a larger ABFR system[23]. It is learnt that the Karlsruhe Nuclear Research Centre and the Japan Atomic Energy Research Institute (JAERI)[24] have recently agreed to jointly pursue the burning of actinides in specially constructed "fast reactor incinerators" as a means of mitigating the long lived actinide waste problem.

PARTITIONING AND RECYCLING ASPECTS

The well known PUREX process used in spent fuel reprocessing is found capable of recovering > 99.5% of the fuel actinides of uranium and plutonium. But the process for the removal of the byproduct actinide elements has so far proved to be formidable not only because of the difficult chemistry involved but also because of the very low concentration levels at which the byproduct actinide elements are present in the dissolver solution. In this context the recently developed TRUEX process[25] for TRansUranics EXtraction from waste streams is considered to be a significant breakthrough in the field of solvent extraction[26], next only to the PUREX process. This process employs a highly selective extractant called

TABLE II: CRITICALITY DATA FOR BARE
FAST ASSEMBLIES OF ACTINIDE NUCLIDES

Nuclide	Z^2/A	K_∞	σ_c^b (g/cm^2)	Density ρ (g/cm^3)	Critical Mass M_c (Kg)
FISSILE (34.10)*					
92-U-235	36.02	2.337	51.53	18.90	43.33
92-U-233	36.32	2.524	36.48	18.90	15.37
94-Pu-241	36.66	2.912	33.20	19.00	12.18
94-Pu-239	36.97	2.956	31.84	19.00	10.13
95-Am-242	37.29	3.238	28.01	11.87	17.65
96-Cm-247	37.31	3.658	23.33	13.51	7.87
96-Cm-245	37.62	3.430	27.07	13.51	12.28
96-Cm-243	37.93	3.487	23.55	13.51	8.10
98-Cf-251	38.26	3.978	24.17	13.84	8.24
98-Cf-249	38.57	3.993	23.62	13.84	7.78
FISSIBLE (34.00)*					
91-Pa-231	35.85	2.199	69.73	15.37	162.31
*92-U-234	36.17	1.477	86.77	19.00	204.63
93-Np-237	36.49	1.746	58.62	20.45	51.18
94-Pu-242	36.51	2.169	55.99	19.00	54.98
94-Pu-240	36.82	2.308	18.77	19.00	36.33
94-Pu-238	37.13	2.884	33.20	19.84	10.54
95-Am-241	37.45	2.519	45.39	11.87	75.09
96-Cm-244	37.77	3.032	32.47	13.51	21.21

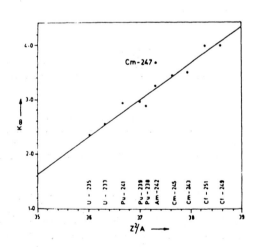

Fig.6 K_∞ Vs (Z^2/A) for Fast Fissile Cores

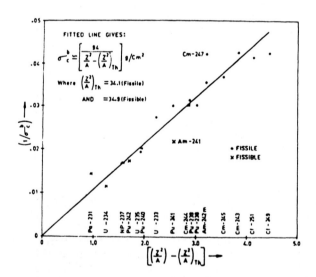

Fig.7 Plot of $(1/\sigma_c^b)$ Vs $[(\frac{Z^2}{A}) - (\frac{Z^2}{A})_{th}]$
For Fast Actinide Assemblies

"CMPO". It was initially found that this solvent undergoes some degradation under the high radiation fields experienced in the reprocessing environment. However adoption of an appropriate mixture of CMPO and TBP in ether has reportedly overcome this problem. It is learnt that deployment of this process for treating wastes from military sites is under active consideration in the USA.

As for the recycle of the separated special actinides back into reactors, there are three possible approaches: In the first the byproduct elements would be homogeneously distributed i.e uniformly mixed with UO_2 and PuO_2, the special actinide content being ~ 1 to 2%. In this approach no new problems in terms of heat generation and removal are expected. In the heterogeneous recycling concept, the special actinides would be mixed with a diluent such as MgO and fabricated into separate fuel pins or subassemblies before loading into the reactor. It is however, generally felt that homogeneous recycling would be more practical. The third approach is to recycle the byproduct actinides in a specially set up Actinide Burning Fast Reactor (ABFR) as mentioned earlier.

SUMMARY AND CONCLUSIONS

The authors recent finding that the infinite neutron multiplication factor (K_∞) of all the actinide nuclides increases monotonically and systematically with their fissility parameter (Z^2/A), has a significant bearing on the management of long term hazards of fission reactor wastes. Each and every one of the special actinide nuclides irrespective of whether it contains odd or even number of neutrons is found to be a better nuclear fuel, from the reactor physics point of view, than the corresponding odd or even neutron number plutonium isotopes. Consequently there is no more any justification to refer to the special actinides as "nuclear waste". The main purpose of the present paper is to draw the attention of the nuclear community to the excellent fissionability characteristics of the special actinides.It is not necessary to resort to the use of any exotic neutron sources to "incinerate" actinide "wastes". The byproduct actinides can be burnt as fuel in any type of fission reactor.

Even if detailed numerical analysis indicates that the radiation dose likely to be received due to geologically disposed HLW by a maximally exposed individual at any time in the future would be less than 10% of the average dose to humans due to natural background radiation, it would still appear to be wiser on our part to minimize the quantum of actinides (fuel plus byproduct) sent into the HLW stream.

The focus of attention of those dealing with the hazards arising from the long lived actinide component of HLW should not be to ask what is the hazard posed by the quantum of special actinides generated in any fuel cycle but rather to arrive at an upper limit to the total amount of all actinides that should be permitted to enter the HLW stream. This will help eliminate atleast one of the commonly voiced objections to nuclear fission energy.

If the actinides are entirely eliminated from the waste stream, the WDV value of the fission products alone would decrease to the uranium ore values in less than 1000 years. It is generally argued that it is possible to predict the tectonic stability of geological formations over time scales of 500 to 1000 years but not over periods of 10^5 to 10^6 years.

While on the subject of actinide hazards it may not be out of place to point out that the generation of transuranics perse is smaller by several orders of magnitude in the Th–^{233}U cycle[27,28]. In this cycle the main byproduct actinide nuclide generated is ^{231}Pa, a nuclide continuously being produced in natural uranium ores following alpha emission by ^{235}U.

REFERENCES

1　C.M. COPLIK, M.F. KAPLAN, B. ROSS, "The Safety of Repositories for Highly Radioactive Wastes," Reviews of Modern Physics, 54, 269 (1982)

2　"A Study of the Isolation System for Geologic Disposal of Radioactive Wastes," Report of National Research Council, Waste Isolation Systems Panel (WISP), National Academy Press, Washington, D.C. (1983)

3　T.H. PIGFORD, "Long Term Environmental Impacts of Geological Repositories," Conf–IAEA–CN–43–185 (1983)

4　B.L. COHEN, "Critique of the National Academy of Sciences Study of the Isolation System for Geologic Disposal of Radioactive Waste," Nucl. Technol. 70, 433 (1985)

5　"Radionuclide Migration Around Uranium Ore Bodies – Analogue of Radioactive Waste Repositories," Australian Atomic Energy Commission Report NUREG/CR–5040, AAEC/C55 (1987)

6　R.D. WALTON and C.A. COWAN, "Relevance of Nuclide Migration at OKLO to the Problem of Geologic Storage of Radioactive Waste," Proceedings of IAEA Symposium, Libreville (1975)

7　H.O. HAUG, "Some Aspects and Long Term Problems of High Level and Actinide Contaminated Spent Fuel Reprocessing Wastes from U–Pu and Th–U Fuel Cycles," Proceedings of IAEA Symposium on the Management of Radioactive Wastes from the Nuclear Fuel Cycle 2, 233 Vienna (1976)

8　J. HAMSTRA, "Radiotoxic Hazard Measure for Buried Solid Radioactive Waste," Nucl. Safety, 16, 180 (1975)

9　B.L. COHEN, "Before It is Too Late, Scientist's Cause for Nuclear Energy," Pergamon Press, New York (1983)

10 "P.E. McGRATH, "Radioactive Waste Management Potentials and Hazards from a Risk Point of View," Report KFK 1992 (1974)

11 "Social and Economic Aspects of Radioactive Waste Disposal — Considerations for Institutional Management," National Academy Press, Washington D.C (1984)

12 "Evaluation of Actinide Partitioning and Transmutation," Technical Reports Series No.214, IAEA, Vienna (1982)

13 "Limits for Intakes of Radionuclides by Workers," International Commission on Radiological Protection Report ICRP–30, Part 1, 1979, Part 2, 1980, Pregamon Press, Oxford.

14 "Public Radiation Exposure from Nuclear Power Generation in the United States," Recommendation of the National Council on Radiation Protection and Measurements, NCRP Report No. 92 (1987)

15 M.SRINIVASAN, K.SUBBA RAO, S.B. GARG , G.V. ACHARYA, "Systematics of Criticality Data of Special Actinide Nuclides Deduced through the Trombay Criticality Formula", Accepted for publication in Nuclear Science and Engineering,(1989)

16 R.E. KELLEY and E.D. CLAYTON, "Fissible: A Proposed New Term in Nuclear Engineering," Nucl. Sci. Eng.91 (1985)

17 H.C. CLAIBORNE, "Neutron–Induced Transmutation of High–level Radioactive Waste," Report ORNL – T.M. 3964 (1972)

18 B. MAGLICH, C. POWELL, J. GOODWIN, J. NERING, L. LIDSKY, "Driven D+D EXYDER as Radioactive Waste Burner," (Present Conf.)

19 E. SCHMIDT, E. ZAMORANI, W. HAGE, S. GUARDINI, " Assessment Studies on Nuclear Transmutations of Byproduct Actinides," Final Report, S.A/1.05 .03 83.13 JRC–issued by Euratom, Ispra (1983)

20 International Conf. on Nuclear Waste Transmutation, Austin, Texas (1980)

21 Transactinium Isotope Nuclear Data, Proc. Third Advisory Group Meeting, IAEA–TECDOC–336 (1985)

22 H. MURATA and T. MUKAIYMA, " Fission Reactor Studies in View of Reactor Waste Programmes," Atomkernenergie– Kerntechinik, 45, No.1, 23 (1984)

23 Progress of Nuclear Safety Research, Japan Atomic Energy Research Institute (1987)

24 New Item Regarding Japan FRG Joint Studies on Burning of Actinides in Fast Reactors, New Scientist, 24th March (1988)

25 E.P. HORWITZ and W.W.SCHULZ,"Application of TRUEX Process to the Decontamination of Nuclear Waste Streams," International Solvent Extraction Conference (ISEC–86), Munich, FRG (1986)

26 D.D. SOOD, M.SRINIVASAN, P.K. IYENGAR, "Crriticality Properties of Transuranium Nuclides and their relevance to Waste Management," IANCAS Special Bulletin, Published by Radiochemistry Division, BARC, Bombay, Vol 5, No.1, 43 (1989)

27 S. RAMAN, "Study of the U–233–Th 232 Reactor as a Burner for Actinide Wastes," Conf–750303–36 (1975)

28 M.SRINIVASAN, M.V. DINGANKAR, V. KALYANSUNDARAM, P.K. IYENGAR, "Long Lived Actinide Waste Problem, Th/233U Cycle and Fusion Breeders," Proc. 4th Int. Conf. on Emerging Nuclear Energy Systems, Madrid, Spain, June 1986, World Scientific Publishing Co., Singapore (1987)

THE SELF-ABSORPTION EFFECT OF GAMMA RAYS IN ^{239}Pu

Hsiao-Hua Hsu
Los Alamos National Laboratory
Los Alamos, New Mexico 87545

ABSTRACT

Nuclear materials assay with gamma-ray spectrum measurement is a well-established method for safeguards. However, for a thick source, the self-absorption of characteristic low-energy gamma rays has been a handicap to accurate assay. I have carried out Monte Carlo simulations to study this effect using the ^{239}Pu α-decay gamma-ray spectrum as an example. The thickness of a plutonium metal source can be considered a function of gamma-ray intensity ratios. In a practical application, gamma-ray intensity ratios can be obtained from a measured spectrum. With the help of calculated curves, scientists can find the source thickness and make corrections to gamma-ray intensities, which then lead to an accurate quantitative determination of radioactive isotopes in the material.

INTRODUCTION

Gamma-ray spectrum measurement is a well-established assay method for nuclear material safeguards. From a gamma-ray spectrum, investigators can identify different radioactive isotopes in the material. In principle, they can also determine quantities of each isotope in the material. However, for quantitative measurement this procedure requires a well-calibrated detector system whose use is restricted to an ideal thin and point radioactive source.

In many practical cases, the source could be a slab of unknown thickness. In such a case, the self-absorption of gamma rays in the material will distort the spectrum and may lead to inaccurate quantitative determinations.

MONTE CARLO SIMULATIONS

I used the computer code CYLTRAN of the integrated TIGER series of Coupled Electron/Photon Monte Carlo Transport Codes[1] for simulations of the self-absorption effect in a plutonium decay gamma-ray spectrum. CYLTRAN combines a condensed-history electron Monte Carlo technique with a conventional single-scattering photon Monte Carlo technique. The code simulates the transport of all generations of electrons and protons with energy between several megavolts and 1.0 keV. The electron transport includes energy-loss straggling, multiple electron scattering, production of knock-on electrons, continuous bremsstrahlung, characteristic x rays, and annihilation radiation. The photon transport includes photoelectric, Compton, and pair-production interactions.

Slabs of bare plutonium metal with varying thicknesses and a density of 19.8 gm/cm^3 were modeled as sources. In the model a detector was located 10 cm from the source surface, and a 2-cm-thick lead collimator between the source and the detector limited the source area to 7.5 cm in diameter.

Gamma rays with selected energies were originated uniformly throughout the source volume and transported isotropically toward the detector. I tallied the spectrum at the detector front surface to avoid alteration of the spectrum by the detector responses. If there were no self-absorption, the number of gamma rays tallied at the detector front surfaace would be proportional to the source thickness. For a given detector, a tally of the pulse-height distribution at the detector can also be compared with the real measured spectrum.

Figure 1 is a plot of gamma-ray intensities as a function of source thickness. The straight line represents the gamma-ray intensity with no self-absorption effect. The deviation from the straight line, as shown for three different gamma-ray energies,

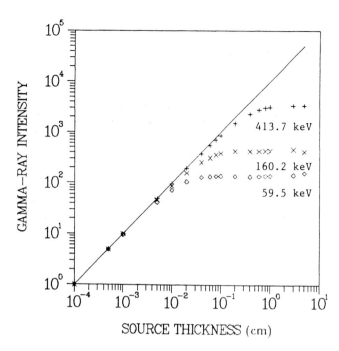

Fig. 1. Gamma-ray intensities as a function of source thickness.

where T is the thickness and R is the gamma-ray intensity ratio. The dots (•) in the plots are 50 interpolations of the function. Calculations are available from the author.

Although each gamma-ray intensity ratio exhibits sensitivity within certain limits of thickness, using the six ratios permits determination of thicknesses ranging from 5×10^{-4} to 5 cm. For an illustration, the measured intensity ratio of 129 keV/413 keV is 2.0 ± 0.1 and that of 203 keV/413 keV is 0.305 ± 0.020. The interpolations of the plots show that the values of the thickness are $(5.00 \pm 0.46) \times 10^{-2}$ cm and $(4.90 \pm 0.15) \times 10^{-2}$ cm, respectively. The results are consitent with each other.

Figure 8 is a plot of the intensity correction factor for the 413.7-keV gamma ray as a function of plutonium sample thickness. In the plot $\diamond$ are calculated values and • are 50 interpolations. Calculations are available from the author. The curves in Figure 8 allow corrections for gamma-ray intensities and determination of the ^{239}Pu quantity in the source. For a thickness of $(5.00 \pm 0.46) \times 10^{-2}$ cm, the intensity of the 413.7-keV gamma ray should be increased by a factor of 1.072 ± 0.008 to obtain the true source intensity.

Plutonium-239 samples usually contain other plutonium isotopes: ^{238}Pu, ^{240}Pu, ^{241}Pu, and ^{241}Am. Determining the amounts of these isotopes is possible by knowing their decay rate and measuring the gamma-ray intensity ratios: 125 keV/146 keV for ^{241}Am/^{239}Pu, 148 keV/146 keV for ^{241}Pu/^{239}Pu, 152 keV/146 keV for ^{238}Pu/^{239}Pu, and 160 keV/146 keV for ^{240}Pu/^{239}Pu. However, for samples thicker than 0.01 cm, the differential absorptions will change these ratios, and corrections factors will be required to obtain the true ratios and to calculate the true contents of these isotopes.

Figure 9 shows plots of these correction factors for gamma-ray intensity ratios as a function of sample thickness. No correction is needed for the 148 keV/146 keV ratio. These correction factors approach constant values for sample thickness larger than 0.25 cm; that is, 0.25 cm is approaching the infinite thickness for gamma rays with energy $\leq$ 160 keV. For the example above, the measured intensity ratios 125 keV/146 keV, 152 keV/146 keV, and 160 keV/146 keV require multiplication by factors of 1.256 ± 0.020, 0.941 ± 0.005, and 0.890 ± 0.006, respectively, to obtain the true ratios.

indicates clearly the energy-dependent, self-absorption effect. These curves start to level off at different thicknesses. Because all principal gamma rays in ^{239}Pu decay are low energy ($\leq$413.7 keV), plutonium metal thicker than 5 cm is essentially considered to have infinite thickness to its own gamma rays and hence is not amenable to quantitative gamma-ray assay.

The intensity ratios between different gamma rays changes as a function of source thickness up to 5 cm because of differential absorption characteristics. I calculated 6 gamma-ray intensity ratios in ^{239}Pu for 17 different thicknesses ranging from 1.0×10^{-4} cm to 5 cm. The ratios were 375 keV/413 keV, 203 keV/413 keV, 146 keV/413 keV, 129 keV/413 keV, 51 keV/413 keV, and 38 keV/413 keV.

RESULTS AND DISCUSSION

I carried out the calculations for gamma-ray intensity ratios as functions of source thickness. A practical applicaiton would be to derive source thickness given the appropriate measured gamma-ray intensity ratios. Figures 2–7 show plots of the source thickness as functions of different gamma-ray intensity ratios. In each plot, $\diamond$ are calculated values that can be fit by a function of the form

$$\ell n T = \Sigma a_i (\ell n R)^i,$$

CONCLUSION

The self-absorption effect, usually considered a handicap in radioactive isotope quantitative assay from gamma-ray spectra, can instead in many cases be used to determine the source thickness with the help of careful Monte Carlo simulations. Such simulations, however, **must** incorporate the actual geometry of the experiments.

REFERENCES

1. J. A. Halbleib and T. A. Mehlhon, "ITS: The Integrated TIGER Series of Coupled Electron/Photon Monte Carlo Transport Codes," Sandia National Laboratories report SAND84-0573 (1984).

2. M. R. Schmorak, "Nuclear Data Sheets for A = 231, 235, 239," Nuclear Data Sheets, Vol. 40 (1), 1983.

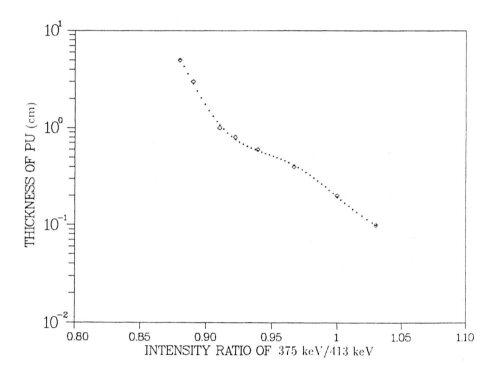

Fig. 2. Sample thickness vs intensity ratio 375/413. Thin source ratio = 1.060 ± 0.008.[2]

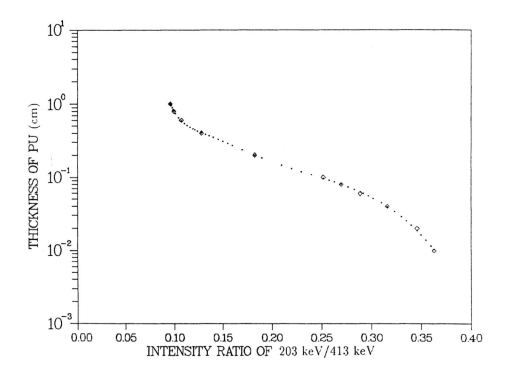

Fig. 3. Sample thickness vs intensity ratio 203/413. Thin source ratio = 0.388 ± 0.003.[2]

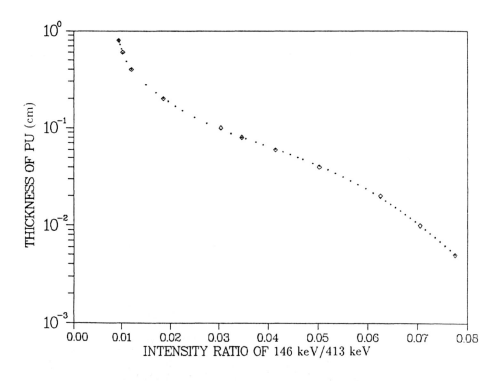

Fig. 4. Sample thickness vs intensity ratio 146/413. Thin source ratio = 0.0812 ± 0.0018.[2]

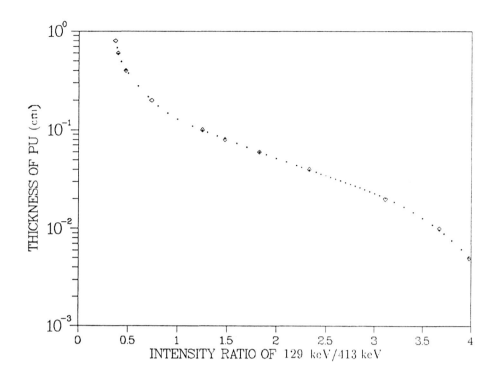

Fig. 5. Sample thickness vs intensity ratio 129/143. Thin source ratio = 4.304 ± 0.052.[2]

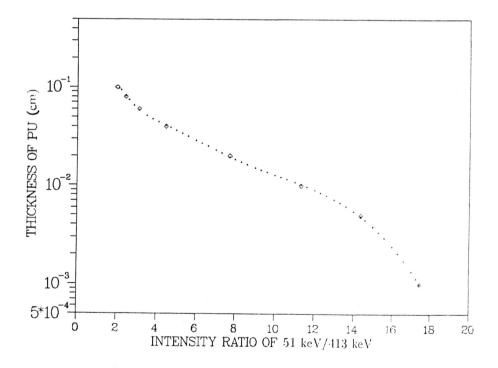

Fig. 6. Sample thickness vs intensity ratio 51/413. Thin source ratio = 18.48 ± 0.35.[2]

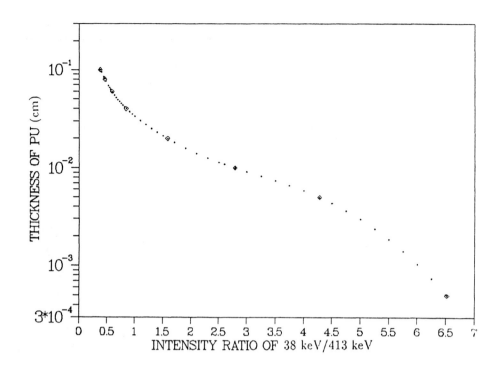

Fig. 7. Sample thickness vs intensity ratio 38/413. Thin source ratio = 7.162 ± 0.143.[2]

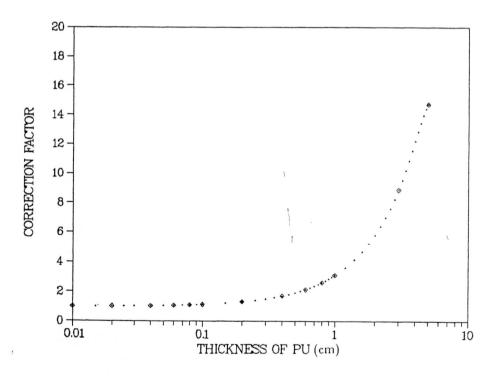

Fig. 8. 413.7-keV gamma-ray intensity correction factor vs sample thickness.

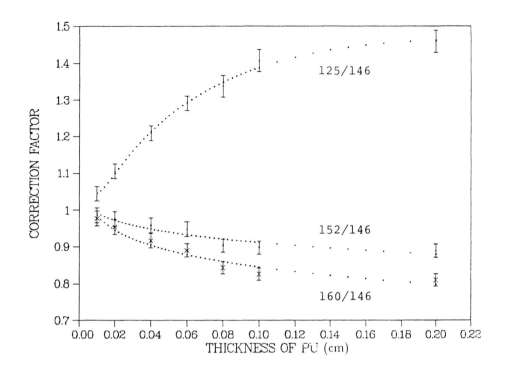

Fig. 9. Intensity ratio correction factor vs sample thickness.

HIGHLIGHTS OF 50 YEARS OF NUCLEAR FUELS DEVELOPMENTS

MASSOUD T. SIMNAD
University of California in San Diego
Mail Code R-011
La Jolla, California, 92093
(916)534-4903

ABSTRACT

The development of nuclear fuels since the discovery of nuclear fission is briefly surveyed in this paper. The fabrication of the uranium fuel for the first nuclear pile, CP-1, is described. The research and development studies and fabrication of the different types of nuclear fuels for the variety of research and power reactors are reviewed. The important factors involved to achieve low fuel cycle costs and reliable performance in the fuel elements are discussed in the historical context.

INTRODUCTION

The first nuclear chain reacting pile, CP-1, reached criticality on December 2, 1942, only three years after the discovery of fission and only one year after the chain reactor program was started in the Manhattan Project. In a coded telephone exchange Arthur Compton informed James Conant that "the Italian Navigator" (Enrico Fermi) had landed in the New World and that "the natives were friendly." The success of this experiment was critically dependent on the development and fabrication of uranium fuel (metal and oxide), the production of pure graphite moderator bricks, and the preparation of the radium-beryllium neutron source. The production of these materials for the CP-1 reactor was successfully achieved by the friendly natives, who were a highly talented group of metallurgists, physicists and chemists. This was a classic example of interdisciplinary research and it served as an important model for subsequent research studies to develop nuclear fuels for reactors.

The development of nuclear fuels is primarily the result of the extensive contributions of pioneers from many countries during the past five decades. The goals of low cost and reliable performance in the fuel elements have been achieved. The nuclear fuel elements have to accommodate the severe operating conditions set by the designs of the reactor cores, including thermal and mechanical stresses and prolonged exposure to the coolants and nuclear irradiation.

THE FIRST DECADE

The self-sustaining controlled nuclear chain reaction was achieved on December 2, 1942, in the CP-1 uranium-graphite reactor, which was constructed on a squash court under the West Stands of Stagg Field at the University of Chicago. The core of this first pile consisted of layers of graphite blocks (1350 tons) with holes about 20 cm apart in some of the blocks in alternate layers, which contained natural uranium metal rods or uranium oxide cylinders and pseudo-spheres. It was not until November 1942 that any appreciable amount of metallic uranium was available. At the rated power the core loading was 5630 kg of metallic uranium (2060 rods, 5.6 cm diameter x 5.6 cm long) and 36,590 kg of uranium oxide in the form of cylinders and pseudospheres. The research and development of fabrication techniques for uranium metal were initiated in 1942. The main objective was to find a system, using normal uranium, in which a chain reaction would occur. The early efforts to produce uranium rods by an extrusion process almost ended in disaster: "The uranium billet was initially inserted into the extrusion press container with some difficulty in handling. The temperature of the billet was too low when the full 700 tons force was used. The uranium metal came through the die into the run-out chute in a shower of flowing pieces the size of marbles glowing red hot. The "pit" man flew up the 20 foot ladder out of the pit, clothing on fire, and giving a profane lecture that if a group of idiot college professors wanted to catch their experimental rods they could!"

During the first decade (1942-1952) extensive research, development, and production studies were carried out in the US on fuel materials. Fuel elements were fabricated for the three Chicago piles (of which CP-1 and CP-2 were small air-cooled graphite-moderated piles, and CP-3 was a heavy-water moderated research reactor built at Argonne National Laboratory), for the production reactors at Hanford, and for the X-10 graphite-moderated air-cooled research reactor at Oak Ridge National Laboratory. These reactors operated with natural uranium fuel. At Los Alamos during this period the aqueous homogeneous water-boiler reactor LOPO, the first reactor to operate with enriched fuel was operated.

By the end of the first decade experience had been gained in the US with natural and enriched uranium and plutonium fuels, the importance of the Th/U-233 cycle had been emphasized, light and heavy water and graphite moderators had been used, and air, water, and liquid metals had been utilized as reactor coolants. Studies of a breeder reactor, a helium gas cooled reactor, and a materials testing reactor had been initiated.

THE NUCLEAR FUEL CYCLE

The nuclear fuel cycle includes (1) production of nuclear fuel (mining, milling, and enrichment),(2) fabrication of fuel elements, (3) reprocessing and recycling of the spent fuel to recover and raise the uranium and plutonium content, and (4) storage of the radioactive waste. The costs of fuel have been reduced by higher burnups, lower fabrication costs, and an increase in the maximum specific power output of the fuel rods. Fuel assembly prices have not risen because fabrication costs have dropped and thus balanced the rising cost of labor and materials costs. The specific fuel costs have actually decreased with the higher burnups.

Howe listed 14 materials that were developed by 1955, including metallic U-based and Pu-based alloy fuel elements, ceramic systems, and fluid fuel systems.[2] The dominant influence of the US Naval Reactors programs on

commercial nuclear technology in the US was initiated in 1946. The successful developments of uranium oxide fuel, of hafnium-free zirconium with low thermal neutron cross-section, and of Zircaloys with good corrosion resistance in water at 300'C were particularly important.

FUEL ELEMENT MATERIALS AND DESIGNS

The nuclear fuels that have been developed for reactors include metallic, ceramic, composite, and liquid fuels. The metallic fuels have been alloyed to improve their resistance to irradiation and corrosion.[5,6] Ceramic fuels have included the oxides, carbides, oxycarbides, nitrides, and hydrides. Composite fuels include two-phase metallic fuels and dispersions of ceramic fuels in metal, ceramic or graphite matrices. The ideal goal of inherent safety in nuclear reactors has been shown to be feasible with the proper choice of fuel elements in the reactor design, such as the hydride fuel in the TRIGA research reactor and the coated-particle fuel dispersed in graphite moderator in the HTGR power reactors.

A 1000-MW(e) LWR is fueled with about 9 million uranium dioxide pellets contained in about 150 km of fuel rods clad in Zircaloy tubing. The design of the fuel elements has aimed to achieve the goals of adequate heat transfer, nuclear reactivity, retention of fission products, inherent safety under accident conditions, and retention of structural and mechanical integrity. This process has always been based on an iterative procedure, whereby information from experimental results and operational experiences are factored into the refinement of the design. The phenomenon of fuel swelling has been studied in great detail. The effects of temperature, thermal gradients, and stress gradients on the nucleation and migration of fission gas bubbles in the fuel matrix have been determined.[7] The bubbles migrate up the thermal gradients toward the fuel center and are held and carried along by lattice defects until they are large enough to escape from or migrate along the defects. Bubble migration has been shown to be by Brownian motion for very small bubbles, by surface diffusion when they are larger, and by an evaporation-condensation process at elevated temperatures in very large bubbles. The phenomenon of fission gas resolution in irradiated fuel has been incorporated into the mechanism.

Computer codes have been developed to predict the behavior of nuclear fuels in power reactors. The codes address the complex processes occurring during the life of operating fuel elements as functions of the power histories by rigorous analyses based on first principles. These codes have been well documented and are on file at Argonne National Laboratory. They can be obtained on tape and IBM cards with user's manual.

The most challenging problem in the development of the modeling codes for fuel elements has been the complex effects of neutron irradiation on materials and fuels.[8,9] The fuel cladding and the structural alloys in fast reactor cores swell through void formation by migration of the vacancies formed by fast neutron irradiation. This leads to a movement of the cladding away from the fuel and thereby to a reduction of fuel-induced stresses. Radiation-induced creep of the cladding and ducts is also a highly complicated phenomenon. Corrosion of stainless steel cladding by certain fission products (iodine, cesium) in fast breeder reactor fuel pins has been experienced and examined in great detail.

There have been very successful developments in recent years to improve fuel performance by means of better fuel management and fuel cycling, advanced fuel design, fuel-cycle cost reduction, and more reliable reactor components. The large-scale production of nuclear fuels, particularly with plutonium and recycled fuel, has involved special mechanized equipment designs, improved shielding, rapid accurate analyses, and continuous accountability. The new fuel element production facilities have automated remotely-controlled fuel pin fabrication processes with computer controlled operation from a centralized control room. Fuel pellets can now be inspected by means of rapid test instruments, which perform complete characterization of 100% of core loading pellets. Quality control and quality assurance is being exercised to an increasing degree of sophistication in all stages of production.

During the past five decades the remedies that have been applied to solve the fuels problems have been quite effective. An important example in the LWRs was the solution to the serious problem of cladding collapse resulting from radiation-enhanced densification of the oxide fuel pellets. Stable fuel pins were developed by control of the grain size, pore structure, and density of the pellets and by back-filling the cladding with pressurized helium gas in order to prevent collapse of the cladding and to improve the thermal conductivity of the gap. Much higher burnups (over 4000 Gj/kg M) and longer fuel cycles (18 to 24 month cycles) have been achieved in recent years in many LWRs. The incorporation of a thin zirconium barrier between the fuel and the cladding has allowed the successful accommodation of power ramps and cycling to peak power.

RESEARCH REACTOR FUELS

The fuels that have been used in research reactors have included uranium and plutonium metal and alloys, oxides, cermets, hydrides, and aqueous homogeneous solutions (uranyl sulfate, nitrate, or phosphate). The limited availability of enriched uranium fuel and of heavy-water moderator in the early days of reactor development led to the design and construction of several natural uranium fueled, graphite moderated, air-cooled research reactors, such as the 3.5-MW X-10 reactor at Oak Ridge and the 28-MW Brookhaven Research Reactor. However, the much higher cost per unit flux did not justify continuing with natural uranium fueled graphite reactors.

The pool- and tank-type light-water moderated and cooled research reactors are the most commonly used in most countries. The prototypes of these reactors were first designed and built at Oak Ridge in 1946 as part of the program to build the materials test reactor (MTR). In a typical MTR-type core, the fuel is composed of enriched uranium in aluminum.

In 1962 the research reactor in Puerto Rico was the first to use U_3O_8 in aluminum cermet fuel. The same fuel was used in the following year in the 250-MW Advanced Test Reactor (ATR) in Idaho. The most sophisticated and complex version of this cermet fuel was fabricated for the 100-MW thermal HFIR at Oak Ridge, which went critical in 1965. It generates the highest thermal neutron flux of any research reactor in the world. It was a remarkable achievement to produce the fuel plates for the HFIR, which are formed as involute curves and fastened in two annular cylinders. The fuel loading in the plates is graded in the radial direction and, in addition, the inner plates contain boron carbide as a burnable poison. These fuel elements have a life of only two weeks in the reactor. The ATR fuel elements are similar to the HFIR elements, except that the uranium oxide loading is unform. However, each fuel plate in the ATR elements has a different radius. A relatively simple, small (10 kW) research reactor, which utilized 20% enriched U_3O_8-aluminum cermet fuel containing 40 wt% U_3O_8 (called Argonaut) was designed and built by Argonne national Laboratory and operated from 1957 to 1972.

Many heavy-water-moderated research reactors have been built in the US and 15 other countries since the CP-3 reactor was built at Argonne in 1944. The fuel elements for these reactors included natural and enriched fuel, and uranium metal, U-Al alloys, and uranium oxide. The 25-MW HBWR, built in Norway in 1959, is the only heavy water moderated research reactor in which the coolant is pressurized boiling heavy water (250'C). It utilizes cylindrical fuel pins with 1.5% enriched uranium oxide pellets clad in Zircaloy-2 and helium bonded. The 33-MW NRX reactor has operated at Chalk River since 1948. Three types of fuel have been used in the NRX: natural uranium metal, enriched U-Al alloy, and Pu-Al alloy. One of the first Pu-Al fuels melted right through two sheaths and the reactor tank! The largest heavy water moderated research reactor is the 200-MW NRU which has operated at Chalk River in Canada. The fuel consists of 305 cm long flat bars of Al-clad natural uranium of variable width and breadth placed in coolant channels. The 60-MW high-flux Grenoble reactor in France uses fully enriched U-Al with boron carbide burnable poison and is clad with an aluminum alloy. The core configuration is annular with plate elements in the shape of involutes of a circle, around a hollow central cylinder. The plutonium recycle test reactor (PRTR) at Hanford was a 70-MW pressure-tube type test reactor cooled and moderated by heavy water. It was used to test U-Pu mixed oxide fuel and operated very successfully from 1960 to 1969, demonstrating the feasibility and economy of recycling plutonium in thermal reactors.

The TRIGA research reactor was conceived and developed at General Atomics after it was founded in 1956. The objective was to provide an inherently safe core composition that had a large prompt negative temperature

coefficient of reactivity such that if all the available excess reactivity were suddenly inserted in the core, the resulting fuel temperature would automatically cause the power excursion to terminate before any core damage resulted. Experiments demonstrated that the integral fuel-moderator system of the uranium-zirconium-hydride fuel possesses a basic neutron-spectrum-hardening mechanism to produce the desired characteristics. This fuel also has a good heat capacity, excellent irradiation stability and fission product retentivity, high chemical inertness in water, and low hydrogen equilibrium pressures at elevated temperatures. The first 100-kW TRIGA reactor was developed and built in just a year and a half and was critical in 1958. The TRIGA reactor was also shown to have the capability of operation under conditions of transient experiments for delivery of high-intensity bursts of neutrons. It was part of the US exhibit at the second Geneva Conference in 1958. Since then, over 60 TRIGA reactors have been operated in 22 countries, the largest one being the 14-MW unit in Romania.

A number of liquid-metal-cooled small experimental fast reactors have been built and operated successfully. These reactors have used Pu, enriched U, or Pu+U mixed fuel and were cooled with air, mercury, sodium, or NaK. The first fast reactor experiment was the 25-kW Clementine at Los Alamos, operated from 1946 to 1953. It was fueled with stabilized delta-phase Pu. The fuel was in the form of nickel-plated rods. The core was surrounded with natural U rods of the same dimensions and was cooled with mercury. Los Alamos also operated the 1-MW LAMPRE-1 reactor from 1961 to 1963. It was fueled with molten eutectic alloy of Pu with 2.4 wt% Fe having a melting point of 410'C, contained in tantalum capsules which were cooled with sodium.

POWER REACTOR FUELS

Carbon Dioxide Gas-Cooled Reactors

The first generation of commercial nuclear power reactors in Britain and France are cooled by carbon dioxide gas and fueled with natural uranium metal rods clad in magnesium alloys. Graphite is the moderator material in these reactors. The first of these reactors (Calder Hall) started generating electricity in 1956. The uranium contained was alloyed (~1%) with small quantities of Fe, Al, C, Si, and Ni to improve its irradiation resistance. The second generation CO_2-cooled graphite moderated reactors in Britain (the AGRs) use slightly enriched UO_2 clad in a special stainless steel. These fuel elements can operate at higher temperatures to much greater burnups, giving higher efficiencies and ratings.

Helium Gas-Cooled Reactors

From 1944 to 1946 a design for an advanced helium gas-cooled power reactor concept was developed at Oak Ridge[1]. The proposal was to use natural uranium carbide as fuel, graphite and BeO as moderators, and helium as coolant with a direct cycle gas turbine energy conversion system. The project was cancelled in 1946, and it was revived a decade later in the US (Peach Bottom, Ft.St. Vrain, UHTREX), Britain (Dragon), and West Germany (AVR, THTR). The high-temperature gas-cooled reactors (HTGR) use helium gas as the primary coolant, graphite as the neutron moderator and fuel element structural material, and coated carbide or oxide fuel particles dispersed in a graphite matrix. The choice of graphite as the moderator and core structural material is based on its unique chemical physical, and mechanical properties at elevated temperatures and on its very low neutron cross section, good radiation stability, ease of fabrication, and low cost. The use of graphite as a diluent of the fuel permits much greater fuel dilution than would otherwise be possible and thereby minimizes radiation damage, increases specific power, and greatly extends the heat transfer surface. The Th/U-233 standard fuel cycle (with U-235 as the initial fissionable fuel) is used because of its potential for achieving a higher fuel utilization.

The coated-particle fuel allows the high-temperature operation of the core to very high burnup (80%) of the fissile fuel, with extremely high retention of the fission products. The average fuel burnup of 100 MWd/kg obtainable is by far the highest of all existing thermal reactor systems. In recent years the design and development effort has been focused on a modular smaller power (130 MWe) concept, the MHTGR. In this second generation nuclear power system the safety and protection will be provided by inherent and passive features, independent of operator actions or the activation of engineered systems.

In the MHTGR the active core region is composed of graphite fuel element blocks that are hexagonal in cross section, 35 cm across the flats and 77 cm long. The fuel is in the form of coated particles, 800 microns in diameter. Each fuel particle consists of a uranium oxycarbide kernel (350 microns in diameter) first coated with a porous graphite buffer, followed by three successive layers of pyrolytic carbon, silicon carbide, and pyrolytic carbon. Similar, but slightly larger coated particles containing a kernel of thorium oxide are also used in the reactor. The coated particles are mixed with a graphitic material, formed into fuel rods, 1.25 cm in diameter and 5 cm long, and then inserted into sealed holes in the graphite fuel element blocks. Vertical coolant holes are also provided in the fuel element blocks. The fuel elements are stacked in columns to make up an annular shaped core. Unfueled graphite blocks surround the active core to form replaceable inner and outer radial and axial reflectors. The massive graphite structure provides a large heat sink during transient conditions.

The inherent safety is also achieved virtue of the single phase and inertness of the helium coolant, and the negative temperature coefficient of reactivity. In addition to the redundancy in the cooling system, the decay heat can be removed passively by means of conduction, radiation, and natural convection without the core temperature exceeding the fuel damage temperature.

In Germany two pebble bed helium cooled reactors (AVR and THTR) have been developed and built with spherical, graphite matrix fuel elements surrounded by bottom and side graphite reflectors. The fuel elements consist of pyrolytic carbon coated carbide fuel particles dispersed in a graphite matrix and encased in spherical graphite balls, 6 cm in diameter. These reactors have performed very well; the AVR operated for about twenty years and attained coolant temperatures of up to 1000'C. The UHTREX reactor at LANL attained 1300'C.

Light Water Reactor Fuels

The light water pressurized and boiling reactors (PWR and BWR) in operation and under construction account for the largest share of nuclear power generation in most countries[10]. The first land-based PWR prototype, the STR, was started in Idaho in 1953. The APS-1 prototype at Obninsk, USSR, was originally operated in 1954 as a PWR power reactor and was later converted for boiling water and nuclear superheat. The Shippingport PWR was authorized in 1954 and commenced operation in 1957.

Although metallic cermet fuels (Zircaloy-2 matrix with 6.3 wt% U) were used in a few of the early PWR cores in the US, the majority are fueled with uranium dioxide clad with Zircaloy. The zirconium alloys were developed for water reactors because of their low neutron cross section, adequate strength in the operating temperature range, and satisfactory resistance to irradiation and to corrosion by water at high temperatures. The many improvements and refinements in core design led to greater power densities, fuel assemblies with higher integrity, more effective fuel management and fuel cycling, chemical shim control (using boric acid in solution in the PWR coolant), and rod cluster control. The Th-U-233 cycle has been shown to improve the conversion ratio significantly. The operational experience with mixed oxide $(U,Pu)O_2$ fuel has been excellent.

The Shippingport PWR cores have provided extensive operating experience on a large-sized PWR nuclear power plant. This reactor furnished the incentive for the development of and the vehicle for evaluation of the Zircaloy-clad uranium oxide fuel rod, which is the basic fuel element for the commercial water-cooled power reactors of the world today. The "seed-and-blanket" core in this reactor consisted of "seed" regions containing fully enriched (93%) uranium surrounded by blanket regions consisting of natural fuel lattices.

The prototype PWR version of the 5-MWe APS first operated in the USSR in 1954 with a fuel which consisted of a 5% enriched U-9%Mo alloy powder dispersed in a magnesium matrix. The fuel elements were annular-tube shaped, with thicker inner and thinner outer claddings of stainless steel. A typical fuel channel consisted of four elements arranged in a square array in a graphite moderator structure, which contained a stainless steel tube in the center for carrying the primary circuit water to the inlet and outlet headers.

The first experimental boiling water reactor in the US, the 5-MWe EBWR, operated from 1956 to 1967 at Argonne. The fuel elements for the initial core included highly enriched rod-type "spike" elements and 1.44% enriched plate-type elements. The fuel in the spike elements was a ceramic oxide fuel clad in Zircaloy-2, and in the plate-type elements the fuel was an alloy of U-5%Zr-1.5%Nb metallurgically bonded to the Zircaloy-2 cladding. In 1966 the EBWR was the first BWR to use Pu fuel in the form of mixed oxide fuel rods in an electricity generating reactor. The 5-MWe Vallecitos BWR was a prototype reactor built and operated by General Electric from 1957 to 1963.

The background of experience with light water reactor fuel exposure by 1985 had reached an estimated 56,000 PWR fuel assemblies (13 million rods) and 10,000 BWR assemblies (6 million rods). Fuel failure rates have decreased from 0.012% to 0.001% in PWRs and from 0.023% to 0.001% in BWRs. Lead test assemblies have been irradiated to over 60 GWd/t in PWRs and to over 45 GWd/t in BWRs. In-reactor exposures of fuel assemblies for as long as six equivalent full power years in a BWR and over five years in a PWR have been achieved. These assemblies appeared to be in excellent condition, and their life expectancy was limited only by the differential growth of the Zircaloy under irradiation. Appropriate design improvements could eliminate such limitations and allow even longer exposures of the fuel assemblies.

In the PWRs fuel damage is primarily caused by fabrication defects, by fretting and wear from the deposition of impurities and debris in the core, and by core baffle-jetting. Handling damage of fuel assemblies has also been a problem during refueling operations, which has led to more accommodating designs and improved operating procedures. In the BWRs in the 1960s and 1970s major losses of capacity factor were experienced as a result of failures caused by clad hydriding and by fuel pellet-clad interaction (PCI) phenomena, as well as by stress corrosion cracking of pipe welds. These problems have been addressed successfully, such that fuel problems are no longer a significant cause of capacity factor losses.

The recent developments have resulted in the design and fabrication of more forgiving fuel elements for water-cooled reactors, such as the incorporation of a thin barrier liner (zirconium) inside the cladding, prepressurization of the fuel pin with helium gas, fuel pellet design changes, and changes in the fuel assembly designs so as to lower fuel temperatures. The use of burnable poisons (Gd) in the fuel has enabled control of the large excess reactivity required at initial startup with high fuel exposure cores.

Heavy Water Reactor Fuels

The use of heavy water as a moderator provides good neutron economy and permits a wide range of possible fuel cycles and fuel management schemes. The most ambitious and pioneering work in the development of heavy water moderated power reactors has been in Canada. The 25-MWe NPD reactor was Canada's first nuclear power demonstration reactor (1962). It was built to demonstrate the concept of a horizontal pressure tube reactor, moderated and cooled by heavy water and fueled with natural uranium dioxide pellets contained in Zircaloy-2 cladding, operating on a once-through basis with on-power refueling. The pressure tubes used were the Zr-2.5%Nb alloy developed in the USSR. The fuel elements have performed very well in the CANDU reactors. The fuel elements are made up of bundles of 28 rods. The maximum fuel rod rating is about 690 W/cm. The fuel temperature is 400'C surface and 2000'C center. A recent modification has significantly improved the fuel's performance. The new fuel rods include a thin layer of graphite between the fuel and the cladding, designated CANLUB fuel. This minimizes local stress concentrations and also protects the cladding against fission product (iodine) attack. Another important contribution was the work on how directionally oriented hydrides in Zircaloy affect the deformation behavior. Specifications were then produced for cladding with controlled hydride orientation.

Fast Breeder Reactor Fuels

The concept of breeding plutonium in a fast reactor dates back to 1944, when Fermi and Zinn discussed the possibility of building a fast neutron breeder reactor. Fast breeder reactors increase fuel usage to over 70% of the uranium employed, compared with about 1% in thermal reactors. In a 30-year period, a fast breeder reactor of 1000-MWe capacity would require about 23 tons of uranium compared with 3000 tons in a light-water-cooled reactor. The fuel cycle cost is also expected to be significantly lower in fast-breeder power reactors than in thermal reactors or in fossil-fueled power stations. The cost of power is not strongly influenced by the cost of uranium in fast breeder reactors. Although the technical feasibility and advantages of the fast breeder reactor have been demonstrated, the goal of the fast breeder reactor programs has been to improve the technology to build economically viable fast breeder reactors in the near future.

In 1946 the developmemt of the experimental breeder reactor, EBR-I, was started at Argonne National Laboratory; construction began in 1949 at the National Reactor Testing Station in Idaho, and the reactor went critical in mid-1951, a total of 5 years! Nowadays it would take that long just for the paper work and the hearings for such a project. The EBR-I reactor produced the first usable amounts of electricity (200 kW) to be generated from a nuclear reactor (December 20, 1951), and demonstrated the feasibility of breeding plutonium in a fast reactor. Fast breeder (FBR) power reactor prototypes have been built in the US, UK, USSR, France, Germany, Japan, and India. The largest operating FBR is the 1300-MWe Super-Phoenix in France.

Following the shutdown of EBR-I in 1963, the 20-MWe EBR-II reactor began operation in 1964. A unique feature of the EBR-II is that it is located adjacent to a fuel cycle facility for pyrometallurgical reprocessing, recovery of the fertile and fissile materials, and reenrichment and refabrication of fuel elements for return to the reactor. The shielded, remotely controlled pyrometallurgical facility can handle high-burnup short-cooled fuels, and thereby improve fuel cycle costs by avoiding high inventory charges. The core-1 fuel loading was the 43% enriched alloy U-11 at% "fissium" corresponding to the mixture of fission products that are not removed in the refining process, and its composition changes as Pu is added or builds into the fuel. The fuel is sodium-bonded to the stainless steel cladding, and an inert gas plenum is provided to accommodate sodium expansion and fuel swelling. The fuel smear density is 75% and the linear heat rating is 20 to 60 Kw/m. Advanced fuels for the EBR-II have included the successful use of U-10Zr, U-8Pu-10Zr and U-19Pu-10Zr, which are compatible with stainless steel cladding up to 800'C. These alloys have tolerated very high burnups of up to 18.4 at.% in the EBR-II when clad with type D9 stainless steel, and 14.3 at.% clad in HT9. Tests are in progress in the FFTR fast test reactor at Hanford, where burnups of up to 10.2 at.% have been achieved with these fuels. The axial swelling of the fuel appears to saturate at ~10% when clad in D9 or HT9. The diametral increase is under 1 % at 10 at.% burnup, and 5 to 8% at 18.4 at.% burnup. About 60 to 80% of the fission gases are released above 6 at.% burnup.

The 12-MWe experimental fast breeder reactor at Dounreay, UK, operated from 1959 to 1980. It was one of the most successful experimental reactors in terms of the wealth of data it provided on fuel elements, materials, kinetics and physics of fast reactors, and the sodium coolant. The fuel elements were vented to allow fission gas release to the sodium coolant. The 300-MWe PFR in the UK has operated successfully as a prototype commercial FBR using uranium-plutonium mixed oxide fuel.

The first prototype FBR in France was the Rapsodie reactor (40-MWe), which started operation in 1967. Since then France has rapidly built up on this experience to design and operate the highly successful 300-MWe Phoenix and the 1300-MWe Super-Phoenix. The fuel used in the FBRs in France is stainless steel clad mixed oxide (25 wt.% PuO$_2$).

In the USSR the development of FBRs has been given a high priority since the 1950's. The 5-MWt SBR-5 reactor is the fifth of a series of small fast reactor experiments. It has operated with stainless steel clad plutonium dioxide, mixed oxide fuel, and with carbide fuel. During 1962 to 1964 the reactor was intentionally operated with leaking fuel elements and the distribution of fission products in the primary system was determined as a function of power level. Large FBRs have also been built and are operating in the USSR at power levels of 300-MWe and 600-MWe.

The 400-MWt Fast Flux Test Facility (FFTF) at Hanford has served as a most powerful tool for irradiation testing of fuels and materials for commercial FBRs. The advanced mixed oxide fuel clad in the stainless steel alloys D9 and HT9 have attained burnups of up to 20%.

The thermionic and thermoelectric direct conversion space nuclear power reactors have been under development in the US and the USSR. The fuels and materials research studies for these systems have been the most challenging. Good progress has been made during the past two decades.

CONCLUSION

The better load following, and the capacity for extended burnups and longer reactor cycles, have been especially important factors in lowering the fuel cycle costs and in improving the economics of nuclear power.

The distinguished metallurgist and pioneer in this field, Dr. Cyril Stanley Smith, has made the cogent comment that metallurgy has gained more than it has contributed in its fruitful association with the field of nuclear energy. He has stated that "the core of the problem is the core of the reactor... the production of serviceable fuel elements, coolants, and moderator... The solution of the materials problems of the reactor core has called for a skill approaching that of the artist in creating a balance between possibilities and needs, and the highest craftsmanship has been evoked in making the finished components."

REFERENCES

1. "History of Nuclear Materials: Memoirs and Surveys," J. Nucl. Matls, 100, 1-148 (1981).

2. J. P. HOWE, ibid, p. 80.

3. J. F. SCHUMAR, ibid, p. 32.

4. E. C. CREUTZ, ibid, p. 83.

5. M. T. SIMNAD, "Fuel Element Experience in Nuclear Power Reactors" Am. Nucl. Soc./AEC Monograph (1971).

6. M. T. SIMNAD and J. P. HOWE, "Materials for Nuclear Fission Power Technology," p.32-180 in "Materials Science in Energy Technology," G. G. Libowitz and M. S. Whittingham, eds. Academic Press, New York (1979).

7. D. R. OLANDER, "Fundamental Aspects of Nuclear Reactor Fuel Elements," TID-26711-P, NTIS, Springfield, VA (1976).

8. J. T. A. ROBERTS, "Structural Materials in Nuclear Power Sysems," Plenum Press, New York (1981).

9. B. R. T. FROST, "Nuclear Fuel Elements," Pergamon Press, New York, (1982).

10. M. T. SIMNAD, "Fuel and Fuel Element Developments for Water-Cooled Nuclear Power Reactors," IAEA, Vienna (1989).

A MULTI-DETECTOR (NaI) SYSTEM FOR NUCLEAR SAFETY IN A PLUTONIUM PROCESSING FACILITY

R. C. Hochel
E. I. du Pont de Nemours & Co.
Savannah River Laboratory
Aiken, SC 29808
803-725-1344

INTRODUCTION

The FB-Line facility of the Savannah River F-Area Purex Plant processes plutonium nitrate solutions into metal by calcium metal reduction of a fluoride/oxide precipitate. Nuclear safety and plutonium accumulation, or holdup, in solution processing tanks must be strictly controlled. In the past, such control was exercised through administrative procedures and periodic sampling or monitoring. However, new Operational Safety Requirements (OSR) call for continuous monitoring of certain process tanks and lines along with appropriate safety interlocks.

The OSR call for monitoring the Pu concentration in eight different tanks, and mechanically preventing transfer of their contents if the concentration exceeds certain limits. Because of the difficulty and cost of modifying or replacing these tanks in an operating facility, a nonintrusive, nondestructive analysis (NDA) approach to the problem was selected. Actually, the problem is very similar to monitoring requirements at seven other locations in the facility which was successfully met with NDA using NaI detectors. These were mostly accumulation monitors tied to an alarming-recorder, but the alarms could be, and in one case was, used to interlock processing equipment. Because of the success of the existing monitors, it was decided to expand and improve the system to include the OSR monitors.

DESCRIPTION OF EXISTING SYSTEM

The existing monitors had been installed over a period of years, and the first several were simple single channel analyzer (SCA) systems. A schematic diagram of a six SCA system is shown in Figure 1. Each consists of a 5 cm. x 5 cm. NaI (T1) detector positioned as close as possible to measure the gamma-ray spectrum from the tank or line to be monitored. Because of the corrosive environment (nitric and/or hydrofluoric acid) in the process, detectors viewed the tank or line through a "Lexan" cabinet panel. Pb shielding and collimation were usually required depending on the location of the detector. Detector electronics were standard NIM modules consisting of a HV power supply, amplifier/SCA, and a ratemeter; and were remote, in some cases as much as 50 meters from the detector. A SCA window was set on the 320-420 keV multiplet of the Pu spectrum, and the window-output was routed to the ratemeter. The analog output from the ratemeter was used to drive a strip-chart recorder with setpoints for high and low level alarms.

Calibration of the monitors depends on their use. Those used for holdup or accumulation were calibrated with a solid Pu source of known mass. This determines the monitor's response, which can be used to set an appropriate alarm limit. Monitors which must alarm at a specified concentration are calibrated insitu. This is done by matching monitor responses to tank concentrations after independent analysis of tank samples.

SCA systems provide an analog signal which is easily interfaced to the process; however, they have some fundamental limitations. The hardware is difficult to keep calibrated because there is no visual display of the spectrum, and changes in background or gain can significantly affect results in ways often unnoticed. However, these problems largely disappear if the detector signal is processed by a multichannel analyzer (MCA). The background subtraction capabilities of the MCA and the visual display are both enormous improvements over an SCA approach, and ones which were essential to contend with the variables expected for the OSR monitors.

DESCRIPTION OF THE MCA SYSTEM HARDWARE

Components of the MCA system replacing the SCA system and adding four of the new OSR monitors are shown schmatically in Figure 2. Because procedures require that these monitors must be operational to run the facility, the standard SCA electronics were retained to assure SCA operation even if the MCA or computer fails. Otherwise, the SCA and ratemeter for each monitor are not used. Instead, the amplifier output is digitized by an analog-to-digital-converter (ADC) and the spectrum stored in the MCA. It is not always necessary to dedicate one ADC to each detector. In Figure 2, the first four detectors are multiplexed by a mixer/router into a single ADC. All four of these detectors are accumulation monitors and normally see little or no Pu. As a result, the duty cycle of ADC 1 is light, so multiplexing causes no serious deadtime or counting loss problems.

The MCA can accommodate up to 32 ADCs using four 8-input collect interface boards. This one has two such boards: one for the seven ADCs shown, and another which will be discussed later. The MCA is capable of data input rates as high as 500k events/second, far in excess of the 30-50 k needed here. Data acquisition is under control of a learn/execute task downloaded from the computer to the MCA. The task starts each ADC for a 60-second count, analyzes two regions of interest (ROIs) in each spectrum,

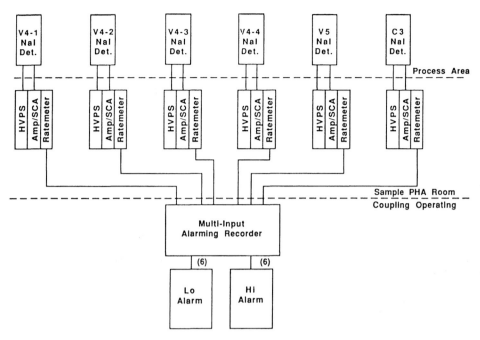

FIGURE 1. Single Channel Analyzer System

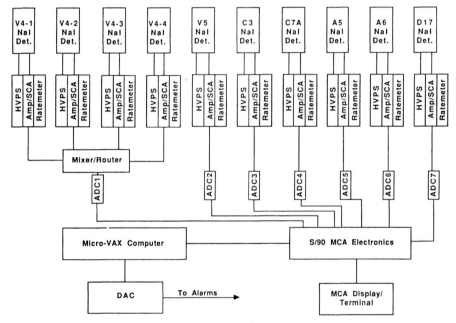

FIGURE 2. 5th Level Series 90 System

reports the results to the computer, clears the data, and then restarts the cycle again.

The system computer performs three main tasks: (1) downloads the learn/execute task to the MCA, (2) scales the digital results from the MCA to appropriate analog signals for output by the digital-to-analog-converter (DAC), and (3) performs various checks on the MCA results to asssure each monitor is properly calibrated and working correctly. In addition, the computer also monitors the status of an uninterruptable power supply (UPS) which powers the system, and can shutdown and restart the system in the event of an extended power outage.

The DAC is the communications interface between the monitors and the process. Analog signals from the DAC are sent to a multi-input recorder to track each monitor and alarm if certain conditions are met.

A schematic diagram of a second system operationally identical to the first, but located in another part of the processing facility, is shown in Figure 3. It includes five monitors, the first two of which are upgrades of previous SCA systems. Again, the duty cycles of two of the monitors are low enough to multiplex them into a single ADC.

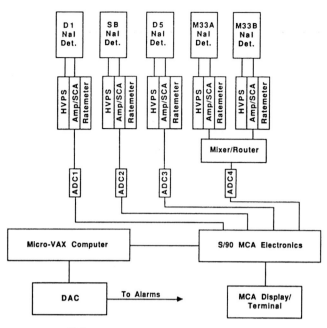

FIGURE 3. 6th Level Series 90 System

SYSTEM OPERATION

Each system is structured to provide maximum flexibility in its operation. It can operate independently in an SCA mode, or in the MCA mode under manual or computer control. Therefore, failure of a monitor, the MCA, or the computer will not force a shutdown of the entire system and consequently the process. If the computer fails, analog signals for the alarms can be taken from the ratemeters, and requires only a readjustment of alarm setpoints to compensate for the lack of background subtraction. The MCA remains available to easily check calibrations and proper operation of each monitor.

Normally, however, the system is under computer control to maximize performance. A typical spectrum from one of the monitors (Figure 4) shows why this is so. The 0-1250 keV spectrum shows several low energy peaks from Pu and Am, the Pu multiplet between the markers (300-470 keV), a Cs-137 reference peak (662 keV), and a Zr/Nb peak (750 keV) from incomplete fission product removal in prior processing. Rather than reading-out the entire spectrum to the computer, MCA firmware is used to analyzed two ROIs in the spectrum. Analysis of Pu multiplet in the first ROI is displayed at the bottom of the spectrum. Comparison of the integral and area counts per second (ICPS vs. ACPS) shows that about half the ROI intensity is due to background. A major disadvantage of the SCA mode, but not the MCA mode, is that results can be significantly affected by large or varying backgrounds. Because the MCA analysis is relatively insensitive to background, a Cs-137 reference source is used on all the monitors to assure proper calibration. A second ROI is set in each spectrum for the Cs peak. ROI information for each monitor is passed to the computer serially via the MCA's printer port. The computer software performs several checks on the ROI data:

- Checks to see that the ROI integral count is not zero
- Checks that the reference ROI integral count is within user-defined limits
- Checks to see that ROI values do not remain totally constant

The first check assures that the monitor detector and electronics are working, the second that each monitor is in proper energy calibration, and the third that the MCA is not "hung" and simply passing identical repetitions of a previous good count.

The computer communicates the results to the process via the DAC output boards. Each Pu-ROI peak count rate is compared to a user-defined minimum and range and is scaled to an analog output voltage between 0.5-5.0 V. If any of the three above ROI checks should fail, the DAC output for that monitor is set to 0 V. Each DAC output is fed into a strip-chart recorder which provides low and high alarms based on appropriate setpoints for the process.

The two systems are each powered by their own UPS. The UPS eliminates powerline fluctuations which are very troublesome in process environments and will provide output power for up to eight minutes following an input power failure. If input power to the UPS fails, a timer in the UPS cabinet is started. If input power to the UPS is not restored within five minutes, the timer signals the computer to begin an orderly shutdown procedure. Also, once input power is restored following a shutdown, the computer will restart itself and instruct the MCA to resume normal operation.

SYSTEM BACKUP CAPABILITIES

As mentioned earlier, the first system has two collect interface boards. The purpose of the second board is to allow the system to function as a backup for an independent gamma pulse height analysis (PHA) system. The PHA system performs Ge-detector analyses of liquid samples for nuclear safety and process control. Its operation, like the OSR monitors, is vital to the operation of the processing facility and must have a ready backup in the event of a failure.

Figure 5 shows a schematic of the backup strategy. Both detectors are used routinely, but a failure of one can be tolerated for a time. Normally the PHA system is under control of the MCA and computer on the left. On the right are duplicate signal processing electronics interfaced to the OSR monitor system as a ready backup. Software for both systems is installed on both computers, as well as the second OSR system, so that the computers are interchangeable.

Indeed, the idea of standardizing components for total interchangeability was a key feature of this work, and one that should be considered carefully in any project. For instance, the computers for the OSR monitors are oversize for those particular functions, but are appropriate considering they can also be used as backups. In a processing facility in particular, adherence to identical hardware wherever possible facilitates maintenance by reducing the number of spare parts to be kept on hand, and minimizing training of support personnel.

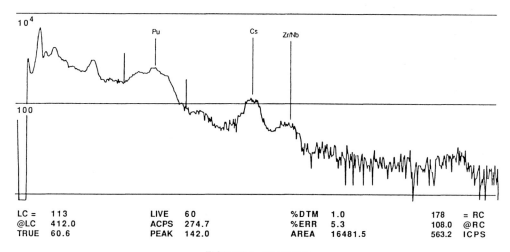

LC =	113	LIVE	60	%DTM	1.0	178	= RC
@LC	412.0	ACPS	274.7	%ERR	5.3	108.0	@RC
TRUE	60.6	PEAK	142.0	AREA	16481.5	563.2	ICPS

FIGURE 4. V5 Monitor

SUMMARY

These systems have been installed and made operational with minimum disruption to the process. They were purposely designed for easy expansion to meet both recognized and anticipated needs. Each was installed during normal periodic maintenance shutdowns of the facility. The first system upgrading six SCA monitors and providing backup for the PHA system has been operating since mid-1986. To date, not one day of processing time has been lost due to a system outage. Despite the harsh environment for electronic equipment in a processing facility, component failures have been few and rarely serious. Installation of the remaining OSR monitors is complete except for final testing and calibration. Again, this is being done in a step-wise fashion to minimize process disruptions. Operability of the newer monitors is expected to be as good as the older ones, and both systems have adequate capacity to handle additional monitors should they be needed in the future.

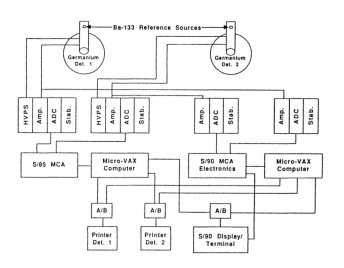

FIGURE 5. Gamma PHA System

The information contained in this article was developed during the course of work under Contract No. DE-AC09-76SR00001 with the U.S. Department of Energy. By acceptance of this paper, the publisher and/or recipient acknowledges the U. S. Government's right to retain a nonexclusive, royalty-free license in and to any copyright covering this paper, along with the right to reproduce and to authorize others to reproduce all or part of the copyrighted paper.

DEVELOPMENT, UTILIZATION, AND
FUTURE PROSPECTS OF MATERIALS TEST REACTORS

Peter v. der HARDT
Commission of the European Communities
Joint Research Centre, Ispra, Italy - Cadarache, France
Phone: 39, 332, 789595
             33, 4225, 4389

ABSTRACT

Reactor radiation affects the chemical and physical properties of materials. These changes can be very drastic in certain cases. Special test reactors have therefore been built since the 1950's and specific skills were developed to expose materials specimens to the precise irradiation conditions required (1), (2).

Materials testing reactors are those research reactor facilities which are designed and operated predominantly for studies into radiation damage. About a dozen plants in European communities (EC) Member States and in the U.S. can be identified in this category, with 5 to 100 MW fission power and neutron fluxes between 5×10^{13} and 10^{15} cm^{-2} s^{-1}.

The paper elaborates common aspects of development, utilisation, and future prospects of U.S. and EC materials testing reactors, and indicates the most significant differences

INTRODUCTION

The original MTR at Idaho Falls (3) gave its name to a category of research reactors, built and operated to study the physics and chemistry of materials in a reactor radiation environment. These facilities traditionally represent the upper power class (10 to 100 MW) of research reactors, and about a dozen plants in the US and in Western Europe fall into this category, a small number among all nuclear reactors in the two areas considered.

Table 1 gives a personal compilation of test reactors in the United States, all operated for the Department of Energy (DOE), and in countries of the European Communities, managed by eight different administrations. They are all used, largely or partially, for the testing of materials. Table 1 also reveals that the average age of these reactors is 25 years. It does not show that about another dozen of reactors in this category have been shut down during the past 20 years, that several of the facilities listed in Table 1 are faced with funding problems, and that no new reactor is under construction in the two regions considered.

GLOSSARY

ATR	Advanced Test Reactor, Idaho Falls, ID, USA
BR 2	Belgian Reactor, Mol, Belgium
DR 3	Danish Reactor, Risø, Denmark
EBR II	Experimental Breeder Reactor, Argonne -West, Idaho Falls, ID, USA
FFTF	Fast Flux Test Facility, Hanford, WA, USA
FRJ 2	Forschungsreaktor Juelich, Germany
HFBR	High Flux Beam Reactor, Brookhaven, USA
HFIR	High Flux Isotope Reactor, Oak Ridge, TN, USA
HFR	High Flux Reactor, Petten, Netherlands
	also: High Flux Reactor, ILL, Grenoble France (RHF in French)
ILL	Institut Laue - Langevin
KNK II	Kompaktes Natriumgekuehltes Kernkraftwerk, Karlsruhe, Germany
MTR	Materials test reactor
MPMTR	Multi-purpose materials test reactor
ORR	Oak Ridge Research reactor, Oak Ridge, TN, USA
R 2	Reactor at Studvik, Sweden (ORR type)
RERTR	Reduced Enrichment for Research and Test Reactors
TRIGA	Testing, Research, Isotopes, General, Atomic

REACTOR	LOCATION	TYPE	POWER, MW	START OF OPERATION	REMARKS
FFTF	Hanford, USA	Fast flux MTR	400	1980	
BR2	Mol, Belgium	MPMTR	100	1961	
HFR	Petten, Nether.	MPMTR	50	1961	Rebuilt, 1984
ATR	Idaho Falls, USA	MTR	250	1967	Classified test program
OSIRIS	Saclay, France	MTR	70	1966	
SILOE	Grenoble, France	MTR	35	1963	Refurbished, 1988
DIDO	Harwell, UK	DIDO type D_2O cooled MP MTR'S	25,5	1956	
PLUTO			25,5	1957	
FRJ2	Jülich, Germany		23	1962	
DR3	Risø, Denmark		10(12)	1960	
HFIR	Oak Ridge, USA	Isotope prod. reactor with MTR capability	100	1966	Vessel embrittlement problems
HFBR	Brookhaven, USA	D_2O cooled neutron beam reactor with MTR capability	60	1965	
PHEBUS	CADARACHE, France	LWR fuel Safety test facility	20(40) Steady state	1975	Refurbished, 1990
CABRI		Fast reactor fuel safety test facilities	25 (20 min.)	1976	Power peak up to 20.000 MW
SCARABEE			80 (20 min.)	1973	
EBR II	Idaho Falls, USA	Prototype fast breeders with MTR capability	62,5	1964	
KNK II	Karlsruhe, Germany		58 (fast core)	1977	

Table 1.

Tentative ordering of test reactors in the US and in EEC countries by decreasing MTR characteristics.

DEVELOPMENT
The early years (1950 - 1970)

Building and operating a research reactor, in the 50's and 60's, was usually based upon a policy decision of a country, research centre or university to acquire expertise in nuclear physics and technology. Building and operating the facility was largely an aim in itself. This explains that standardization never got very far: Besides the triplet ORR-HFR-R 2, the DIDO's and the TRIGA's (the highly successful TRIGA (4) is outside the scope of this paper), many "one-of-its-kind" were built, at high construction and running costs. Once taken into service power increases pushed most of the reactors to higher and higher neutron fluxes, twice to three times the initial design levels, and to rising operating expenses.

Maturity (1970-1990)

The absence of an economic, businesslike, approach to MTR management, inadequate long-term planning and the lack of univoque licensing criteria are among the main phenomena leading to the crisis of the 70's with the first shut-downs for lack of funding and/or because of new safety requirements.

Virtually all surviving facilities have implemented upgrading programs (5), (6), (7), fighting against technical obsolescence and meeting increasing safety problems. Extended recent safety reviews were carried out in the US (8), (9), (10) in France (11) and in Germany (12). The new issues range from earthquake hazards and neutron embrittlement to prompt criticality accidents, flow instability analyses, and advanced fission product release studies.

Conversion of research and test reactors to low-enriched uranium fuel has been another development of the 80's. Starting as a political issue-non-proliferation of potential nuclear weapon material (13) - the US RERTR program (14) has been successful in a large international collaboration (15),(16), in the fields of development, reactor physics and safety analyses (17). These developments also come in support of potential future high-enrichment, high density, fuel elements (18).

UTILIZATION

Test reactors have been highly successful in their original working areas, viz. the development of engineering materials resisting power reactor operating conditions (1), (2). They generated the data bases for all nuclear materials in fission and fusion reactor technology, including synergetic effects like radiation-enhanced corrosion, displacement+helium embrittlement and fission-enhanced fuel creep. These areas, however, have been subject to a number of significant developments.

The variety of power reactor types has decreased: with minor exceptions for gas cooled reactors (19), (20), work is now limited to light water reactors and fast breeders. Consequently, research programmes were terminated or reduced. New demands have appeared with safety-related programs inside and beyond design base accident scenarios. The beginning research into materials for fusion reactor added new test requirements in the 80's (21).

The overall result, however, has been a steady decrease of the traditional irradiation "market". Together with increasing operating costs resulting from the developments mentioned earlier (upgrading, safety requirements, core conversion) funding problems became inevitable. The way out was found for the surviving reactors by diversification into areas outside the traditional irradiation testing. A few examples follow:

Nuclear and solid state physics.

The demand for neutron beams has consistently remained beyond the capacity of specialised facilities like HFBR or the ILL reactor. MTR facilities equipped with neutron beam tubes have therefore frequently been upgraded by cold neutron sources and new instruments (22).

Neutron radiography (23), (24).

Often develloped for in-house use this technique opens numerous application possibilities in nuclear and non-nuclear industry as shown during three World Conferences (1981,1986,1989).

Radioisotopes and activations analysis.

Traditional by-products of MTR operation these applications have considerably developed during the past 20 years, following increasing industrial, medical and scientific consumption. Harwell runs a sizeable silicon doping facility (25), and Oak Ridge used to be the only producer of transuranium isotopes (26).

Boron neutron capture theraphy.

There has been a renewed international interest in this method as documented by three symposia between 1983 and 1988. Groups are active in the US (27) and in Europe (Harwell and CEC Petten). Their success will depend a.o. on the flawless collaboration between biochemists, neurosurgeons, radiotherapists, reactor physicists and nuclear engineers.

Inside the traditional materials testing area, however, an opposite development has taken place, i.e. a trend to specialize on irradiation services for which reactor and connected hot laboratories are suited and for which the special expertise is on site. Typical examples are in-pile sodium loops in BR 2, in-pile water loops at OSIRIS, highly-instrumented fuel and materials capsules for HFR, the PLUTO in-pile gas loops,...... giving the facility in question a leading position in a narrow market sector.

FUTURE PROSPECTS

Assuming a "normal" progress of nuclear fission and fusion energy during the following 20 years one can postulate a continuing need for materials testing under reactor conditions. The challenge will be to assess the future market beyond the present institutional limits, to be aware of new competing technologies, and to upgrade the most promising facilities.
Competition

Many tests are now carried out in power reactors with the advantage of lower cost, larger volumes, and reduced interpretation problems.

New competitors are :

- accelerators, particularly cyclotrons, undergoing a rapid development to higher performance and lower cost,
- super computers capable of predicting reactor radiation damage, using e.g. molecular dynamics codes, into domains not yet covered by irradiation testing,
- possibly, accelerator-based neutron sources.

New reactors

As stated earlier in this paper, no new test reactor is under construction in the areas considered. The Advanced Neutron Source (ANS) project in the U.S. (28) and the Munich Compact Core Reactor (29) are essentially beam tube facilities with neutron scattering as the major anticipated field of activity.

Another recent large reactor, the MPR 30 in Indonesia (30) carries the programmatic name "multi-purpose reactor".

The next Twenty Years

There is a case for a thorough quantitative analysis of future irradiation testing needs, both in the U.S. and Western Europe. Tentatively, under the assumption of unperturbed development and keeping the long-term fusion programs in mind, each of the two areas is estimated to require two reactor-years per year. It can be seen under this hypothesis that the U.S. market might just be covered by the combined possibilities of the DOE plants (Table 1, ATR excluded), accounting for contributions from university reactors. It will be necessary, however, to design testing capability into new projects like the ANS.

In the EC countries, on the other hand, the present overcapacity is obvious, and will be reduced to the required level by closing down one or two reactors of Table 1 and by diversifying into other research areas. The underlying analysis and management will cut across institutions and frontiers. The ILL reactor at Grenoble has demonstrated the feasibility of international collaboration over 22 years (31), (32).

A European consensus in the field of materials irradiation testing would not necessarily lead, in a forseeable future, to a new reactor project. It has been demonstrated that the life of an existing facility can be considerably extended by replacing degraded and obsolete components.

CONCLUSION

Materials test reactors have contributed to the economy and safety of present power reactors, and a number of them were shut down after successfully accomplishing their mission.

Their future role will be determined by continued diversification into new research areas, improved management schemes and increased international mobility of expertise and competences.

The new universal non-power reactor will combine the traditional features of research, training, and test reactors into one facility.

REFERENCES

1. P. von der HARDT, "Radiation effects experiments at test reactors" Int. Symp. on the Use and Development of Low and Medium Flux Research Reactors. Cambridge, MA, USA, October 16-19, 1983.
2. J. AHLF, "Forschungsreaktoren fur die Entwicklung von Reaktorwerksstoffen" Atomwirtsschaft (Jan. 1988)
3. D.R. DEBOISBLANC, "Engineering Test Reactor Technology", these Proceedings.
4. W.L. WHITTEMORE, " Research reactors: A product of the past, the pathway to the future", these Proceedings.
5. R.M. MOON, " A review of current and proposed reactor upgrades", IAEA-CN-46 1028 (Jan. 1985)
6. B.H. MONTGOMERY, K.R. THOMS, and C.D. WEST, " Final report of the HFIR irradiation facilities improvement project", ORNL/TM - 10501 (September 1987)
7. N.G. CHRYSOCHOIDES et al., " High flux testing reactor Petten. Replacement of the reactor vessel and connected components". EUR 10194 EN (1985)
8. "Safety Issues at the DOE Test and Research Reactors", National Accademic Press Washington (1988)
9. H.P. PLANCHON et al., "Results and implications of the EBR II inherent safety demonstration test", Nucl. Sci. Engrg. 100,549-557 (1988)
10. Q.L. BAIRD et al., "Operational safety experience and passive safety testing at the FFTF", Nucl. Safety, 29 nr. 3 (July- Sept. 1988)
11. F. MERCHIE, personal communication (February 1989)
12. W. HAJEK, H. J. KRIKS, and W. KRULL, "Backfitting safety measures in FR Germany", Nucl. Eng. Intern. (December 1988)
13. P. von der HARDT, " Problems related to the conversion of research and test reactors to low-enriched uranium fuel", Atomkernenergie - Kerntechnik, Vol. 48 (1986) nr.4
14. A. TRAVELLI, " Status of the RERTR Program", RERTR Meeting San Diego, CA, USA (Sept. 1988)
15. H.J. ROEGLER and A. STROEMICH, " Research reactor conversion in Germany....", ANS Annual Meeting, San Diego, CA, USA (June 1988)
16. J.R. DEEN and J.L. SNELGROVE, " LEU fuel cycle analyses for the Belgian BR 2 research reactor" ibid.
17. M. BELHADJ, T. ALDEMIR, and R.N. CHRISTENSEN. "Onset of nucleate boiling in research reactors...", Nucl. Technol., Vol 82 (Sept 1988)
18. J.L. SNELGROVE and G.L. HOFMAN, "Fuel for the ANS - performance testing and fabrication development", ANS Winter Meetg., Washington, DC, USA, (Oct-Nov. 88)
19. G. POTT et al., " Qualification of HTR fuel and graphite in European material testing reactors", IAEA-SM-300/20 (October 1987)
20. J.WILLIAMS, "Advanced gas cooled reactor research and development", ATOM 386 (Dec. 1988)
21. P. von der HARDT, "International radiation damage tests in fusion materials: The Oak Ridge and BEATRIX exchange schemes", J. Nucl. Mater. 155-157 (1988),. 789 793
22. R. THEENHAUS et al., " Past, present and future reactor neutron research requirements at the KFA Juelich...", IAEA-SM 300/22 (Oct. 1987)
23. H. BERGER, "Advances in neutron radiography", ANS Winter Meeting, Washington, DC, USA (November 1986)
24. J.P. BARTON, "Neutron radiography", HFR Petten Colloquium, Petten, Netherlands (April 1989)
25. N. CRICK, "Silicon irradiations in Harwell reactors", Atom 336 (April 1987)
26. D.C. HOFFMAN, "Transuranium isotopes", LBL-21015 (Dec. 1985)
27. O.K. HARLING and J.A. BERNARD, "A clinical trial of neutron capture therapy for brain cancer", IAEA-SM-300/082 (Oct. 1987)
28. C.D. WEST, "Overview of the ANS Project", ANS Winter Meeting, Washington, DC, USA, (Oct.-Nov. 1988)
29. K. BOENING, "The compact core reactor project of the Technical University of Munich", ANS Winter Meeting, Washington, DC, USA, (Oct.-Nov. 1988)
30. N. MANDERLA, "Der Mehrzweckforschungsreaktor G.A. Siwabessy (MPR - 30)", Atomwirtschaft (Jan. 1988)
31. W. GLAESER, "The ILL: An example of international co-operation in neutron beam research", IAEA-SM-300/100 (Oct. 1987)
32. " 20 years ILL", brochure (1987)

POSTER SESSION: GENERAL RESEARCH, INSTRUMENTATION, AND BY-PRODUCTS

ESOL FACILITY FOR THE GENERATION AND RADIOCHEMICAL
SEPARATION OF SHORT HALF-LIFE FISSION PRODUCTS[a]

R. J. GEHRKE, D. H. MEIKRANTZ, J. D. BAKER,
R. A. ANDERL, V. J. NOVICK, R. C. GREENWOOD
Idaho National Engineering Laboratory
EG&G Idaho, Inc.
P. O. Box 1625
Idaho Falls, Idaho 83415
(208) 526-4155

ABSTRACT

A facility has been developed at the Idaho
National Engineering Laboratory (INEL) for the
generation and rapid radiochemical separation of
short half-life mixed fission products. This
facility, referred to as the Idaho Elemental
Separation On Line (ESOL), consists of electroplated sources of spontaneously fissioning
^{252}Cf with a helium jet transport arrangement
to continuously deliver short half-life, mixed
fission products to the radiochemistry
laboratory for rapid, computer controlled,
radiochemical separations.

I. INTRODUCTION

Nuclear structure and radiochemical
separations have been of long standing interest
(>30 years) to the Nuclear Physics personnel
located at the Materials Test Reactor Area at
the INEL. The study of fission products,
because of their relevance to reactor safety,
and of the deformed rare-earth radionuclides
has been of special interest. When the
Materials Test Reactor was permanently shut
down in 1970, another source of short half-life
fission products and rare-earth radionuclides
had to be found. The other materials test
reactors at the INEL were designed to be very
efficient for materials testing with in-pile
loop experiments but they left no flexibility
for the installation of rapid irradiation
facilities for nuclear structure studies.
Hence, a new radionuclide production facility
specifically designed for nuclear structure
studies was required. The facility selected
utilizes electroplated ^{252}Cf spontaneously

fissioning sources that can be coupled via a
helium-jet transport system to either an on-
line elemental separation (ESOL) or an on-line
mass separation (ISOL) facility. In this paper
we discuss only the ESOL facility. With this
facility a number of experiments can be
performed, including the measurement of
radionuclide half-lives, gamma-ray energies and
relative intensities, decay energies (Q_β) and
gamma-gamma coincidences. A description of the
ISOL system can be found in reference 1.

The helium jet recoil method for the rapid
transportation of radionuclei from the production target to remotely located counting
instrumentation was first developed in the
early 1960's.[2-4] As illustrated in Figure 1,
nuclear reaction products escape from the
target or source by recoil and become
thermalized in a gas-filled chamber surrounding
the target or source. If the gas (other gases
besides helium may be used with ESOL), which
flows continuously through the target/source
chamber, is seeded with aerosols,[b] the
thermalized radionuclei rapidly attach
themselves to the aerosols and are entrained in
the gas flow from the target/source chamber
through a small diameter capillary. If the gas
flow is laminar in the capillary the
radionuclei can be transported, via the aerosol
carriers, with high efficiency, to a remote
laboratory where they can be collected,
purified and studied. The gas exits the
capillary at sonic velocity into an evacuated

---

[a]This work was performed under DOE contract
DE-AC07-76ID01570.

[b]Solid aerosols (vs. liquid), and especially
NaCl[5] became the aerosol of choice for many
facilities employing the gas jet transport
technique because of their stability and the
ease of generating aerosols of an optimum size
for transport (~0.05 to ~1.0 micrometer
diameter).

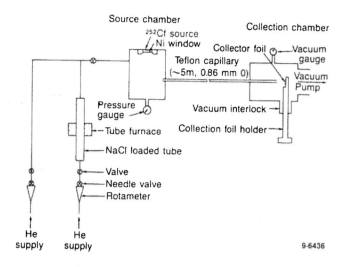

FIG. 1   BLOCK DIAGRAM OF A GAS JET RECOIL
         TRANSPORT SYSTEM.

collection chamber in the form of a gas jet.
The carrier gas is exhausted from the
collection chamber by a high volume mechanical
vacuum pump, and the relatively massive
aerosols emerge from the capillary with a small
divergence angle and impact upon a collection
surface located a few millimeters from the
capillary.

II. DEVELOPMENT OF THE INEL ESOL

The idea to apply the gas-jet technique at
the INEL to a spontaneously fissioning
^{252}Cf source was proposed by one of the
authors (RCG) in the mid 1970's. Sufficient
quantities of ^{252}Cf were available to the DOE
laboratories on a loan basis from Oak Ridge
National Laboratory (ORNL), and the technique
of electrodepositing tens of micrograms of
californium with good adhesion onto a platinum
backing was already being developed at ORNL for
other applications. A special hot cell to
accommodate the large ^{252}Cf sources was designed
and built[6] in a radiochemical laboratory at
the INEL which was already equipped to handle
large quantities of actinide materials. This
hot cell (see Figure 2) was completed in the
late 1970's and within six months of completion
the first electroplated ^{252}Cf source (50
micrograms) was received from ORNL. The
proposal for this new facility was to couple
on-line, via the helium jet transport system,
the ^{252}Cf produced fission products to a mass
separator. (The mass separator was located in
the same laboratory wing and had been used to
obtain highly enriched stable and radionuclide
target materials for neutron cross section
studies.) It soon became clear that the effort
required for a ^{252}Cf spontaneously fissioning
source to be coupled via a helium-jet recoil
transport system to an on-line mass separation

FIG. 2   HOT CELL DESIGNED TO CONTAIN UP TO 2
         mg OF ^{252}Cf.

system would take several years of research and
development. In order to perform nuclear
structure studies far from the line of beta
stability prior to the completion of the
on-line mass separator system, several of the
authors proposed that a rapid radiochemical
separation facility could be developed in
parallel.

The INEL ESOL facility became
operational in early 1979 with a computer-
controlled radiochemical separation system,
based on HPLC, for the rapid separation of
individual rare-earth fission product
fractions. Less than one year later the rapid,
computer-controlled solvent-solvent extraction
radiochemical separation system, based on
centrifugal contactors, was in operation. The
following timely advances in separation
chemistry played an important role in the
implementation of a rapid radiochemical
separation facility at INEL.

   A.   Extractants for Removal of Actinides
         from Processed Spent Fuel Effluent

Development of special solvent
extractants for the separation of actinides
from commercial light water reactor wastes
advanced significantly during the late 1960's
and early 1970's.[7,8] These new extractants,
unlike the old, allowed the extracted actinides
to be back-extracted into an aqueous phase
under mild chemical conditions. Our laboratory

834

developed a commercial purification method for the bidentate compound dihexyldiethylcarbamylmethylene phosphate (DHDECMP).[a,9] Because of the chemical similarity of the rare-earths and actinides, DHDECMP can be used to separate within seconds the rare-earth fission products as a group from ^{252}Cf mixed fission products by solvent extraction or extraction chromatography.

B.   High Pressure Liquid Chromatography

Advances in high pressure pumps, computer-controlled gradient elution and newly developed anion and cation exchange resins of a 5 to 20 micron particle diameter during the 1960's and 1970's allowed separation of individual rare-earth fission products within minutes by high pressure liquid chromatography (also referred to as high performance liquid chromatography, HPLC).

C.   Liquid-Liquid Extractions

Laboratory scale models of plant-size in-stream centrifuges for solvent extraction were developed during the 1970's to allow studies of extraction techniques for radioactive waste processing.[10,11] Laboratory-scale in-stream centrifugal contactors were built for the Idaho ESOL system based on the design developed at Argonne National Laboratory, Argonne, Illinois.[12]

III. ^{252}Cf GAS-JET FISSION PRODUCT GENERATION AND TRANSPORT

Other research groups have also studied short half-life fission products, but have generally carried out these studies by mass or elemental separation using thermal neutron fission in ^{235}U. The facility at the INEL has been designed to complement these other facilities in that the fission products are generated from spontaneously fissioning ^{252}Cf. With this source the yields of fission product radionuclides between ~110 and ~125 atomic mass units (AMU) and above ~145 AMU are enchanced relative to ^{235}U or ^{239}Pu as shown in Figure 3. Direct yield ratios of fission products in the rare-earth region, relative to those of ^{235}U, exceed 1000 for some radionuclei.

A.   Fission Product Generation

The ^{252}Cf sources are located in a hot cell (Figure 2) which has been designed to contain up to two milligrams of ^{252}Cf.[6] The interior of the cell is 1.2 m deep x 1.2 m wide

<hr/>

[a]Dihexyldiethylcarbamylmethelene phosphate (80% purity) obtained from Bray Oil Company, Los Angeles, California, U.S.A. Further purified at the INEL.

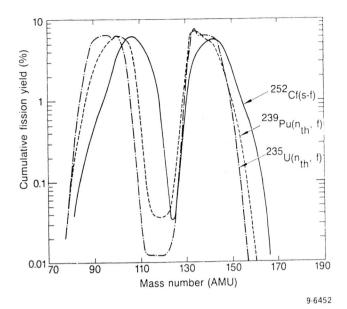

9·6452

FIG. 3   COMPARISON OF THE CUMULATIVE YIELDS FOR THE SPONTANEOUS FISSION OF ^{252}Cf AND THERMAL NEUTRON FISSION OF ^{235}U AND ^{239}Pu.

x 1.5 m high and lined by a stainless steel box. Between the inner and exterior sides of the cell is a completely enclosed shield structure containing 3.8 cm thick lead sheet and 90 cm thick borated gypsum. The cell has a large 52 cm x 52 cm window providing a view of 80% of the cell interior, two master-slave manipulators and a shielded air-lock door. In addition, it is equipped with service access tubes, internal cell lighting, a HEPA filtered ventilation system and appropriate monitor and control instrumentation.

The spontaneously fissioning ^{252}Cf sources are electrodeposited as the hydroxide onto platinum disks (~2 cm diameter deposit). They were prepared at ORNL.[13] Each source has a deposit of up to 1000 micrograms of ^{252}Cf. The sources are each mounted in a stainless steel holder and these holders can be screwed into the ends of the cylindrical stainless steel source chamber (8.25 cm x 7.6 cm long). To reduce the possibility of transport of recoiling actinide nuclei from the source chamber to the collection chamber in the chemistry laboratory, a replaceable, thin (1.3 μm) nickel foil window covers each source and is located ~0.6 cm from each ^{252}Cf electrodeposit. The nickel foil is held in place with a retaining ring fastened to the source holder as shown in Figure 4. The recoiling actinide nuclei lack the energy to penetrate the nickel foil and are thereby segregated from the main source chamber. The chamber is pressurized with helium to ~2 atmospheres (2 x 10^5 Pa).

FIG. 4. THE ²⁵²Cf SOURCE CHAMBER AND A ²⁵²Cf
SOURCE HOLDER WITH ATTACHED Ni WINDOW
HELD IN PLACE BY AN ANNULAR RETAINING
RING.

B. Gas Jet Transport

A NaCl aerosol loaded helium gas
stream is used in the ESOL setup. The helium
flow rate is ~40 cc/sec at STP. The solid NaCl
aerosols are produced by passing helium gas
over a NaCl filled ceramic boat that is placed
inside a tube furnace operated at 600°C (a
variety of other solid aerosols have also been
produced using this same technique, e.g., AgCl,
Ag, Sm, etc.). By operating the furnace at
~600° a sufficient number of NaCl aerosols are
produced to provide high transport efficiencies
(~79%) without causing the gas-jet transport
capillary to become plugged over extended use.

The teflon capillary, 1.35 mm ID x
25 m long, is contained in a sealed stainless
steel conduit that runs from the hot cell to
the fume hood in the radiochemistry laboratory
as shown in Figure 5. The conduit provides
secondary containment of the fission products
during transfer between laboratories and

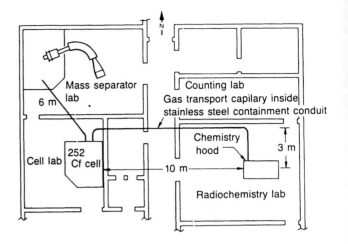

FIG. 5   SCHEMATIC FLOOR PLAN OF THE
LABORATORIES CONTAINING THE ²⁵²Cf
HOT CELL, THE MASS SEPARATOR AND THE
CHEMISTRY HOOD.

protects the fragile capillary from damage.
The fission products exit the capillary at
sonic velocity into an evacuated collection
chamber located inside the fume hood. The
carrier gas is exhausted by a large 76 L/S
mechanical pump while the relatively heavy
aerosols impact and stick to a collection
tape. Magnetic computer tape has been found to
serve as a convenient and inexpensive
collection tape. Figure 6 is a diagram of the
collection chamber assembly. The moving tape
mechanism allows the transfer of the collected
aerosol and fission products from the
collection chamber to a dissolution vessel.

C. Dissolution of Aerosols and Attached
Fission Products.

At the end of a collection period, the
collection tape section containing the aerosol
deposit (~3 mm diameter) travels under
microprocessor control from the evacuated
collection chamber through a sliding vacuum
seal to a small dissolution vessel where the
activity is washed from the tape. The vacuum
seal is simply a piece of thin flexible rubber
gasket with slits cut to allow the tape to pass
through it. To protect the aerosol deposit
during transfer through the sliding seal, a
second tape covers the deposit during movement
of the collection tape from collection point to
dissolution point. In the dissolution vessel
the individual layers of tape separate exposing
the collected radioactivity to the wash
solution as illustrated in Figure 7.

IV. AUTOMATED RADIOCHEMICAL SEPARATIONS

The movement of the collection tape at the
end of a collection period and the sequential
radiochemical separation steps are computer
controlled to assure rapid, accurate and

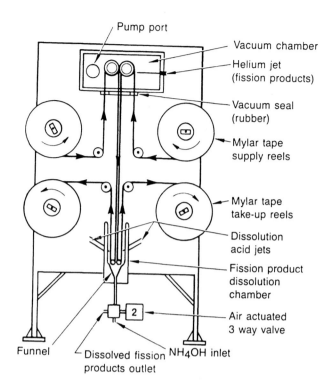

FIG. 6   AUTOMATED FISSION PRODUCT COLLECTION
         AND DISSOLUTION APPARATUS.

reproducible timing sequences. The
microcomputer can be programmed with a set of
simple time sequenced commands that
automatically control the subsequent chemical
separation steps at precise times predetermined
relative to the end of the collection period.
The Idaho ESOL facility is primarily based on
two types of radiochemical separation schemes:
1) column chemistry, and 2) solvent-solvent
extractions.

    A.   Column Chemistry

        Columns that can be effectively used
in purification schemes include columns to
carry out oxidation or reduction, extraction
chromatography and anion/cation exchange.
Column chemistry is rapid, simple, and
elementally specific. High purification
factors can be realized so that the fission
product element of choice can often be selected
with one column.

        The system used for rare-earth
purifications is illustrated in Figure 8. This
system is composed of two HPLC's coupled in
series to perform a two-step purification of
individual rare-earth elements. Collection
times from 3 to 5 minutes were chosen to
optimize the yield. The fission products,
dissolved in ~1 mL of warm 3.0 M HNO_3, are

FIG. 7   CLOSE UP OF DISSOLUTION VESSEL FOR
         DISSOLVING THE AEROSOLS FROM THE
         COLLECTION SPOT ON THE MAGNETIC TAPE.

placed onto an extraction chromatography column
using an injection valve. The extraction
chromatography column consists of 20 micrometer
Vydac C_9 resin[a] which is saturated with
DHDECMP. This column, which is slurry
packed,[14] is 5 cm long and 3.2 mm inside
diameter. A pump capable of operating up to 30
MPa delivers DHDECMP-saturated 3.0 M HNO_3 at a
flow rate of 5.0 mL/min to the extraction
chromatography column. The rare-earth elements
are absorbed on this column while most (~97%)
other fission products are washed through
within ~1 min under the above conditions. The
rare-earth fraction is subsequently eluted by
injecting ~2 mL of H_2O onto the extraction
chromatography column. A chromatogram of the
rare-earth group separation is shown in Figure
9. The yield through this first separation
step is ~25% with ~3% contamination from other
fission products viz. Tc, Ru, and I). By
minimizing the volume and acidity of the
separated rare-earth sample, optimized

[a]Trademark of Separations Group, Hesperia,
California, 92345, U.S.A.

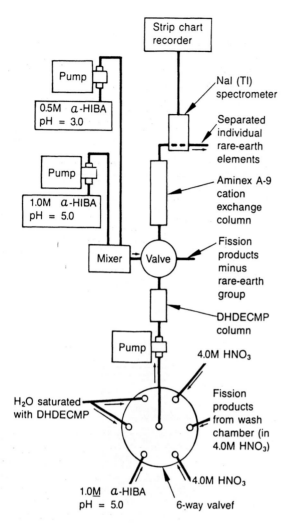

9-6433

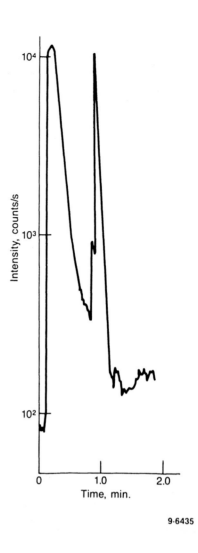

9-6435

FIG. 8   SCHEMATIC DIAGRAM OF THE RADIOCHEMICAL
SEPARATION SYSTEM USED TO SEPARATE
INDIVIDUAL RARE-EARTH FISSION PRODUCT
ELEMENTS FROM MIXED FISSION PRODUCTS.

resolution of the individual rare-earth
elements can be achieved in the second
separation step.

Specific separation of the individual
rare-earth elements is accomplished by cation
exchange. The output from the DHDECMP column
passes through a pneumatically operated stream-
splitting sample-injection valve which is
connected to a cation-exchange column. The
rare-earth fraction from the DHDECMP column is
captured in a sample loop in the injection
valve and is sequentially injected onto the
cation-exchange column where the individual
rare-earth elements are separated. The
cation-exchange column is a 25 cm long x 3.2 mm
inside diameter stainless steel tube which is
slurry packed[14] with 11.5 micrometer Aminex

FIG. 9   CHROMATOGRAM OF GROUP RARE-EARTH
SEPARATION FROM MIXED FISSION
PRODUCTS. TIME ZERO CORRESPONDS TO
THE END OF FISSION PRODUCT COLLECTION.

A-9 cation exchange resin.[a] By elevating the
temperature of the Aminex A-9 column from
17°C (ambient) to 90°C with a thermostatically-
controlled jacket the resolution between the
individual rare-earth elements is increased by
~50%.

Two high-pressure pumps, capable of
operating up to 80 MPa, are used under
microprocessor control to deliver alpha
hydroxisobutyric acid (α-HIBA) of varying
concentrations and pH to the cation-exchange
column. The gradient starts at pH 3.2, 0.7 M
α-HIBA, which allows the rare-earth elements to
adhere to the column, and smoothly increases
within seven minutes to pH 5.0, 1.0M α-HIBA
thereby eluting the rare-earth elements in

[a]Trademark of Bio-Rad Laboratories, Richmond,
California, 94894, U.S.A.

inverse order of atomic number (Z) as shown in Figure 10. The yield through this column is estimated to be >90%. Thus the yield through the entire system is >22%.

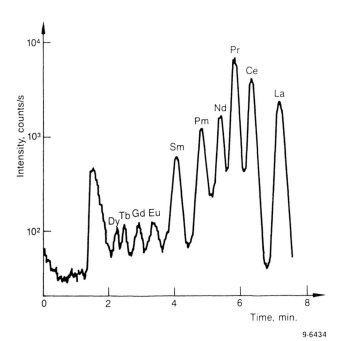

FIG. 10   CHROMATOGRAM OF A SEPARATION OF INDIVIDUAL FISSION-PRODUCT RARE-EARTH ELEMENT PRODUCED BY THE FISSION OF ^{252}Cf. THE TIME SCALE CORRESPONDS TO THE END OF THE FISSION PRODUCT COLLECTION PERIOD AND INCLUDES ALL OF THE CHEMICAL SEPARATION STEPS.

As they are eluted from the column, the individual rare-earth elements are monitored with a shielded 3.81 cm diameter x 3.81 cm thick NaI(Tl) detector which has a 4.76 mm diameter hole drilled diametrically through it for in-stream use. The output of this NaI(Tl) detector is connected via a count-rate meter to a strip chart recorder. The rare-earth fraction of interest contained in ~0.5 mL can either be collected manually or directed through capillary tubing to the detector system by a computer controlled valve. Data acquisition is controlled by the data acquisition computer and is automatically initiated when it receives a signal from the microprocessor that controls the on-line chemistry.

B.   Solvent-Solvent Extraction

The solvent-solvent extraction system is based on the use of in-stream laboratory-scale mixer centrifuges called centrifugal contactors. A block diagram of a centrifugal contactor is shown in Figure 11. It has an effective volume of ~12 mL with ~4 mL in the mixer stage and ~8 mL in the separation stage. The centrifugal contactors are each

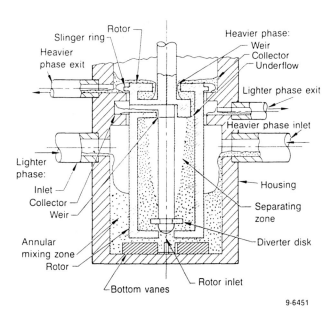

FIG. 11   CROSS-SECTION VIEW OF A CENTRIFUGAL CONTACTOR SHOWING THE INLET AND OUTLET PORTS AND THE MIXING AND SEPARATION CHAMBERS.

individually driven by 1/20 H.P. transistorized motors (0 to 5000 rpm) which offer precise (±1%) speed control even with changing load and line voltage conditions. The time required for one separation stage (i.e., to mix and separate phases) is ~10 s for a two-phase flow rate of 80 mL/min. The weir, whose dimensions control the position of the interface of the two phases, is fixed; however, the weir dimensions are satisfactory as long as the ratio of the densities of the lighter to heavier phase is between ~0.7 to ~0.9. At optimum phase flow rates and contactor rotor speed the purity of each output phase is >99%. To permit some flexibility in the use of various mineral acids and organic solvents three centrifugal contactors were constructed from 304L stainless steel and three were constructed from C-276 Hastalloy.

The chemical separation scheme used for the purification of fission product palladium (see Figure 12) will be described as an example of the use of three centrifugal contactors used in series to extract, strip and back-extract an element of interest. It is based on the method of Alexander, Schindewolf and Coryell.[15] After a two-minute collection the aerosol deposit is moved to the dissolution chamber where the fission products are dissolved in a warm (70°C) solution of 8 M HNO$_3$-0.1 M HCl containing 0.1 mg/mL of Pd, Ru, Rh, and Te carriers. Upon entering the complexation vessel the solution is adjusted to a pH ~1 with 1 M NH$_4$OH. The Pd is then complexed by adding several mL of 1% dimethylglyoxime (DMG)$_2$ in methanol to form

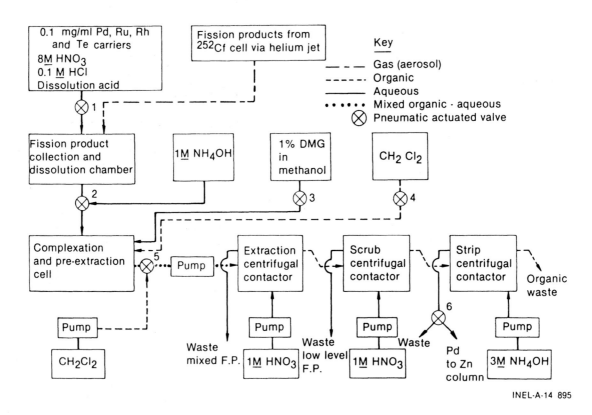

Key

— — — Gas (aerosol)
‑‑‑‑‑‑ Organic
——— Aqueous
• • • • • Mixed organic - aqueous
⊗ Pneumatic actuated valve

FIG. 12   CHEMICAL SEPARATION SCHEME WITH ELAPSED TIME FROM THE END OF FISSION PRODUCT COLLECTION INDICATED AT THE VARIOUS CHEMICAL STEPS.

palladium dimethylglyoxime complex [Pd(DMG)$_2$]. This complex is very specific to nickel and Pd and at pH ~1 forms a precipitate. Vigorous stirring of the mixture and the addition of 15 mL of dichloromethane (CH$_2$Cl$_2$) takes the Pd(DMG)$_2$ up into solution and prevents the plateout of the precipitate onto the container walls. The mixture is then pumped directly into the first contactor.

The first centrifugal contactor completes the extraction of the Pd complex from the fission product solution. The Pd(DMG)$_2$ CH$_2$Cl$_2$ extract from the outlet of the first contactor is gravity fed to the second contactor where it is scrubbed by 1 M HNO$_3$. In the third contactor the Pd(DMG)$_2$ complex is stripped into 3 M NH$_4$OH to separate it from the radioiodine which remains in the organic phase. Following the output of the strip contactor, three different types of radiochemical isolation of the Pd and/or Ag (daughters of short half-life palladium fission products) can be employed for the purpose of distinguishing the parent Pd from the daughter Ag radioactivities.

1. Collection of Palladium and Silver. The Pd and Ag radionuclides are both reduced by passing the 3 M NH$_4$OH strip outlet solution through a 30 mesh zinc column

measuring 0.6 cm dia. x 3.2 cm long. The separation time, from the end of the fission product collection to the start of the first count, is 135 s.

2. Collection of Silver. In this experiment the Ag daughters are isolated by isotopic exchange on a preformed AgCl column (0.6 dia. x 3.2 cm long). The aqueous outlet strip solution is collected in a vessel and acidified with 8 M HNO$_3$ before introduction to the AgCl column (see Figure 13). The Ag is collected on this column before the Pd(DMG)$_2$ begins to form a precipitate. The Ag daughters which had accumulated since the strip stage (third contactor) are thus trapped on the column with the Pd parent activities passing through the AgCl column to waste. The total separation time is 165 s.

3. Collection of Palladium with Silver Initially Removed. The Pd(DMG)$_2$ precipitate is reformed in this experiment by acidifying the outlet strip solution in a collection vessel to pH ~1. The concentration of Pd carrier used for this separation was doubled to provide ample precipitate. After the precipitate formed it was collected by vacuum filtration on a column of glass wool (see Figure 13). The Ag activities which formed while the Pd(DMG)$_2$ was in solution were washed through the column. However, any

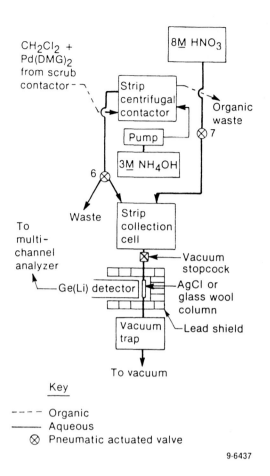

CH$_2$Cl$_2$ +
Pd(DMG)$_2$
from scrub
contactor

Strip
centrifugal
contactor

8$\underline{M}$ HNO$_3$

Organic
waste

Pump

7

3$\underline{M}$ NH$_4$OH

6

Waste

To
multi-
channel
analyzer

Strip
collection
cell

Vacuum
stopcock

Ge(Li) detector

AgCl or
glass wool
column

Vacuum
trap

Lead shield

To vacuum

Key

---- Organic
——— Aqueous
⊗ Pneumatic actuated valve

9-6437

FIG. 13 ISOLATION SCHEME FOR AgCl ISOTOPIC
EXCHANGE AND Pd(DMG)$_2$ PRECIPITATION
EXPERIMENTS.

Ag activities formed after the Pd(DMG)$_2$
precipitate was produced were physically bound
by the precipitate, permitting the observation
of the growth and decay of the Ag daughter
activities. This isolation required 150 s.

V. DATA ACQUISITION AND ANALYSIS

Following each radiochemical isolation
method, sources are prepared or directed to the
detector and counted with a coaxial Ge(Li)
spectrometer by spectral time multiscaling
(i.e., acquisitions of a set of spectra
sequenced in time). As soon as the counting
sequence of one source is complete, another
source is prepared and counted. However,
instead of adding these spectra to the
respective multiscaled spectra previously
accumulated, the multiscaled spectra are all
individually stored on a 43 megaword (12 bit
words) disk. At the end of each experiment,
the individual spectra are examined for the
presence of contaminants or other problems that
would invalidate the data. The respective
spectra, that are acceptable, are then combined
to produce a set of spectra sequenced in time

with improved statistics. These spectra are
subsequently analyzed in the normal manner for
gamma-ray energies, emission rate and
radionuclide assignment.

The 4096 x 4096 channel coincidence
measurements are made with two Ge(Li)
spectrometers accumulating both singles data as
well as coincidence information. The system is
based on a slow-fast coincidence circuit using
zero crossover timing with the data stored
event-by-event on disk or magnetic tape in the
list mode. After the experiment the
accumulated channel pairs are sorted and
spectra in coincidence with particular energy
gates are examined in order to reconstruct the
level scheme. The decay schemes of [157]Sm,

[158]Sm, [152]Pm and [154]Pm have been studied with
this system.

VI. SUMMARY

In this paper we have described a novel
radiochemical separation facility for the study
of short half-life fission products. The
system has been operating reliably and
effectively during the time required for many
experiments. The He-jet system has operated
reliably for periods of one year with
essentially no maintenance. The collection
chamber with moving tape and the in-stream
switching valves have seldom malfunctioned.

To date, the INEL ESOL system has been used
to identify five new rare-earth radionuclides[16,17]
with half-lives as short as 42 s and has been
used to provide separated sources for decay
scheme studies of several rare-earth and other
fission product radionuclides (e.g., [113-115]Pd).
In 1986 the INEL ISOL system became operational
and within a three-year period has identified
seven additional new rare-earth radionuclides[18]
with half-lives as short as ~4 s.

In conclusion there are many advantages to
the present ESOL [252]Cf fission product
generation system for studies of short-lived
fission products: 1) it is less expensive to
operate than alternate fission product
generators (i.e., nuclear reactors), and 2) the
[252]Cf fission product yield curve has a
narrower valley between peak yields and
significant enhancement in the yields of the
heavier rare-earth elements (see Figure 2). As
a result the ESOL facility provides an
opportunity to study those radionuclides that
are not easily observed from [235]U or [239]Pu
fission.

ACKNOWLEDGEMENTS

Many individuals have assisted in the development of this facility. We are particularly grateful to the following individuals: E. G. Grafwallner, E. E. Owen, B. R. Heuring and D. R. Staples.

REFERENCES

1. R. A. ANDERL, J. D. COLE and R. C. GREENWOOD, Nucl. Instr. and Methods, B26 (1978) 333.

2. A. GHIORSO, "Techniques Used for the Production and Identification of the Transplutonium Elements" Lawrence Radiation Laboratory (Berkeley) Preprint UCRL-8714 (1959) p. 21. Talk given at Mendelew Chemistry Conference, Moscow, USSR, March 1959.

3. R. D. MacFARLANE and R. G. GRIFFIOEN, Nucl. Instr. and Methods, 24 (1963).

4. R. D. MacFARLANE, R. A. GOUGH, N. S. OAKEY and D. F. TORGERSON, Nucl. Instr. and Methods, 23 (1964) 285.

5. A. GHIORSO, J. M. NITSCHKE, J. R. ALONSO, C. T. ALONSO, M. NURIMA, G. T. SEABORG, E. K. HULET and R. W. LOUGHEED, Phys. Rev., 33 (1974) 1490.

6. R. A. ANDERL and C. H. CARGO, Proceedings of 27th Conference on Remote Systems Technology (1979).

7. L. D. McISAAC, J. D. BAKER and J. W. TKACHYK, Actinide Removal from ICPP Wastes, U.S. ERDA Report ICP-1080 (1975).

8. L. D. McISAAC, J. D. BAKER, J. F. KRUPA, R. E. LA POINTE, D. H. MEIKRANTZ and N. C. SCHROEDER, Study of Bidentate Compounds for Separation of Actinides from Commercial LWR Reprocessing Waste, U.S. DOE Report ICP-1180 (1979).

9. N. C. SCHROEDER, L. D. McISAAC and J. F. KRUPA, U.S. ERDA Report ENICO-1026 (1980).

10. R. A. LEONARD, G. J. BERNSTEIN, A. A. ZIEGLER and R. H. PELTON, "Annular Centrifugal Contactors for Solvent Extractions", presented at the Symposium on Separation Science and Technology for Energy Application, Gatlinburg, TN (Oct. 1979). To be published in Separation Science and Technology.

11. A. A. SICZEK, J. H. MEISENHELDER, G. J. BERNSTEIN and M. J. STEINDLER, "Solvent Extraction Studies in Miniature Centrifugal Contactors," Radiochim. Acta, 27 (1980) 51.

12. G. J. BERNSTEIN, Argonne National Laboratory, Argonne, Illinois, private communication.

13. ^{252}Cf sources made available through J. E. Bigelow, Coordinator for the National Transplutonium Element Production Program, Oak Ridge, TN, 37830, U.S.A.

14. N. A. PARRIS, Instrumental Liquid Chromatography, Elsevier, New York, (1976) p. 37.

15. J. M. ALEXANDER, U. SCHNIDEWOLF and C. D. CORYELL, Phys. Rev., 111 (1958) 228.

16. R. J. GEHRKE, R. C. GREENWOOD, J. D. BAKER and D. H. MEIKRANTZ, Z. Phys. A-Atoms and Nuclei, 306 (1982) 363.

17. R. C. GREENWOOD, R. J. GEHRKE, J. D. BAKER, D. H. MEIKRANTZ and C. W. REICH, Phys. Rev., 27 (1983) 1266.

18. R. C. GREENWOOD, R. A. ANDERL, J. D. COLE and M. A. LEE, "Nuclei Far From Stability," 5th International Conference, Rosseau Lake, Ontario, Canada (1988) AIP Conference Proceeding 164 (NY, 1988) p. 782.

THE ROLE OF RESEARCH REACTOR UTILIZATION

Isao AOYAMA
Japan Atomic Energy Research Institute
Tokai-mura
Naka-gun, Ibaraki-ken, 319-11
0292(82)5096

Yoshiaki FUTAMURA
Japan Atomic Energy Research Institute
Oarai-machi
Higashi-Ibaraki-gun, Ibaraki-ken, 311-13
0292(67)4300

Eiji SHIRAI
Japan Atomic Energy Research Institute
Tokai-mura
Naka-gun, Ibaraki-ken, 319-11
0292(82)5548

ABSTRACT

The first fission reactor in Japan, called
Japan Research Reactor No.1 (JRR-1), attained
the initial criticality in Aug. 1957. Commissionings of the other three research reactors
succeeded it at Tokai, JAERI. Scientists and
engineers from within and outside JAERI have
utilized these reactors for general research
and development for more than 30 years.
Research subjects are widespreading — fundamental, applied for industry and nuclear
related studies. Two techniques, neutron activation analysis and neutron scattering, are
prominent in these research reactor utilization.
The upgraded JRR-3 will be reoperable in 1990.
The demands expected in the 1990s will almost
be satisfied. Some views of future are considered.

INTRODUCTION

Research reactor operation is an application of fission reaction. It can supply
neutron fields for irradiation and experiment
to many fields of researchers.

The first fission reactor in Japan, called
Japan Research Reactor No.1 (JRR-1), attained
the initial criticality in August 1957, which
was nearly 20 years after the discovery of
fission by Hahn and Strassman. The utilization
with this reactor resulted the breakthrough of
the nuclear research in Japan. Commissionings
of the other three research reactors succeeded
it at the Tokai Research Establishment, Japan
Atomic Energy Research Institute (JAERI).

Scientists and engineers from within and
outside JAERI have utilized these reactors for
general research and development for more than

30 years. This presentation aims at reminding
many researchers of the usefulness of research
reactor with current record of Japan Research
Reactors (JRRs).

Safety operation of research reactors is a
key factor of promoting research reactor utilization. Some news relating to the progress of
competitive research tools let us consider
about the future of the research reactor utilization.

HISTORY OF JRRs

JAERI was at first established as a foundation on 30 November 1955, and was reborn as a
quango on 15 June 1956. Japan Atomic Energy
Committee decided the introducing plan of
research reactors into Japan which are one as
water boiler type and another one as CP-5 type
on 13 January 1956. JAERI contracted with a
company called NAA (USA) to import the former
as JRR-1 on 26 march 1956, and with a company
called AMF (USA) to do the latter as Japan
Research Reactor No.2 (JRR-2) on 15 November
1956.

The above statement describes that the
introduction of research reactors was a
starting point for the peaceful uses of atomic
energy in Japan and also JAERI. Our Japanese,
our members of JAERI, learned at first how to
control the nuclear fission by the operation of
JRR-1.

The third reactor called Japan Research
Reactor No.3 (JRR-3), was designed and constructed domestically except the manufacturing
of reactor fuel and the import of heavy water.
After three years of its construction, it
reached the initial criticality in September

1962. The experience gained through its construction was valuable for the advancement to the next step. JAERI contracted with a Japanese company, HITACHI Works to construct the fourth reactor called Japan Research Reactor No.4 (JRR-4) in January 1962.

Thereafter we had good utilization with these JRRs. JRR-1 was utilized for the fundamental research, especially reactor physics experiments and neutron activation analyses, production of radioisotopes and training of reactor engineers during 11 years. Since the termination of its operations of March 1969, the building and the reactor components left after the mothballing of JRR-1 have been kept as a monument.

JRR-2 has been operated since its initial criticality of October 1960 though it suffered some interuptions. The enrichment of its reactor fuel was reduced from 93% to 45% in November 1987. Its operation is normally 13 cycles/year, 12 days (265.5 h)/cycle with maximum thermal neutron flux 2×10^{14} n/cm^2·s. Its utilization field is neutron beam experiments with eight neutron scattering instruments and a neutron radiography facility, and much irradiation for production of radioisotopes, neutron activation analyses and Research and Development (R&D) of nuclear fuel and materials.

JRR-3 was utilized during 21 years until the termination of operation of March 1983, JRR-3 is now under modification since that time. New JRR-3 will be reoperable in March 1990. The utilization of old JRR-3 was neutron beam experiments with six neutron scattering instru-

ments and two low temperature irradiation loops, which had been utilized for the study of radiation damage and radiation chemistry; tests of neutron detectors and neutron radiography and a treatment of neutron therapy for a brain tumor with a thermal column. Much irradiation were conducted for production of radioisotopes, neutron activation analyses, the study of radiation damage and the study of fission product diffusion with a gas loop.

JRR-4 was constructed as a shielding research reactor. From its initial criticality of January 1965 until 1974, it was utilized mainly for the study of shielding at a thermal level of 1 MW and 2.5 MW though training of reactor operation for nuclear engineers was added because of the coping with the termination of JRR-1 operation. This special purpose utilization was changed to common utilization service in 1974. The rated thermal power was raised to 3.5 MW after the common utilization at 2.5 MW during two and 3/4 years. This reactor has been operated normally 43 weeks a year, four days a week and 6 hours a day with scarcely unscheduled shutdown. The reactor power can be held at a requested level from users within the rated power of 3.5 MW. JRR-4 has been utilized actively, especially for short-term irradiation since the transfer to the common utilization service.

Summary of this section is as follows. JRR-2 and JRR-4 are yet alive. JRR-1 was retired already. JRR-3 was terminated operations, but it will be reborn soon. History of JRRs is shown in FIG. 1.

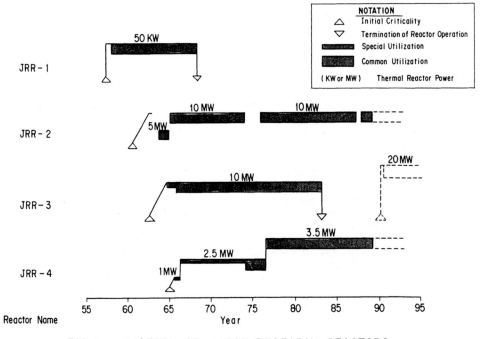

FIG.1   HISTORY OF JAPAN RESEARCH REACTORS

CURRENT UTILIZATION

A wide variety of studies and tests have currently been conducted with JRR-2 and JRR-4 though JRR-3 was terminated operations in 1983. Researchers from within and outside JAERI are composed of physicists, chemists, agriculturists, fishery scientists, medical scientists, dentistry scientists, geologists, applied engineers, nuclear scientists and engineers, and etc..

Research subjects are also widespreading. An example of these ones are listed as refering to the record of FY 1986, as follows.

1. properties of condensed matter
2. radiation damage of solid
3. trace element analysis
4. dynamics of iodine in the soil and plant system
5. effective feeding material for cultivating fishes
6. accumulation of some elements in a liver
7. maps of elemental distribution
8. nuclear fuel and materials study
9. radiation shielding
10. inspection
11. production of radioisotopes
12. neutron transmutation doping (NTD) of silicon
13. training of reactor operation

Many and different substances have also been examined.[1]

Utilization facilities for irradiation and experiment play the role of commonage for these scientists and engineers, who are aiming to study a wide variety of research. The technique of neutron activation analysis (NAA) has been utilized with the pneumatic tube facility since the utilization with JRR-1 for more than 30 years. And also Japanese physicists have nearly 30 year experience on neutron scattering study with the horizontal beam facilities installed in JRR-2 and JRR-3.[2]

These two techniques, NAA and neutron scattering, are prominent in our research reactor utilization as shown in FIG. 2. This tendency resembles the utilization of NBS reactor, USA.[3]

Continuous production of radioisotopes and NTD silicon requires irradiation with both short-term and long-term irradiation facilities throughout a year. Operation schedules of plural reactors can be arranged in consideration of these demands of production. It is advantageous to fulfill these services that there are plural reactors in a center.

Users of FY 1986 are classified as follows: 14 departments within JAERI, 50 faculties of 38 universities, 12 national or related institutes and 14 companies. They are from 65 organizations in total. These organizations are distributed in many places of Japan, as shown in FIG. 3.

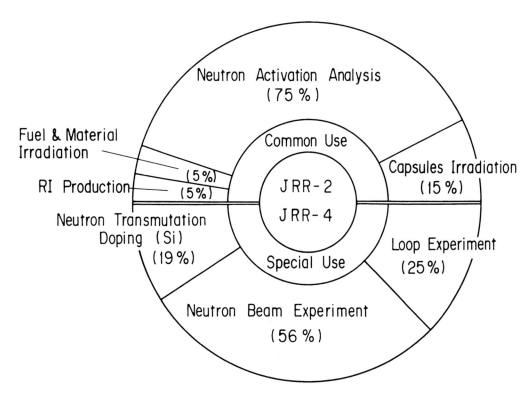

FIG. 2 USER PARTICIPATION AT JAPAN RESEARCH REACTORS IN 1986

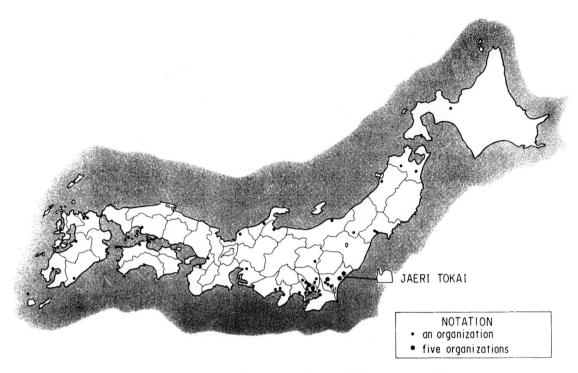

NOTATION
• an organization
• five organizations

FIG.3 USER DISTRIBUTION OF JAPAN RESEARCH REACTORS

JAERI TOKAI

It was not true that all things turned to good direction. There was a low temperature irradiation loop in JRR-3. It had been utilized for the study of radiation damage by physicists within JAERI untill the termination of JRR-3 operation. It was unhappy that they have not continued their study with it since 1984 because their valuable loop became a useless one.

NEW JRR-3

In the 1980s the department of research reactor operation surveyed the utilization trend in reply to the request presented from the users to let JRR-3 raise the neutron flux and modernize its utilization facilities, especially a cold neutron source installation and a new guide hall. The upgrading of JRR-3 was decided after some conceptual design works and has been in progress since 1984. This reactor will be reoperable at the new power level of 20 MW, double the previous level in 1990.

New JRR-3 is a low enriched uranium, light water cooled and moderated, swiming pool-type reactor, which can produce 2×10^{14} n/cm^2·s of maximum thermal neutron flux. Its core is surrounded by a heavy water tank, in which a liquid hydrogen cold neutron source is installed. A beam guide hall in a experimenter building is connected with a reactor room in a reactor building. Seven horizontal beam tubes deliver thermal neutrons to the reactor room.

Two beam guide tubes lead thermal neutrons to the beam hall, where eight windows are arranged for the experimentation. Three beam guide tubes lead cold neutrons to the beam hall, where eight windows are arranged for the experimentation.

Neutron beam experiments will be active in new JRR-3. Twenty instruments will be installed for neutron scattering research by JAERI and universities. An instrument will be installed for ultracold neutron research by a national laboratory. Two instruments will be installed for neutron radiography by JAERI. An instrument will be installed for prompt gamma analysis by JAERI.

New JRR-3 is equipped with following irradiation facilities: 2 hydraulic rabbit facilities, 2 pneumatic tube facilities, 1 activation analysis facility, 1 uniform irradiation facility, 1 rotating irradiation facility, 10 capsule irradiation facilities.

The reoperation of this reactor will satisfy the users in the 1990s.

FUTUR PERSPECTIVE

Many experimenters visit our JRRs from within and outside JAERI. They do their experimentation eagerly all the time of reactor operation. The number of capsules for NAA is increasing, as shown in FIG. 4. How will be research reactor utilization in future?

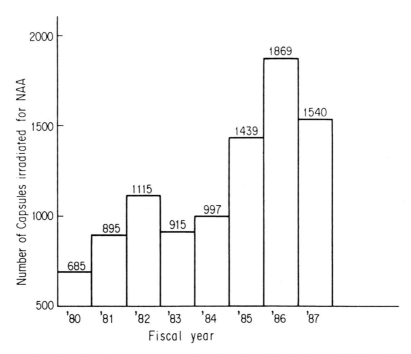

FIG.4 RECORD OF CAPSULES IRRADIATED FOR NAA IN JAPAN RESEARCH REACTORS

Following factors are considered in reply to this question.

1. Number of Researchers and Research Subjects

According to the statistics, annual increasing rate of researchers in Japan is from 3 to 8% during past 20 years. Number of Researchers and Research Subjects is in proportional relation. Therefore it is conceivable that Number of Researchers and Research Subjects will increase gradually.

2. Competitive Research Tools

Recent news about rapid progress of accelerator technology, a début of synchrotron orbit, and the application of Particle Induced X-ray Emission analysis, light quantum activation analysis and Inductively Coupled Plasma-Mass Spectrometry, is interesting. Research reactor utilization still had the large market share, but these competitors are growing fast.

3. Neutron Flux Level

Performance of research reactors relates to the quality and speed of research achievement. The thermal neutron flux of JRR-3 will be 2×10^{14} n/cm^2·s, but there are higher flux $(1-2) \times 10^{15}$ n/cm^2·s reactors as HFIR (ORNL, USA), High Flux reactor (ILL, France) in the world. The Advanced Neutron Source project in USA aims at constructing a highest flux $(8-10) \times 10^{15}$ n/cm^2·s reactor.

4. Number of Reactor Operating Cycle

Some researchers request to increase number of reactor operating cycle. But increasing number of reactor operating cycle will basically result increasing the required number of reactor fuel and the finance for operating a reactor.

5. Reactor Fuel

Japan depends on foreign countries for receiving the supply of fresh enriched uranium and reprocessing of spent research reactor fuel. Smooth progression of these two things is most important for operating research reactors steadily.

6. Finance

There are three finances, which are for reactors, utilization facilities and users, to be considered. These three ones, of course, require sufficient amount for attaining active utilization.

It must be stressed on the third one that the expenses on research for individual users must be increased because they are suffering from travelling and staying fees for experimentalizing at Tokai, JAERI.

Though these factors will be interconnected with each other, the authors personally conclude that research reactor utilization will advance at a slow but steady speed.

CONCLUSION

Research reactor utilization has played an important role in general research and development. Japanese engineers and researchers have gained plenty of experience for utilizing JRRs.

Operation of new JRR-3 will begin within a year. It is a time to remind many researchers of the usefulness of research reactors.

Although the utilization of research reactors in future will be affected by several factors, research reactor utilization will advance well because there are many active researchers representing many fields of research.

REFERENCES

1. I. AOYAMA, H. SAKURAI, and Y. FUTAMURA, "Status of Multi-purpose Research Reactors at the Tokai Research Establishment," in International Atomic Energy Agency ed. Multipurpose Research Reactors. IAEA, Vienna, Austria, 435, (1988)

2. S. HOSHINO, "Progress in Japan," in G.E. BACON ed. Fifty Years of Neutron Diffraction. Adam Hilger, Bristol, 113 (1983)

3. F.J. SHORTEN ed, "NBS Reactor: Summary of Activities July 1983 to June 1984," PB-85-184836, National Technical Information Service (1985)

FIFTY YEARS OF FAST CHEMISTRY:
STUDY OF SHORT-LIVED FISSION PRODUCTS

Krishnaswamy Rengan
Chemistry Department
Eastern Michigan University
Ypsilanti, MI 48197
(313) 487-0106

ABSTRACT

Discovery of nuclear fission by Hahn and Strassmann provided an abundant source of neutron-rich nuclides. The complexity of fission product mixture has been a challenge to nuclear chemists. In the fifties and sixties nuclides with half-lives in the range of several minutes were studied with manual procedures. However the interest in the study of nuclides with half-lives of several seconds led to the development of autobatch and continual chemical separation techniques. The autobatch separation procedures available for fission products are briefly reviewed. Gas-jet systems available for continuous delivery of fission products within a second and techniques available for fast continuous separations are also reviewed.

I.INTRODUCTION

Ever since the discovery of radioactivity, nuclear chemists have been fascinated by the study of short-lived nuclides. Rutherford used a gas-flow system to separate emanation from thorium compounds. Precipitation of MnO_2 was used by Livingood and Seaborg[2] to separate manganese activities from deutron irradiated iron and chromium and from ^4He bombarded vandadium. The discovery of fission by Hahn and Strassmann provided an abundant source of neutron-rich nuclides and initiated a new era in nuclear chemistry.

Nuclear fission produces several hundred nuclides belonging to elements ranging from zinc (Z = 30) to gadolinium (Z = 64). Separating short-lived nuclides from such a complex mixture and studying their decay characteristics has been a challenge to nuclear chemists. Ideally, the nuclide of interest for decay studies should be isolated by both chemical and mass separations. Even in recent years only a few such separations have been achieved. During the first two decades after the discovery of fission fast radiochemical separations provided the only possible means for studying short-lived nuclides. Development of various ion-sources and on-line mass separation techniques have made possible study of short-lived isotopes of several elements. Chemical separation still provides the only possible approach for studying isotopes of a number of elements like selenium for which no suitable ion-source is available.

II. BATCH PROCESSES

In the 1950's and 1960's nuclear chemists were studying nuclides with half-lives in the range of tens of minutes. Radiochemical separation procedures used were those adapted from standard procedures utilized for the analysis of elements. Development of new solvent extraction systems and ion-exchange resins made faster separations possible. The typical procedures took several minutes or longer. Kusaka and Meinke[3] have reviewed the techniques used and included a collection of fast procedures in their Radiochemical Techniques Monograph.

Nuclear chemists turned their attention to nuclides with half-lives of several minutes in the late 1960's and the early 1970's. In order to reduce the separation time the standard techniques were modified. For example, smaller ion-exchange columns were used by Ghiorso et al.[4] to achieve faster separation of actinides while Rengan and Meinke[5] used them for the separation of lanthanides. By proper selection of solvents quicker phase separations were achieved in procedures utilizing solvent extraction. Rengan and Griffin[6] reported a solvent extraction procedure for the separation of praseodymium which took about three minutes.

Most of the procedures developed for studying nuclides with half-lives of several minutes used solvent extraction and/or ion-exchange techniques. The procedures are too slow for studying nuclides with half-lives in seconds. The manual operations, e.g. mixing the phases for solvent extraction, operating the stop cocks, transferring the liquid etc., are slow. For the study of shorter-lived nuclides new, faster procedures had to be developed. Two different approaches have been used. The slower batch procedures were adapted and automated leading to what are known as "**Autobatch**" procedures. An entirely different approach, especially useful for studying nuclides with half-lives in the range of a few seconds, has been to have continuous delivery and separation of fission products. The following sections briefly reviews the techniques used for each category.

III. AUTOBATCH PROCEDURES

Interest in studying fission-product nuclides decaying with half-lives of tens of seconds led nuclear chemists to search for ways to reduce manual handling which are invariably slow. Greendale and Love[7] designed a semi-automated system and used it for the study of short-lived arsenic, tin and antimony. The system transferred the irradiated solution to a chemistry apparatus in about 2 s. By manually operating a few stopcocks they were able to generate hydrides and achieve separation of arsenic, antimony and tin in about 10 s.

Schussler et al.[8] used the first completely automated system for fast separation of halogens from fission products. The entire operation was performed with the use of syringes, stopcocks and valves operated automatically by an electronic programmer. The cerenkov radiation accompanying the neutron burst of the Triga reactor was used to initiate the sequence of operations.

A good illustration of the adaptation of solvent extraction for autobatch process is the procedure used by Trautmann et al.[9] for the separation of technetium from fission products. A schematic of the procedure is shown in **Figure 1**. the capsule containing the irradiated solution was smashed by the impact on the walls of the apparatus and the solution was sucked through two layers of preformed AgCl. The halogen fission products were removed by exchange with AgCl. The AgCl layers were washed with 2 mL of 0.1 M HNO_3 containing tartaric acid (TaA). The fission product solution was collected in 2 mL of $(NH_4)_2S_2O_8$ containing $AgNO_3$. Technetium was oxidized to pertechnetate by persulfate. Next the solution was passed through a layer of chromosorb 202 containing 0.025 M tetraphenyl arsonium chloride (Ph_4AsCl) in $CHCl_3$. The chromosorb layer was washed by 15 mL of 0.1 M HNO_3 containing TaA. The pertechnetate extracted by Ph_4AsCl was then eluted using 10 mL of 2M HNO_3 containing $(NH_4)_2ReO_4$. The washing and elution

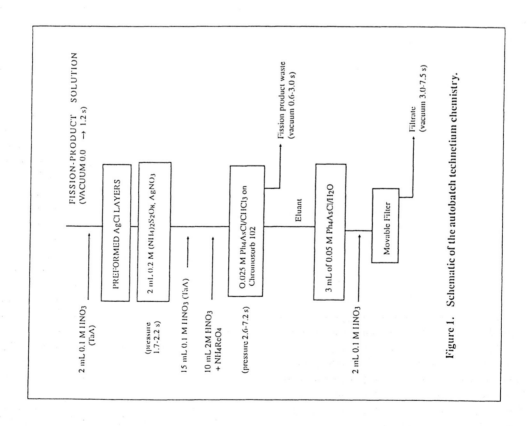

Figure 1. Schematic of the autobatch technetium chemistry.

were accomplished by a combination of pressure and vacuum. The eluant was collected in 3 mL of 0.05 M Ph4AsCl in H2O; under these technetium coprecipitated with Ph4AsReO4. The precipitate was filtered, washed and transferred for counting. The operation of the stopcocks and the application of pressure and vacuum were controlled by electronic programmer.

Production of volatile hydrides followed by selective decomposition and/or trapping had been used for a number of elements. **Figure 2** shows the time sequence of the chemistry steps used by Meyer et al.[10] for the study of arsenic and antimony isotopes. The chemical operation took about 1.9 s. The entire cycle, from the loading of the rabbit to the cleaning of the chemistry apparatus took 30 s, and was controlled by a microprocessor. They carried out over 10,000 cycles of arsenic chemistry using this system.

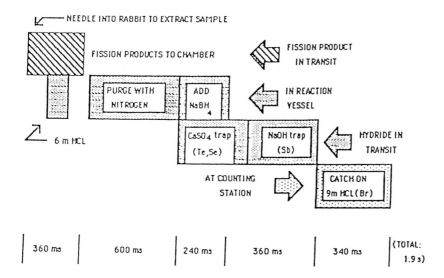

Figure 2. Time sequence of the autobatch arsenic-antimony chemistry.

An autobatch procedure for the separation of lanthanides from fission products developed by Baker et al.[11] used high pressure liquid chromatography. The lanthanides were separated from fission products by extraction chromatography; the separation of individual lanthanides was achieved using cation exchange resin. The separations could be completed in 3 to 5 minutes. They have used the system for studying a number of short-lived lanthanide isotopes.

If the half-life of the nuclide is less than a few seconds autobatch procedures become tedious. Continuous production and separation techniques, if available, are more efficient for such nuclides. The following section briefly discusses the options available for such systems.

IV. CONTINUOUS PROCEDURES

Helium gas-jet systems have been used for a number decades in particle accelerators to transport nuclear reaction products. To carry fission products from a target chamber in the reactor to a chemistry box gas-jet systems have been adapted successfully. The carrier gas should have aerosols for transporting nonvolatile fission products efficiently. Alkali halides and gases containing clusters (e.g. ethylene) have been used. If the continuous separation procedure uses aqueous chemistry, alkali halide aerosol is preferable. Details of gas-jet systems and aerosols are presented in a review article by Rengan and Griffin[12].

Gas-jet systems provide continuous delivery of fission products to a chemistry system in about one second. It is essential that the chemistry system is capable of extracting the fission products form the gas stream and isolate the product of interest in a time comparable with the half-life. Two different approaches have been used in the last two decades for achieving continuous separation. The first approach uses solvent extraction procedures utilizing developments in low-volume, high speed centrifuges for phase separations. The second approach is based on continuous gas phase separation procedures. Both approaches are briefly discussed in the following sections.

A. Continuous Solvent Extraction

Solvent extraction technique is well known. A large volume of literature is available and specific solvent extraction procedures can be identified for essentially all the elements. The phase separation is generally slow and the development of high speed centrifuge[13] has overcome this difficulty. The low volume centrifuges developed recently[14] has further helped to reduce the time required for separation. The high speed centrifuges were initially used in solvent extraction studies[13] and the apparatus is known as the **AKUFVE**, a Swedish abbreviation for "apparatus for continuous measurement of distribution factors in solvent extraction." The system for the study of short-lived fission products is referred to as the **SISAK**, **S**hort **L**ived **I**sotopes **S**tudied by the **AKUFVE** technique. A number of procedures are available and generally the procedures require 2 to 20 s. An example of the technique is described in the following paragraph.

Broden et al.[15-17] have developed a SISAK procedure for the separation of bromine from fission products and used it for the study of $^{86-89}$Br. **Figure 3** shows a schematic of the separation system. Nitrogen gas containing KCl aerosol was used to carry the fission products (FP) from the target chamber to the separation system. The FP were extracted in the degassing unit (Dg) with an acid solution containing iodide and bromide carriers. The solution leaving the degassing was mixed with NaNO2 and passed onto the first mixer-centrifuged separation unit (C1). Iodine and noble gases were extracted into chloroform. The aqueous solution leaving the first unit was mixed with HNO3-KBrO3 solution before entering

the second unit (C2). The bromine was extracted with CCl4 in the second unit. The CCl4 phase was counted as it passes onto the third unit where the bromine was stripped with a reducing solution containing NaHSO3. The aqueous phase was also counted. Buildup of longer-lived bromine was avoided in the aqueous phase. The entire procedure took about 7 s. The applications of the SISAK system for the study of short-lived nuclides have been reviewed by Skarnemark et al.[18].

B. Continuous Gas Phase Separations

The second approach for continuous separations is based on gas phase chemical reactions. Volatile products have been produced by allowing fission products to interact with reactive gases outside the target chamber. The generated products are frequently separated using thermochromatographic technique[19,20] or by selective adsorption[21]. Volatility of the halides formed the basis of such separations. Zendel et al.[21,22] studied selenium and tellurium using volatile products formed outside the target chamber at ~860°C. By appropriate use of adsorbent traps they could study selenium or tellurium.

Volatile products can also be generated *in situ* in the target chamber by reaction of the fission fragments with a reactive gas present in the carrier gas. Separation of the volatile products is achieved by selective adsorption. Rengan et al. have developed procedures for the separation of selenium[23,24] and bromine[25] from fission products in a few seconds. The bromine procedure is described briefly in the following paragraph.

The gas jet set up in the Ford Nuclear Reactor has a ^{235}U target covered by ~2.7 mg cm^{2} aluminum foil; the foil retains heavy fission fragments and provides an enhancement factor of 100 for light fission fragments. A mixture of nitrogen and ethylene was used as the carrier gas. The clusters present in ethylene carried most of the fission products. Selenium, bromine and iodine formed volatile products. A schematic of

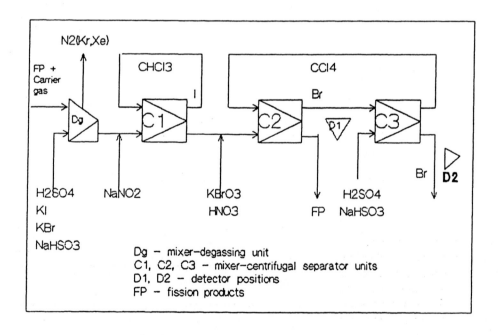

Figure 3. Schematic of continuous bromine extraction system.

the separation is shown in **Figure 4**. A quartz wool filter retained the nonvolatile fission products carried by clusters. The gas stream was then passed through a trap containing quartz wool coated with AgNO3 which retained selenium. An anion exchange trap in front of a HPGe detector selectively retained bromine while most of the iodine along with krypton and xenon passed through. The separation time is about 2 s.

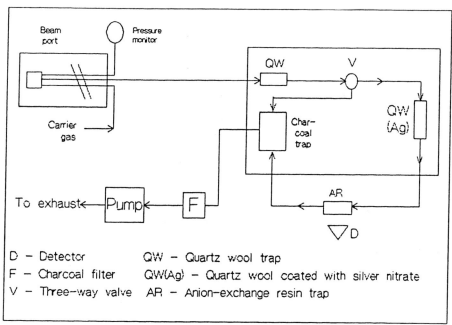

Figure 4. Schematic of continuous gas-phase bromine chemistry system.

The nature of the chemical interaction taking place between the fission fragments and the carrier gas is not known. Experiments are in progress in our laboratory to elucidate the type of reactions in the target chamber. The study will help in the development of gas-phase, fast separations of elements in the fission product mixture.

This paper has given a panoramic view of fast chemical separations - from the early precipitation procedures to the current continuous chemical systems. The development in the last two decades has been dramatic. Future developments may lead to a combination of mass and chemical separation for all the fission product elements. A radiochemistry monograph[26] reviewing the fast radiochemical separations is under preparation.

V. REFERENCES

1. E. RUTHERFORD, "A Radioactive Substance Emitted from Thorium Compounds," *Phil. Mag., Series 5, xlix*, 1 (1900).

2. J.J. LIVINGOOD and G.T.SEABORG, "Radioactive Manganese Isotopes," *Phys. Rev., 54*, 391 (1938).

3. Y. KUSAKA and W.W. MEINKE, *Rapid Radiochemical Separations, National Academy of Sciences Radiochemistry Techniques Monograph, NAS-NS-3104* (1961).

4. A. GHIORSO, B.G. HARVEY, G.R. CHOPPIN, S.G. THOMPSON and G.T. SEABORG, "New Element Mendelevium, Atomic Number 101," *Phys. Rev., 98*, 1518 (1955).

5. K. RENGAN and W.W. MEINKE, "Rapid Radiochemical Separation and activation Analysis of Rare Earth Elements, "*Anal. Chem., 36*, 157 (1964).

6. K. RENGAN and H.C. GRIFFIN, "Rapid Radiochemical Isolation of Praseodymium from Fission Products," *Radichem. Radioanal. Lett., 29*, 253 (1977).

7. A.E. GREENDALE and D.L. LOVE, "A System for Rapid Handling of an Irradiated Solution," *Nucl. Instr. Meth., 23*, 209 (1963).

8. H.D. SCHUSSLER, W. GRIMM, M. WEBER, V. THARUN, H.O. DENSCHLAG and G. HERRMANN, "A system for Rapid Radiochemical Separations from Aqueous Solutions," *Nucl. Instr. Meth., 73*, 125 (1969).

9. N. TRAUTMANN, N. KAFFRELL, H.W. BEHLICH, H. FOLGER, G. HERRMANN, D. HUBSCHER, and H. AHRENS, "Identification of Short-Lived Isotopes of Zirconium, Niobium, Molybdenum and Technetium in Fission by Rapid Solvent Extraction Techniques," *Radiochem. Acta., 18*, 86 (1972).

10. O.G. LIEN III, P.C. STEVENSON, E.A. HENRY, R.P YAFFE and R.A. MEYER, "Autobatch: I. System Description for the Automated Batchwise Isolation and Study of Short-Lived Fission Products," *Nucl. Instr. Meth., 185,* 351 (1981).

11. J.D. BAKER, R.J. GEHRKE, R.C. GREENWOOD, and D.H. MEIKRANTZ, "Advanced System for the Separation of Rare-Earth Fission Products," *J. Radioanal. Chem. 74,* 117 (1982).

12. K. RENGAN and H.C. GRIFFIN, "Gas Jet System for the Radiochemical study of Fission Products," *Artificial Radioactivity,* K. Narayana Rao and H.J. Arnikar (editors), Tata McGraw-Hill, New Dehli.

13. H. REINHARDT and J. RYDBERG, "Solvent Extraction Studies by the AKUFVE Method. II. A New Centrifuge for Absolute Phase Separation," *Acta Chem. Scand., 23,* 2773 (1969).

14. G. SKARNEMARK, P.O. ARONSSON, D. BRODEN, J. RYDBERG, T. BJORNSTAD, N. KAFFRELL, E. STENDER and N. TRAUTMANN, "An Improved System for Fast, Continuous Chemical Separations ("SISAK 2") in Nuclear Spectroscopic Studies," *Nucl. Instr. Meth., 171,* 323 (1980).

15. K. BRODEN, "Some Applications of the SISAK Technique to Nuclear Sepctroscopic Studies, PhD. thesis submitted to Chalmers University, Goteborg, 1984.

16. K. BRODEN, G. SKARNEMARK, T. BJORORSTAD, D. ERIKSEN, I HALDORSEN, N. KAFFRELL, E. STENDER and N. TRAUTMANN, "Rapid Continuous Separation Procedures for Zirconium, Niobium, Technetium, Bromine and Iodine from Complex Reaction Product Mixtures," *J. Inorg. Nucl. Chem., 43,* 765 (1981).

17. G. SKARNEMARK, K. BRODEN, N. KAFFRELL, S.G. PRUSSIN, N. TRAUTMANN, K. RENGAN, D. ERIKSEN, D.F. KUSNEZOV and R.A. MEYER, "Subshell Closure Effects on the Collectivity of ^{88}Kr and the Beta Decay of ^{88}Br to Levels in ^{88}Kr," *Z. Phys. A., 323,* 407 (1986).

18. G. SKARNEMARK, M. SKALBERG, J. ALSTAD and T. BJORNSTAD, "Nuclear Studies with the Fast On-Line Chemical Separation system SISAK," *Physica. Seripta, 34,* 597 (1986).

19. J. ZVARA, O.L. KELLER, Jr., R.J. SILVA and J.R. TARRANT, "Thermochromatography of Bromides. A Proposed Technique for the Study of Transactinide Element Chemistry," *J. Chromatog., 103,* 77 (1975).

20. U. HICKMANN, N. GREULICH, N. TRAUTMANN, G. GAGGLER, H. GAGGLER-KOCH, B. EICHLER and G. HERRMANN, "Rapid Continuous Radiochemical Separations by Thermochromatography in Connection with a Gas-Jet Recoil-Transport System," *Nucl. Instr. Meth., 174,* 507 (1980).

21. M. ZENDEL, E. STENDER, N. TRAUTMANN and G. HERRMANN, "Chemical Reactions in a Gas-Jet Recoil-Transport System: Continuous Separation Procedure for Selenium and Tellurium from Fission Products," *Nucl. Instr. Meth., 153,* 149 (1978).

22. M. ZENDEL, N. TRAUTMANN, and G. HERRMANN, "Decay of ^{85,88}Se to Levels in $^{85-88}$Br," *J. Inorg. Nucl. Chem., 42,* 1387 (1980).

23. K. RENGAN, J. LIN, M. ZENDEL and R.A. MEYER, "On-Line System for the Isolation and Study of 0.5 to 30 second Selenium Fission Products with Simultaneous Suppression of Daughter Bromine Activity," *Nucl. Instr. Meth., 197,* 427 (1982).

24. K. RENGAN, J. LIN, T.N. MASSEY, M. ZENDEL, and R.A. MEYER, "Use of Organo-Metallic Reactions for the Isolation and Study of Short-Lived Selenium Fission Products and Simultaneous Suppression of Daughter Bromine Activity," *Radiochem. Radioanal. Lett., 50,* 383 (1982).

25. K. RENGAN and H.C. GRIFFIN, "A Gas-Jet System for the Study of Short-Lived Light Fission Products," *J. Radioanal. Nucl. Chem., 98,* 255 (1986).

26. K. RENGAN and R.A. MEYER, "Ultrafast Chemical Separations," *Radiochemistry Techniques Monograph* to be published by the National Academy of Sciences.

Acknowledgments

The author wishes to acknowledge Drs. R. A. Meyer and G. Skarnemark for giving permission to reproduce figures 2 and 3 respectively.

THE CORNELL UNIVERSITY COLD NEUTRON BEAM FACILITY

DAVID D. CLARK, TAKASHI EMOTO, CAROL G. OUELLET, ELISSA PEKRUL, J. SCOTT BERG
Cornell University
Ward Laboratory
Ithaca, NY 14853-7701
(607)255-3480

ABSTRACT

A cold neutron beam facility nearing completion at the Cornell University 500-kW TRIGA Mark II reactor is described. Designed to optimize beam quality for basic and applied research in which low backgrounds are especially important, it uses a cold neutron source in the reactor reflector and a curved 13-m neutron guide. The only operating US cold sources are at Brookhaven and NIST and emphasize long-wavelength neutrons for condensed matter research. Our system has a different purpose: a nearly pure subthermal beam with no fast neutrons or gamma rays and a target station remote from other experiments. Cold sources are generally considered to be complex, costly and hazardous. For a medium power university reactor we chose mesitylene as a proven cold moderator safer than hydrogen or methane and cool it with copper cold fingers instead of circulating helium gas. Design details, initial operating tests, and experimental plans are described.

I. INTRODUCTION

A project to design and construct a cold neutron beam facility at the Cornell University 500-kW TRIGA Mark II reactor is in its final phase. The goal of the project is to make available a low background neutron beam for basic and applied research. Cold sources and neutron guides were developed in Europe and are relatively common there. (References to the early work are listed by Clark.[1]) In the US only the Brookhaven 60-MW High Flux Beam Reactor and the National Institute of Standards and Technology (NIST) 20-MW reactor have operating cold sources; the University of Missouri at Columbia plans one as part of an upgrade to 30 MW. A major driving force behind those plans is the use of cold neutron/neutron guide (CN/NG) systems that emphasize long-wavelength neutrons for condensed matter research using instruments such as small angle neutron scattering apparatus and triple axis spectrometers. The utility of CN/NG systems for such research has been amply demonstrated and such programs are very appropriate for large

high flux reactors with 24-hour-per-day operation.

However, the superiority of cold source/neutron guide systems for beam research has not been as fully exploited. Our aim is to serve those other experiments for which CN/NG systems also have unique and valuable properties -- namely, experiments requiring a beam of subthermal neutrons with negligible contamination by fast neutrons and gamma rays. If, as in our plans, it is also possible to locate the target station for the emergent beam in an isolated area, remote from other experiments, a very low background facility is obtained, suitable for a variety of experiments in basic and applied areas.

A secondary goal of the project is to show that a moderate power university reactor (7.5×10^{12} n/cm^{2}s central flux) can be competitive and useful in state-of-art research. Cold neutron sources are generally considered to be complex, costly, and potentially hazardous systems, feasible only at national laboratories. In our design we have chosen mesitylene as the cold moderator, located in a chamber inside a beam tube within the reflector region of the reactor; unlike hydrogen and methane, mesitylene is liquid at room temperature and is not explosive. It is known[2] to be an effective moderator at cryogenic temperatures. We cool it by copper cold fingers connected to a cryogenic refrigerator outside the biological shield of the reactor, avoiding the circulation of cryogenic liquids or gases within the shield.

In a series of in-pile tests begun in November 1988 and continuing currently, design parameters relating to nuclear heating, radiation effects, and moderating efficiency of the source geometry are being measured and interpreted in terms of simple models including Monte Carlo simulations. The results of these tests and calculations will lead to the final design. That design, as well as our operating experience with the final system will be available to others for possible adaptation to their reactors.

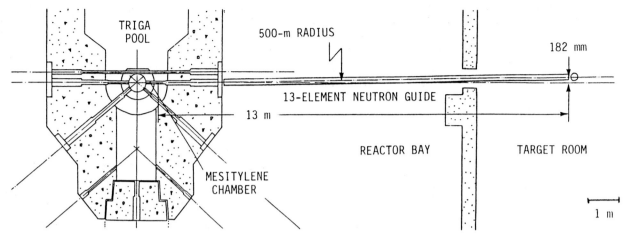

FIGURE 1. PLAN VIEW OF REACTOR, NEUTRON GUIDE, AND TARGET ROOM.

II. DESCRIPTION OF THE FACILITY

The overall layout is shown in Figure 1. The reactor is a Mark II TRIGA with 20%-enriched 8-wt% UZrH stainless-steel-clad fuel elements. The core proper is surrounded by a 30.5-cm wide graphite reflector. At the licensed maximum power of 500 kW the approximate values of the unperturbed fluxes at the cold source position are 1.5×10^{12} n/cm^{2}s thermal (using Au foils), 1.9×10^{11} epithermal (using Cd-covered Au), and 1.5×10^{11} fast (using Ni, threshold = 2.9 MeV). The gamma-ray field is ~8×10^6 R/hr. The principal components of the system are discussed in the following subsections.

A. Cold Source

The chamber for the cold mesitylene moderator is a thin-walled aluminum container within the graphite reflector; it is positioned inside a 15.4-cm beamport about 21 cm from the core edge. Connected to it are stainless-steel filling and draining tubes and copper-rod cold fingers; appropriate shields to reduce nuclear heating by the gamma-ray field and to reduce heat transfer by thermal radiation are provided.

Mesitylene, which is 1,3,5-trimethyl-benzene, has been studied as a cold moderator by Utsuro et al.[2] It is sufficiently effective for our purposes and is much safer and simpler for use at a medium-sized on-campus reactor than liquid hydrogen or solid methane. Because it freezes at 228K and boils at 437K, the handling system for it, consisting of cold chamber, connecting tubing, and storage reservoir does not have to be designed to withstand large or abrupt pressure changes in the event of loss of cooling. The system is closed, to avoid either contaminating the mesitylene or releasing it, since it is carcinogenic and mildly toxic.

The exact geometry of the cold chamber (and of the nuclear and thermal heat shields) has yet to be decided on the basis of current tests and calculations, but the chamber will be similar to the existing 500-cm^3 capacity trial model, which is a right circular cylinder, 12 cm ID by 5 cm deep with a 2.5 cm by 5.5 cm by 3 cm deep re-entrant hole on the downstream face -- i.e., facing the entering end of the first neutron guide element. Monte Carlo simulations using moderating parameters for cold mesitylene from work by Utsuro[3] show that the final chamber, optimized for efficacy in providing cold neutrons, can be smaller than the trial model. (Note that because the source is required to supply neutrons to only one guide, it can be smaller than most other cold sources.) This simplifies fitting the source, its nuclear and thermal heat shields, and their supports into the 15.4-cm ID beam port.

The chamber, its filling and draining tubes, parts of the cooling system (see next sub-section), and the first guide element are all housed together with their support structure in a single vacuum enclosure that forms the upstream section of the beamport plug that contains all the in-reactor components of the system.

B. Cryogenic System

The cyrogenic system is comprised of a cryogenic refrigerator outside the biological shield of the reactor and oxygen-free, high-conductivity (OFHC) copper heat conductors between the refrigerator and the cold chamber and its heat shield. This method of cooling avoids the operational, safety, and regulatory problems of circulating cryogenic liquids or gases within the reactor shield. The simplicity of cooling by conduction is partially offset by the limited rate of heat removal by conduction (and by the generation of heat within the copper conductors by nuclear radiation), but the rate can be sufficient if there is not a strict requirement that the neutrons be the coldest possible. This applies in our case, since the additional downward shift in the neutron energy spectrum obtained by lowering the physical temperature of the mesitylene much below 40K is slight.[2]

In the present design, the cold chamber is cooled by two 1.43-cm diameter copper rods, ~270 cm long, connected to the 20K stage of a cryogenic refrigerator. A thin-walled cylindrical copper "active" heat shield surrounding the chamber is cooled by two 1.91-cm ID, 2.54-cm OD copper tubes, ~270 cm long, connected to the 77K stage of the refrigerator. These tubes surround the rods and so also act as their "active" heat shields. All the copper parts are OFHC. The "active" shields are wrapped in "passive" heat shields consisting of layers of reflecting material separated by insulating layers. The term "active" denotes shields that are connected to a refrigerator, whereas "passive" shields are merely reflecting and insulating layers. In regions of low ambient gamma-ray flux the passive shields can be aluminized Mylar, but that material disintegrates readily in high fluxes, where the layers can, for example, be aluminum foils separated by stainless-steel mesh as an insulator.

The refrigerator that has been available to us in the developmental phases has been a rather well-worn second-hand hydrogen liquefier. It will have to be replaced by a new unit for us to reach the desired moderator temperature of 40K or below. A permanent unit will be purchased once its specifications can be established after the current tests and calculations for the cold chamber and heat shield designs are completed.

C. Neutron Guide

The guide will consist of 13 1-m long elements of a standard design purchased from Neutronentechnik.[4] The reflecting surface is Ni evaporated on glass; the internal dimensions are 2 cm wide by 5 cm high. The elements are to be placed in the formation of a sequence of tangents to a circle of 500-m radius. The first three are located within the reactor shield, and the guide will extend across the reactor bay into an adjacent room which is well-isolated from all other experimental areas that use or generate nuclear radiations. The interior of the guide will be evacuated to avoid scattering and absorption of the neutrons. The elements outside the reactor shield are to be covered with a borated plastic, and a 15.2-cm by 17.1-cm tunnel of 1.27-cm thick lead shield will surround the guide. Properties of neutron guides are well-known. We have used Monte Carlo

methods to calculate for our particular geometry both the transmission of the guide, and the spatial distribution across the exit aperture as functions of neutron energy. The transmission is defined as the fraction of neutrons entering the guide within the critical angle for total external reflection that emerge from the guide.

III. LOW-POWER TRIALS

Low-power trials using the current version of the cold source have been conducted to assess the adequacy of our design methods and models, to observe some operating characteristics of the system, and to measure nuclear heating and other radiation effects before completing the design of the final, permanent system. These trials were considered worthwhile even though the lowest temperature attainable with the current model has been limited to 110K by the inadequate cooling capacity of the old refrigerator. (An earlier "bench" model, shorter in length and somewhat less complex, had been built and tested by Lydia Young[5] when the refrigerator was in better condition; it had reached 23K.) The results of the trials have been very valuable for the final design phase.

Runs were conducted over a two-week period in November 1988 at 5kW with mesitylene in the cold source chamber at 300K and at 140K. The runs were carried out to measure the neutron spectrum at the exit of a temporarily installed guide of five meters total length. A slow chopper was mounted at the exit, and a Li-6 glass scintillator neutron detector was placed two meters downstream from the chopper. The chopper consists of a stator and a rotating disk, both with a Gd-loaded coating except for a narrow slit. The spatial distribution across the exit was measured with a narrow BF_3 counter. Both the shift in the neutron energy spectrum and the spatial distribution agreed within experimental error with calculated values corresponding to the moderator temperature and the guide tube length that were used.

During the same two-week period short runs were conducted at 100 kW to measure radiolysis of the mesitylene and nuclear heating of cold source components. The former was small, within expected values from the literature. The gamma-ray heating was large, showing that a careful design of the shielding will be necessary for the permanent system. Currently further heating and shielding tests are being carried out with a special probe designed for the purpose instead of using the complete cold source beamport plug.

In the current (final) design phase the size and shape of the mesitylene chamber and of the nuclear heating shield will be optimized using Monte Carlo simulations and the results of the low-power trials.

IV. ANTICIPATED PROPERTIES OF THE BEAM

The neutron beam at the guide exit in the target room can be expected to be a subthermal beam with an average intensity equivalent to a thermal neutron flux of about 5×10^7 n/cm^{2}s and to be nearly purely subthermal, with very few fast neutrons and gamma rays. Both basic and applied experiments in which low background is a requirement will be greatly facilitated. For example, most capture gamma-ray experiments are of that type. The usual external beams from a reactor have fast neutron and gamma ray components that originate in the core along with the desired thermal neutrons. Filters, collimators, and shielding help, but one still finds many detector events occur due to gamma rays in the beam that scatter from the sample itself and from structural parts, shielding, and beam stop, to fast neutrons in the beam that do the same things, and to thermal neutrons in the beam that scatter from the sample and then produce capture gamma rays in structure, shielding and beam stop instead of being absorbed in the sample to produce the desired gamma rays. Capture gamma experiments done with the cold neutron beam will show none of these interferences except those due to the last effect, (sub)thermal neutrons scattered by the sample. Because only subthermal neutrons will be present, collimators, shielding, and beam stop can be much less bulky, and less likely to produce background, since absorption mean free paths are short and no moderating properties are required.

Absence of background production is a major advantage, but there are two more advantages, both of which improve the sensitivity (i.e., count rate per milligram): the detector can be placed much closer to the target since the beam is so much cleaner, and reaction rates are larger than for thermal neutrons since capture cross sections are nearly always proportional to 1/v. The closer placement of detectors, and the higher reaction rate, make the use of coincidence methods feasible without a severe loss in counting rates, especially if one uses large-memory multiparameter multichannel analyzers for data acquisition and analysis, so that the selection of which combinations of gamma-ray lines are most useful can be done in the subsequent off-line analysis.

V. ANTICIPATED USES OF THE BEAM

Both basic and applied uses of the beam are foreseen. Among the basic nuclear physics experiments are capture reaction studies, both gamma-ray and conversion electron, for decay scheme data. We expect to do studies of isomeric states -- in particular, fission isomers -- using a timing detector, previously developed and used by us,[6,7] that is specifically designed for timing the moment of neutron capture. Another category is the measurement of low cross section reactions such as the subthermal cross section for the U-238 (n,f) reaction.

Considerable use of the beam will be for analytical applications. A major technique to be exploited is prompt gamma neutron activation analysis (PGNAA). Lindstrom and others have pointed out in several papers[8,9] the large gains in sensitivity for PGNAA that cold neutron beams provide. The gains over existing PGNAA facilities can be one to two orders of magnitude. Development of coincidence methods will also extend the technique. We expect to see PGNAA used for analyses of multi-element geological samples on the one hand and for measurements of trace amounts in nearly pure samples of materials science interest on the other hand.

Another existing technique that will be more widely used with the availability of the cold neutron beam is neutron depth profiling (NDP). This useful technique exploits neutron reactions that result in the emission of monoenergetic alpha particles or protons -- for example, the B-10(n,α)Li-7 reaction to determine the depth of boron layers by correlating the reduced energy of an emerging alpha particle with the length of its path from the point of origin to the surface of the sample. As currently practiced, the method is limited, however, to those few elements, all of the low atomic number, which exhibit a suitable exothermic reaction.

We plan to explore and develop an extension of NDP to a much greater range of elements and depths by exploiting the prompt conversion electrons (PCEs) that are emitted by many elements undergoing neutron capture. The favorable aspects of using PCEs are (1) they are emitted in monoenergetic groups ranging from a few to several hundred keV, (2) they are emitted with usable intensities by many elements with atomic number above about 20, (3) elements can be identified by their PCE spectra, and (4) above about 20 keV their energies can be measured with cooled Si(Li) detectors with high intrinsic efficiency and FWHM resolution around one keV. There is even a tantalizing but remote prospect of spatial localization of the nuclei emitting PCEs. Unfavorable aspects are (1) PCE spectra are often complex and (2) the straggling in range and in energy loss per unit path for electrons could present a problem. At this stage we have begun compiling a list of possibly useful nuclides, and will shortly begin some experimental trials using radioactive nuclides. These trials will draw upon our previous experience with conversion electron studies in neutron capture reactions and in radioactivity studies. An initial list of some elements and their properties appears in Table 1. As far as we know this will be the first attempt to use PCEs as an analytical tool.

TABLE 1. SOME POSSIBLE ELEMENTS FOR DEPTH PROFILING WITH CONVERSION ELECTRONS.

Z	Element	Target Isotope	Natural Abund. %	Cross Section barns	Electron Energy keV	Electron Intensity %/capture in element	Range in Si μm	Energy Loss in Si keV/μm	Level Half-life
26	Fe	Fe-56	91.72	2.6	7.4	> 44.	0.7	5.6	98 ns
					115	0.088	70	0.7	8.6 ns
45	Rh	Rh-103	100	11	28.2	13.2	7	1.9	
					54.3	3.9	21	1.15	
					74	11.5	34	0.92	
64	Gd	Gd-157	15.65	2.55 X 10³	29	25	7.4	1.85	2.53 ns
					72	26	32.5	0.95	2.53 ns
69	Tm	Tm-169	100	105	30	25.7	7.6	1.8	1.7 ns
					90.3	5	47	0.82	
					145	3.14	100	0.39	
73	Ta	Ta-181	99.988	20.5	46.9	70	16	1.25	
75	Re	Re-187	62.6	77.8	34.2	7.1	9.6	1.6	
					51.3	19.2	18.5	1.2	
					93.4	1.2	49	0.8	
79	Au	Au-197	100	98.7	21.52	15.0	4.3	2.35	
					40.84	24.6	12.6	1.4	
					41.46	11.8	13	1.4	
					43.27	10.6	14	1.35	
					87.54	6.16	45	0.85	
					111.70	3.08	68	0.73	
					180.54	2.94	140	0.355	

VI. ACKNOWLEDGMENTS

The project was conceived in 1979 and has been carried forward as a thesis project by two successive Ph.D. students, with a two-year hiatus between them. Accounts of their work have been published.[1,5] Funding has been from University sources only. Dr. W. L. Whittemore of General Atomic called our attention to the studies of mesitylene by Utsuro. We thank the staff of Ward Laboratory for reactor operations and other assistance.

REFERENCES

1. D. D. CLARK and T. EMOTO, "Low-background Neutron-capture Gamma-ray Facility," p. 596 in Capture Gamma-Ray Spectroscopy 1987, K. ABRAHAMS and P. VAN ASSCHE, editors. Institute of Physics, Bristol and Philadelphia, (1988).

2. M. UTSURO, M. SUGIMOTO, and Y. FUJITA, "Experimental Study on a Cold Neutron Source of Solid Methylbenzene," Annu. Rep. Res. Reactor Inst. Kyoto Univ. 8, 17 (1975).

3. M.UTSURO, "A Simple Neutron Scattering Study of Proton Motion in Methyl Compounds," J. Phys. C: Solid State Phys. 9, L171 (1976).

4. Neutronentechnik, Oststrasse 5, Bad Wörishofen, FRG (Dr. E. Steichele).

5. LYDIA YOUNG, "The Design and Construction of a Cold Neutron Source for Use in the Cornell TRIGA Reactor," Ph.D. Thesis, Cornell University, 1982; LYDIA YOUNG and DAVID D. CLARK, "Design and Test of a Cryogenic System for a Cold Neutron Source for the Cornell TRIGA Reactor," Atomkernenergie Kerntechnik 44 (Supplement), 383 (1984).

6. DAVID D. CLARK, V. O. KOSTROUN, and NORMAN E. SIEMS, "Identification of an Isomer in Ag-110 at 1-keV Excitation Energy," Phys. Rev. C12, 595 (1975).

7. D. D. CLARK, J.R. BOYCE, E.T. CASSEL, and S. C. MCGUIRE, "Low-Lying Levels of U-236 from Investigation of the $K^\pi = 4^-$ Two-quasineutron Isomer in (n,γ) and (n,e) Experiments," p. 586 in Neutron Capture Gamma-ray Spectroscopy, R. E. CHRIEN and W. R. KANE, editors. Plenum Press, New York (1979) and STEPHEN CRAIG MCGUIRE, "An Experimental Investigation of the $K,J^\pi = 4,4^-$ K-Forbidden Isomer in U-236 via Thermal Neutron Capture," Ph.D. Thesis, Cornell University, 1979.

8. R. M. LINDSTROM and D. L. ANDERSON, "Analytical Neutron-Capture Gamma-Ray Spectroscopy," p. 810 in Capture Gamma-Ray Spectroscopy and Related Topics 1984, S. RAMAN, editor. American Institute of Physics, New York (1985).

9. R. M. LINDSTROM, R. ZEISLER, and M. ROSSBACH, "Activation Analysis Opportunities Using Cold Neutron Beams," J. Radioanal. Nucl. Chem. 112, 321 (1987).

NEUTRON-GAMMA HODOSCOPE DETECTION OF FISSILE MATERIALS

A. DeVolpi
Argonne National Laboratory
9700 South Cass Avenue
Argonne, IL 60439
(312) 972-4598

ABSTRACT

The neutron-gamma hodoscope has been developed to make use of two aspects of the fission process that occur during severe safety testing of nuclear reactor fuel: fission-product heating that induces realistic effects in the fuel and penetrating radiation that enables the imaging of fuel behaviour. During in-pile transient reactor experiments, the radiation which escapes from the test fuel, its surrounding coolant, and a thick-walled container is detected by a large collimated array that produces cineradiographic images. Phenomena observed in hundreds of destructive experiments have included pre-failure fuel motion, cladding breach, and post-failure fuel motion. On the basis of this successful 25-year experience, application of hodoscope techniques to arms control treaty verification is now being studied.

INTRODUCTION

The fission process provides unique signatures that are widely utilized in the detection and quantification of fissile and fertile materials. In addition to nuclear materials accountancy and safeguards, extensive application has occurred in demonstrating operational and safety limits of nuclear reactor fuels[1] by means of cineradiography.[2] In-pile radiographic imaging of reactor fuel under transient conditions was devised for the purpose of observing destructive motion of the fuel sealed in containers or flow loops. This paper describes the development of the neutron-gamma hodoscope array, which continues to gather fuel behaviour cineradiographic information from expensive experiments that are stressed to destruction. The first hodoscope was installed at the TREAT reactor in Idaho; a similar system has since been placed into operation at the CABRI reactor in France; various hodoscope designs have been considered for other facilities.[3]

FUEL-MOTION DIAGNOSTICS

Fuel-motion diagnostics is a highly sophisticated application of the fission process: Penetrating radiation from fission is used to image the internal effects of fission heating within the sample. Because of the reactive nature of the coolants (typically liquid sodium) and the radiological nature of the fuel, samples are protected by thick-walled containers, as shown for example in Fig. 1.

Fission heating, if induced beyond operational levels, can cause the following effects in nuclear fuel: internal fuel motion before cladding failure, breach of the cladding, post-failure fuel and cladding motion, and flow blockages. These and other effects in a sample inserted in a nuclear reactor might also result in changes in axial power profiles and power-coupling to the fuel. Fuel samples range from fuel pins or slugs to multiple-pin assemblies. The fast-neutron and gamma-ray hodoscope has been able to collect data on these and other effects, resulting in diagnostic data that have given direct insight into time-dependent behaviour relevant to reactor fuel safety.

Conventional radiography uses x-ray, gamma, or neutron transmission to provide high-resolution images. The hodoscope in the reactor safety program depends largely on fission neutrons emitted by the fuel under test. A cutaway view of the TREAT reactor is shown in Fig. 2. The hodoscope yields cineradiographic data by recording two-dimensional images at millisecond intervals. Therefore, specific phenomena can be identified, such as the time and location of cladding failure and the quantity of displaced fuel. Up to now the hodoscope has been used thousands of times in hundreds of experiments with a high degree of reliability.

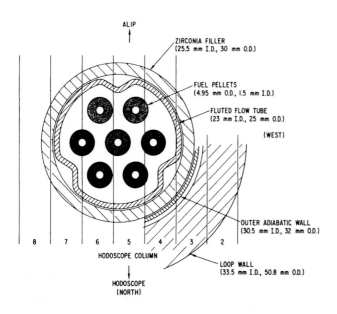

FIGURE 1   EXAMPLE OF A THICK-WALLED CONTAINER FOR TREAT EXPERIMENTS

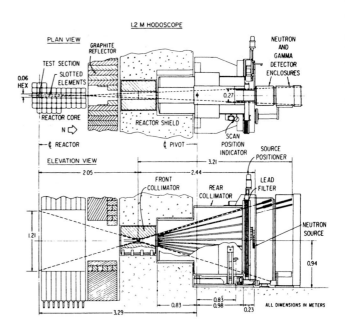

FIGURE 3   PLAN AND ELEVATION VIEWS OF 1.2 M HODOSCOPE AT TREAT

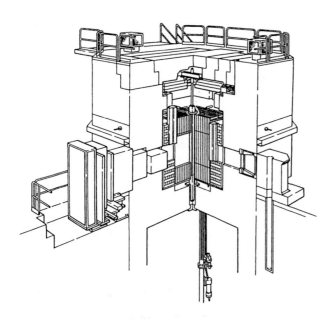

FIGURE 2   TREAT LAYOUT, SHOWING HODOSCOPE AT ONE (LEFT-HAND) SIDE OF REACTOR

As an instrument system, the primary features of the hodoscope are a multichannel collimator, an array of detectors, associated signal processing and data collection electronics, and ancillary equipment for shielding and scanning. The present 360-channel collimator (Figs. 3 and 4) is stationary during transient experiments, but it can be scanned either vertically or horizontally to improve image resolution during steady-state radiography.[4]

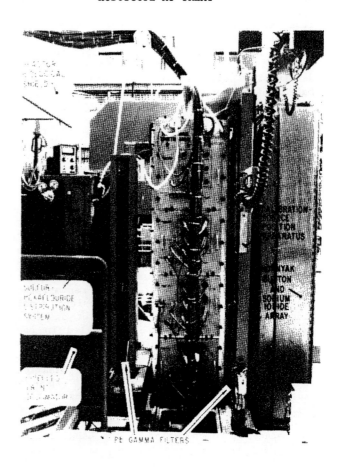

FIGURE 4   PHOTOGRAPH OF EXTERNAL EQUIPMENT OF TREAT HODOSCOPE

Although the system has a capacity for over 1000 detectors, normal complement is closer to 500, consisting of methane-filled proportional counters and Hornyak-button scintillation detectors for fast-neutron detection and up to 100 sodium-iodide gamma detectors. Up to three detectors can be mounted in tandem. Each detector has separate electronics that culminate in a gated scaler which dumps data on a disk every millisecond or so as programmed. The entire system is controlled to commence data recording in phase with the reactor transient. Despite the large number of detectors to calibrate and maintain, availability and reliability for experiments has been very high.

To cope with typical reactor transient bursts and imaging requirements of experiments, the hodoscope has nominal 1 ms time resolution, 0.2 mm horizontal resolution, 2 x 100 cm area coverage, wide dynamic range, and 0.1 g mass sensitivity. Fission neutrons that escape though containers up to 2 cm thick are detected. An early example of steady-state scanning results is shown in Fig. 5. The signal/background ratio depends on a number of factors, including the fissile content of the fuel. The ratio normally varies from less than one up to ten. Figure 6 is an example of reconstructed scan data, as is Fig. 7 which indicates at one corner the unexpected detection of the absence of about 0.5 g of Pu at that location.

This powerful instrument, which was designed for the hostile thermal and radiation environment of a transient reactor, is a basis for adaptations now being developed for nuclear arms control treaty verification.

TYPICAL HODOSCOPE RESULTS

Development of a new generation of safer reactors is being pursued by the U.S. Department of Energy.[5] Metallic fuels for a sodium-cooled fast reactor are now being extensively tested at conditions causing fuel failure. The hodoscope provides detailed data on fuel-pin dimensional changes that affect reactivity prior to cladding failure.[6] Figures 8, 9, and 10 display some typical time-resolved cineradiographic data for single and multiple pin tests. The latter figure indicates one means of displaying multiparameter data.

In Fig. 11 is shown some capabilities of the hodoscope in distinguishing different enrichments of U-235: 0.4%, 9%, and 93% by weight when enclosed in a thick container. The gamma-ray part of the hodoscope detects capture gamma rays from steel vessels, as shown in Fig. 12. Detection of fission-product gamma rays is depicted in Fig. 13.

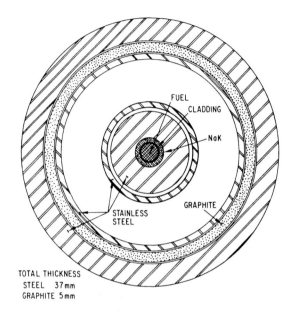

TOTAL THICKNESS
STEEL 37mm
GRAPHITE 5mm

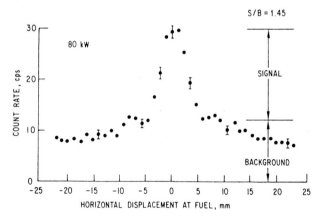

FIGURE 5 STEADY-STATE HODOSCOPE SCANNING DATA FOR A SINGLE PIN IN A THICK-WALLED CONTAINER

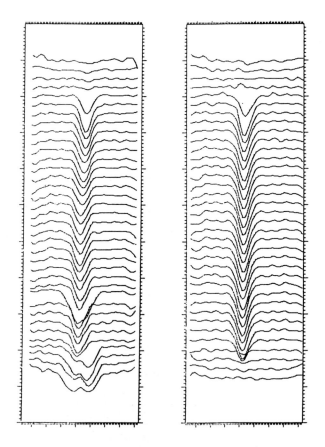

FIGURE 6   RECONSTRUCTION OF SINGLE-PIN DATA
DERIVED FROM STEADY-STATE SCANNING,
SHOWING ORIGINAL PIN ON LEFT AND
DESTROYED PIN ON RIGHT

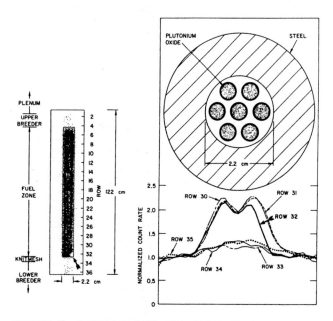

FIGURE 7   SCANNING DATA FOR SEVEN PLUTONIUM PINS
IN A THICK-WALLED CONTAINER, WITH A
RECONSTRUCTED IMAGE ON LEFT THAT INDI-
CATES ~0.5 G MISSING AT THE ARROW IN
THE LOWER RIGHT CORNER. TOTAL FUEL IS
ABOUT 1 KG.

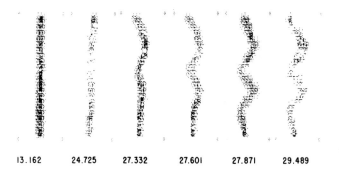

13.162   24.725   27.332   27.601   27.871   29.489

FIGURE 8   TIMEWISE PORTRAYAL OF FUEL REDISTRI-
BUTION RECONSTRUCTED FROM HODOSCOPE
DATA. ONLY SELECTED FRAMES ARE SHOWN,
TAKEN FROM A MUCH LARGER NUMBER OF
COLLECTED TIME FRAMES.

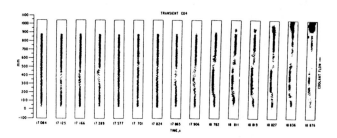

FIGURE 9   TIMEWISE PORTRAYAL OF FUEL DISTRI-
BUTION, SHOWING RECONSTRUCTIONS AT 40
OR SO MILLISECOND INTERVALS. THE ORI-
GINAL FUEL WAS SUBJECTED TO A BURST OF
RADIATION THAT INTENTIONALLY INDUCED
EXTENSIVE MOVEMENT AND REDISTRIBUTION.

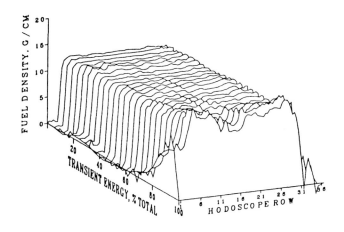

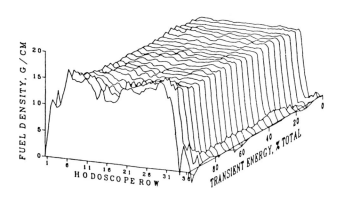

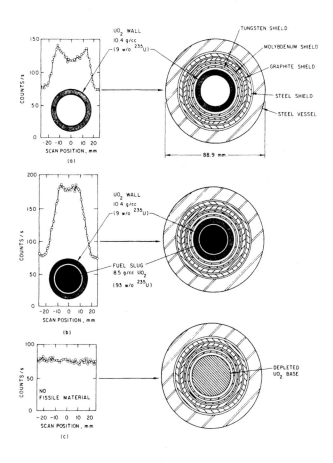

FIGURE 10   THREE PARAMETER RECONSTRUCTION OF
TRANSIENT DATA, SHOWING CHANGES IN
FUEL DENSITY AT DIFFERENT ELEVATIONS
AS THE TOTAL TRANSIENT ENERGY BUILDS
UP

FIGURE 11   EXAMPLES OF SENSITIVITY TO VARIOUS
FUEL DENSITIES: AT TOP, ANNULUS OF
9% U^{235} SLUG INSERTED WITHIN THE 9%
ANNULUS; AT BOTTOM, A 0.4% U^{235}
DEPLETED SLUG REPLACING THE OTHER
SAMPLES

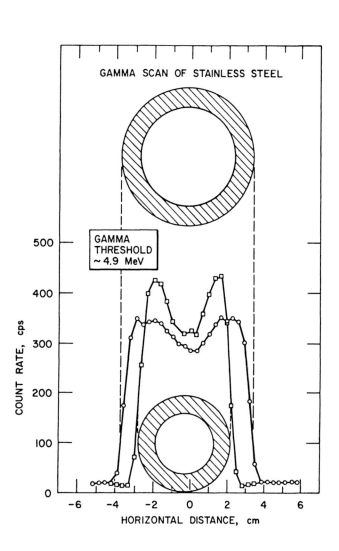

FIGURE 12   CAPTURE GAMMA RAY IMAGING OF STAIN-
LESS STEEL ANNULI

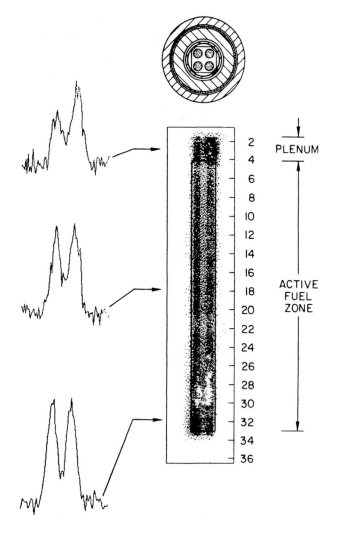

FIGURE 13   FISSION-PRODUCT-DECAY IMAGING OF
FISSILE MATERIAL

ARMS CONTROL VERIFICATION APPLICATIONS

The design principles that have made the
hodoscope highly successful in its current role
have been evaluated for application to arms
control treaty verification.[7] Radiation detection and imaging play a role in the Intermediate
Nuclear Forces (INF) treaty. For short-notice
inspection, neutron detectors are used to differentiate between two types of Soviet missiles
based on the differences in spontaneous fission
output rate. A hodoscope-type array would be an
appropriate alternative that could expedite the
inspection process. For monitoring rocket-
motors at a production facility, some type of
non-damaging image-producing radiography system

may be used. A hodoscope radioactive-source transmission array might be more fieldable and less expensive than a large linear-accelerator "cargo scan" system.

Other impending potential hodoscope applications for treaties under discussion or consideration include the counting of nuclear reentry vehicles, distinguishing between nuclear and conventional warheads on sea-launched cruise missiles, and nuclear warhead dismantlement. What began as a technical fix for a difficult problem in energy security 25 years ago might now turn out to be useful in current national security problems.

ACKNOWLEDGMENTS

Work supported by the U.S. Department of Energy, Technology Support Programs under Contract W-31-109-Eng-38.

REFERENCES

1. C. E. DICKERMAN, E. S. SOWA, D. OKRENT, J. MONAWECK, and L. B. MILLER, ANL-6334, Argonne National Laboratory (1961).

2. A. DEVOLPI, "Applications of Cineradiography to Nuclear-Reactor Safety Studies," Rev. Sci. Instrum., 55(8), 1197-1220 (1984).

3. A. DEVOLPI, "Proceedings Conference on Fast, Thermal and Fusion Experiments," (American Nuclear Society, LaGrange, IL, 1982).

4. A. DEVOLPI, U.S. Patent No. 4 092 542 (May 30, 1978).

5. A. E. WRIGHT, T. H. BAUER, W. R. ROBINSON, and A. E. KLICKMAN, "Techniques of Metal Fuel Transient Testing in TREAT," Intl. Topical Meeting on Safety of Next Generation Power Reactors, Seattle, May 1988 (Proceedings to be published).

6. A. DEVOLPI, R. C. DOERNER, C. L. FINK, J. P. REGIS, E. A. RHODES, and G. S. STANFORD, "Fuel-Motion Diagnostics in Support of Fast-Reactor Safety Experiments," Science and Technology of Fast Reactor Safety, BNES, London (1986).

7. A. DEVOLPI, "Neutron Radiographic Techniques for Nuclear Arms Control Applications," Proceedings of the Second World Conf. on Neutron Radiography, D. Reidel (1987).

FISSION RATE MEASUREMENTS IN FUEL PLATE

TYPE ASSEMBLY REACTOR CORES[†]

JW ROGERS
Idaho National Engineering Laboratory
EG&G Idaho, Inc.
P. O. Box 1625
Idaho Falls, ID 83415-7111
(208) 526-4252

ABSTRACT

The methods, materials and equipment have been developed to allow extensive and precise measurement of fission rate distributions in water moderated, U-Al fuel plate assembly type reactor cores. Fission rate monitors are accurately positioned in the reactor core, the reactor is operated at a low power for a short time, the fission rate monitors are counted with detectors incorporating automated sample changers and the measurements are converted to fission rate distributions. These measured fission rate distributions have been successfully used as baseline information related to the operation of test and experimental reactors with respect to fission power and distribution, fuel loading and fission experiments for approximately twenty years at the Idaho National Engineering Laboratory (INEL).

INTRODUCTION

A technique was developed for measuring fission rates in fuel plate type assembly reactors utilizing small uranium-aluminum (U-Al) alloy monitors.[1] This technique allows measurements to be made extensively throughout the reactor with fine spatial resolution and with negligible perturbation by the fission rate monitors. Upwards of 500 individual monitor measurements can be obtained in a single day. A principal advantage of this technique is the direct correlation between the fission rates of the monitors and the adjacent reactor zone (fuel, moderator, reflector, structure, etc.). This technique has some distinct advantages over other techniques which employ other monitors and require major corrections for response and perturbation.

[†]The work performed under DOE contract DE-AC07-76ID01570.

This technique is normally applied at low reactor powers (typically less than 500 watts).

This technique depends on a completely standardized and calibrated system including the monitors, the counting equipment and the conversion factors. The system currently in use is setup for use in light water moderated, beryllium or water reflected, ^{235}U enriched (93%) fueled plate type assembly reactors.

The fission-rate data which have been obtained using this technique have provided basic information for test and experimental reactors at the INEL for approximately twenty years. Measurements have been made using these fission monitors to support the Advanced Test Reactor (ATR), the Engineering Test Reactor (ETR), their associated critical facilities (ATRC and ETRC), the Advanced Reactivity Measurement Facility (ARMF) and the Coupled Reactivity Measurement Facility (CFRMF).[2,3,4]

FISSION MONITORS

The fission rate monitors have a standardized geometry of 0.102 cm diameter and 0.635 cm length. They are made of 10 weight percent uranium in aluminum alloy. The uranium is isotopically enriched to 93 percent ^{235}U. A typical monitor contains about 1.45 mg of enriched uranium and about 3.45E18 atoms of ^{235}U.

It is important that the ^{235}U atom concentration is uniform in the U-Al alloy monitors so that accurate fission rate data can be obtained. The uniformity of these monitors was checked by measuring the relative fission product activity of individual monitors which had been equally irradiated. These measurements showed that the standardized monitors produced relative results with a standard deviation of $\pm$ 0.7 percent (2σ). The relative natural radioactivities of the ^{235}U in unirradiated monitors were also measured and produced similar results. Based on these results it is estimated that the ^{235}U content of the monitors does not vary by more than one percent.

This geometry and material was selected to allow the monitors to be conveniently used in the moderator channels of the fuel assemblies and to have low neutron self-shielding and perturbation properties. A principal advantage of these monitors is the direct correlation between the fission rates of the monitor and the adjacent fuel zone.

COUNTING EQUIPMENT

The counting equipment used for these fission rate measurements consists of a set of five thin window (1.11 mg/cm²) methane gas flow proportional counters and their associated electronics. This is a master/slave system where each of the four slave counters has a sample changer. The data acquisition and sample changing functions are controlled by a microprocessor computer. The counting data are stored and analyzed with a laboratory computer. A block diagram of the system is shown in Figure 1.

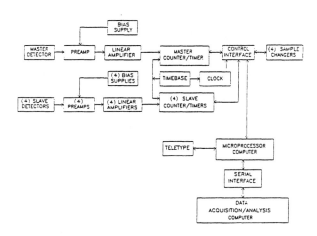

FIG. 1   FISSION RATE MONITOR COUNTING
          EQUIPMENT DIAGRAM

FISSION PRODUCT BETA DECAY

To determine the fission product beta decay curve for the fission rate monitors they were irradiated in a well thermalized neutron energy spectrum ($R_{cd} > 1000$) field for the standardized time (20 min.). It was necessary to allow one hour for the ^{28}Al and ^{27}Mg activation products due to the aluminum to decay to insignificant levels. This was determined by comparing pure aluminum material with the U-Al alloy material. Using the

counting equipment, the fission product gross beta activity was carefully measured as a function of the decay time in order to establish the decay curve. The results from these measurements are illustrated in Figure 2. Also shown is the inverse of the activity which was found to be nearly linear during the initial eight hours of decay.

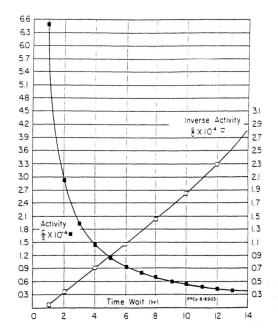

FIG. 2   FISSION PRODUCT BETA ACTIVITY CURVE
          FOLLOWING A 20-MINUTE IRRADIATION

CALIBRATION TECHNIQUE

The calibration of the U-Al fission monitors was accomplished by irradiating them and standardized gold neutron monitors in the same well thermalized neutron field ($R_{cd} > 1000$) for the standardized time (20 min.). The $^{197}Au(n,\gamma)^{198}Au$ reaction rate with a 98.8 barn cross section was used to obtain the scalar fluence rate to an accuracy of $\pm$ 1 percent (1σ). The fission rate was then obtained using the following expressions:

$$\text{fission rate} = N \int_0^\infty \sigma_f(v) \, M(v) \, v dv \qquad (1)$$

$$= gN\sigma_0 (nv_0) \qquad (2)$$

$$= gN\sigma_0 \frac{KA_0}{t_{exp}} \qquad (3)$$

where:

N = number of ^{235}U atoms/gm of ^{235}U

$\sigma_f(v)$ = neutron velocity dependent ^{235}U fission cross section

v = neutron velocity

$M(v)$ = Maxwellian-Boltzmann neutron distribution

g = Westcott's g factor for ^{235}U

σ_0 = 2200 m/s fission cross section

nv_0 = conventional 2200 m/s scaler neutron fluence rate

K = nvt calibration factor for a standard gold foil

A_0 = beta activity of a standard gold foil at zero decay time

t_{exp} = exposure time in seconds.

Since the ratio between the gold standard neutron monitor and the U-Al fission rate monitor activities was established as a function of the waiting time following the end of irradiation (20 min.), the fission rate can be obtained from the U-Al monitor fission product beta activity using the following expression:

$$\text{fission rate} = K_{fr}(t) A_u(t) = A_u(t) \sum_{i=0}^{6} B_i t^i \quad (4)$$

where:

$A_u(t)$ = fission product activity (counts/s) of standard U-Al monitors following a 20 minute irradiation period

$K_{fr}(t)$ = fission rate "constant" which corrects the U-Al fission product activity for decay and converts the counts/s to fission/s/gm ^{235}U

B_i = calibration coefficients obtained from a least-squares fit of the decay data

t = waiting time in hours.

From Equations (3) and (4):

$$gN\sigma_0 = \frac{KA_0}{t_{exp}} = A_u(t) K_{fr}(t) \quad (5)$$

$$K_{fr}(t) = \frac{gN\sigma_0 K}{t_{exp}} \frac{A_0}{A_u(t)} \quad (6)$$

where:

$$K_{fr}(t) = \sum_{i=0}^{6} B_i t^i \quad (7)$$

for a set of standardized and calibrated conditions.

The values of the above parameters which were used to determine the fission rate for one set of conditions were:

g = 0.975 $\pm$ 0.002

σ_0 = 577.1 $\pm$ 0.9 barns

K = 8.25 x 10^8 cm^{-2}·s

N = 2.56 x 10^{21} atoms/gm

t_{exp} = 1200 s

$\dfrac{A_0}{A_u(t)}$ = 18.7 $\pm$ 0.2.

The calibration coefficients resulting from a least squares fit of the decay data were:

B_0 = -17443.198

B_1 = 68943.940

B_2 = -573.85056

B_3 = -30.338487

B_4 = 12.617695

B_5 = -0.52854141

B_6 = 0.0068458056

The relationship of the conversion factor, $K_{fr}(t)$, to the wait time, t, is illustrated in Figure 3.

When changes are made in the fission monitor material (such as using another alloy melt), the counting equipment (such as changing sample carrier or detector windows) or the irradiation time a recalibration or correction may be necessary.

For small deviations (plus or minus up to five minutes) from the prescribed twenty minute irradiation (at approximately the same neutron level), a linear correction factor of $1200/t_{exp}$ can be applied to the data. For longer

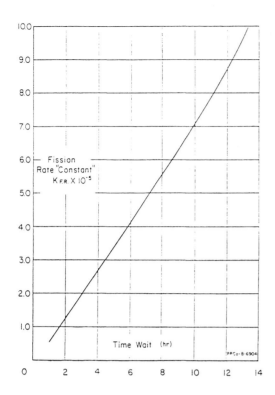

FIG. 3   FISSION RATE CONVERSION FACTOR VERSUS
          WAITING TIME

irradiations (greater than twenty-five minutes)
it is necessary to wait longer for the
short-lived isotopes to decay. If irradiations
of greater than about twenty-five minutes are
encountered it is necessary to wait at least
five hours before counting the monitors and
using the linear correction.

The U-Al fission rate monitor calibration
was checked by comparing the results from these
monitors with a National Institute of Standards
and Technology (NIST) ^{235}U fission chamber.
The U-Al monitors and NIST fission chamber were
placed in the same neutron field and
irradiated. The fission rates obtained with
the U-Al monitors calibrated in the way
described above agreed with the fission rates
obtained from the NIST fission chamber to
within 0.33 percent where the uncertainty on
each is estimated to be $\pm$ 1.5 percent at the
2σ confidence level.

NEUTRON SPECTRAL EFFECTS

It is known that the fission product yield
for some fission products vary with incident
neutron energy or with different neutron energy
spectra.[5,6] Some tests were conducted to
determine the sensitivity of this method to
variations in neutron spectra. Fission rate
monitors were irradiated in a "thermal" reactor
reflector neutron field with and without

cadmium neutron filters. There was no
observable difference in the fission product
beta-decay rates of these tests.

Another spectral test was conducted in
conjunction with an NIST ^{235}U fission chamber
in the "fast" neutron spectrum found in the
CFRMF at INEL.[7] The average neutron energy
of this spectrum was 0.72 MeV. The fission
rates obtained with the monitors in this
spectrum were in excellent agreement with that
obtained from the NIST fission chamber.

Based on these tests these fission rate
monitors can be successfully used in a variety
of neutron spectra based on this calibration
technique.

APPLICATIONS

The fission-rate data which have been
obtained using this technique have provided
basic information for test and experimental
reactors at the INEL for approximately twenty
years.

For the test reactors such as the Advanced
Test Reactor (ATR), the Engineering Test
Reactor (ETR) and their associated critical
facilities (ATRC and ETRC) these data have been
used to: (a) establish the absolute power
levels and reverify them, (b) study the effects
of control devices and test assemblies on the
local and overall fission rate distribution of
the various core loadings of these reactors,
(c) study fission rates in the development of
fuel types and assemblies, (d) provide fission
rate data for in-core experiment assemblies,
and (e) provide experimental data for
comparison with calculated data in the
development of reactor models and computer
codes.[2,3,4]

For the experimental reactors such as the
Advanced Reactivity Measurements Facility
(ARMF) and Coupled Reactivity Measurements
Facility (CFRMF) these data have been used to:
(a) establish the absolute power levels and
reverify them, (b) measure the power
distribution of different core configurations,
and (c) study fission rates associated with
various experiment geometries.

Figure 4 is a cross-sectional diagram of
the ATRC core and Figure 5 is an illustration
of an ATR type fuel assembly. Figure 6 shows a
typical measured radial fission power profile
at the midplane elevation of an ATRC fuel
assembly which was obtained using the fission
rate monitors.

Figure 7 is a cross-sectional diagram of
the CFRMF core at midplane. Figure 8 shows
axial fission rate profiles which were measured
with the fission rate monitors in the filtered

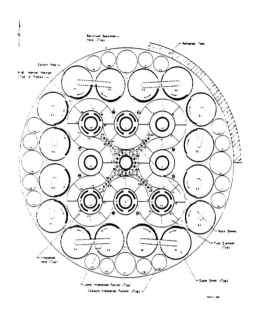

FIG. 4   CROSS-SECTIONAL DIAGRAM OF ATRC CORE

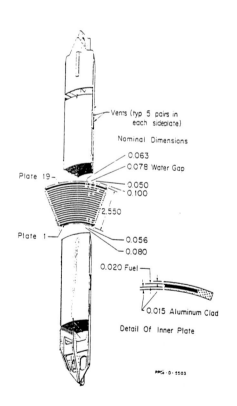

FIG. 5   ATR FUEL ASSEMBLY

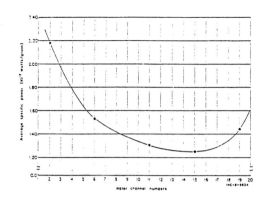

FIG. 6   TYPICAL AVERAGE SPECIFIC POWER RADIAL PROFILE AT MIDPLANE IN AN ATRC FUEL ASSEMBLY

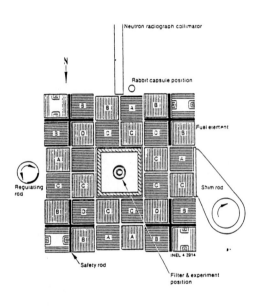

FIG. 7   CFRMF MIDPLANE CROSS-SECTIONAL DIAGRAM

neutron experiment position with and without ^{10}B end plugs.

CONCLUSIONS

These fission rate monitors along with their standardization and calibration have proven to be valuable in the characterization of fuel plate type assembly reactor cores and in reactor experimental facilities. They can provide measurements in fine spatial detail with accuracies in the range of two to five percent provided they are used as standardized and calibrated. They are useful in a wide

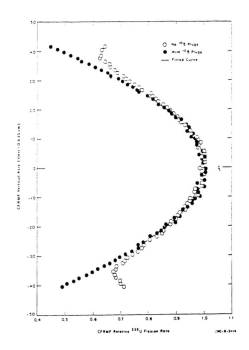

FIG. 8   PROFILES OF ^{235}U FISSION RATE ALONG
THE VERICAL AXIS OF CFRMF FAST NEUTRON
SPECTRUM ZONE WITH AND WITHOUT ^{10}B
END PLUGS

range of neutron spectral conditions (highly
thermalized to fast neutrons). The primary
limitation is the fact that they can only be
used at low neutron levels (up to about
10^{10} n/cm²/sec) under the standardizations and
calibrations described herein.

ACKNOWLEDGEMENTS

The author is grateful for the contributions
by C. H. Hogg, B. W. Howes, J. L. Durney, the
staffs of ATRC, ARMF, CFRMF and the Radiation
Measurements Laboratory at INEL. The
contributions by J. A. Grundl of NIST are also
appreciated.

REFERENCES

1. B. W. HOWES and C. H. HOGG, "Uranium Fission
    Rate Monitors," TREE-1141, (February 1978).

2. J. L. DURNEY and N. C. KAUFMAN, "Calculating
    Reactor Power from Activation Techniques as
    Applied to an Unusual Fuel Geometry,"
    IN-1047, (January 1967).

3. J. W. HENSCHIED, ET AL., "ATR Startup,
    Zero-Power Experiments and Comparison with
    ATRC," IN-1136 (December 1967).

4. N. C. KAUFMAN, ET AL., "Reactor Physics
    Results from Low-Power Measurements in the
    ATR," IN-1260 (February 1969).

5. K. T. FALER and R. L. TROMP, "Variation in
    ^{235}U Mass Yields at Neutron Energies
    Below 0.5 eV," The Physical Review, 131, 4
    (August 1963) pp 1746-1749.

6. G. LAMMER and M. LAMMER, "Status of Fission
    Product Yields . . .," IAEA-208 (November
    1976) pp 301-318.

7. JW ROGERS, ET AL., "CFRMF Neutron Field Flux
    Spectral Characterization," Nuclear
    Technology, 25 (February 1975) pp. 330-348.

EXPLOITING FISSION EVENT DETECTION IN THICK DISKS TO DEVELOP A
HIGH EFFICIENCY FAST NEUTRON THRESHOLD DETECTOR

R. A. AUGUST, G. W. PHILLIPS
Code 4616, U.S. Naval Research Laboratory
4555 Overlook Avenue, Washington, DC 20375-5000
(202)767-5692

J. H. CUTCHIN
Sachs/Freeman Associates Inc.
1401 McCormick Drive, Landover, MD 20785
(202)767-5692

ABSTRACT

Experiments at the Naval Research Laboratory (NRL) show that 1mm thick ^{238}U disks backed by charged particle detectors have a significant count rate increase when exposed to a fast (MeV energy range) neutron flux. This count rate is higher than would be expected considering only detection of the short range primary fission fragments, which are detected in a standard fission chamber neutron detector. We believe the excess count rate can be understood in terms of longer range particles resulting from the highly energetic and prolific nature of the fission reaction and the decay of its daughter products, which yield many neutrons, γ's, β's, etc. We are investigating exploiting these results to develop a fast neutron detector with an efficiency of several percent.

INTRODUCTION

Neutron counters using materials sensitive to neutron induced fission have been around for many years.[1] As a simple example, a counter sensitive to thermal neutrons could be constructed by depositing a thin coating of ^{235}U metal on the interior wall of a gas filled proportional counter. The ^{235}U deposit should be thin enough that the primary fission fragments can escape the metal and be detected in the proportional counter. A neutron counter that is sensitive to fast neutrons can be made by using a material with a higher threshold for neutron induced fission, like ^{238}U. The cross section for neutron induced fission of ^{238}U rises rapidly from about 2.5×10^{-4} b (barns) at 0.5 MeV incident neutron energy to about 0.5 b at 2.0 MeV.[2] Therefore, a counter using ^{238}U as the sensitive material would only be sensitive to neutrons with incident energies above this cross section threshold (i.e. a "threshold detector").

Consider the neutron detection efficiency of a fast neutron threshold detector. A typical deposit of ^{238}U in such a neutron counter is 1 mg/cm^2 which is approximately 0.5 microns thick.[3] Deposits thicker by a factor of 10 or more could be used but would result in a significantly smaller probability of the fission fragment escaping the deposit and being detected.[1] As an example, consider a flux of 8 MeV neutrons passing through a 1 mg/cm^2 layer. The neutron induced fission cross section in this case is about 1 b, corresponding to a fission probability of 0.00024%.[2] Considering only a single layer deposit of ^{238}U, this sets an upper limit on the neutron detection efficiency of 0.00024%. If we wanted to construct a high efficiency fast neutron threshold detector it would require a minimum of over 4000 such layers of ^{238}U just to approach 1% neutron detection efficiency. Clearly such a detector could be better constructed if we were able to use ^{238}U layers that were 200 to 2000 times thicker (0.1 to 1 mm). To consider such a possibility we must first look at the energetics of the neutron induced fission reaction.

The neutron induced fission of a heavy nucleus in the uranium region results in a release of about 200 MeV of energy shared by a variety of reaction products.[4] The breakdown of this is shown in Table 1. The total amount of energy released and its breakdown will vary somewhat depending on the exact nucleus that is undergoing fission and the kinetic energy of the neutron that induced the fission.[5] In our case, however, we are interested only in the general breakdown of energies for the fission of nuclei in the uranium region for which Table 1 is a sufficient guide.

The largest amount of energy released is that contained in the kinetic energy of the fission fragments: 165 ± 5 MeV. It is these fission fragments that typically are detected in neutron counters made with fissionable materials. However, while these products are energetic they have very short ranges within the fissionable material. There is a wide range of possible candidates for these fission fragments, which depend to some extent on the energy of the neutron inducing the fission. For fission of ^{238}U induced by neutrons with energies of 2 - 3 MeV (just above the fission threshold) the most likely situation is to have two fission fragments with mean mass numbers of 98 ± 16 and 139 ± 16 and with kinetic energies (in MeV) of 98 ± 29 and 65 ± 19 respectively.[5,6] This results in ranges that are short enough to require the thin layers of fissionable materials previously mentioned.[1,5,7]

Table 1.   Distribution of Fission Energy[4]

	Energy [MeV]
Kinetic energy of fission fragments	165 ± 5
Instantaneous γ-ray energy	7 ± 1
Kinetic energy of fission neutrons	5 ±.5
β Particles from fission products	7 ± 1
γ-rays from fission products	6 ± 1
Neutrinos from fission products	10
Total energy per fission	200 ± 6

It is clear that if we want to make a high efficiency fast neutron detector using thicknesses of ^{238}U on the order of 1 mm, then detection of the fission fragments will be an insufficient way of detecting a neutron induced fission event in the ^{238}U. We must therefore look at Table 1 and consider the other reaction products.

A kinetic energy of about 5 MeV is carried away by fission neutrons. In a fission of ^{238}U there are about 2 - 4 neutrons released per fission, depending on the energy of the neutron which induced the fission.[8] The problem of detecting such neutrons is the object of this study. It is therefore not feasible to use them to indicate the presence of a fission in the ^{238}U.

The γ-rays released instantaneously and by the fission products carry away about 13 MeV of energy from the reaction. These γ-rays bring up two considerations. Firstly, γ-rays are more penetrating and generally more difficult to detect than charged particles. Secondly, it is undesirable to detect γ-rays in this case. The reason for their undesirability is that there are some strong low energy (below the fission threshold) $^{238}U(n,\gamma)$ resonances.[2] Therefore, γ-rays will be produced as a result of neutrons with energies below the energy threshold we are seeking in this neutron detector. It is then actually desirable to minimize detection of γ-rays in our neutron counter.

Clearly the energy carried off by the very penetrating neutrinos is not easily detected. This leaves the about 7 MeV of energy released in β particles from fission products. We believe that it these β particles which may make the use of ^{238}U thicknesses on the order of 1 mm possible. It should be mentioned before discussing these β particles, that they are not the only electrons presents. When the energetic fission fragments are slowed down in the ^{238}U a shower of electrons known as δ-rays are produced along the path of the fission products.[9] It is, however, easily shown that the ranges of these δ-rays within the ^{238}U are insufficient for our purposes.[9,10]

β DECAY OF FISSION PRODUCTS

The number of possible fission products and the β decays they can undergo are so numerous that it is not meaningful to try and discuss all the individual possibilities. In this case a statistical treatment is more useful. "The number of radioactive fission products is so large that the decay characteristics of the ensemble can be treated statistically for decay times up to about 50 days, after which time the number of fission products remaining may become to small for accurate results by this method."[11]

From Table 1 we see that 7 ± 1 MeV of energy per fission is expended in β particles from fission products. To get an idea of the amount of energy that can be expected per β we need to know the total number of β decays per fission. We can get an idea of this by looking at a study which estimates the total number of β particles emitted per fission of ^{235}U to be in the range from 4 to 8 for the prominent heavy and light fission chains, with the average weighted by the % yields of the various chains being 6.1 β's per fission.[11,12] These results are for ^{235}U and not ^{238}U, however, comparison of fission yields for the two nuclei show that it is reasonable to expect similar behavior in both.[5] This leads to the conclusion that the probability is high that at least some of the β's from these fission fragments will have energies in the range from several hundred keV to several MeV.

The decay rate of β's from fission products drops rapidly following a fission, being down by 2 orders of magnitude within 100 seconds following a fission.[11] The same is true of the total energy released per second per fission (β, γ, and neutrino) by the fission products, which starts at several MeV per second per fission and is also down by 2 orders of magnitude within 100 seconds following fission.[11] It follows from this that the more energetic β's are most likely to be emitted within 100 seconds or so following a fission.

This statistical treatment of the β's that result from decay of the fission products leaves us with several expectations. There should be several delayed β's per fission. At least some of these β's should have energies in the hundreds of keV to several MeV region. These energetic β's should decay within about the first 100 seconds following a fission. Table 2 gives us an idea of the ranges that can be expected from these β's in ^{238}U.[7] This table makes it clear that the ranges of these energetic β's are long enough that we can expect the following: a fission occurring at some random point inside a 1 mm thick deposit of ^{238}U will result in delayed β's, some of these will be energetic enough to have a significant probability of escaping that deposit.

Table 2. Range in ^{238}U of energetic β's[7]

β Energy [MeV]	Range [mm]
0.5	0.08
1.0	0.22
2.0	0.50
3.0	0.79

EXPERIMENTAL DESIGN AND TECHNIQUES

The above discussion shows that it may indeed be possible to make a threshold detector for fast neutrons out of deposits of ^{238}U with thicknesses on the order of 1 mm. To test this we designed a series of experiments using 1 mm thick disks of ^{238}U. Natural uranium is 99.3% ^{238}U and 0.7% ^{235}U.[13] The ^{238}U available to us had a ^{235}U impurity that was reduced by a factor of 2 or more compared with natural uranium, but the exact purity was not known. This makes it critical to our experiments to understand the behavior of both ^{238}U and ^{235}U in the presence of a neutron flux.

The neutron source used in our experiments is the radioisotope ^{252}Cf. The spectrum of neutrons from this source is well known, it is an approximately maxwellian distribution with a mean neutron energy of 2.2 MeV.[14] The cross sections for neutron induced fission of the uranium isotopes are also well known.[2] A computer program was developed to determine the number of fissions that a flux of neutrons from a ^{252}Cf source would induce when passing through a thickness of ^{238}U with a ^{235}U impurity. The program varied the amount of the ^{235}U impurity, and reported the percent increase in fission rate as a function of ^{235}U impurity. Figure 1 is a plot of the output from the program where

the % increase in the rate of fission (compared to the 100% ^{238}U rate) is plotted versus the % ^{235}U impurity in a 1 mm thickness of ^{238}U.

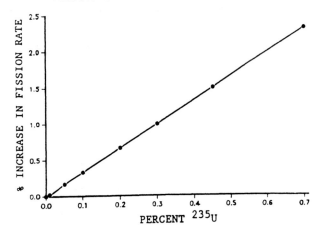

FISSION IN U INDUCED BY ^{252}Cf NEUTRONS

FIGURE 1 % INCREASE IN RATE OF FISSION OVER THE 100% ^{238}U RATE VERSUS THE % ^{235}U IMPURITY IN A 1 MM THICKNESS OF ^{238}U.

Figure 1 shows that the effect of the ^{235}U in this case is only a few percent. The program also showed that these results are insensitive to the thickness for thicknesses of several mm or less. These results show that the degree of uncertainty about the purity of the ^{238}U we used in our experiments was not large enough to significantly effect the results. This is true only when a bare source of ^{252}Cf is used. If any neutron attenuating materials are present between the neutron source and the ^{238}U disk then the energy spectrum of the neutron flux the disk is seeing is changed. In such a case the effect of the ^{235}U impurity can be more significant, since the cross section for neutron induced fission does not drop off at lower neutron energies in ^{235}U as it does in ^{238}U. In fact the cross section in ^{235}U increases as neutron energy decreases, reaching 693 b at thermal neutron energies.[2]

The detectors used were transmission mounted silicon solid state charged particle detectors. The charged particle detector used in most experiments was 2000 microns thick, although some experiments were run with thinner detectors to gauge what effect this might have. ^{238}U disks were cut from 1 mm thick sheets such that they were the same size as the active area of the detector to which they were to be mounted. The disks were mounted right up against the detector face, with a disk mounted on both sides of the transmission mount detector. This was done to maximize the count rate in the charged particle detector.

Only one disk/detector assembly was tested at a time. The disk/detector assembly was put into an evacuated chamber and placed with one face parallel to a flat wall of the chamber at a distance of 1 cm. The wall of the chamber was 1.6 mm thick stainless steel. Two ^{252}Cf sources were used in these experiments, both had been previously calibrated to be 136 and 582 μCi. When a neutron source was in use it was placed outside the vacuum chamber normal to the center of disk/detector assembly. The distance between the neutron source and the disk/detector assembly was varied between 5 cm and 15 cm. When we wanted to moderate the neutron source, 1.3 cm thick, 61 cm x 61 cm polyethylene sheets were placed on the outside of the vacuum chamber between the neutron source and the disk/detector assembly.

Standard nuclear electronics were used and included a solid state detector power supply, preamplifier, spectroscopy amplifier, and electronic pulser for calibration. The data were collected on a Nuclear Data ND66 multichannel analyzer with its own ADC. An ^{241}Am source was used as the calibration source for the charged particle detectors.

All experiments were performed following the same method. After setting up the disk/detector assembly in the vacuum chamber, a background spectrum was taken. This gave a spectrum of the natural background of the ^{238}U disks which is dominated by α particle decay. The neutron source (and polyethylene sheets if being used) was then put in place and a spectrum collected. The evacuated chamber was then opened and the disks removed. The charged particle detector was then replaced in the chamber without the disks and a spectrum was collected. This was done to check for the effects of the neutron flux on the charged particle detector. The neutron source was then removed and a spectrum was collected to check for any additional sources of background (none were found).

The detection events due to neutron induced events in the ^{238}U disks were then determined by comparing the summed counts in the spectrum taken when both the ^{238}U disks and neutron source were present with the other spectra taken. All spectra were taken for a length of time that assured a statistical accuracy of no worse than 0.5%. In practice this could vary anywhere between 20 minutes and several hours depending on the parameters of the set-up in use.

Many experimental parameters were varied: amplifier gain, low energy discriminator level, neutron source, amount (if any) of polyethylene for neutron flux moderation, disk/detector to neutron source distance, geometry of the local environment, and thickness of the charged particle detector. After each variation spectra were taken following the experimental method just described.

Some of the variations just mentioned require further explanation. When experimenting with neutrons there is always concern that neutron scattering in the local environment can bias the results. To check for this the environment around the experimental set-up was varied by moving objects and moving the set-up itself. The polyethylene moderator was used to help determine if the neutron induced events in the disks were indeed due to the fast neutron component of the incident neutron flux, or if there was a significant contribution due to the slow/thermal components of the flux. A low energy discriminator level was set on the signal from the solid state detector in order to keep the experiments from being distorted by low energy noise. The thickness of the solid state detector was varied to help determine that the effects being seen were due to charged particles from the ^{238}U disks being stopped in the charged particle detector rather than being due to energy deposited by γ-rays passing through the charged particle detector.

EXPERIMENTAL RESULTS

After a series of initial tests the amplifier gain was set to 8 MeV full scale and the lower level discriminator was set at 600 keV for the duration of these experiments. This discriminator setting was somewhat higher than was absolutely necessary, but we felt that it was more important to insure a clean spectrum in these tests than to try and maximize event detection efficiency.

The first spectrum to be considered is a ^{238}U disk background when no source was present. The disk/detector background count rate (summed over the entire spectrum) was 584.6 $\pm$ 0.4 counts/second. This is somewhat higher than would be expected purely from α decay of ^{238}U, but is not unexpected since it has already been stated that the ^{238}U available to us was not of high isotopic purity. Techniques to suppress the α's electronically or otherwise were not attempted in these preliminary experiments.

The high background count rate forced us to use the larger neutron source and place it 2.5 inches from the detector when taking neutron spectra in order to obtain good counting statistics. Although spectra were taken with the neutron source further away they required longer counting times and produced results with less statistical accuracy. However, they were consistent with the reported 2.5 inch results. In future experiments we plan to use disks that are isotopically pure and expect that the disk background counts should be reduced significantly by this.

When spectra were taken with the strong neutron source 2.5 inches from the detector the count rate (summed over the entire spectrum) represented a 6.2 ± 0.1 % increase over the background counting rate. This is clearly a significant increase. Spectra that were collected in the presence of the neutron source but without the ^{238}U disks showed a count rate that was 3.2 ± 0.4 % of the background counting rate. Comparing this with the result obtained when the disks were present shows that 3.0 ± 0.4 % of the increase in the count rate in the solid state detectors can only be due to neutron induced events in the ^{238}U disks. This corresponds to a count rate of 17.5 ± 2.3 counts per second in the charged particle detector. Figure 2 shows one of the spectra of counts resulting from neutron induced events in the ^{238}U disks; this is a spectrum taken with the disks in and the neutron source present, minus spectra that were taken of the disk background and of the events due to neutron interactions in the charged particle detector.

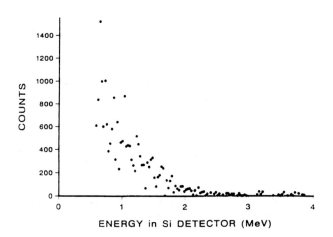

FIGURE 2   SPECTRUM OF COUNTS IN THE CHARGED PARTICLE DETECTOR RESULTING FROM NEUTRON INDUCED EVENTS IN THE ^{238}U DISKS. THIS IS A SPECTRUM OF THE DISK/DETECTOR ASSEMBLY WHEN EXPOSED TO THE NEUTRON SOURCE, WITH THE VARIOUS BACKGROUND SPECTRA (SEE TEXT) SUBTRACTED OUT.

It is important at this juncture to make a point about ^{238}U disk backgrounds. After each spectrum taken while the disk/detector assembly was exposed to the neutron source, the neutron source was removed from the area and a background spectrum was taken of the disk/detector assembly. The background counting rate of the disk/detector assembly never varied. Therefore any delayed β decays from the fission products during these background collections were of a low enough energy that they could

either not escape the disk or not be detected above the 600 keV energy discriminator threshold that was being used in our experiments. This is in agreement with what was stated in the discussion about β decay. The more energetic β decays should occur within about the first 100 seconds following fission.

During these experiments the charged particle detectors were periodically checked with the ^{241}A$_m$ source to look for possible effects from neutron damage. We found no evidence during the course of these experiments that the neutrons were adversely effecting the performance of the charged particle detectors. As explained in the previous section, the environment around the experimental set-up was varied; every time this was done the entire set of experiments were repeated. Using this method we found no evidence that neutron scattering in the environment was biasing our results.

To provide an indication that the interactions we have seen in the ^{238}U disks are indeed due to fast rather than slow/thermal neutrons, the experiments were repeated with polyethylene sheets between the neutron source and the disk/detector. Two total thicknesses of polyethylene were tested, 1.3 cm and 2.5 cm. With the 1.3 cm sheet the bare source count rate increase of 3.0 ± 0.4 % over background was reduced to 2.0 ± 0.4 %. With the 2.5 cm sheet present this was reduced to 0.7 ± 0.4 %. As mentioned previously ^{252}Cf has an approximately maxwellian spectrum centered at 2.2 MeV. From this we can estimate the attenuation of the fast neutron flux from the polyethylene moderator using fast neutron attenuation data.[7,15] This estimate showed that the fast neutron component of a ^{252}Cf flux passing through our polyethylene moderator should be reduced by a fraction which is consistent with our experimental results.

To make a similar estimate for the expected behavior of the slow/thermal flux is a far more complex calculation; the process of thermalization creates many slow/thermal neutrons, also, the local scattering environment becomes critically important in such calculations. Also, as mentioned previously, ^{235}U has a very large cross section for thermal neutron induced fission which makes the small ^{235}U impurity in our ^{238}U disk much more important. However, it seems highly unlikely that the change in the slow/thermal flux due to the moderator would result in a reduction in count rate in the disk/detector assembly that is exactly the same as the reduction we would expect from the fast neutron flux, especially since we have already mentioned that our experiments were insensitive to variations in the local scattering environment. This indicates that the reduction in neutron induced events in the disk/detector assembly when the neutron source was moderated is consistent with the neutron induced events in the ^{238}U disks being due to fast neutron interactions in the disk, with little apparent contribution from slow/thermal neutrons. However, detailed calculations of the effect of the polyethylene on the neutron flux would be necessary to provide quantitative proof of this statement.

We then took the 17.5 ± 2.3 counts per second in the charged particle detector that we found to be due to neutron induced events in the ^{238}U disks, and compared this number to the rate at which we expected neutron induced fissions to be occurring in the disks. We knew the dimensions of the source to disk/detector geometry, and as we have already mentioned, the ^{252}Cf neutron energy distribution is well known. Therefore, it is a fairly simple calculation to fold this distribution into the known cross section distribution for neutron induced fission in ^{238}U, and to obtain a fast neutron induced fission rate in the disks.[2] Comparing this to our count rate indicates that 45% of the neutron induced fissions in the ^{238}U disks result in a signal in the charged particle detector. An accurate estimate of the error on this event detection efficiency number would require neutron scattering calculations. However, we feel confident that the event detection efficiency for this disk/detector set-up is approximately 50%.

CONCLUSIONS

Our experiments have shown that when our system of two 1 mm thick ^{238}U disks sandwiching a solid state charged particle detector is exposed to a flux of neutrons, a significant count rate can be seen in the charged particle detector attributable to neutron induced events in the disks. Our experiments are consistent with these neutron induced events being due to fast neutron induced fission of ^{238}U. We surmise that we are detecting the more energetic β decays of the fission products which occur within about the first 100 seconds following fission. The efficiency with which neutron induced events in the disks produced signals in the charged particle detector is calculated to be approximately 50%.

This suggests the possibility of constructing fast neutron threshold detectors from thickness of ^{238}U on the order of 1mm. A flux of 7-8 MeV neutrons passing through a 1 mm thick layer of ^{238}U has roughly a 0.5% probability of inducing a fission. If a detector could detect these fission events about 50% of the time, then the overall neutron detection efficiency would be about 0.25%. This number is large enough that it would be possible to construct a fast neutron threshold detector with a several percent efficiency without using an unreasonably large number of layers.

FUTURE WORK

We plan to continue this work in order to more completely understand the process of detection of fission events in thick layers of ^{238}U. This work will use high isotopic purity ^{238}U disks of varying thicknesses. We will also consider fast neutron fissionable isotopes other than ^{238}U. Sources of neutron flux in addition to ^{252}Cf will be employed. We also plan to closely monitor neutron fluxes using a neutron scintillator as a spectrometer. Detailed neutron multiple scattering and absorption calculations will aid in the interpretation of our results.

We also plan to fully investigate the possibilities for constructing a fast neutron threshold detector from such thick layers of fast neutron fissionable material. This will include investigating methods of suppression of the background in these disks due to α particle decay and also determining the best type of charged particle detector to use. We used solid state charged particle detectors in our experiments because they are an ideal research tool, however, they are most likely not the idea choice in an actual detector due to their sensitivity to neutrons and their expense. In order to enhance the threshold nature of such a detector we plan to use passive shielding designed to suppress slow/thermal neutrons.

REFERENCES

1. J.B. Marion and J.L. Fowler, Fast Neutron Physics Part I, Vol. IV, Interscience Publishers, (1960), ch. III.E, pp. 449-506.

2. J.R. Stehn, et al., Neutron Cross Sections Vol. III, Z=88 to 98, Brookhaven National Laboratory, BNL 325, NY, (1965).

3. TGM DETECTORS, INC., Short Form Catalog (REV.2), TGM DETECTORS, INC., Waltham, MA, (1988).

4. Harald Enge, Introduction to Nuclear Physics, Addison-Wesley Publishing Co., Inc., Reading, MA, (1966), p. 440.

5. H. Soodak, Reactor Handbook Volume III, Interscience Publishers, NY, (1962), ch. 1, pp. 3-59.

6. E.K. Hyde, The Nuclear Properties of the Heavy Elements Vol. III, Dover Publications, Inc., NY, (1971), ch. 4, pp. 87-140.

7. J.B. Marion and F.C. Young, Nuclear Reaction Analysis, John Wiley & Sons, NY, (1968), ch. I & V, pp. 1-27, 97-105.

8. R.B. Leachman, <u>Emission Probabilities of</u>
    <u>Prompt Neutrons from Spontaneous and</u>
    <u>Neutron-induced Fission</u>, USAEC Report
    LA-1863, Los Alamos Scientific Laboratory,
    Los Alamos, NM, (1954).

9. E.J. Kobetich and R. Katz, "Energy
    Deposition by Electron Beams and δ Rays,"
    <u>Phys. Rev. 170</u>, 391 (1968).

10. W.J. Stapor and P.T. McDonald, "Practical
    approach to ion track energy distribution,"
    <u>J. Appl. Phys. 64</u>, 443 (1988).

11. C.D. Coryell and N. Sugarman, <u>Radiochemical</u>
    <u>Studies: The Fission Products, Book 1</u>,
    McGraw-Hill Book Co., Inc., NY, (1951),
    p. 341, 436-458.

12. K.Way and E.P. Wigner, "Rate of Decay of
    Fission Products," <u>Phys. Rev. 73</u>, 1318
    (1948).

13. R.C. Weast, editor, <u>Handbook of Chemistry</u>
    <u>and Physics</u>, Edition 56, CRC Press, (1975),
    pp. B39-B40.

14. T. Wiedling, "Microscopic Fission Neutron
    Spectra Measurements", <u>Proceedings of the</u>
    <u>Neutron Standards and Flux Normalization</u>
    <u>Symposium</u>, Argonne, IL, (1970), pp. 437-451.

15. H. Goldstein, <u>Fundamental Aspects of Reactor</u>
    <u>Shielding</u>, MA:: Addison-Wesley Publishing
    Company, (1959), ch. 6, pp. 243-342.

STUDIES OF FRAGMENT CHARGE AND ENERGY

CORRELATIONS IN SPONTANEOUS FISSION OF ^{252}Cf

M. N. Rao
Institute of Physics
Bhubaneswar
India, 751005

D. C. Biswas, R. K. Choudhury
Bhabha Atomic Research Centre
Bombay
India, 400 085

ABSTRACT

Fragment charge and energy correlations in fission provide useful information on the shell and pairing effects and the dynamics of the fission process. In the present experiment, fragment charge measurement was done by the energy loss technique using a gas detector telescope. A charge resolution (FWHM) of 1.8 charge units was achieved for the light fragments in spontaneous fission of ^{252}Cf. The odd-even Z effect (δ) in the charge yields was determined from the measured charge distributions as a function of kinetic energy of the fragments. It is seen that δ depends on the excitation energy of the fragments. The average kinetic energy, however, has no noticeable odd-even charge effect.

INTRODUCTION

Nuclear fission process involves large scale rearrangement of nuclear matter and offers the possibility of studying both the microscopic and macroscopic properties of the nucleus undergoing fission. At low energies. the shell and pairing effects are quite dominant and govern the characteristics of the fission fragments. Experimental studies of mass, charge and energy correlations of the fragments can provide useful information on the shell and pairing effects as well as on the dynamics of the fission process. Radiochemical methods have been extensively used in the past to measure the fragment charge yields. Among the physical methods, the measurement of x-rays and γ-rays emitted by the fission fragments provide information on the charge of the fragments. Recently, attempts have been made to carry out fragment charge and energy measurements using gas detector telescopes.[1] Optimum charge resolution in the range of fission fragment energies can be achieved by measuring the detector response function as a function of charge and energy of fission fragments. The present experiment is aimed at studying the energy loss behavior of fragments in a gas medium and measurement of charge,

energy correlations using a gas detector telescope. The results are discussed on the basis of the fission mechanism and the role of pairing correlations in the fission process.

EXPERIMENTAL SETUP AND DATA ANALYSIS

The detector telescope consisted of a gas ionization chamber (10 cm active length) for energy loss (DE) and a surface barrier detector for residual energy (E_R) measurements as shown in Fig. 1. The ^{252}Cf source was mounted inside the detector, and P-10 gas was filled at 110 torr pressure. The surface barrier detector was collimated to detect the fragments in a narrow cone in order to minimize the dispersion in the path length in the gas detector. The pulse height information from the DE and E_R detectors were recorded for about 8×10^6 events.

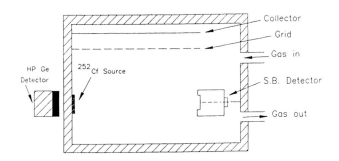

Fig. 1. Schematic diagram of the experimental set up.

In order to determine the response of the gas detector to different charge (Z) and energy of fragments, the DE and E_R data were also collected in coincidence with x-rays detected in a HPGe detector. A total of 2.2×10^5 triple coincidence events were recorded. Data analysis was carried out only for the events in which light fragments were detected in the telescope and heavy fragment x-rays were detected in the HPGe detector. In this case,

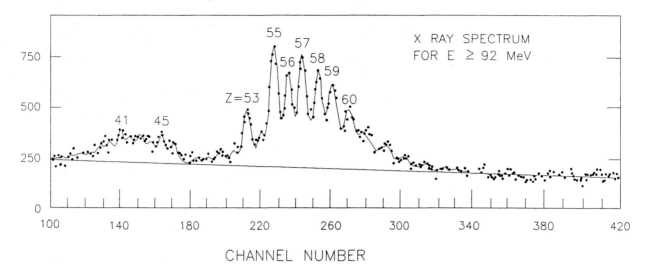

Fig. 2.   X-ray spectrum of fragments in ^{252}Cf fission measured in coincidence with
light fragments entering the gas detector.   (See text).

the doppler shift of the x-rays is eliminated, thereby improving the energy resolution of x-ray detection.   Fig. 2 shows the x-ray spectrum measured in this manner.   The peaks corresponding to each fragment charge have been identified in the figure.   The energy loss (DE) distribution for each fragment charge and 1 MeV window on the light fragment energy ($E=DE+E_R$) was determined after correcting for the continuum background under each peak.   The most probable energy loss (DE_p) is shown in Fig. 3 as a function of E for different fragment charges.   These results provide important data for understanding the energy loss behavior of fission fragments in a gas medium.

The energy loss in a given gas length (L mg/cm^2) can be written as

$$DE = \int_0^L \frac{dE}{dx} \, dx$$

where $\dfrac{dE}{dx} = \dfrac{K Z_{eff}^2}{\beta^2} \dfrac{Z_M}{A_M} \ln \left(\dfrac{m_e \beta^2 c^2}{I} \right),$

Z_M, A_M and I are the atomic number, mass number and mean ionization energy of atoms in the medium, m_e is electron mass.   The effective charge Z_{eff} is given by the simple Bohr expression as

$$Z_{eff} = \gamma Z = Z \left(1 - a_1 \exp \left(-a_3 V_R \right) \right)$$

where $V_R = \dfrac{V}{V_o} Z^n$, and V_o is orbital velocities of electrons in the first Bohr orbit of hydrogen atom; a_1, a_3 and n are constants.

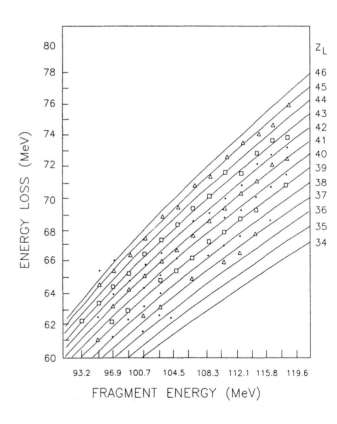

Fig. 3.   Most probable energy loss in the gas detector as a function of E and Z of the fragment.

882

The present data on dEp versus E for various fragment charges could not be well reproduced by the above simple expression. However, much better fit could be achieved by adding small correction terms to the coefficients of the above expression as given by

$$Z_{eff} = Z \left(1-(a_1+a_2/E^2) \exp \left(-a_3V_R+a_4V_R^2\right)\right)$$

and the results of the fit are shown in Fig. 3.

The above expression was, therefore, used to determine Z event by event. The response function of the detector to different charges was measured by calculating the Z distribution for windows on various x-ray peaks, which are shown in Fig. 4, after correcting for the continuum background under each peak. The resolution in Z as obtained from the widths of these distributions is 1.8 charge units for all charges and kinetic energies of fragments. The calculated Z-distributions from the DE-E data is unfolded using the measured response function to obtain the fragment charge yields. The unfolding method was tested by determining the charge yield in coincidence with x-rays, which agreed quite well with the k x-ray yields of the x-ray spectrum. The full DE-E data were analyzed by the above procedure to obtain the primary fission fragment charge yields.

RESULTS AND DISCUSSION

The charge yield distribution of light fragments for all events is shown in Fig. 5. The odd-even effect can be quantitatively defined to be the difference between the yields of even and odd charges normalized to the total yield as given by

$$\delta = (\Sigma_e - \Sigma_o)/(\Sigma_e + \Sigma_o)$$

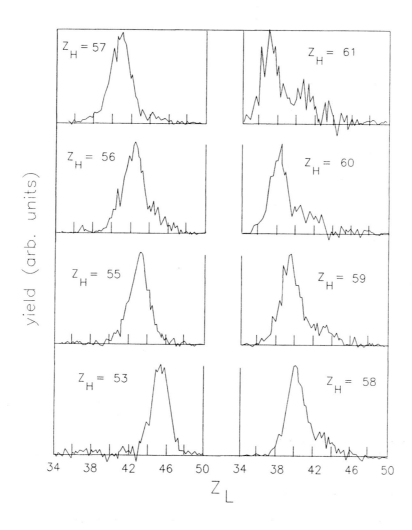

Fig. 4. Response function of the gas detector for different heavy fragment K X-ray windows.

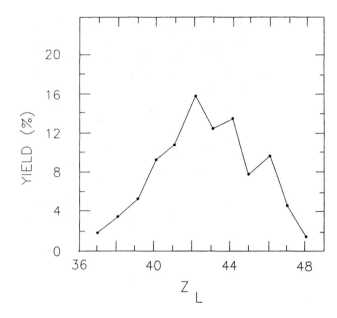

Fig. 5.   Distribution of light fragment charge
yields.

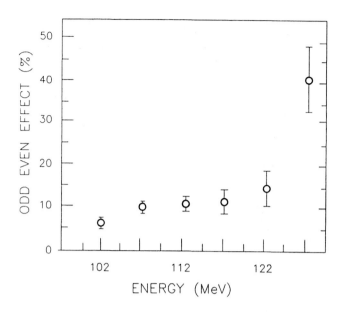

Fig. 6.   Odd-even effect (δ) as function of
fragment kinetic energy.

The average odd-even effect for all events
is seen to be 0.12±0.01 and agrees well with
the results obtained earlier by Mariolopoulos
et al.[2]   The variation of the odd-even effect
with excitation energy is studied by
determining the value of δ for different
kinetic energy windows, as shown in Fig. 6.   It
is seen that for very high kinetic energies, δ
increases sharply to about 0.4 so that the
yield of even charges is more than twice the
yield of odd charges.   Similar variations have
also been seen in thermal neutron fission of
^{229}Th and ^{235}U.[2,3]   Enhanced yield of even-Z
fragments over the odd-Z fragments arises due
to the fact that for production of odd-Z
fragments, it is necessary to break a proton
pair in the fissioning nucleus.   The
probability of breaking a pair depends on the
excitation energy and the pairing gap.   It is
also seen from earlier experiments[2] that the
odd-even effect depends strongly on the
fragment charge, suggesting that pair breaking
occurs closer to the scission point where
fragment pairs are formed rather than at the
saddle point.   Also since δ is fairly
independent of kinetic energy, the excitation
energy at scission point is fairly independent
of the final kinetic energy except for the cold
fission events corresponding to the highest
kinetic energy window.

It is also interesting to estimate the
odd-even effect on the kinetic energy
distribution of the fragments.   This is related
to the question of odd-even effect in neutron
and gamma emission.   Recently it was shown by

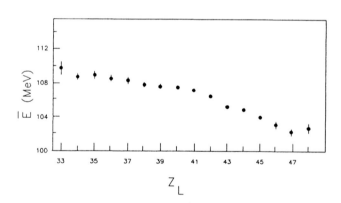

Fig. 7.   Average fragment kinetic energy as
function of charge.

Walsh[4] that the excess energy available for the
even-Z nuclei over the odd-Z nuclei due to Q
value difference appears in the form of neutron
and gamma ray yields.   Present results on the
average fragment kinetic energy as function of
Z (Fig. 7) show that there is no noticeable
odd-even effect on the kinetic energy of
fragments supporting the observation of Walsh.

SUMMARY

Fragment charge, energy measurements have been carried out using a gas detector telescope. The results on the energy loss of light fragments in the gas detector for various Z and kinetic energy were used to determine an empirical expression for Z_{eff} of the fission fragments. The measured detector response function was used to unfold the Z-distribution to obtain the primary fragment charge yields. The odd-even effect (δ) is seen to be fairly independent of kinetic energy of the fragments except at very large kinetic energies corresponding to cold fission events. It is also seen that there is no noticeable odd-even effect on the kinetic energy of the fission fragments.

ACKNOWLEDGEMENT

One of the authors (RKC) wishes to thank Prof. J. B. Natowitz for his kind hospitality at Texas A&M University, where this paper was written. The financial support of The Welch Foundation during the stay at Texas A&M is also gratefully acknowledged.

REFERENCES

1. G. MARIOLOPOULOS, J. P. BOCQUET, R. BRISSOT, H. NIFENECKER, CH. RISTORI, A. PECQUET, J. GIRARD, "A New Experimental Method to Measure the Charge Distributions of Fission Products," Nucl. Instr. and Meth., 180, 141 (1981).

2. G. MARIOLOPOULOS, CH. HAMELIN, J. BLACHOT, J. P. BOCQUET, R. BRISSOT, J. CRANCON, H. NIFENECKER, CH. RISTORI, "Charge Distributions in Low Energy Nuclear Fission and their Relevance to Fission Dynamics," Nucl. Phys., A361, 213 (1981).

3. H. G. CLERC, W. LANG, H. WOHLFARTH, H. SCHRADER, K. H. SCHMIDT, "Detailed Study of the Nuclide Yields in ^{235}U (N_{th},f) and Their Relation to the Dynamics of the Fission Process," Proc. 4th IAEA Symposium on Physics and Chemistry of Fission, Julich, Vol. II, 65 (1979).

4. R. L. WALSH, "Variation of Even-Odd Proton Effects with Excitation Energy in Fission of ^{252}Cf: Confirmation of Fine Structure in V(A)," Nucl. Phys. A469, 333 (1987).

YTTRIUM-90 FOR CANCER

RADIOIMMUNOTHERAPY

H.B. Hupf, P.M. Wanek, B. Barbosa, J.K. Poggenburg
Hybritech Incorporated
P.O. Box 269006
San Diego, California 92126-9006
(619) 578-9800

ABSTRACT

An ideal radiopharmaceutical for cancer therapy must provide a sufficient radiation dose to destroy all the viable malignant cells while sparing normal cells of critical body organs. The strategy implies a radionuclide with high linear energy transfer, a moderate range in tissue and a high equilibrium dose constant be delivered specifically to target cells. Yttrium-90 coupled with tumor-cell-specific antibody approaches the ideal product necessary for radioimmunotherapy. Yttrium-90 is separated from its fission by-product parent Sr-90, purified and aseptically coupled with an antibody conjugate to prepare a therapy radiopharmaceutical. The same antibody conjugate is labeled with In-111 and used after injection for estimating tumor targeting and therapy planning. A dedicated robotic facility has been constructed for safe handling of the large quantities of radioactive materials used. Several Phase I clinical protocols using the Y-90 and In-111 antibody labeled matched pair have been initiated, providing excellent safety results and several tumor remissions.

INTRODUCTION

When an incident particle transfers sufficient energy to a critical area within a cell the result is cell death. The mechanism of the energy transfer is through active radicals and the critical area is the nucleus. Insufficient energy transfer or transfer to a non-critical cell area ususally leads to total recovery of the cell. Between cell death and cell recovery, there is an area of reproductive cell death where the struck cell is physically present and apparently intact, but unable to synthesize DNA. Radiation doses of 200 rad or cGy can often produce reproductive cell death[1]. Successful therapy with radionuclides must deliver a sufficient radiation dose to produce reproductive cell death in all the viable malignant cells while delivering a sub-critical dose to normal healthy cells of critical body organs. The delivery system for the radionuclide must, therefore, exhibit a high degree of specificity for tumor cells vs. normal cells and must remain associated with the malignant cells during the useful life of the radionuclide. Our strategy for therapy is to couple a radionuclide with beta decay and a high equilibrium dose constant to a monoclonal antibody having a demonstrated high affinity for tumor cells and low affinity for normal tissue. The goal is to deliver 20 Gy to the tumor mass. The paper describes portions of our work to achieve cancer radioimmunotherapy with Y-90.

RADIONUCLIDES

Numerous radionuclides have been mentioned as potential candidates for radiotherapy and include Cu-67, Y-90, I-131, Sm-153, Re-186, Re-188 and At-211[2]. Table 1 is a comparison of some of their important properties. The characteristics of an ideal therapy radionuclide will vary somewhat depending upon the clinical use and its biodistribution, but can be listed generally as follows: high linear energy transfer (LET), high equilibrium dose constant, single imageable gamma emission, 3 to 5 day half-life, readily available in large quantities at a reasonable cost and moderate range in tissue (0.2 to 0.6 cm).

Both alpha and beta emitters have a place in radiotherapy, however, for different uses. Alpha particles produce a high number of ion-pairs per micron path and will generally destroy a struck target cell. Alpha particles in the 5 MeV range have a path length in tissue approximately equal to one cell diameter, which limits their usefulness in solid or soft tissue tumors, but may be very useful for destroying micrometastases. On the other hand, beta particles in the range of 2 MeV produce about 5 ion-pairs per micron path, have an average range of about 30 cell diameters and should be useful for tumor radiotherapy[3]. A cell strike by a beta particle may cause temporary damage followed by complete recover of the cell necessitating use of the highest radiation dose tolerable for effective therapy.

Yttrium-90 (T1/2=64.1 h, Emax (beta)=2.28 MeV, 1.99 gm-rad/uCi-hr) is nearly ideal for tumor radiotherapy. It is readily available in large quantities obtained through chemical separation from its radioactive parent Sr-90 (T1/2=28.6 Y), a by-product of fission reactors. The absence of a gamma for imaging and Y-90's potential for bone marrow toxicity need to be addressed. Hybritech has addressed these issues by using chelation chemistry which binds Y-90 and In-111 in a stable complex which is covalently bound to a polyclonal or monoclonal antibody. The antibody isothiocyanatobenzyl DTPA chelate conjugate[4] binds In-111 (T1/2=67.4 h, 171 & 245 keV gammas) which is used for imaging and assessment of the Y-90 activity required for therapy. Initial specific activities between 30 and 60 mCi Y-90 per mg antibody have been prepared and used for animal and clinical studies. The stability of the Y-90 antibody complex has been studied over a 5 day storage period. There is approximately 1% loss of antibody-bound Y-90 per day when stored between 2 and 8° C. No significant loss of immunoreactivity is incurred during the labeling stage.

Curie quantities of Y-90 are separated from Sr-90 by solvent extraction techniques using di-(2 ethylhexyl) phosphoric acid in dodecane and 0.1 M hydrochloric acid. It is necessary to further purify the Y-90 chloride to obtain consistently high incorporation into conjugated antibodies. To accomplish this task, we constructed a shielded facility containing a robot programmed to perform the additional purification, remove appropriate test samples and dispense the product into a serum vial for sterilization by autoclaving. The antibody labeling procedure is performed aseptically in a class 100 shielded glove box.

ANTIBODIES

Polyclonal antibodies are prepared by immunizing animals, such as rabbits or pigs, with the appropriate antigen and harvesting the in-vivo produced antibodies from the sera. Following purification, the immune globulin product may contain only a small fraction of the desired antibody. Monoclonal antibodies are prepared by immunizing mice with the appropriate antigen, removing antibody-secreting spleen cells and fusing them with mouse myeloma to form hybridomas[5]. After selecting the hybridomas producing the antibody with the desired tissue reactivity, the hybridomas may be grown in mouse ascites or in fermentation tanks where they will secrete the desired antibodies. Furthermore, the hybridomas may be stored frozen for long periods, thawed and grown again when needed. Purification from ascites or media results in a product having 70 to 95% of the specific monoclonal antibody. The high percent immunoreactivity of the product, when compared with polyclonals, generates optimism that sufficient specificity will be achieved using monoclonal antibodies for effective tumor therapy when coupled with Y-90.

RADIATION DOSIMETRY

Estimation of absorbed dose to tumor and normal tissues is an integral part of radiotherapy. The general formula for calculating absorbed dose rate in rad/hr is[6]:

$$D* = \bar{A}/m \times \Delta \quad \text{where}$$

$\bar{A}$ is tissue activity in uCi, m is target mass in gm and Δ is the equilibrium dose constant in gm-rad/uCi-hr; a constant for each radionuclide. Total dose in rads can be calculated by integration over time if the tissue kinetics are known. Determination of the kinetics, $\bar{A}$ and m is not difficult using mice or rats since the target tissues can be dissected, weighed and assayed at various time points. Figures 1 and 2 are typical biodistributions in normal mice at 4 and 48 hours with Y-90 and In-111. Therapy can be demonstrated through the use of transplanted tumor models. In one of numerous studies, we transplanted T380 tumors into 5 groups of nude mice. When the tumors were between 0.3 and 0.5gm, each group was injected with either saline, Y-90-DTPA, unlabeled specific antibody (ZCE025), Y-90 specific antibody (ZCE025) and Y-90 ZME018 antibody specific for a different tumor type. The average tumor doubling time for all groups except the Y-90 specific antibody was ten days. For a single 200 uCi injection of Y-90 specific antibody, the tumors decreased to less than 0.1 mg and began to increase slowly after about 80 days. Many of the mice in the control groups were dead by 80 days. Figure 3 is a typical tumor response curve.

For non-penetrating radiation (alphas, betas, conversion and auger electrons) the total absorbed dose, D, can be simplified to:

$$D = A \Delta \quad \text{where}$$

A is the cumulated activity per gram in the tissue or organ and Δ is the equilibrium dose constant for the particular radionuclide. The value of A depends upon the physical half-life of the radionuclide and its in-vivo distribution kinetics. For a simple kinetic model of near exponential decrease of activity in the tumor or organ with respect to time, A becomes:

$$A = 1.44 \, T_{eff} \, Ao \, (1-\exp(-0.693t/T_{eff})) \quad \text{where}$$

T_{eff} = effective half-life and Ao is the activity in the tissue at time t=0. Assuming 1 uCi of a Y-90 labeled antibody per gm tissue is bound to the tumor for 10 days ($T_{eff} = T_{1/2}$), the total dose becomes:

$$D = 1.44 \, T_{1/2}(1-\exp(-0.693 \times 240/T_{1/2})) \times \Delta$$

$$D = 85.41 \text{ uCi-hr/gm} \times 1.99 \text{ gm-rad/uCi-hr} = 170 \text{ rad}$$

CLINICALS

Determination of kinetics and tissue activity

to calculate rad doses in humans is more complicated. Computer software to estimate the parameters necessary to calculate absorbed dose using I-131 imaging and CAT scanning has been developed[7] and modified for the In-111/Y-90 system. Regions of interest are identified and dose rates to tumor and normal tissues are estimated at various time points. Several Phase I/II clinical therapy protocols primarily designed to evaluate Y-90 safety have been initiated. Over 100 hepatoma patients have been imaged with In-111 labeled polyclonal antiferritin[8]. Of these, 46 exhibited tumor/normal targeting ratios permitting treatment with the Y-90 labeled radiopharmaceutical. Doses typically were 20 mCi, with some patients receiving second and third courses. Safety of the chelated radiopharmaceutical was established with no evidence of release of the radioisotope in-vivo, and a reversible suppression of blood element formation as the main radiotoxic effect which was consistent with that observed with equivalent exposure from external radiation beams. One patient showed remission for over a year, and 5 others showed partial remissions with several conversions to resectable disease[9]. While clinical efficacy has not justified a continuance of this protocol, the safety of the system has been demonstrated. The same radiopharmaceutical has had more promising results in a continuing trial with Hodgkins' disease patients who have failed primary chemotherapy[10]. Of ten patients treated with 10 to 40 mCi Y-90 antiferritin, 3 had complete remission, one partial response and two progressed. The additional patients have not been evaluated yet.

Clinical studies using In-111 and Y-90 labeled T-101 monoclonal antibodies for potential treatment of cutaneous T cell lymphoma and chronic lymphocytic leukemia are underway at the National Cancer Institute. Additionally, radio-labeled anti-idiotype monoclonal antibodies against idiotypic B cell lymphomas have been initiated[11].

REFERENCES

1. E.J. HALL, Radiobiology for the Radiologist, 2nd ed. Harper and Row, New York, (1978).
2. E.L. SAENGER, J.G. KEREIAKES, V.J. SODD et al., "Radiotherapeutic Agents: Properties, Dosimetry and Radiobiologic Considerations," Sem. Nucl. Med. IX:72-84, 1979.
3. F. HOSAIN and P. HOSAIN, "Selection of Radionuclides for Therapy," in R.P. SPENCER, Ed., Therapy in Nuclear Medicine. Grune & Stratton, New York, (1978).
4. C.F. MEARES, M.J. McCALL, D.T. REARDAN, et al., "Conjugation of Antibodies with Bifunctional Chelating Agents," Anal. Biochem., 142,68-78 (1984)
5. G. KOHLER and C. MILSTEIN, " Continuous Cultures of Fused Cells Secreting Antibody of Predefined Specificity," Nature 256, 494-497 (1975).
6. R.J. CLOUTIER, E.E. WATSON, and J.L. COFFEE, "Radiopharmaceutical Dose Calculation," In J. HALBERT and A. DaROCHA (Eds): Textbook of Nuclear Medicine, Vol. 1, 2nd ed., Lea & Febiger, Philadelphia, (1984).
7. P.K. LEICHNER, J.L. KLEIN, J.B. GARRISON et al., "Dosimetry of I-131 Labeled Antiferritin in Hepatoma," Int. J. Radiat. Oncol. Biol. Phys., 71, 323-333 (1981).
8. S.E. ORDER et al., "Yttrium-90 Antiferritin - A New Therapeutic Radiolabeled Antibody," Int. J. Radiat. Oncol. Biol. Phys., 12, 277-281 (1986)
9. J.V. SITZMAN, et al., "Conversion by New Treatment Modalities of Non-resectable to Resectable Hepatocellular Cancer," J. Clin. Oncol. 5, 1566-1573 (1987).
10. H.M. VRIESENDORP, J.M. HERPST, R.N. LEICHNER et al., "Polyclonal 90-Yttrium Labeled Antiferritin for Refractory Hodgkins Disease," Presented at Annual ASTRO Meeting, New Orleans, October (1988).
11. B.A. PARKER, A.B. VASSOS, S.E. HALPERN et. al., "Radioimmunotherapy of Human B Cell Lymphoma with 90-Yttrium Conjugated Anti-iodiotype Monoclonal Antibody," Submitted to Cancer Research, December, 1988.

TABLE I. COMPARISON OF THERAPY RADIONUCLIDES

	^{67}Cu	^{90}Y	^{131}I	^{153}Sm	^{186}Re	^{188}Re	^{211}At
Equilibrium Dose Constant Δ, $g\text{-}rad/\mu Ci\text{-}hr$	0.3	1.99	0.99	0.48	0.69	1.63	5.21
Range in Tissue, cm non-penetrating radiation	0.02	0.3	0.03	0.04	0.11	0.03	0.01
Readily Available In Quantity	Y/N	Y	Y	N	Y	N	N
Relative Cost	MED	LOW	LOW	HIGH	HIGH	HIGH	V. HIGH
Half-life, hr	61.8	64.1	192	46.7	90.6	17	7.2
Imageable Gamma	Y	N	Y	Y	Y	Y	N
Relative LET	+	++	+	+	+	+	++++

β Range in Tissue, 2 MeV max: About 30 cell diameters
α Range in Tissue, 5 MeV: About 1 cell diameter

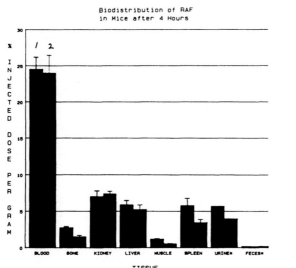

Biodistribution of RAF
in Mice after 4 Hours

FIGURE 1   % TOTAL INJECTED DOSE

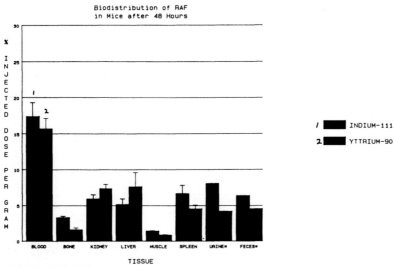

Biodistribution of RAF
in Mice after 48 Hours

FIGURE 2   % TOTAL INJECTED DOSE

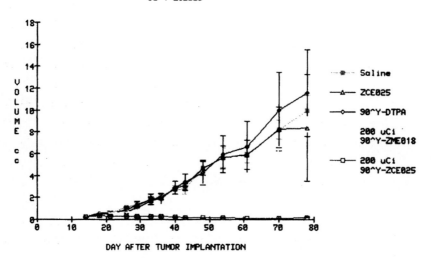

RESPONSE OF T380 XENOGRAFTS IN NUDE MICE TO
90^Y-ZCE025

FIGURE 3

URANIUM TRACE ANALYSIS IN HUMAN BLOOD USING

FISSION TRACK TECHNIQUE

Y. CHENG, J. LIN, L. ZHENG
Institute of Nuclear Research
Academia Sinica
P. O. Box 8204,
Shanghai 201849 China
950998

H. TANG, Z. WENG
Institute of Radiation Medicine
2094 Xietu Road,
Shanghai China
372620

ABSTRACT

Fission track technique makes the measurement of the content of uranium in human blood. By choosing solid state nuclear track detectors of the high sensitivity, uranium can be determined using $U(n,f)$ reaction. Blood samples are directly taken from finger (0.02ml) and irradiated in a nuclear reactor at a thermal neutron flux of 3.5×10^{16} n/cm^2.

In normal human blood, the uranium contents varied from 2.43 to 3.80 $\times$ 10^{-10} g/ml, the average of the values is $(3.06 \pm 0.10) \times 10^{-10}$ g/ml. In U-exposed workers blood, it varied from 3.07 to 5.57 $\times 10^{-10}$ g/ml, the average value is $(4.53 \pm 0.12) \times 10^{-10}$ g/ml. In leukaemia patients blood, 3.90 to 12.07 $\times 10^{-10}$ g/ml, the mean U-content is $(7.74 \pm 0.15) \times 10^{-10}$ g/ml, which is 2.5 times higher than the mean of normal human blood.

These results show a possible relation between the leukaemia and the uranium content in the blood. If there is such a relationship, the Nuclear Fission Track Technique will be an important diagnostic tool in Medicine.

INTRODUCTION

Several techniques are described in the literature for the determination of trace uranium by alpha-counting, fluorometry, and activation analysis. The last technique is especially attractive in that it offers a variety of methods for trace analysis which are fast and simple and have good sensitivity. Of course, the fission track technique seems to be the most favorable because there is no requirement for yield correction or for testing radiochemical purity by half-life measurement. This technique is successfully used to determine the U-content in biological materials.

Man-made mica is chosen as the fission track detector. By exposing the samples only to a thermal neutron flux, fission tracks can be produced using U(n,f) reaction. This eliminates interference by thorium which undergoes only fast neutron fission. Plutonium would interfere, but is very unlikely to be present. The advantages of the fission track method are sensitivity and selectivity for determining U-content in human blood.

The whole biotic community of our biosphere can not avoid the radiation effects. Among the different radioactive isotopes, uranium is the heaviest trace element occuring in nature. Uranium and its salts are highly toxic. The tetravalent form of natural uranium is unstable and is oxidized to the more toxic hexavalent form. Hence, the presence of uranium in any biological material even in traces may have some radiation effects. Blood is the fluid medium through which the toxic substances are transfused to be deposited in or removed from other organs, particularly uranium in blood. It is prudent that U-exposure even at low levels for a long period brings about some harmful effects. It is therefore of great importance to investigate the U-content in blood of diseased patients and normal human. The investigation is directly linked to the development of nuclear technology and the necessity for establishing background values of U-content in blood.

EXPERIMENTAL TECHNIQUES

Nuclear Track Detector. Fission fragments arising from the fission of uranium and other heavy elements will produce tracks in polycarbonate, and mica. These detectors are also insensitive to protons, deuterons, and alpha particles, all of which are commonly produced in nuclear reactions. The U-content in the man-made mica is the lowest value ($X 10^{-14}$ g/cm^2) for most detectors. This is the reason man-made mica is chosen as the Solid State Nuclear Track Detector.

Blood Samples Preparation. Known volumes of blood samples (0.02 ml) were directly taken from finger, and pipetted onto a man-made mica detector (thickness >50 um, diameter 1.4 cm). The whole blood on the detectors were then dried at room temperature. After drying, the samples were covered with detectods of same diameter. All samples were stacked as a cylindrical unit, along with blank detectors, in an aluminium container whose cap was tightly screwed to ensure a good contact between blood samples and detectors, and irradiated in the nuclear reactor at a thermal neutron flux of $3.5 X 10^{16}$ n/cm^2.

To determine the blank contribution of uranium from environment, these blank slides were irradiated and etched along with the blood sample slides. The blank slides were found to contain $2.5 X 10^{-13}$ g/cm^2.

Etching. After irradiation, the blood layer was removed and the mica detectors were etched for 6 minutes in 48% HF at $(70 \pm 5)^{o}C$. The enlarged fission tracks were then counted with the aid of an optical microscope. Standard deviation of tracks counting was between 5 and 10%.

U-content Evaluation. By the fission track technique, U-content in blood can be determined using the U(n,f) reaction. After putting the values of

TABLE 1   U-CONTENT IN HUMAN BLOOD

SAMPLES	NO.	AGE	TOTAL TRACKS	U-CONTENT ($\times 10^{-10}$ G/ML)
NORMAL HUMAN				
	1	32	1155	3.56 ± 0.10
	2	45	995	3.06 ± 0.09
	3	34	790	2.43 ± 0.08
	4	48	950	2.93 ± 0.09
	5	42	1220	3.76 ± 0.11
	6	28	1230	3.80 ± 0.11
	7	30	873	2.69 ± 0.09
	8	33	815	2.51 ± 0.09
	9	36	1030	3.17 ± 0.10
	10	49	895	2.76 ± 0.09
MEAN VALUE			995	3.06 ± 0.09
U-EXPOSED WORKERS				
	1	47	998	3.07 ± 0.10
	2	49	1755	5.41 ± 0.13
	3	45	1320	4.07 ± 0.11
	4	48	1810	5.57 ± 0.13
MEAN VALUE			1471	4.53 ± 0.12
LEUKAEMIA				
	1	35	1265	3.90 ± 0.11
	2	28	3920	12.07 ± 0.19
	3	49	2353	7.25 ± 0.15
MEAN VALUE			2513	7.74 ± 0.15

TABLE 2   THE MEAN VALUES OF U-CONTENT IN BLOOD ($\times 10^{-10}$ G/ML)

COUNTRY	NORMAL HUMAN	U-EXPOSED WORKERS	LEUKAEMIA	SAMPLES PREPARATION
DENMARK	4.8		30.5	FREEZE DRY
MEXICO	9.1	9.8	17.1	FREEZE DRY
CHINA	3.1	4.5	7.7	TO BE TAKEN FROM FINGER

893

constants in the formula given by Fleisher,[1] the U-content in the blood samples is calculated by the following relation:

$$U_c = 186.4 \; T/V\varnothing \; g/ml$$

where
T = total number of tracks
V = volume of the blood taken
$\varnothing$ = thermal neutron flux

RESULTS AND DISCUSSION

The estimated values of U-content in various blood samples are shown in table 1. The uranium level in normal human blood is estimated to be (2.43 to 3.80) X 10^{-10} g/ml with over all average value (3.06 ± 0.10) X 10^{-10} g/ml. In U-exposed workers blood, it varied from 3.07 to 5.57 X 10^{-10} g/ml with average value (4.53 ± 0.12) X 10^{-10} g/ml, this result is 48% higher than the mean of the normal human blood. In leukaemia patients blood, 3.90 to 12.07 X 10^{-10} g/ml. The average value is (7.74 ± 0.15) X 10^{-10} g/ml, it is 2.5 times higher than the mean of the normal human.

Results reported by Koul,[2] Segovia[3] and the present work are shown in table 2. These results show a possible relation between the leukaemia and the U-content in the blood. In these results the sampling was scarce (3 cases reported by Koul, 8 cases by Segovia and 3 cases in the present study) and lacking in medical history. A larger sampling is in project in which both leukaemia and other diseased blood will be analyzed. If there is such a relationship the Nuclear Fission Track Technique will be an important diagnostic tool in Medicine.

ACKNOMLEDGEMENTS

The authors are grateful to Prof. Jiahua Zhang and senior engineer Guigang Wu for many valuable discussions , and to Xiuhong Hao for the reactor irradiations.

REFERENCES

1. R. L. FLEISCHER, D. B. LOVETT, "Uranium and Boron Content of Water by Particle Track Etching", Geochimica et Cosmochimica Acta, 32, 1126 (1968).

2. S. L. KOUL, L. T. CHADDERTON, "Uranium in Blood", Radiation Effects Letters, 50, 19 (1979).

3. N. SEGOVIA, M. E. OLGUIN, M. ROMERO "Studies of U in the Blood of two Population Samples", Nuclear Tracks, 12, 797 (1986).

POSTER SESSION:
FISSION DATA, ASTROPHYSICS, AND SPACE APPLICATIONS

PRODUCTION RATES OF COSMOGENIC NUCLIDES IN STONY METEORITES*

M. Divadeenam
Brookhaven National Laboratory
Upton, NY 11973

O. Lazareth
Brookhaven National Laboratory
Upton, NY 11973

T.E. Ward
Brookhaven National Laboratory
Upton, NY 11973

T. A. Gabriel
Oak Ridge National Laboratory
Oak Ridge, TN 37831

M. S. Spergel
York College, CUNY
Jamaica, NY 11451

ABSTRACT

Intranuclear Cascade Model Monte Carlo calculations of ^{26}Al and ^{53}Mn production due to spallation induced by cosmogenic protons in model meteorite composition similar to L Chondrite has yielded predictions which are consistent with the observed decay rates in L Chondrite stony meteorites. The calculated ^{26}Al production rate (54 dpm/kg) in a 1 m diameter meteorite is within 1/2 S.D. of the mean (49 ± 11 dpm/kg) taken from 100 bulk determinations in L Chondrite samples compiled in Nishiizumi (1987). Similarly calculated average value for ^{53}Mn (223 dpm/kg) is consistent within one S.D. of the mean in the widely scattered ^{53}Mn data (362 ± 113 dpm/kg) compiled by Nishiizumi (1987). The production rates of ^{12}C, ^{13}C, and ^{14}C are also predicted. A physically meaningful sampling of the galactic cosmic ray proton spectrum warrants an extensive set of Monte Carlo calculations.

INTRODUCTION

In our calculations, use is made of Monte Carlo techniques for identifying nuclear collisions and specific nuclear reactions as well as establishing the transport of the incident nucleon and its generated nucleons. It is thus possible to use an integrated calculational approach in predicting the cosmogenic nuclide production rate and depth dependence. Previous calculational approaches have examined the production of nuclides by separating the collision into spallation, neutron capture and fragmentation processes. The calculations use a transport type mechanism for predicting the depth dependence of the cosmic ray induced nuclides (i.e. cosmogenic nuclides). One of the problems in predicting the production of cosmogenic nuclides, as a function of depth in meteorites, has been the need to determine the numerous nucleon–nuclear cross sections and then the subsequent nuclide excitation rates. In the case of neutron capture induced nuclides these difficulties have led many authors (e.g. Eberhardt et al., 1963, Lingenfelter and Ramaty, 1967, Reedy and Arnold, 1972, Reedy et al., 1979 and Reedy, 1985, Spergel et al., 1986) to utilize the similarity in the shape to the production of ^{3}H for predicting the production of neutrons. These tritium rates were normalized to neutron production observations either for the Moon or for Chondrite meteorites.

In particular, the High Energy Intranuclear Cascade (INC) and Internuclear Cascade Transport Code, HETC (Armstrong et al., 1972) is used to calculate directly the nuclide production rate due to spallation. Fast fission process was not considered in the present set of calculations. It is planned to link the neutron source results generated with HETC to the low energy neutron transport code, MORSE. The neutron induced cosmogenic nuclide production will be calculated without the resort to extrapolations of excitation functions.

INC MODEL CALCULATIONS

The isotropic irradiation of a stony asteroid in space is modeled by utilizing the observed cosmic ray proton spectrum up to 200 GeV to select energy and frequency via Monte Carlo techniques. The composition of the bombarded asteroid is taken to be an L Chondrite like composition (Mason, 1979): Oxygen (37%), Iron (22%), Silicon (19%), Magnesium (15%) with lesser amounts of other refractory elements. The HETC code follows the incident particle and its subsequent descendent light particles (A < 5) until they are absorbed, exit the meteorite (presently set at 1 m diameter) or drop below the low energy cut off. The neutrons generated in collisions which are below their 15 MeV cut off, are recorded at their site of production with their kinematic descriptors.

*Work performed under the auspices of the Department of Energy under contract nos. DE–AC02–76CH00016 (BNL) and DE–AC05–84OR21400 (ORNL).

These neutrons are stored in a file for subsequent neutron capture studies. The nuclei produced are recorded at their collision sites with their production energy. The abundance and distribution of these nuclei, essentially the spallation induced nuclei, are presently analyzed in 5 shells of equal volume. The HETC calculations were performed for 48000 proton source particles sampled from an observed cosmic ray proton spectrum.

The analysis of the history events generated by HETC utilizes 4 outer shells down to a depth of 30 cm and the central sphere to yield the production rate of ^{26}Al at 3.1810×10^{-2} no. sec^{-1} cm^{-3} which is equivalent to 54 dpm/kg for the decay rate predicted. The predicted ^{53}Mn production rate is 2.91×10^{-2} no. sec^{-1} cm^{-3}. Here the decay rate is calculated using the accepted Bogou standard: kg (Fe +1/3Ni), to give 223 dpm/kg for the ^{53}Mn decay rate.

DISCUSSION

Depth dependent neutron source spectra are calculated for a 1 m diameter meteorite in order to calculate the neutron capture contribution to nuclide production. Spallation and neutron induced production of cosmogenic nuclides both have to be examined in detail for measured radiogenic nuclides. It is expected that the spallation contribution will dominate near the surface while neutron induced contributions will dominate deep within the meteorite. Since cosmogenic nuclide ratios are less sensitive to incident flux normalization, selected isotopic ratios will be examined to give insight into inherent properties of the meteorite, such as pre-atmospheric-exposure size. In the present work only the spallation reaction product nuclei production rates are presented.

Monte Carlo calculations of ^{26}Al and ^{53}Mn production in model meteorite composition similar to L Chondrite has yielded predictions which are consistent with the observed decay rates in L Chondrite stony meteorites (Nishiizumi, 1987). The calculated ^{26}Al production rate (54 dpm/kg) in a 1 m diameter meteorite as seen in fig. 1, is within 1/2 S.D. of the mean (49 ± 11 dpm/kg) taken from 100 bulk determinations in L Chondrite samples compiled in Nishiizumi (1987). Similarly calculated average value for ^{53}Mn (223 dpm/kg) is consistent (cf fig. 2) with one S.D. off the mean in the widely scattered ^{53}Mn data (362 ± 113 dpm/km) compiled by Nishiizumi (1987).

An examination of the depth dependence of these nuclei are seen in figs. 3 and 4. According to the HETC predictions, there is a gradual rise in the rate of production for ^{26}Al up to a depth of about 8 cm, (or 25 g/cm^2) as seen in fig. 1 (bottom). The production rate as a function of depth shown for ^{53}Mn displays an "expected" behavior, rising as a function of depth shown in fig. 1 (top). In addition to the ^{26}Al and ^{53}Mn, spallation calculations have also been done for the cosmogenic nuclei ^{12}C, ^{13}C, and ^{14}C in the meteorite.

Carbon isotope production is most unusual, one would not have expected it in this L chondrite meteorite, but it is produced at low levels by the spallation reactions as seen in rays is about 1.5 m. Any extreme deviation from the mean value of the production rate may not be expected at depths of 1/10 or less of the bombarding particles' mean free path.

In conclusion, considering the success of the HETC calculations in general and the level of statistical confidence presently generated, it is felt that the calculations must be performed with larger number of cascade particles. It may well be that the physical requirement to sample the large range of energies (40 MeV to 200 GeV) seen in the galactic cosmic ray spectrum demands more cascade particles.

REFERENCES

Armstrong, T.W., R.G. Alsmiller Jr., K.C. Chandler, and B.L. Bishop, (1972) Monte Carlo Calculations of High Energy Nucleon–Meson Cascades and Comparison with Experiment, Nuc. Sci. and Eng. 49, 82–92.

Eberhardt, P., J. Geiss, and M. Lutz (1963) Neutrons in Meteorites, Earth Science and Meteorites, J. Geiss and E.D. Goldberg, eds., pp. 143–168.

Lingenfelter, R.E., and R. Ramaty, (1967) High Energy Nuclear Reactions in Solar Flares, High Energy Nuclear Reactions in Astrophysics, ed., B.P. Shen, pp. 99–158.

Mason, B. (1979) Cosmochemistry; Part 1. Meteorites, Data of Geochemistry, Sixth edition; Chapter 8, U.S. Geological Survey Professional Paper 440–B–1.

Nishiizumi, K. (1987) ^{53}Mn, ^{26}Al, ^{10}Be and ^{36}Cl in Meteorites: Data Compilation, Nucl. Tracks Radiat. Meas., Vol. 13, No. 4, pp. 209–273.

Reedy, R.C. and J.R. Arnold (1972) Interaction of Solar and Galactic Cosmic Ray Particles with the Moon, J. Geophys. Res., 77, 537–585.

Reedy, R.C., G.F. Herzog, and E.K. Jessberger (1979) The Reaction Mg (n, α) Ne at 14.1 and 14.7 MeV: Cross Sections and Implications for Meteorites, Earth Planet. Sci. Lett., 44, 341–348.

Reedy, R.C. (1985) A Model for GCR Particle Fluxes in Stony Meteorites and Production Rates of Cosmogenic Nuclides, J. Geophys. Res. 90, C722–728.

Spergel, M.S., R.C. Reedy, O.W. Lazareth, P.W. Levy, and L.A. Slatest (1986) Cosmogenic Neutron Capture Produced Nuclides in Stony Meteorites, J. Geophys. Res., 91, D483–520.

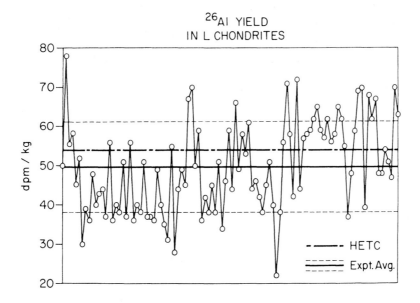

Fig. 1. ^{26}Al production rate: One hundred experimental data points taken from Nishiizumi's compilation are plotted to demonstrate the degree of fluctuation from the mean value (——). The HETC calculated mean value (-·——·) over the meteorite volume is shown for comparison.

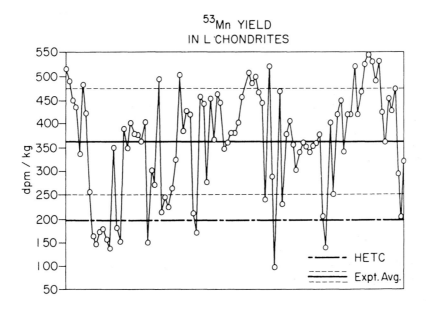

Fig. 2. ^{53}Mn production rate: One hundred experimental data points taken from Nishiizumi's compilation are plotted to demonstrate the degree of fluctuation from the mean value (——). The HETC calculated mean value (-·——·) over the meteorite volume is shown for comparison.

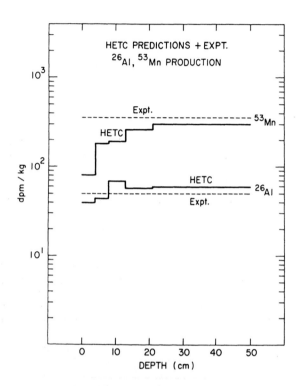

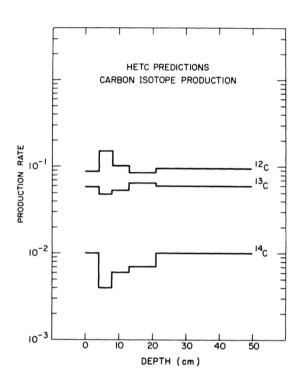

Fig. 3. Production, rate of ^{26}Al (bottom) and ^{53}Mn (top) as a function of meteorite depth: Comparison of experimental mean value with HETC predicted average over the meteorite volume. Conversion of production rate to dpm/kg units in the case of ^{53}Mn by making use of the Bogou standard.

Fig. 4. HETC calculated spallation product production rates for carbon isotope ^{12}C, ^{13}C, and ^{14}C as a function of meteorite depth.

PLUTONIUM-244 DATING

OF THE EARLY SOLAR SYSTEM

P.K.KURODA
Environmental Protection Agency
and the University of Nevada
Las Vegas, Nevada, 89154
(702)739-1318

ABSTRACT

The carbonaceous chondrites Allende and Renazzo appear to have started to retain their xenon approximately 4750 million years ago, when the ^{244}Pu to ^{238}U ratio in the solar system was 0.058 $\pm$ 0.018 (atom/atom). Formation of the solar system began roughly 4800 million years ago when the initial $^{244}Pu/^{238}U$ ratio was approximately 0.100(atom/atom). Chondrites and some of the oldest achondrites formed 200 million years later when the initial $^{244}Pu/^{238}U$ was 0.011 $\pm$ 0.001(atom/atom) and some of the youngest achondrites formed when the ratio decreased to about 0.00013(atom/atom).

INTRODUCTION

When I met Professor Glenn T.Seaborg for the first time on August 29, 1949, I asked him what he thought was the most important future research topic in the field of nuclear chemistry. He paused for a while and then told me that he thought that it would be the nuclear reactions involving the light elements. His answer puzzled me because I knew then he was trying to discover new elements with atomic numbers approaching 100. I had just arrived at San Francisco from Japan on the previous day and I was technically an enemy alien. I therefore felt that perhaps Professor Seaborg was attempting to divert my attention from what he was really doing under the support of the Atomic Energy Comission.

Two years later in 1951,however, the peace treaty between the U.S. and Japan was signed and I became a faculty member at the University of Arkansas in 1952. The first hydrogen bomb was tested in the same year and Hess et al[1,2,3] at Argonne National Laboratory discovered ^{244}Pu in the debris from the 1952 thermonuclear test conducted in the South

Pacific. Soon thereafter, it became obvious that some of the transuranium elements should have been synthesized in supernovae[4,5] and a nuclide such as ^{244}Pu must have been present in nature during the early history of the solar system[6,7]

Twenty five years ago in 1964, a strange fission-like xenon component was discovered in the carbonaceous chondrite Renazzo[8]. The discovery of the so-called Renazzo-type fission xenon was followed by the Pasamonte-type fission xenon by Rowe and Kuroda[9] in 1965. While the latter soon became accepted as the spontaneous fission product of ^{244}Pu which existed in the early solar system, the origin of the former became the focus of heated controversies for many years. Although most investigators in the field of cosmochemistry now believe that the Renazzo-type xenon component is the product of the r- and p-process nucleosynthesis[10], it can be shown to be a mixture of ^{244}Pu fission xenon and mass-fractionated primitive xenon. If this interpretation of the xenon isotope data, which was first proposed by the writer[11,12] in 1971, is accepted, it becomes possible to utilize the ^{244}Pu as a nuclear clock to date the events which took place in the early history of the solar system.

PLUTONIUM-244 FISSION XENON IN METEORITES

The isotopic compositions of the so-called trapped xenon found in meteorites and in lunar samples can be expressed in the form of mathematical equations[13,14,15] as shown below:

$$(1 + 12\mu).^{124}Q = {}^{124}P + s_{123} \quad \text{------(1)}$$

$$(1 + 10\mu).^{126}Q = {}^{126}P + s_{125} \quad \text{------(2)}$$

$$(1 + 8\mu)^{128}Q = {}^{128}P + s_{126} + s_{125} \quad \text{--(3)}$$

$$(1 + 7\mu) \cdot {}^{129}Q = {}^{129}P + s_{129} + n_{129} -- (4)$$

$$(1 + 6\mu) \cdot {}^{130}Q = {}^{130}P + s_{130} + n_{130} --(5)$$

$$(1 + 5\mu) \cdot {}^{131}Q = {}^{131}P + s_{131} + n_{131} --(6)$$

$$(1 + 4\mu) \cdot {}^{132}Q = {}^{132}P + s_{132} + n_{132} --(7)$$

$$(1 + 2\mu) \cdot {}^{134}Q = {}^{134}P \quad -------------(8),$$

where ${}^iP$ and ${}^iQ$ are the ${}^i Xe/{}^{136} Xe$ ratios of the spallation-corrected atmospheric xenon(see Tables 1,2 and 3) and of the xenon found in meteorites, respectively; μ is a mass-dependent fractionation factor; the s_i's are the alterations due to spallation reactions; the n_i's are the alterations due to neutron-capture reactions. The following values of cosmic-ray-production ratios[1] can be used for the s_i's:

$$s_{124}: s_{126} : s_{128} : s_{130} : s_{131} : s_{132} =$$

$$0.60 : 1.00 : 1.43 : 0.93 : 3.49 : 0.58$$

$$-------(9).$$

Table 1 shows the isotopic composition of xenon in the carbonaceous chondrite Murray[17] calculated from the above equations. Note that the values of n_i for i = 128,129,130,131 and 132 are all positive. This means that the relative abundances of these isotopes are all markedly enhanced by the neutron-capture reactions.

Table 2 shows the isotopic composition of the xenon fraction released at 800°C from the carbonaceous chondrite Allende.[18] The values of s_i for this xenon fraction is greater than those for the bulk Murray by a factor of about

1.5 and the value of n_{132} is -0.219. Moreover, the value of n_{131} is also much smaller than that of the bulk Murray. The difference in the isotopic compositions of xenon in the bulk Murray and in the 800°C fraction of Allende is attributable to the presence of an appreciable amount of ${}^{244}Pu$ fission xenon in the latter. The Murray meteorite contains as much as 4,710 x 10^{-12} cc STP of ${}^{136}Xe$ per gram meteorite, whereas the ${}^{136}Xe$ content of the Allende 800°C fraction is only 8.55 x 10^{-12}cc STP per gram. It is therefore to be expected that the presence of even a small amount of ${}^{244}Pu$ fission xenon in the latter should alter its isotopic composition quite considerably.

Table 3 shows the isotopic composition of the 800°C fraction of Allende corrected for the presence of ${}^{244}Pu$ fission xenon. It is assumed here that 18 percent of ${}^{136}Xe$ in this sample is ${}^{244}Pu$ fission xenon. The abundances of ${}^{131}Xe$, ${}^{132}Xe$ and ${}^{134}Xe$ were also corrected for the ${}^{244}Pu$ fission xenon using the following values of their fission yields reported by Alexander et al[19]:

$$^{131}Xe : {}^{132}Xe : {}^{134}Xe : {}^{136}Xe =$$

$$24.6 \pm 2.2 : 87.0 \pm 3.1 : 92.1 \pm 2.7$$

$$: 100 \quad --------------------------(10).$$

It is interesting to note in Table 3 the value of n_{132} for the fission-corrected 800°C fraction of Allende now becomes positive and is in essential agreement with the value for the bulk Murray. These calculations show that the amount of ${}^{244}Pu$ fission xenon in the 800°C fraction of Allende is (8.55 x 10^{-12}) x (0.18) = 1.54 x 10^{-12}(cc STP ${}^{136f}Xe$ per gram meteorite).

TABLE 1   ISOTOPIC COMPOSITION OF XENON IN THE MURRAY METEORITE

	${}^iQ$	$(1 + i \cdot \mu){}^iQ$	${}^iP$	s_i	n_i
${}^{126}Xe$	0.01314	0.01237	0.0024	0.0100	---
${}^{128}Xe$	0.2578	0.2458	0.205	0.0143	0.0265
${}^{129}Xe$	3.222	3.091	2.981	----	(0.110)
${}^{130}Xe$	0.5064	0.4888	0.453	0.009	0.0268
${}^{131}Xe$	2.572	2.497	2.361	0.035	0.101
${}^{132}Xe$	3.122	3.050	3.028	0.006	0.016
${}^{134}Xe$	1.1908	1.177	1.177	----	----
${}^{136}Xe$	1.000	1.000	1.000	----	----

TABLE 2   ISOTOPIC COMPOSITION OF THE 800°C XENON FRACTION OF THE ALLENDE METEORITE

	^iQ	$(1 + i\,\mu)^iQ$	^iP	s_i	n_i
^{126}Xe	0.0095	0.0170	0.0024	0.0146	----
^{128}Xe	9.174	0.284	0.205	0.021	0.058
^{129}Xe	2.666	4.140	2.981	----	(1.159)
^{130}Xe	0.334	0.492	0.453	0.014	0.025
^{131}Xe	1.732	2.416	2.361	0.051	0.004
^{132}Xe	2.141	2.818	3.028	0.009	-0.219
^{134}Xe	1.019	1.177	1.177	----	----
^{136}Xe	1.000	1.000	1.000	----	----

TABLE 3   CALCULATION OF THE AMOUNT OF PLUTONIUM-244 FISSION XENON IN THE 800°C FRACTION OF THE ALLENDE METEORITE

	^iQ	^{244}Pu fission xenon removed	$(1 + i\,\mu)^iQ$ [a]	^iP	s_i	n_i
^{126}Xe	0.0095		0.0192	0.0024	0.0168	----
^{128}Xe	0.174		0.324	0.205	0.024	0.095
^{129}Xe	2.666		4.751	2.981	----	(1.770)
^{130}Xe	0.334		0.568	0.453	0.016	0.099
^{131}Xe	1.732	(- 0.044)	2.737	2.361	0.059	0.317
^{132}Xe	2.141	(- 0.157)	3.058	3.028	0.010	0.020
^{134}Xe	1.019	(- 0.166)	1.177	1.177	----	----
^{136}Xe	1.000	(- 0.180)	1.000	1.000	----	----

a ^{244}Pu fission component removed and re-normalized to ^{136}Xe = 1.000.

The amounts of ^{244}Pu fission xenon released from Allende at 600°C and 1,000 C°can be similarly calculated to be 0.77 x 10^{-12} and 8.75 x 10^{-12} (cc STP ^{136f}Xe per gram meteorite). The fissiogenic xenon is released from the Allende meteorite only at 600, 800 and 1,000°C and hence the total amount of ^{244}Pu fission xenon in Allende corresponds to (0.77 + 1.54 + 8.75) x 10^{-12} = 11.06 x 10^{-12} (cc STP ^{136f}Xe per gram).

Table 4 shows that there is a beautiful relationship between the concentrations and the isotopic compositions of xenon in carbonaceous chondrites, ordinary chondrites and achondrites. The concentration of xenon in carbonaceous chondrites ranges from 540 to 4,710 x 10^{-12} (cc STP/g), whereas that of xenon in achondrites between only 10 to 37 x 10^{-12} (cc STP/g) and in ordinary chondrites between 32 to 83 x 10^{-12} (cc STP/g). The values of n_i for the achondrites are mostly negative indicating that they contain appreciable quantities of ^{244}Pu fission xenon. Three out of four ordinary chondrites have negative values of n_{132}, indicating that they also contain appreciable amounts of ^{244}Pu fission xenon.

It is interesting to recall that Reynolds and Turner[8] attributed the difference between the isotopic compositions of the xenon released at 900°C from the Renazzo meteorite and of the average

TABLE 4 RELATIONSHIP BETWEEN THE CONCENTRATIONS AND THE ISOTOPIC COMPOSITIONS OF XENON IN METEORITES

No. Sample	^{136}Xe (10^{-12}ccSTP/g)	s_{126}	n_{128}	n_{129}	n_{130}	n_{131}	n_{132}
(a)Carbonaceous chondrites							
(1)Murray[10]	4,710	-0.0058	0.0100 2	0.027 2	0.110 22	0.027 6	0.101 8	0.016 19
(2)Murray[13]	4,100	-0.0058	0.0099 1	0.026 2	0.155 20	0.028 3	0.096 15	0.020 19
(3)Renazzo[8]	1,110	-0.0015	0.0101 3	0.032 2	0.470 19	0.026 5	0.074 8	0.007 11
(4)Allende[20]	575	+0.0056	0.0106 1	0.036 1	3.390 42	0.028 2	0.092 11	-0.013 2
(5)Allende[11]	560	+0.0060	0.0101 2	0.043 2	3.770 59	0.033 4	0.082 18	-0.004 18
(6)Allende[21]	540	+0.0047	0.0105 1	0.035 1	2.522 11	0.028 1	0.086 3	-0.013 2
(b)Chondrites							
(7)Bruderheim[22]	83	+0.0008	0.0133 10	0.128 7	0.628 14	0.023 2	0.016 10	-0.026 9
(8)Bruderheim[23]	73	-0.00042	0.0151	----	0.928 23	0.006 4	0.036 12	-0.012 15
(9)Bruderheim[24]	46	-0.0013	0.0144	0.046	0.685	0.030	0.098	0.052
(10)Bruderheim[25]	32	-0.0100	0.0154 9	0.008 19	1.442 27	-0.002 3	-0.023 12	-0.065 12
(c)Achondrites							
(11)Stannern[24]	37	+0.0126	0.0716	-0.006	0.012	-0.021	-0.047	-0.074
(12)Juvinas[24]	18	+0.0742	0.1150	-0.075	-0.077	-0.226	-0.767	-0.897
(13)Kapoeta[26]	14	+0.1005	0.0431 45	-).113 8	-1.340 53	-0.294 11	-1.288 16	-1.111 45
(14)Sioux County[24]	13	+0.0302	0.1246	-0.020	-0.121	-0.068	-0.318	-0.298
(15)Pena Blanca Spring[24]	13	+0.0030	0.0298	-0.010	1.131	-0.027	-0.077	-0.130
(16)Petersburg[24]	13	+0.0781	0.300	-0.179	-1.119	-0.357	-1.713	-1.131
(17)Moore County[24]	12	+0.0541	0.0813	-0.083	-1.193	-0.249	-1.062	-0.927
(18)Shalka[24]	11	-0.0025	0.0087	0.006	-0.056	-0.011	-0.019	-0.036
(19)Mount Padbury[24]	10	+0.0725	0.357	-0.086	-0.557	-0.213	-0.791	-0.837
(20)Pasamonte[24]	10	+0.0311	0.0361	-0.011	-0.328	-0.086	-0.442	-0.462

TABLE 5   CALCULATION OF THE AMOUNTS OF PLUTONIUM-244 FISSION XENON
IN THE RENAZZO AND ALLENDE METEORITES

	i_Q	^{244}Pu fission xenon removed	$(1 + i \mu)i_Q$	i_P	s_i	n_i
			(a)Renazzo			
^{126}Xe	0.0127		0.0125	0.0024	0.0101	----
^{128}Xe	0.254		0.252	0.205	0.014	0.033
^{129}Xe	3.488		3.461	2.981	----	(0.480)
^{130}Xe	0.492		0.490	0.453	0.009	0.028
^{131}Xe	2.489	(-0.003)	2.480	2.361	0.035	0.084
^{132}Xe	3.059	(-0.009)	3.050	3.028	0.006	0.016
^{134}Xe	1.1805	(-0.009)	1.177	1.177	----	----
^{136}Xe	1.000	(-0.010)	1.000	1.000	----	----
			(b)Allende			
^{126}Xe	0.0124		0.0133	0.0024	0.0109	----
^{128}Xe	0.251		0.265	0.205	0.016	0.044
^{129}Xe	6.479		6.823	2.981	----	(3.842)
^{130}Xe	0.479		0.502	0.453	0.010	0.039
^{131}Xe	2.404	(-0.005)	2.508	2.361	0.038	0.109
^{132}Xe	2.959	(-0.017)	3.056	3.028	0.006	0.022
^{134}Xe	1.163	(-0.020)	1.177	1.177	----	----
^{136}Xe	1.000	(-0.020)	1.000	1.000	----	----

carbonaceous chondrite xenon(AVCC) to the presence of the Renazzo-type fission xenon in the latter. Table 4 shows, however, that the isotopic composition of xenon in Renazzo is intermediate between Murray and Allende. This means that the difference in the values of n_{132} is caused by the presence of ^{244}Pu fission xenon in these meteorites. The effect of the presence of ^{244}Pu fission xenon is more clearly visible in Allende than in Renazzo, because the ^{136}Xe content of the former is twice the content in the latter. As it was pointed out earlier, the amount of ^{244}Pu fission xenon in Allende is 11 x 10^{-12}(cc STP/g) or about 2 percent of the amount of ^{136}Xe in this meteorite. If it is assumed that the uranium content and the initial ^{244}Pu to ^{238}U ratio of Renazzo are the same as those of Allende, the former should also contain about 11 x 10^{-12}(cc STP ^{136f}Xe /g), which corresponds to 1.0 percent of the total amount of ^{136}Xe in Renazzo.

Table 5 shows that the xenon found in Renazzo and Allende corrected for these amounts of ^{244}Pu fission xenon is almost identical to that of the xenon found in the Murray meteorite.

PLUTONIUM-244 DATING OF THE EARLY SOLAR SYSTEM

Table 6 shows the initial ratios of ^{244}Pu to ^{238}U for a total of 14 meteorite and lunar samples calculated from the contents of uranium and ^{244}Pu fission xenon. The ^{244}Pu ages of these samples were calculated from the initial ratios of ^{244}Pu to ^{238}U using that of the Kapoeta howardite(pyroxene-plagioclase achondrite) studied by Rowe[26] as a reference standard. The Kapoeta meteorite is unique among achondrites in that it contains accurately measurable amounts of both radiogenic(from ^{129}I decay) and fissiogenic(from ^{244}Pu decay) xenon. Furthermore, it has K-Ar and Rb-Sr ages that place its formation and last major

TABLE 6   PLUTONIUM-244 DATING OF THE EARLY SOLAR SYSTEM

Sample	Uranium (ppb)	$^{136f}Xe/U$ (10^{-5}cc STP/g)	$(^{244}Pu/^{238}U)_o$ (atom/atom)	Age (10^6 years)
(1)Lunar fines 10084,12	450 ±140	136 ± 42	0.096 ±0.030	4809 +32 −44
(2)Lunar fines 10084,59	450 ±140	134 ± 42	0.094 ±0.029	4807 +32 −44
(3)Allende	13.4	82.5 ±25.6	0.058 ±0.018	4749 +26 −44
(4)Bruderheim	12	21 ±11	0.015 ±0.008	4563 +71 −64
(5)Pena Blanca Spring	13.1	17.6 ± 0.5	0.0124 ±0.0003	4561 +1 −1
(6)Kapoeta	64	16.7 ± 2.0	0.0117 ±0.0014	= 4560
(7)Moore County	45 ± 6	13.8 ± 1.8	0.0097 ±0.0013	4537 +16 −14
(8)Petersburg	103 ± 6	10.7 ± 0.6	0.0075 ±0.0004	4507 +6 −7
(9)Shalka	5.6 ±1.2	9.46 ±2.00	0.0067 ±0.0014	4493 +28 −22
(10)Pasamonte	78 ±28	6.67 ±2.39	0.0047 ±0.0017	4453 +54 −35
(11)Juvinas	210 ± 18	6.14 ±0.52	0.0043 ±0.0004	4441 +9 −10
(12)Mount Padbury	109 ± 10	5.69 ±0.52	0.0040 ±0.0003	4433 +12 −10
(13)Sioux County	107 ± 10	5.61 ±0.52	0.0039 ±0.0004	4431 +12 −10
(14)Stannern	176 ± 16	1.88 ±0.17	0.0013 ±0.0001	4301 +11 −11

heating episode near the very begining of our solar system between 4.55 and 4.57 billion years ago.[27] Moreover, the initial ratio of ^{244}Pu to ^{238}U for Kapoeta is in essential agreement with those of Pena Blanca Spring(aublite or enstatite achondrite) and Bruderheim(olivine-hypersthene chondrite.

It is interesting to note in Table 6 that the lunar fines 10084,12[28] and 10084,59[29] have the highest initial ^{244}Pu to ^{238}U ratio and hence the oldest ^{244}Pu

ages of about 4.8 billion years. According to Tatsumoto and Rosholt,[23] the lead-lead age of the Apollo 11 samples is 4660 +70 −160 million years. The ^{244}Pu age of the lunar fines is somewhat greater than the lead-lead age. The ^{244}Pu age of Allende, on the other hand, is about 50 million years younger than the lunar fines. Drozd et al[21] have reported, however, that the initial $^{244}Pu/^{238}U$ ratio for the pink inclusions and fine grained inclusions of Allende to be greater than 0.14 ±0.02 and 0.087 ± 0.011(atom/atom), respectively. These results indicate that some of the mineral inclusions of Allende may have started to retain their xenon about 100 million years earlier than the bulk meteorite.

The achondrites, on the other hand, seem to have formed much later and their ^{244}Pu ages fall in the range between 4300 and 4560 million years ago. These results indicate that the condensation of the solar system began about 4800 million years ago and lasted for 500 million years until about 4300 million years ago.

It is perhaps worthy of note here that Table 6 shows that the ^{244}Pu age of the achondrite Pasamonte is 4453 million years, whereas Unruh et al[30] have reported that the age of Pasamonte to be (4580 ± 120) million years(Sm/Nd method) and (4530 ± 30) million years(Pb/Pb method). They noted,however, that a brecciation of this meteorite took place 4200 to 4450 million years ago and this seems to indicate that the ^{244}Pu dating method is dating the time of this brecciation.

The uncertainties in the ^{244}Pu dating method originate mainly from the uncertainties associated with the determination of the uranium contents of the meteorites. If the uranium content of a meteorite is accurately known, the ^{244}Pu dating method should enable us to date an object formed 4 to 5 billion years ago within few million years.

CONCLUDING REMARKS

The year 1989 marks the 50th anniversary of the discovery of fission by Hahn and Strassmann. It is a remarkable coincidence that this year also marks the 200th anniversary of the discovery of uranium by Martin Heinrich Klaproth(1743-1817) and the 100th anniversary of the publication of the 1889 paper entitled "The Relative Abundance of the Chemical Elements" by Frank Wigglesworth Clarke[31] (1847-1931). When Clarke read his paper before the Philosophical Society of Washington on October 26,1889, he was attempting to prove his hypothesis that "the chemical elements were originally developed by a process of evolution from much simpler forms of matter, as is indicated by the progressive chemical complexity observed in passing from the nebula through the hot stars to the cold planets".

I wish to express my deep gratitude to Professor Glenn T.Seaborg for inviting me to this important conference. If I may be allowed to add a personal note here, This year also marks the 40th anniversary of my first visit to Professor Seaborg's laboratories at Berkeley on August 29,1949.

REFERENCES

1. D.C.HESS, G.L.PYLE, S.FRIED, AND M.INGHRAM, ANL-MGI-48, November 25 (1952)

2. M.H.STUDIER, P.R.Fields, P.H.SELLERS A.M.FRIEDMAN, C.M.STEVENS, J.H.MECH, H.DIAMOND, J.SEDLET, and J.R.HUIZENGA, Plutonium-244 from pile-irradiated plutonium, Phys.Rev. 93,1433(1954).

3. H.DIAMOND and R.F.BARNES, Alpha half-life of ^{244}Pu, Phys.Rev. 101,1064 (1956).

4. G.R.BURBIDGE, F.HOYL, E.M.BURBIDGE, R.F.CHRISTY, and W.A.FOWLER, Californium-254 and supernovae, Phys.Rev.103, 1145(1956).

5. E.M.BURBIDGE, G.R.BURBIDGE, W.A.FOWLER, and F.HOYLE, Synthesis of the elements in stars, Rev.Mod.Phys. 29,547(1957).

6. P.K.KURODA, Nuclear fission in the early history of the earth, Nature 187,36(1960).

7. P.K.KURODA, The time interval between nucleosynthesis and formation of the earth, Geochim.Cosmochim.Acta 24,40 (1961).

8. J.H.REYNOLDS and G.TURNER, Rare gases in the chondrite Renazzo, J.Geophys. Res.69,3263(1964).

9. M.W.ROWE and P.K.KURODA, Fissiogenic xenon from the Pasamonte meteorite, J. Geophys.Res.70,709(1965).

10. O.K.MANUEL, E.W.HENNECKE, and D.D. SABU, Xenon in carbonaceous chondrites, Nature Physical Science 240,99(1972).

11. P.K.KURODA, Temperature of the sun in the early history of the solar system, Nature Physical Science 230, 40(1971).

12. P.K.KURODA, M.A.REYNOLDS, K.SAKAMOTO, and D.K.MILLER, Nature Physical Science 230,42(1971).

13. P.K.KURODA, R.D.SHERRILL, D.W.EFURD, and J.N.BECK, Xenon isotope anomalies in the carbonaceous chondrite Murchison, J.Geophys.Res.80,1558(1975).

14. P.K.KURODA, The Origin of the Chemi-
cal Elements and the Oklo Phenomenon,
Springer-Verlag, Berlin, Heidelberg,
New York,1 82,pp.133-140.

15. P.K.KURODA and Z.Z.SHENG, Isotopic
composition of xenon in the solar
system, Geochem.J.20,241(1986).

16. R.S.CLARK, M.N.RAO, and P.K.KURODA,
Fission and spallation xenon in meteorites, J.Geophys.Res.72,5143(1967).

17. P.K.KURODA, J.N.BECK, D.W.EFURD, and
D.K.MILLER, Xenon isotope anomalies
in the carbonaceous chondrite Murray,
J.Geophys.Res. 79 3981(1974).

18. O.K.MANUEL, R.J.WRIGHT, D.K.MILLER,
and P.K.KURODA, Isotopic compositions
of rare gases in the carbonaceous
chondrites Mokoia and Allende, Geo-
chim.Cosmochim.Acta 36, 961(1972).

19. E.C.ALEXANDER,Jr.,R.S.LEWIS, J.H.
REYNOLDS, and M.C.MICHEL, Plutonium-
244:confirmation as an extinct radioactivity, Science 172,837(1971).

20. R.S.LEWIS, J.GROS, and E.ANDERS,
Isotopic anomalies of noble gases in
meteorites and their origin, 2, Separated minerals from Allende, J.Geo-
phys.Res.82,779(1977).

21. R.J.DROZD, C.J.MORGAN, F.A.PODOSEK,
G.POUPEAU, J.R.SHIRCK, and G.J.TAY-
LOR,Plutonium-244 in the early solar
system?, Astrophys.J. 212,567(1977).

22. P.K.KURODA, M.W.ROWE, R.S.CLARK,
and R.GANAPATHY, Galactic and solar
nucleosynthesis, Nature 212,241(
1966).

23. J.L.MEASON, M.N.RAO, and P.K.KURODA,
Plutonium-244/xenon-136 and iodine-
129/xenon-129 decay intervals of the
Bruderheim meteorite, Preprint, University of Arkansas, 1967.

24. C.MERRIHUE,Xenon and krypton in the
Bruderheim meteorite,J.Geophys.Res.
71,263(1966).

25. W.B.CLARKE and H.G.THODE, Isotopic
anomalies in xenon from meteorites
and xenon from natural gases, in
"Isotopic and Cosmic Chemistry",edi-
ted by H.Craig, S.L.Miller and G.J.
Wasserburg, North-Holland,Amsterdam,
1964,page 471.

26. M.W.ROWE, Evidence for decay of extinct ^{244}Pu and ^{129}I in the Kapoeta
meteorite,Geochim.Cosmochim.Acta
1019(1970).

27. P.K.KURODA and M.W.ROWE, Plutonium-
244 and iodine 129 in the Kapoeta
meteorite: a new interpretation,
Essays in Nuclear, Geo- and Cosmochemistry, edited by M.W.Rowe, Bur-
gess International Group Inc.,1988
page 172.

28. F.A.PODOSEK, J.C.HUNEKE, D.S.BUR-
NETT, and G.J.WASSERBURG, Isotopic
composition of xenon and krypton in
lunar soil and in the solar wind,
Earth Planet.Sci.Lett.10,199(1971).

29. J.H.REYNOLDS, C.M.HOHENBERG, R.S.
LEWIS, P.K.DAVIS, and W.A.KAISER,
Isotopic analysis of rare gases
from stepwise heating of lunar
fines and rocks, Science 167, 545
(1970).

30. D.M.UNRUH, N.NAKAMURA, and M.TATSU-
MOTO, History of the Pasamonte
achondrite: relative susceptibility
of the Sm-Nd, Rb-Sr and U-Pb systems to metamorphic events, Earth
Planet.Sci.Lett.37,1(1977).

31. FRANK WIGGLESWORTH CLARKE, The relative abundance of the chemical
elements, Bull.Phil.Soc.Washington
11,131(1889).

PLUTONIUM-244 FISSION XENON IN THE SOLAR SYSTEM

William A. Myers
Department of Chemical Engineering
University of Arkansas
Fayetteville AR 72701
(501) 575-5977

P. K. Kuroda
Environmental Protection Agency &
University of Nevada, Las Vegas
Las Vegas NV 89154
(702) 739-1318

ABSTRACT

Re-examination of the xenon isotope data for approximately 900 analyses of meteorite and lunar specimens which have been accumulated since the 1960's indicates that ^{244}Pu fission xenon is widely distributed in the solar system. It is commonly found in achondrites and ordinary chondrites, as well as in mineral inclusions and acid residues of the carbonaceous chondrites.

INTRODUCTION

In the fall of 1952 one of us (W.A.M.) was a freshman chemical engineering student and the other a relatively junior Assistant Professor of Chemistry. On November 1 of that year an event occurred in the South Pacific that impacted significantly on both of our careers. The first thermonuclear explosion, "Mike", was the vanguard of the thermonuclear weapons that were of daily concern to one of us (W.A.M.) during 28 years as an officer in the United States Air Force. Analysis of the debris[1] produced by Mike revealed the existence of a very long lived species that decayed by spontaneous fission. The announcement[2,3] of the discovery of this species, ^{244}Pu, gave the other (P.K.K.) a piece of a puzzle that has required over 30 years to complete.

Twenty-five years ago in 1964, a strange, fission-like component was discovered by Reynolds and Turner[4] in the carbonaceous chondrite Renazzo. The discovery of the so-called Renazzo-type fission xenon was followed in 1965 by the discovery of ^{244}Pu fission xenon in the achondrite Pasamonte by Rowe and Kuroda[5]. The Renazzo-type fission xenon, now called CCF or CCFX, is generally attributed to the products of galactic nucleosynthesis, which were not uniformly mixed when the solar nebula began its condensation[6].

An alternative interpretation for the origin of CCFX xenon was offered by one of us (P.K.K.)[7] in 1971, according to which the CCFX xenon is a mixture of ^{244}Pu fission xenon and mass-fractionated primitive xenon. This theory of xenology was, however, rejected by the scientific community of the 1970's and has long been ignored by other researchers.

Meanwhile, mass-spectrometric determinations of the isotopic composition of xenon have been carried out in many laboratories. Over 1000 analyses from material, mineral inclusions, acid residues and temperature fractions of meteorites and lunar samples have been reported. In the present study, we have re-examined much of the existing xenon isotopic data which accumulated since the 1960's. The results indicate that ^{244}Pu fission xenon is widely distributed in the solar system. Aside from the group of meteorites called achondrites, it is commonly found in ordinary chondrites as well as in most mineral inclusions and acid residues of the carbonaceous chondrites and quite often in lunar samples.

Table 1. Isotopic Compositions of Xenon from Various Sources (After Takaoka[8])

	I	II	III	
^{124}Xe	(0.018)	0.0158±0.0002	0.0143±0.0004	
^{126}Xe	(0.016)	0.0144±0.0003	0.0128±0.0002	
^{128}Xe	$0.31^{+0.03}_{-0.01}$	0.279±0.002	0.255±0.005	
^{129}Xe	---	---	---	
^{130}Xe	$0.61^{+0.03}_{-0.01}$	0.547±0.002	0.501±0.005	
^{131}Xe	$2.99^{+0.14}_{-0.07}$	2.731±0.015	2.545±0.032	
^{132}Xe	$3.63^{+0.15}_{-0.08}$	3.320±0.016	3.115±0.037	
^{134}Xe	$1.29^{+0.02}_{-0.01}$	1.233±0.006	1.190±0.016	
^{136}Xe	≡ 1.00	≡ 1.000	≡ 1.000	

I) Primitive Xenon, II) Solar Xenon, III) Average Carbonaceous (AVCC) Xenon, IV) Atmospheric Xenon.

RESULTS AND DISCUSSION

Table 1 shows a comparison (after Takaoka)[8] of the isotopic compositions of xenon from various sources within the solar system. Figure 1 shows the 3-isotope plots of $^{i}Xe/^{136}Xe$ vs. $^{134}Xe/^{136}Xe$ for i = 124, 126, 128, 129, 130, 131 and 132. The relationships between the isotopic compositions of atmospheric xenon, Takaoka's primitive xenon[8] and ^{244}Pu fission xenon[9] are illustrated here. The line AM represents the isotopic compositions of mass-fractionated atmospheric xenon. The line representing the least squares fit to the data points for carbonaceous chondrites intersects the extension of the mass-fractionation line AM at P. The isotopic composition of Takaoka's primitive xenon[8] lies in the vicinity of the point P. The line PF is a mixing line between ^{244}Pu fission xenon F[9] and P. The line PX is a mixing line between CCFX xenon X and P.

One of us (P.K.K.)[7] used a similar plot of $^{i}Xe/^{136}Xe$ vs. $^{134}Xe/^{136}Xe$ in 1971. The array of published xenon isotope data was quite limited at that time, but we have a vastly different situation today. For example, 894 data points are plotted in Figure 1e. The great majority of the data points lie in the area between PX and PF. The point P is the intersection of the mass-fractionation line PM and the line PX, the best fit to 309 data points from 33 different carbonaceous chondrites. These analyses include bulk samples, acid residues and temperature fractions. More than thirty data points lie above the line PX. These are the xenon fractions whose isotopic compositions have been markedly altered by spallation and neutron-capture processes which occurred during an early irradiation period of the solar system. As shown in Table 2, the 10 KeV neutron-capture cross section of ^{129}Xe is much greater than that of the neighboring stable isotope ^{130}Xe. On the other hand, the cosmic abundance of ^{129}Xe is 6.5 times that of ^{130}Xe. Thus, the relative abundance of ^{130}Xe can easily be enhanced by neutron-capture reactions, as well as by spallation reactions.

A total of 906 data points are plotted in Figure 1g. These data are much less scattered than are those in the $^{130}Xe/^{136}Xe$ vs. $^{134}Xe/^{136}Xe$ plot. The reasons for this are threefold: a) the cosmic abundance of ^{132}Xe is 6.7 times that of ^{130}Xe; b) the cosmic-ray-production ratio of ^{132}Xe is the smallest among the xenon isotopes with masses ranging from 124 to 132 (see Table 2); and c) even though the 10 KeV neutron-capture cross section of the neighboring stable isotope ^{131}Xe is more than 5 times that of ^{132}Xe, the effect of neutron-capture reactions is relatively small, because the cosmic abundance of ^{132}Xe is greater than that of ^{131}Xe.

Table 2. Isotopic Compositions of Cosmic-Ray-Produced Xenon, ^{244}Pu Fission Xenon and the Values of 10 KeV Neutron-Capture Cross-Sections

	Cosmic Abundance[18]	Cosmic-ray produced Xenon[19]	^{244}Pu Fission Xenon[9]	10 KeV Neutron-Capture Cross-Sections (barns)[20]
^{124}Xe	0.0106	0.60	---	0.826
^{126}Xe	0.0098	≡1.00	---	0.555
^{128}Xe	0.213	1.43	---	0.197
^{129}Xe	2.933	---	---	1.12
^{130}Xe	0.453	0.93	---	0.290
^{131}Xe	2.374	3.49	0.246±0.022	1.08
^{132}Xe	3.011	0.58	0.870±0.031	0.195
^{134}Xe	1.173	---	0.921±0.027	0.101
^{136}Xe	≡1.000	---	≡1.000	0.00406

Figure 1f shows that the $^{131}Xe/^{136}Xe$ vs. $^{134}Xe/^{136}Xe$ plot is similar to that of $^{130}Xe/^{136}/Xe$ vs. $^{134}Xe/^{136}Xe$ except that at least fifty data points lie above the line PX and scatter in the data is more than was seen in the latter plot. The $^{i}Xe/^{136}Xe$ vs. $^{134}Xe/^{136}Xe$ plots for the light xenon isotopes, i = 124 - 129, shown in Figure 1 a,b,c and d are quite similar to each other in that a very large number of data points lie above the line PX, indicating that the relative abundances of the light xenon isotopes have been severely altered by the addition of spallation produced xenon isotopes. Decay of the 1.6 x 10[7]- year ^{129}I which existed in the early solar system may have been responsible for the upward scatter of some of the data in the plot for i = 129, but the fact that similar deviations are observed for i = 124, 126 and 128 as well indicates that the effects on the isotopic composition of xenon of spallation reactions caused by high-energy particle irradiations in the early solar system were quite considerable.

It is important to note here that of all the plots of $^{i}Xe/^{136}Xe$ vs. $^{134}Xe/^{136}Xe$ shown in Figure 1, that of $^{132}Xe/^{136}Xe$ vs. $^{134}Xe/^{136}Xe$ is unique in that a) it shows the least scatter in the data points and b) it is the only one in which the line PX lies below the line PM. The fact that the plot for i = 132 shows the least scatter of the data points strongly suggests that this plot best illustrates the relationships between the isotopic compositions of xenon from various sources in the solar system.

It is interesting to note in Figure 1 that none of the data points lies in the vicinity of the point X. During the past two decades, researchers have attempted to enrich the strange xenon component called CCFX, first by releasing xenon from the meteorites in step-wise heating experiments and later by treating the meteorite samples with various acids. Initially the results appeared encouraging, but progress virtually stopped more than a decade ago.

Table 3. Attempts to Enrich the CCFX Xenon Component

Year	Reference	Sample	$^{134}Xe/^{136}Xe$ (Observed)	Enrichment Factor α (Percent)
1964	Reynolds, and Turner[4]	Renazzo 800°C	1.158±0.011	21.3
1968	Rowe[21]	Mokoia 600°C	1.109±0.006	29.2
1971	Phinney[22]	Allende 600°C	1.038±0.016	40.7
1972	Manual et al.[23]	Allende 800°C	1.019±0.016	43.8
1975	Lewis et al.[10]	Allende residue 3C54	0.960±0.011	53.3
1977	Lewis et al.[11]	Allende residue 4C56, 1,000°C	0.925±0.006	59.0
1984	Ott et al.[12]	Allende residue BA3-H	0.895±0.025	63.6
1988	Lewis and Anders[13]	Allende residue = DK, 1600°C	0.913±0.001	60.9
		Allende residue = DM, 1600°C	0.910±0.001	61.4
		Allende residue = DN, 1600°C	0.913±0.001	60.9

Table 3 shows the lowest values of $^{134}Xe/^{136}Xe$ reported for the xenon fractions released or isolated from various carbonaceous chondrites. The enrichment factor (α) was calculated here from the equation

$$\alpha = \frac{(^{134}Xe/^{136}Xe)_{obs.} - (^{134}Xe/^{136}Xe)_p}{(^{134}Xe/^{136}Xe)_x - (^{134}Xe/^{136}Xe)_p} \quad (1)$$

where the subscripts p and x refer to the ratios for primitive xenon and CCFX, respectively. Values of $^{134}Xe/^{136}Xe = 1.29$ reported by Takaoka[8] for primitive xenon and of $^{134}Xe/^{136}Xe = 0.671$ reported by Lewis et al.[10] for the CCFX xenon were used in these calculations. In 1977, Lewis et al.[11] reported that the xenon fraction released at 1,000°C from the Allende residue 4C56 had a $^{134}Xe/^{136}Xe$ ratio as low as 0.925±0.006 and it appeared as if they had succeeded in isolating a xenon fraction in which CCFX was enriched to 59 percent. Attempts to further increase the enrichment of CCFX have made little progress, however. Ott et al.[12] in 1984, observed a $^{134}Xe/^{136}Xe$ ratio of 0.895±0.025 in the Allende residue BA3-14 and in 1988 Lewis and Anders[13] reported xenon isotopic ratios from stepwise heating of different carbon fractions separated from Allende. The minimum $^{134}Xe/^{136}Xe$ ratio observed was 0.910±0.001 in the 1600°C release from fraction DM. These results indicate that a limit had been reached beyond which CCFX xenon could not be further

enriched. This most likely means that CCFX xenon does not really exist as such within the solar system.

The reason why CCFX xenon can not be enriched beyond a limiting value of approximately 60 percent can be explained in terms of the process of a mass-dependent fractionation. The extent of rare gas isotope ratio variations can be estimated from calculations of the separation of a mixture of two gases by diffusion. Aston[14] used the theory of Lord Rayleigh[15] to calculate the enrichment of ^{22}Ne relative to ^{20}Ne by diffusion and found agreement between experiment and theory. If m_1 and m_2 are the masses of the lighter and heavier isotopes, respectively, and r is the enrichment of the second component in the residue, then Aston's formula is

$$r = \frac{m_2 + m_1}{m_2 - m_1} \sqrt{\frac{\bar{V}_1}{\bar{V}_2}} \quad (2)$$

where $\bar{V}_1$ and $\bar{V}_2$ are the initial and the final volume of the gas.

Table 4 shows the relationship between the ^{136}Xe content and the $^{134}Xe/^{136}Xe$ ratio for 20 samples of meteorite and lunar material. Note that the lunar fines with very high ^{136}Xe contents have the highest $^{134}Xe/^{136}Xe$ ratios and there is a general trend that a decrease in the ^{136}Xe content is accompanied by a decrease in the $^{134}Xe/^{136}Xe$ ratio. Assuming that a mass-dependent fractionation accompanied by the diffusive loss of xenon is responsible for the enrichment of the heavier isotope ^{136}Xe relative to the lighter isotope ^{134}Xe, we have calculated the $^{134}Xe/^{136}Xe$ ratios from the ^{136}Xe contents of the material using Equation (2). In this calculation, it was assumed that there existed initially a hypothetical meteorite parent body, which contained a primitive xenon, whose isotopic composition was that of Takaoka's primitive xenon[8], shown in Table 1, and that the ratio of xenon to silicon in the meteorite parent body was the same as the ratio of the cosmic abundances of xenon and silicon. Kuroda and Sheng[16] have calculated the ^{136}Xe content of such a hypothetical meteorite parent body to be 2.88×10^{-5} (CC STP ^{136}Xe per gram of meteorite). Introducing this value into $\bar{V}_1$ and the ^{136}Xe content of the meteorites into $\bar{V}_2$ in Equation (2), we first obtained the values of r and calculated the $^{134}Xe/^{136}Xe$ ratio for the meteorites from the value of $^{134}Xe/^{136}Xe = 1.29$ for Takaoka's primitive xenon[8].

Table 4. Relationships Between the ^{136}Xe Content and
the ^{134}Xe/^{136}Xe Ratio in Meteorites
and Lunar Samples

Sample	^{136}Xe (10^{-12} cc STP/g)	^{134}Xe/^{136}Xe (Observed)	(Calculated)
Lunar fines 10084,12[24]	15,300	1.233	1.223
Lunar fines 10084,59[25]	13,700	1.236	1.222
Novo Urei[26]	7,360	1.191	1.214
Murray[27]	4,710	1.191	1.208
Murchison[28]	3,970	1.191	1.206
Renazzo[4]	1.110	1.181	1.201
Mokoia[23]	899	1.164	1.196
Allende[23]	560	1.163	1.189
Shallowater[17]	78	1.193	1.154
Bruderheim[17]	46	1.180	1.148
Stannern[17]	36.7	1.148	1.146
Sioux County[17]	20.5	1.110	1.143
Juvinas[17]	18.2	1.025	1.143
Cumberland Falls[17]	13.6	1.169	1.142
Petersburg[17]	13.4	1.018	1.142
Pena Blanca Spring[17]	13.4	1.170	1.142
Moore County[17]	11.9	1.006	1.142
Shalka[17]	10.5	1.183	1.141
Pasamonte[17]	10.4	1.108	1.141
Mt. Padbury[17]	10.0	1.028	1.141

Table 4 shows that the agreement between the observed and calculated ^{134}Xe/^{136}Xe ratios is reasonably good considering the nature of the assumptions made during the calculation. It is interesting to note here that, for a number of meteorite samples the observed ^{134}Xe/^{136}Xe ratio is definitely lower than the calculated value. These are meteorites with unusually high uranium and thorium concentrations belonging to the group called achondrites. The uranium contents of the achondrites Juvinas, Petersburg, Moore County and Pasamonte are (210 ± 18), (103 ± 6), (45 ± 6) and (78 ± 28) parts per billion, respectively[17]. These achondrites are, therefore, expected to contain appreciable quantities of ^{244}Pu fission xenon with ^{134}Xe/^{136}Xe = (0.921 ± 0.027), as shown in Table 2. This is the reason why observed ^{134}Xe/^{136}Xe ratios for these meteorites are intermediate between the calculated ^{134}Xe/^{136}Xe ratio of about 1.141 and the value of 0.921 for the ^{244}Pu fission xenon.

We now turn out attention to the low ^{134}Xe/^{136}Xe ratios observed over the last decade in the various Allende acid fractions shown in Table 3. The values of ^{134}Xe/^{136}Xe = 0.895 ± 0.025 to 0.913 ± 0.001 observed in Allende fraction, BA3-H, DK, DM and DN are very similar to that of the ^{244}Pu fission xenon, whose ^{134}Xe/^{136}Xe ratio is 0.921 ±

0.027. If we are to attempt to obtain a xenon fraction in which the heavier isotope ^{136}Xe is enriched relative to the lighter isotope ^{134}Xe to the extent that the ^{134}Xe/^{136}Xe ratio is very low, say about 0.915, we must carry out an experiment on an astronomical scale with a huge reservoir of primitive xenon. Let us therefore use Kuroda and Sheng's[16] hypothetical meteorite parent body as a starting material and calculate the extent to which the outgassing process should proceed using Aston's equation (2). The concentration of ^{136}Xe in the starting material is 2.88×10^{-5} cc STP ^{136}Xe per gram which is equivalent to 7.8×10^{20} atoms of ^{136}Xe per ton of meteorite. The required enrichment factor $\underline{r}$ is 1.29/0.915 = 1.41. Introducing these values into equation (2), we find that $\bar{v}_2$ should be smaller than $\bar{v}_1$ by a factor of 10^{20}, or the final concentration of the residual ^{136}Xe to be only about 8 atoms per ton of meteorite! Apparently a limit has been reached beyond which no further outgassing can take place and this probably explains why the CCFX xenon component cannot be enriched beyond this limit.

SUMMARY

Re-examination of the xenon isotope data for approximately 900 analyses of meteorite and lunar specimens which have been accumulated since the 1960's leads to the conclusion that (a) the so-called CCFX xenon is a mixture of ^{244}Pu fission xenon and mass-fractionated primitive xenon and (b) ^{244}Pu fission xenon is widely distributed in the solar system. The reason why the attempts by various investigators during the past two decades have failed to enrich the CCFX xenon component is explained. The results of the present study support the arguments put forward by one of us (P.K.K.)[4] in 1971 that the processes of a) mass-fractionation, b) spallation and c) neutron-capture reactions play important roles in the alterations of the isotopic compositions of xenon found in the solar system.

REFERENCES

1. D. C. HESS, G. L. PYLE, S. FRIED AND M. INGHRAM, ANL-MGI-48, Argonne National Laboratory, November 25, 1952.

2. M. H. STUDIER, P. R. FIELDS, P. H. SELLERS, A. M. FRIEDMAN, C. M. STEVENS, J. F. MECH, H. DIAMOND, J. SEDLET, and J. R. HUIZENGA, "Plutonium-244 from Pile-Irradiated Plutonium," Phy. Rev. 93, 1433 (1954)

3. H. DIAMOND and R. F. BARNS, "Alpha Half-Life of Pu^{244}," Phy. Rev. 101, 1064 (1956).

4. J. H. REYNOLDS and G. TURNER, "Rare Gases in the Chondrite Renazzo," J. Geophys. Res. 69, 3263 (1964).

5. M. W. ROWE and P. K. KURODA, "Fissiogenic Xenon from the Passamonte Meteorite," J. Geophys. Res. 70, 709 (1965).

6. O. K. MANUEL, E. W. HENNECKE and D. D. SABU, "Xenon in Carbonaceous Chondrite," Nature 240, 99 (1972).

7. P. K. KURODA, "Temperature of the Sun in the early History of the Solar System," Nature 230, 40 (1971).

8. N. TAKAOKA, "An Interpretation of General Anomalies of Xenon and the Isotopic Composition of Primitive Xenon," Mass Spectroscopy 20, 287 (1972).

9. E. C. ALEXANDER, JR., R. S. LEWIS, J. H. REYNOLDS and M. C. MICHEL, "Plutonium-244: Confirmation as an Extinct Radioactivity," Science 172, 837 (1971).

10. R. S. LEWIS, B. SRINIVASAN and E. ANDERS, "Host Phase of a Strange Xenon Component in Allende," Science 190, 1251 (1975).

11. R. S. LEWIS, J. GROS and E. ANDERS, "Isotopic Anomalies of Noble Gases in Meteorites and their Origin, 2. Separated Minerals from Allende," J. Geophys. Res. 82, 779 (1977).

12. U. OTT, J. KRONENBITTER, J. FLORES, and S. CHANG, "Colloidally Separated Samples from Allende Residues: Noble Gases, Carbon and an ESCA-Study," Geochim. Cosmochim. Acta 48, 267 (1984).

13. R. S. LEWIS and E. ANDERS, "Xenon-HL in Diamonds from the Allende Meteorite-Composit Nature," LPSC XIX 679 (1988).

14. F. W. ASTON, Mass Spectra and Isotopes, Edward Arnold & Co. London, 220 (1933).

15. LORD RAYLEIGH, "Theoretical Consideration Respecting the Separation of Gases by Diffusion and Similar Processes," Phil. Mag., 42, 493 (1896).

16. P. K. KURODA and Z. Z. SHENG, "The Occurrence of CCFX Xenon in the Earth's Interior," Geochem. J. 21, 187 (1987).

17. P. K. KURODA, M. W. ROWE, R. S. CLARK and R. GANAPATHY, "Galactic and Solar Nucleosynthesis," Nature 212, 241 (1966).

18. H. E. SUESS and H. C. UREY, "Abundances of the Elements," Rev. Mod. Phys. 28, 53 (1956).

19. R. S. CLARK, M. N. RAO, AND P. K. KURODA, "Fission and Spallation Xenon in Meteorites," J. Geophys. Res. 72, 5143 (1967).

20. J. A. HOLMES, S. E. WOOSLEY, W. A. FOWLER and B. A. ZIMMELMAN, "Atomic Data and Nuclear Tables," 18, 305 (1976).

21. M. W. ROWE, "On the Original Excess Heavy Xenon in Primitive Chondrite," Geochim. Cosmochim. Acta 32, 1317 (1968).

22. D. L. PHINNEY, PhD Thesis, University of Minnesota (1971).

23. O. K. MANUEL, R. J. WRIGHT, D. K. MILLER and P. K. KURODA, "Isotopic Compositions of Rare Gases in the Carbonaceous Chondrites, Mokoia and Allende," Geochim. Cosmochim. Acta 36, 961 (1972).

24. F. A. PODOSEK, J. C. HUNEKE, D. S. BURNETT and G. J. WASSERBURG, "Isotopic Composition of Xenon and Krypton in the Lunar Soil and in the Solar Wind," Earth Planet. Sci. Lett. 10, 199 (1971).

25. J. H. REYNOLDS, C. M. HOHENBERG, R. S. LEWIS, P. K. DAVIS and W. A. KAISER, "Isotopic Analysis of Rare Gases from Stepwise Heating of Lunar Fines and Rocks," Science 167, 545 (1970).

26. KURT MARTI, "Isotopic Composition of Trapped Krypton and Xenon in Chondrites," Earth Planet. Sci. Lett. 3, 243 (1967).

27. P. K. KURODA, J. N. BECK, D. W. EFURD and D. K. MILLER, "Xenon Isotope Anomalies in the Carbonaceous Chondrite Murray," J. Geophys. Res. 79, 3981 (1974).

28. P. K. KURODA, R. D. SHERILL, D. W. EFURD, and J. N. BECK, "Xenon Isotope Anomalies in the Carbonaceous Chondrite Murchison," J. Geophys. Res. 80, 1558 (1975).

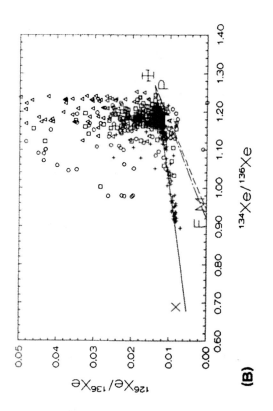

(A)

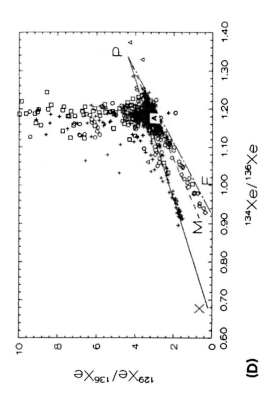

(B)

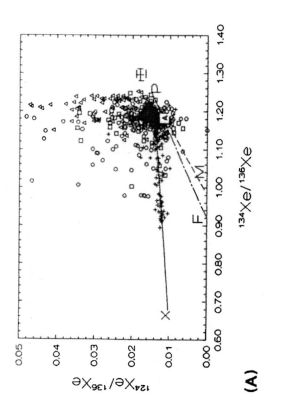

(C)

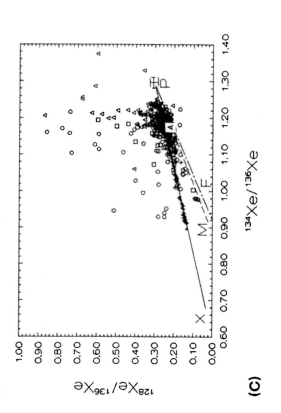

(D)

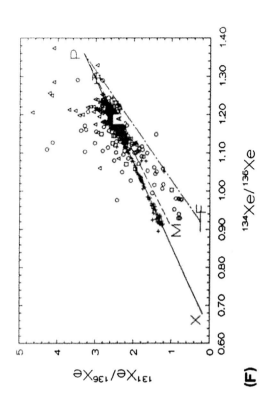

(E)

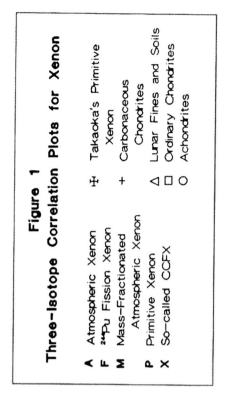

Figure 1
Three-Isotope Correlation Plots for Xenon

A   Atmospheric Xenon
F   ²⁴⁴Pu Fission Xenon
M   Mass-Fractionated
     Atmospheric Xenon
P   Primitive Xenon
X   So-called CCFX

⊞   Takaoka's Primitive
     Xenon
+   Carbonaceous
     Chondrites
△   Lunar Fines and Soils
□   Ordinary Chondrites
○   Achondrites

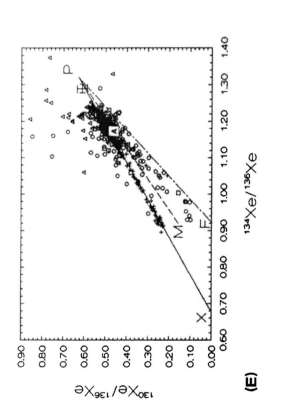

(F)

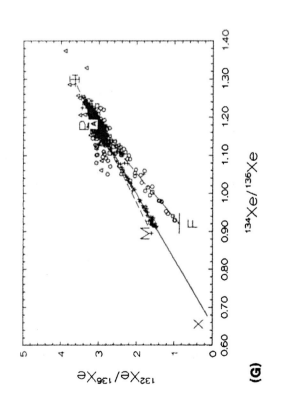

(G)

915

ON THE APPLICATION OF
NUCLEAR FISSION TO SPACE POWER

GARY L. BENNETT
National Aeronautics and Space Administration
Propulsion, Power and Energy Division
Code RP
Washington, D. C. 20546
(202) 453-2847

ABSTRACT

From the beginning of planning for the space age it was recognized that space exploration would depend on the availability of reliable power sources. In the 1950s, the U. S. initiated development of both space reactors and space radioisotope power sources. The first use of a space reactor was SNAP-10A which was launched on 3 April 1965. The SNAP-10A reactor program successfully demonstrated the feasibility of safe operation of a nuclear reactor in space and paved the way for subsequent space reactor programs.

INTRODUCTION

The discovery of fission opened to mankind the possibility of having compact power sources that could produce large amounts of power independent of the environment. Such power sources were considered by a number of investigators to be ideal for space applications.

Early studies, such as "Utility of a Satellite Vehicle for Reconnaissance" conducted by the Rand Corporation for the U. S. Air Force (USAF), considered the feasibility of obtaining satellite power from fissioning uranium and from radioisotopes produced in fission reactors. Subsequent industry studies completed in 1952 for the U.S. Atomic Energy Commission (AEC) concluded the technical feasibility of powering satellites with fission or radioisotope power sources.[1,2]

The U. S. space nuclear power program began in 1955 with the selection of the former Martin Company (now Teledyne Energy Systems) to design the 500-We radioisotope generator SNAP-1 and the selection of the Atomics International Division of what was then North American Aviation, Inc. (now Rockwell International) to design the 3-kWe sodium-potassium (NaK)-cooled, mercury Rankine cycle SNAP-2 space reactor. (The acronym SNAP stands for Systems for Nuclear Auxiliary Power. The odd-numbered SNAP power sources used radioisotope fuel and the even-numbered SNAP power sources used fission reactors.)[1,3]

Several additional reactor design concepts were investigated including a joint AEC-National Aeronautics and Space Administration (NASA) mercury Rankine cycle reactor power plant designed for 35 kWe (SNAP-8) and the 300-We conductively cooled thermoelectric converter SNAP-10 power plant. Subsequently the SNAP-2 and SNAP-10 concepts were in effect merged to produce a 500-We reactor known as SNAP-10A.[2]

The following sections provide more information on the SNAP-10A flight program.

SNAP-10A DESIGN

The SNAP-10A reactor power plant consisted of two major subsystems -- the compact thermal reactor heat source and the thermoelectric power conversion unit (PCU). The heat produced in the reactor core was transported to the PCU by a closed NaK heat transfer system using a thermoelectric-powered DC conduction-pump with no moving parts. The cycle rejection heat was radiated directly to space through an overall radiator area of 5.8 m^2. The nuclear radiation field was appropriately attenuated by a steel-reinforced lithium hydride shadow shield.[2] The system design parameters are listed in Table 1.[2]

The safety philosophy governing the SNAP-10A program was to keep the reactor subcritical in accident situations. Thus, the reactor was not operated at power before launch or until the final orbit was achieved. The final orbit was chosen to be one with an orbital lifetime of over 3000 years, well beyond the time required for the decay of the majority of the fission products. The reactor was designed to have a permanent shutdown system so that if it were to shut down it could not be restarted.[2,4]

As shown in Figure 1, the completed SNAP-10A power system had the shape of a truncated cone with an overall length of 3.48 m and a mounting base diameter of 1.27 m. This configuration was dictated by minimum mass shield requirements, especially the requirement to eliminate neutron scattering around the shadow shield.

The base diameter was established by the Agena launch vehicle payload and the upper diameter was determined by the effective area of the reactor. The length was determined by the total radiator area requirement. The total system mass of the final flight unit (known as FS-4) was 435 kg including the shield.[2]

TABLE 1
FLIGHT SYSTEM DESIGN PARAMETERS[2]

System Characteristics	Design Parameters
Electrical power	533 We (min)
Reactor thermal power	43.8 kWt (nom.)
Design life	1 year
Fuel	$ZrH-^{235}U$
Reflector	Beryllium
System mass (shielded)	440 kg
Overall length	3.5 m
Mounting base diameter	1.3 m
Radiator area	5.8 m^2
Coolant	NaK-78
Coolant flow rate	0.8 l/s
Reactor outlet temperature	827 K
Reactor inlet temperature	790 K
Power conversion unit (PCU)	
Thermoelectric material	Silicon-Germanium
Voltage	30.3 V

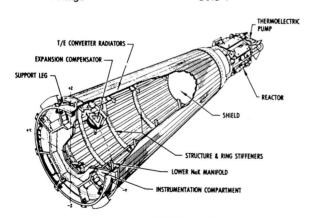

Figure 1. Cutaway of the SNAP-10A Reactor Power System (The term "T/E" stands for "thermoelectric")

The SNAP-10A reactor subsystem, which is shown in Figure 2, consisted of five major subassemblies: (1) the reactor structure; (2) the reflector assembly; (3) the reactor core; (4) the radiation shield; and (5) associated control equipment. The core contained 37 hydrided zirconium fuel rods enriched with ^{235}U and packed inside a cylindrical stainless-steel vessel of dimensions 0.23-m diameter by 0.41-m long. The fuel was clad with 3.18-cm-diameter Hastelloy-N tubing and had an overall length of 0.32 m. For minimum mass, the reactor core was reflected by beryllium and controlled by variation of the effective reflector thickness through the angular rotation of four semicylindrical beryllium control drums.[2]

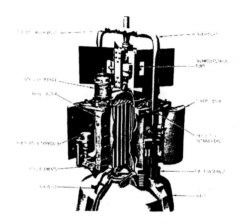

Figure 2. SNAP-10A Reactor Subsystem

The PCU essentially consisted of 2,880 silicon-germanium (SiGe) thermoelectric elements mounted in groups of 72 along 40 stainless steel tubes through which the NaK coolant flowed. Figure 3 shows the overall thermodynamic cycle including a thermoelectric module. Despite its lower figure of merit at the SNAP-10A operating temperatures SiGe was chosen over lead telluride because of (1) its stability to higher temperatures; (2) its potential for future performance growth; (3) its ease of manufacture; and (4) its mechanical properties. The converter hot side operating temperature was about 780 K and the mean radiator temperature was about 610 K.[2]

SNAPSHOT

In 1960, the USAF and the AEC initiated the Space System Abbreviated Development Plan for Nuclear Auxiliary Power Orbital Test (SNAPSHOT) Program. Under the program the USAF was to furnish the launch and satellite vehicles and the AEC was to furnish the SNAP-10A reactor units. The reactor was to provide not less than 500 We with a one-year operating lifetime. Atomics International built the reactor units for the AEC. General Dynamics built the Atlas booster and Lockheed Missiles and Space Company built the Agena satellite vehicle for the USAF.[2]

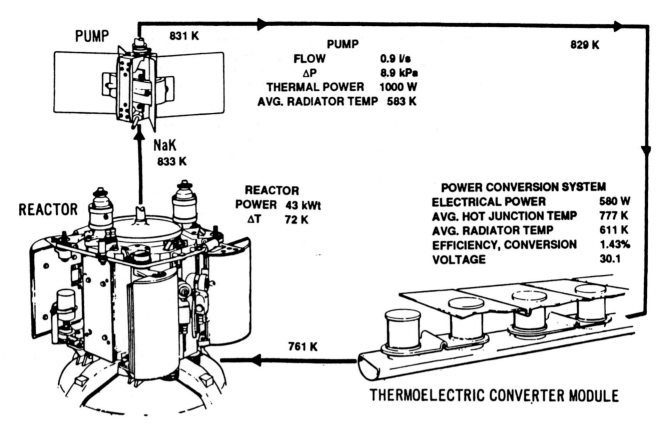

PUMP 831 K

PUMP
FLOW 0.9 l/s
ΔP 8.9 kPa
THERMAL POWER 1000 W
AVG. RADIATOR TEMP 583 K

829 K

NaK 833 K

REACTOR

REACTOR
POWER 43 kWt
ΔT 72 K

POWER CONVERSION SYSTEM
ELECTRICAL POWER 580 W
AVG. HOT JUNCTION TEMP 777 K
AVG. RADIATOR TEMP 611 K
EFFICIENCY, CONVERSION 1.43%
VOLTAGE 30.1

761 K

THERMOELECTRIC CONVERTER MODULE

Figure 3. Schematic of the SNAP-10A thermodynamic cycle

Included among the objectives of the SNAP-10A/SNAPSHOT program were to[2]

• Demonstrate, proof test, and flight qualify SNAP-10A for subsequent operational use;

• Demonstrate the adequacy and safety of ground handling and launch procedures; and

• Demonstrate the adequacy and safety of automatic reactor startup in orbit.

To aid in accomplishing these and other objectives, the original SNAP-10A program included three prototype test systems, three electrically heated nonnuclear qualification test systems, one nuclear qualification test system and three flight systems (originally two flights were to be made and the third flight system was a spare).[2]

On 3 April 1965, SNAP-10A was placed into a 1288 km by 1307 km polar orbit by an Atlas/Agena launch vehicle. Once it was confirmed that SNAP-10A was in a very long-lived orbit, the AEC authorized startup of the reactor.[2] Figure 4 is an artist's concept of SNAP-10A in space with the Agena. The reactor was successfuly started up and used to power a small ion-propulsion unit, telemetry, and other experiments.[2]

The flight objectives were to demonstrate[2]

• capability of SNAP-10A to survive launch and ascent;

• capability to attain safe orbit for nuclear operation;

• capability to initiate reactor startup remotely and monitor system performance;

• capability to stabilize at rated power;

• adequacy of nuclear safety provisions;

• operational capability of 90 days of SNAP-10A/Agena orbital system

and to determine

• space effects on thermal-control coatings;

• nuclear-radiation-shield effectiveness;

• thermal capability; and

• effects of high-temperature vacuum operation.

Figure 4. Artist's conception of the SNAP-10A reactor
mounted on the Agena launch vehicle in space

In addition the microgravity operations were to be monitored and certain scientific and engineeering experiments were to be performed.

SNAP-10A achieved full power approximately 12 hours after launch and initially produced more than 600 We. After 43 days of successful operation, the reactor was shutdown by the safety system as the result of a high-voltage failure sequence in the electrical system of the Agena spacecraft. At the time of its shutdown, SNAP-10A was producing about 533 We. Table 2 summarizes the SNAP-10A performance in space.[2]

Even though the flight test reactor did not achieve 90 days of operation, a twin to the flight reactor operated successfully on the ground without any control adjustments for 10,000 h thereby demonstrating the capability of SNAP-10A to operate unattended for a year. Among the more significant achievements of the SNAP-10A program were[2]

- First application of a nuclear reactor in space;

- First develoment of a reactor thermoelectric power system and the first use of such a system in space;

- First remote automatic startup of a nuclear reactor in space;

- First application of a high-temperature (810 K) liquid-metal-transfer system in space and the first application of a high-temperature spacecraft in space;

TABLE 2
SNAP-10A PERFORMANCE IN SPACE[2]

Parameter	Initial Performance		Final Performance	
	Measured	Predicted	Measured	Predicted
Total Electrical Energy Generated (kW-hr)			570	
Total Thermal Energy Produced (kW-hr)			44,000	
Reactor Outlet NaK Temperature (K)	827-845*		827	830
Reactor Average NaK Temperature (K)	792-809*		790	791
Reactor Thermal Power (kW)	42.5-45.5*		42.2	42.4
Flow (l/s)	.94-.95		.84	.83
Converter Isolation Resistance (ohms)	300	6,000	34	2,200
Electrical Power Output (W)	590-650*		533	530
Converter Voltage (V)	30.3	29.8	30.25	29.75
Reactor Thermal Power at Average Reactor Temperature of 801 K (kW)	43.9	43.9	43.8	43.9
Flow at Reactor Outlet Temperature of 833 K (l/s)	.94	.94	.85	.83
Electrical Power Output at Average Converter NaK Temperature of 800 K (W)	596	601	565	565
Overall System Thermal Efficiency (%)	1.36	1.37	1.26	1.26
Pump Degradation at Constant Temperature (%)			10.0	9.8
Converter Power Degradation at Constant Temperature (%)			4.2	5.0

*Approximate response to insertion of two control drum steps after control temperature switch reached its normal set point.

- First use of a nuclear shadow shield in space;

- Development and application of the highest powered thermoelectric power system to that time and the first use of a thermoelectric system of that size in space; and

- First thermoelectric-powered liquid-metal pump and the first use of such a pump in space.

SUBSEQUENT PROGRAMS

The success of SNAP-10A led to a succession of other U. S. space reactor programs as listed in Table 3, with powers reaching into the megawatt range.[4] The Soviet Union has subsequently flown at least 30 nuclear reactors, reportedly based on a thermoelectric conversion system that may bear some conceptual similarities to SNAP-10 and SNAP-10A.[5,6] For completeness, all of the U. S. space nuclear power launches (SNAP-10A and the radioisotope power sources) are tabulated in Table 4. As can be seen, the use of nuclear sources of electrical power for space applications has been a key element of some of the more ambitious and spectacular astronautical undertakings of the United States. The radioisotope power sources obtained their heat from plutonium-238, which was a very useful byproduct of nuclear fission reactors. The power performance of the radioisotope power sources has been documented elsewhere.[8]

The National Commission on Space report and other studies have recognized the need for nuclear reactors to explore and maintain permanent bases on other planets.[7] Nuclear reactors powering electric propulsion systems extend the capability to explore the solar system (especially the outer planets) and to perform solar escape missions. The unique characteristics of nuclear reactors -- compact size, low mass for high powers, self-sufficiency, hardness against natural environments (e.g., radiation belts), and long life -- can enable the operation of scientific spacecraft and bases.[3,4]

CONCLUSION

The use of fission reactors has profoundly enhanced the U.S. space program. The SNAP-10A reactor program successfully demonstrated the feasibility of safe operation of a nuclear reactor in space and paved the way for subsequent space reactor programs as well as plans for future space missions. The production of plutonium-238 in fission reactors allowed the U. S. to conduct a number of important space missions to the Moon, Mars, Jupiter, Saturn, Uranus, Neptune, and beyond the solar system.

REFERENCES

1. W. R. CORLISS, "Nuclear Reactors for Space Power," U. S. Atomic Energy Commission booklet (1971).

2. D. W. STAUB, "SNAP-10A Summary Report," NAA-SR-12073, Atomics International (1967). [Note: A more recent and more readily available summary may also be found in G. L. SCHMIDT, "SNAP-10A Test Program," DCN:SP-100-XT-0002, Rockwell International (1988).]

3. G. L. BENNETT, J. J. LOMBARDO, and B. J. ROCK, "Development and Use of Nuclear Power Sources for Space Applications," The Journal of the Astronautical Sciences, XXIX (4), 321 (1981).

4. G. L. BENNETT and D. BUDEN, "Use of Nuclear Reactors in Space," The Nuclear Engineer, 24 (4), 108 (1983).

5. N. L. JOHNSON, "Nuclear Power Supplies in Orbit," Space Policy, 2, 223 (1986).

6. G. L. BENNETT, "A Look at the Soviet Space Nuclear Power Program," Proceedings of the 24th Intersociety Energy Conversion Engineering Conference, Washington, D. C., 6-11 August 1989.

7. NATIONAL COMMISSION ON SPACE, Pioneering the Space Frontier, The Report of the National Commission on Space, Bantam Books, New York (1986).

8. G. L. BENNETT, J. J. LOMBARDO, and B. J. ROCK, "US Radioisotope Thermoelectric Generators in Space," The Nuclear Engineer, 25 (2), 49 (1984).

TABLE 3
PRINCIPAL U.S. SPACE NUCLEAR REACTOR PROGRAMS[4]

Power Plant	Purpose	Power Level	Operating Temp (K)	Period	Type Reactor	Fuel	Converter	Development Level
Rover (Includes NERVA)	Propulsion	365-500 MWt	2,450	1955-1973	Epithermal	UC		Twenty reactors tested. Demonstrated all components of flight engine >2 hr. Ready for flight engine development.
Fluidized Bed Reactor	Propulsion	1000 MWt	3,000	1958-1973	Thermal	UC-ZrC		Cold flow, bed dynamics experiments successful.
Gaseous Core Reactors	Propulsion and Electricity	4600 MWt	10,000 / 1,500	1959-1978	Fast	Uranium plasma UF$_6$	Brayton	Successful critical assembly of UF$_6$.
SNAP-2	Electricity	3 kWe	920	1957-1963	Thermal	Uranium zirconium hydride	Mercury Rankine	Development level. Tested two reactors with longest test reactor operated 10,500 hrs. Precursor for SNAP-8 and —10A.
SNAP-10A	Electricity	0.5 kWe	810	1960-1966	Thermal	Uranium zirconium hydride	Thermoelectric	Flight tested reactor 43 days. Tested reactor with thermoelectrics in 417-day ground test.
SNAP-8	Electricity	30-80 kWe	976	1960-1970	Thermal	Uranium zirconium hydride	Mercury Rankine	Tested two reactors. Demonstrated 1 yr operation. Non-nuclear components operated 10,000 hr and breadboard 8,700 hr.
Advanced Hydride Reactors	Electricity	5 kWe	920	1970-1973	Thermal	Uranium zirconium hydride	Thermoelectric and Brayton	PbTe thermoelectrics tested to 42,000 hrs.
SNAP-50	Electricity	300-1200 kWe	1,365	1962-1965	Fast	UN, UC	Potassium Rankine	Fuels tested to 6,000 hr.
Advanced Metal-Cooled Reactor	Electricity	300 kWe	1,480	1966-1973	Fast	Uranium nitride	Brayton and potassium Rankine	Non-nuclear potassium Rankine cycle components demonstrated to 10,000 hr. Ready for breadboard loop.
710 Gas Reactor	Electricity and propulsion	200 kWe	1,445	1962-1968	Fast	UO$_2$	Brayton	Fuel element tested to 7,000 hr.
In-Core Thermionic Reactor	Electricity	5-250 kWe	2,000	1959-1973	Fast or thermal driver	UO$_2$, UC-ZrC	In-core thermionics	Integral fuel element, thermionic diode demonstrated >1 yr operation.
Nuclear Electric Propulsion	Electricity	400 kWe	1,675	1974-1981	Fast	UO$_2$	Out-of-core thermionics	Limited testing on thermionic elements.
SPAR/SP-100	Electricity	100 kWe	1,500	1979-present	Fast	UN	Thermoelectric	Limited testing on core heat pipes and advanced thermoelectric materials

TABLE 4 - SUMMARY OF SPACE NUCLEAR POWER SYSTEMS LAUNCHED BY THE UNITED STATES

POWER SOURCE	SPACECRAFT	MISSION TYPE	LAUNCH DATE	STATUS
SNAP-3B7	TRANSIT 4A	NAVIGATIONAL	29 JUNE 1961	RTG operated for 15 years. Satellite now shutdown but operational.
SNAP-3B8	TRANSIT 4B	NAVIGATIONAL	15 NOV. 1961	RTG operated for 9 years. Satellite operation was intermittent after 1962 high-altitude nuclear test. Last reported signal in 1971.
SNAP-9A	TRANSIT 5-BN-1	NAVIGATIONAL	28 SEPT. 1963	RTG operated as planned. Non-RTG electrical problems on satellite caused satellite to fail after 9 months.
SNAP-9A	TRANSIT 5-BN-2	NAVIGATIONAL	5 DEC. 1963	RTG operated for over 6 years. Satellite lost navigational capability after 1.5 years.
SNAP-9A	TRANSIT 5-BN-3	NAVIGATIONAL	21 APRIL 1964	RTG operated as planned. Mission was aborted because of launch vehicle failure.
SNAP-10A (Reactor)	SNAPSHOT	EXPERIMENTAL	3 APRIL 1965	Reactor operated successfully as planned. Satellite electrical problem shutdown reactor after 43 days.
SNAP-19B2	NIMBUS-B-1	METEOROLOGICAL	18 MAY 1968	RTGs operated as planned. Mission was aborted because of range safety destruct. RTGs recovered.
SNAP-19B3	NIMBUS III	METEOROLOGICAL	14 APRIL 1969	RTGs operated for over 2.5 years (no data taken after that).
SNAP-27	APOLLO 12	LUNAR	14 NOV. 1969	RTG operated for about 8 years (until station was shutdown).
SNAP-27	APOLLO 13	LUNAR	11 APRIL 1970	Mission aborted on way to Moon. Heat source returned intact to South Pacific Ocean.
SNAP-27	APOLLO 14	LUNAR	31 JAN. 1971	RTG operated for about 6.5 years (until station was shutdown).
SNAP-27	APOLLO 15	LUNAR	26 JULY 1971	RTG operated for over 6 years (until station was shutdown).
SNAP-19	PIONEER 10	PLANETARY	2 MAR. 1972	RTGs still operating. Spacecraft successfully operated to Jupiter and is now beyond orbit of Pluto.
SNAP-27	APOLLO 16	LUNAR	16 APRIL 1972	RTG operated for about 5.5 years (until station was shutdown).
TRANSIT-RTG	"TRANSIT"(TRIAD-01-1X)	NAVIGATIONAL	2 SEPT. 1972	RTG still operating. Satellite shutdown
SNAP-27	APOLLO 17	LUNAR	7 DEC. 1972	RTG operated for almost 5 years (until station was shutdown)
SNAP-19	PIONEER 11	PLANETARY	5 APRIL 1973	RTGs still operating. Spacecraft successfully operated to Jupiter, Saturn, and beyond.
SNAP-19	VIKING 1	MARS	20 AUG. 1975	RTGs operated for over 6 years (until Lander was shutdown).
SNAP-19	VIKING 2	MARS	9 SEPT. 1975	RTGs operated for over 4 years until relay link was lost.
MHW-RTG	LES 8	COMMUNICATIONS	14 MAR. 1976	RTGs still operating.
MHW-RTG	LES 9	COMMUNICATIONS	14 MAR. 1976	RTGs still operating.
MHW-RTG	VOYAGER 2	PLANETARY	20 AUG. 1977	RTGs still operating. Spacecraft successfully operated to Jupiter, Saturn, Uranus, Neptune, and beyond.
MHW-RTG	VOYAGER 1	PLANETARY	5 SEPT. 1977	RTGs still operating. Spacecraft successfully operated to Jupiter, Saturn, and beyond.

SNAP stands for Systems for Nuclear Auxiliary Power. All odd-number SNAP power sources use radioisotope fuel. Even-numbered SNAP power sources have nuclear fission reactors as a source of heat. MHW-RTG stands for the Multihundred Watt Radioisotope Thermoelectric Generator.

/

U-235 FISSION NEUTRON SPECTRUM AVERAGED CROSS SECTIONS MEASURED FOR SOME THRESHOLD

REACTIONS ON Mg, Al, Ca, Sc, Ti, Fe, Co, Ni, Zn, Sr, Mo, Rh, In AND Ce

O. HORIBE, Y. MIZUMOTO, T. KUSAKABE
DEPARTMENT OF REACTOR ENGINEERING
KINKI UNIVERSITY
HIGASHIOSAKA, 577 JAPAN
06(721)2332

H. CHATANI
RESEARCH REACTOR INSTITUTE,
KYOTO UNIVERSITY
KUMATORI-CHO, OSAKA, 590-04
JAPAN, 0724(52)0901

ABSTRACT

The thirty four averaged cross sections of (n,p), (n,α), (n,n') and (n,2n) reactions are measured by the activation method relative to that of ^{27}Al(n,α)^{24}Na reaction. The samples were irradiated by fission neutrons generated with a U-235 fission plate. The following various kinds of corrections were done for the photo peak areas measured without causing random coincidence; (1) cascade coincidence summing effect due to cascade gammas, (2) contribution of gammas from impurities in the samples and (3) the photo peak efficiencies of a detector due to sizes of the samples. The 34 reaction rate ratios are best estimated from the 113 measured ratios considering correlations between the experimental data. The cross sections obtained assuming the reference one to be 0.705 mb and their correlation matrix are given.

INTRODUCTION

Experimentally measured data of the average cross sections for the standard neutron fields such as those with the U-235 and Cf-252 fission neutron spectra are currently used for intergal evaluations of the dosimetry file data such as JENDL, ENDF, IRDF and so on. In the evaluation, for instance, some of spectrum averaged cross sections calculated from IRDF-82 data files are still different from experimentally measured cross sections exceeding the experimentally quoted uncertainties. This indicates that more precise knowledge of these spectra and further evaluations are still needed.

At the same time, recomfirmations of the measured integral data would be still important. Furthermore, many other averaged cross sections will be similarly needed, because many kinds of elements are becoming to be newly used as constituents of fission and fusion reactor materials. Among these data, however, there are many cross sections which are difficult or hopeless to obtain experimentally. Therefore study on the prediction of unmeasurable ones is important and then many measured data are helpful for the study. On the other hand, averaged cross sections measured or predicted are useful for validation of energy dependent cross sections predicted more physically by the methods based on for instance the Weisskopf-Ewing theory, which are still very approximate. Accordingly, precisely measured values of averaged cross sections are needed as many as possible.

In the intercomparison of many measrured values of any cross section, systematic errors of these measured values must be as small as possible. Possible systematic errors usually encountered in the measurements are those due to both ambiguities of spectrum shapes of the irradiation neutrons used and of many kinds of corrections needed for obtaining correct reaction rates from the measured activities of irradiated samples.

To minimize the systematic errors due to the spectrum shape, we have used the U-235 fission neutrons produced by a U-235 fission converter plate provided with a heavy water thermal column of the Kyoto University Reactor (KUR), because of the following aspects.

Main feature of the facility for irradiation of the fission neutrons is that the plate is set in a room as large as 2.4m×2.4m×2.4m. Consequently, in irradiating samples on the plate by the fission neutrons, interference of neutrons scattered from the surrounding wall with the irradiations should be enough small. Moreover, neutrons well thermalized in the column can be used to irradiate the plate. Accordingly, The facility is one of those useful for the cross section measurements in the U-235 fission neutron standard field.

We had to measure most of activities of irradiated samples at a close detector-source distance, because the irradiation neutron flux is about 10^9 n/cm^2 sec and the activities then attainable for isotopes in the natural samples were usually weak. In such close measurements, coincidence summings due to incident gammas in prompt cascade with the interesting gamma can not be disregarded independently of intensities of the gammas incidnet on the detector. Similarly, if sizes of the samples differ largely from those of the sources used in the calibration of the photo peak efficiencies of the detector, the photo peak efficiencies must be corrected to be suitable for the sizes of the samples.

If the (n, γ) reaction product of a impurity in a target sample is identical with that of the interesting reaction, then contribution of gammas due to the impurity was substructed from the photo peak area observed.

The coincidence summing corrections can be done correctly only for the photo peak areas observed without random coincidence summings. Therefore, intensities of gammas incident on the detector must be limited within such a level as that photo peak areas measured are proportional to the number of incident gammas to avoid the random coincidences.

In the present measurements, we have obtained the reaction rates of irradiated samples by taking account of the various kinds of the corrections mentioned above, and then the (n,p), (n,α), $(n,2n)$ and (n,n') reaction cross sections of the following nuclei have been measured several times; for (n,p) reaction, ^{24}Mg, ^{27}Al, ^{42,43}Ca, ^{46,47,48}Ti, ^{54,56}Fe, ^{59}Co, ^{58,60,61}Ni, ^{64,67}Zn, ^{84,86}Sr, ^{90,95,96}Mo, ^{103}Rh, ^{115}In and ^{140}Ce; for (n,α) reaction, ^{45}Sc, ^{50}Ti, ^{54}Fe, ^{59}Co and ^{68}Zn; for $(n,2n)$ reaction, ^{59}Co, and for (n,n') reaction, ^{103}Rh, ^{113}In and ^{115}In.

By using the photo peak areas thus precisely obtained, we estimated the ratios of reaction rates of the irradiated samples to that of the Al sample in each measurement.

In the data processing, uncertainties taken into account are those of mass determination, counting statistics, photo peak efficiency and decay gamma intensity. The measured reaction rate ratios and the correlation matrix were calculated according to the procedure described in the report by Kobayashi et al.[3] We assumed the cross section of ^{27}Al$(n,\alpha)^{24}$Na to be 0.705 mb as reference. Final results of the cross sections were calculated by using a coumputer code, BOLIK[4] taking account of correlation between the experimental data.

Results thus obtained were compared with other experimental data and also the spectrum averaged cross sections calculated using ENDF/-B-V and JANDL-2 data files and several spectrum shapes proposed.

Among the experimental data, those obtained by 1984 had been preliminary used to obtain the cross sections which were presented at Santa Fe conference, 1985.[5]

EXPERIMENTALS

(1) Enriched Uranium Converter Plate

Specifications of the plate are as follows; circular disk shape with 27 cm in dia. and 1.1 cm in thickness, equivalent thickness of uranium of 1.95 g/cm^2 and 90% enriched U-235 of UO_2-Al cermet.

In our irradiations of the samples, however, a quarter of the plate was used by applying a thermal neutron collimator to decrease the number of fission neutrons scattered inside the plate as well as scattered neutrons from the wall, which perturb the spectrum shape of the fission neutrons. A region on the plate at which the fast fluxes distribute uniformly was thus restricted to a circular region of about 3 cm in rad. Then attainable fast flux at surface of the plate is about 10^9 n/(cm^2 sec) at power level of 5 MW.[6]

(2) Samples and Irradiations

Specification of the samples used are the same with those shown in TABLE I of our report presented at Snta Fe conference[5]. Powder and pebble samples were shaped into thin disks wrapped with polyethlene films. Some of them were attached to the surface of the plate and then irradiated at a power level of 5 MW for around 74.5 h. The irradiations were done similarly six times.

(3) Photo Peak and Total Detection Efficiencies

For the photo peak efficiencies of the LEPS detector and the high purity Ge detector used, we had measured them at three source-detector distances 15, 30 and 70 mm, and at four source-detector distances 8, 30, 51 and 81 mm, respectively using several IAEA gamma standard sources and other calibrated sources. When the gamma sources used for the calibrations accompanied with cascade gammas, coincidence summings due to the cascade gammas had been corrected for the photo peak areas observed.

The values of the efficiencies ε for each source-detector distance were fitted by the following function of gamma energy E.

$$\ln \varepsilon = \sum_{i=o}^{6} a_i (\ln E)^i,$$

where a_i's denote fitting parameters and values of these parameters were fitted by the least squares method. We have thus obtained the detection efficiencies for any gamma energies.

For the total gamma detection efficiencies of the Ge detector, we had measured by using single gamma emitter sources other than Co-60 and Na-24 sources, showing in Fig. 1 together with the sources used, which efficiencies were used for calculations of correction factors for cascade coincidence summings.

(4) Measurements of Gamma Spectra

The spectra of the gammas of the irradiated samples were measured by the LEPS and also the Ge detector attached with a 5mm thick acrylite plate to the front surface using a 1024 channel pulse height analyzer (PHA).

In measuring gamma spectra, intensities of incident gammas on the detectors were usually limited so as an indication of the dead time of the PHA to be less than 3% (about 2500 cps). This is because above the 3% dead time, the photo peak areas measured are disproportional to a number the gammas then incident on the detectors. The measurements were usually possible to be done at the source-detector distance 8 mm, and those in Nos. 5 and 6 experiments were done inside a Pb shield housing, of which attenuation factor is about 0.2 for 1460 keV gamma.

CORRECTION FACTORS

(1) Correction Factor due to Sample Size

To obtain correction factors of photo peak efficiencies due to source sizes, preliminary measurements had been done at the specified source-detector distances by using gamma sources having various different gamma energies and several circular sizes. From these results systematically obtained for the gamma energies and the sizes, correction factors due to any sizes and energies can be obtained by interpolation. The correction factors thus obtained for the present samples and their gamma energies were all around 0.98 for the Ge detector at 8mm from the samples and negligible at the other distances. While, those for the Rh samples were about 0.95 for the LEPS at 15mm from the samples. This relatively large correction is due to small detection area of the LEPS relative to the Rh sample size.

TABLE 1. CALCULATED FACTORS OF CASCADE GAMMA COINCIDENCE SUMMINGS OF THE Ge DETECTOR.

Nuclide	γ-energy (keV)	Source-detector distance (mm)			
		8	30	51	81
Na - 24	1368.6	1.102	1.026	1.012	1.006
Mg - 27	843.8	1.002	1.001	1.000	1.000
K - 42	1524.6	1.003	1.001	1.001	1.000
K - 43	372.9	1.155	1.048	1.020	1.010
	617.8	1.144	1.046	1.020	1.010
Ca - 47	1297.1	0.996	0.999	1.000	1.000
Sc - 46	889.3	1.102	1.033	1.014	1.008
Sc - 48	983.5	1.246	1.073	1.031	1.017
Mn - 56	846.75	1.039	1.012	1.006	1.003
Fe - 59	1099.2	1.012	1.004	1.002	1.001
Co - 58	810.8	1.040	1.013	1.006	1.003
Co - 60	1173	1.098	1.031	1.014	1.007
	1332	1.101	1.032	1.014	1.008
Ni - 65	1481.8	0.9900	0.9966	0.9983	0.9992
Rb - 85	881.6	1.039	1.013	1.006	1.003
Cd - 115 m	933.6	1.019	1.007	1.003	1.001
La - 140	1596.2	1.155	1.048	1.021	1.010

(2) Correction Factors due to Cascade Gammas

For the correction factors, we used the coincidence probabilities of photo detection events of the interesting gamma with any of all detection events of the prompt cascade gammas, which were calculated by using the photo peak and total detection efficiencies obtained from the above data assuming isotropic emission of the gammas. Validity of the calculation had been experimentally tested. Values of the coincidence correction factors thus obtained are shown in Table 1.

(3) Correction Factor due to Self-shieldings

The factors for the samples were neglected other than that for the Rh samples, because thicknesses of the samples were so thin to attenuate gamma rays of the samples. The factors for 20 keV X-ray and 40 keV gamma of the Rh samples were obtained from the following calculations to be both 0.604 using the mass-absorption coefficients of Rh, 14.9 and 14.8 cm^2/g for these rays[7], respectively. We calculated self-shielding factors of five divided concentric circular zones of the sample taking each oblique thickness of the zones and then obtained the averaged value of these factors weighting with solid angles for detections of the gammas from each zone and with zone areas.

(4) Corrections for Impurity Gammas

The corrections due to Mn impurities contained in both Fe and Co samples and of La in the CeO_2 samples were calculated by using specific activities of pure impurity samples and the interesting ones which were each irradiated at the fission plate and the thermal column of KUR. Contributions due to the impurity gammas were obtained to be 1.2% for $^{56}Fe(n,p)^{56}Mn$, 10% for $^{59}Co(n,\alpha)^{56}Mn$ and 29% for $^{140}Ce(n,p)^{140}La$, owing to a large $^{55}Mn(n,\gamma)$ cross section and about 10^5 n/cm^{2}sec thermal neutron flux.

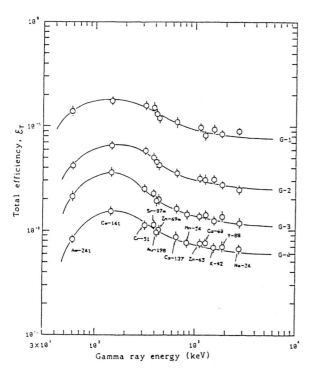

FIGURE 1. PLOT OF TOTAL DETECTION EFFICIENCIES MEASURED BY THE Ge DETECTOR. G-1, 2, 3 and 4 CORRESPOND TO SOURCE-DETECTOR DISTANCES 8, 30, 51 AND 81 mm.

DATA PROCESSING

Reaction rate P can be given by the equation below assuming constant irradiation flux.

$$P = \frac{AC\lambda T_m \exp(\lambda T_c)}{Nf\varepsilon I \Gamma_s (1-\exp(-\lambda T_m))(1-\exp(-\lambda T_i))},$$

where

A; Photo peak area measured,
N; Number of target nuclides,
ε; Photo peak efficiency,
f; Correction factor for ε due to sample size,
C; Correction factor due to coincidence summing,
Γ_s; Correction factor due to self-shielding,
I; Absolute gamma ray intensity,
T_i; Duration of irradiation,
T_c; Cooling time to measurement,
T_m; Duration of measurement,
λ; Decay constnat.

We calculated reaction rates of the irradiated samples from this equation using the photo peak efficiencies, the correction factors calculated above and the nuclear data as shown in Table 2.

Covariances in detection efficiencies and correlation matrix for interpolated efficiencies were obtained similarly as in the report by Kobayashi et al.[3] Similarly we also calculated the variances and covariances for the ratio measurements.

RESULT

We have finally obtained the correlation matrix, dimensioned 114×114 by combining those matrixes obtained for Nos. 1, 2, 3, 4, 5 and 6 experiments, as well as the experimentally determined ratios and the standard deviations.

To calculate the best estimates of the 34 reaction rate ratios from the results of 113 ratio measurements on the basis of the Bayes theorem,[8] we used computer code, BOLIK[4] for this calculation. The final results of the cross sections were obtained by multiplying these best estimated ratios by the references cross section of 0.705 mb to compare other measured values. The cross sections thus obtained are shown in Table 3(a) and (b).

DISCUSSIONS

(1) Comparison of Our and Other Data

Large error margins of our results were resulted from our estimates for errors such as we have allocated enough errors to background counts of photo peaks to safely cover areas of the peaks and from that in our spectral measurements, the intensities of gammas incident on the detector were restricted to be less than 3% dead times. In consequence, those for weak photo peaks become more larger. In the cases of the $^{68}Zn(n,\alpha)$ and $^{115}In(n,p)^{115m}Cd$

TABLE 2. NUCLEAR DATA USED IN ESTIMATING REACTION RATE.

Reaction	Isotope abandance (%)	Half-life	Measured γ-ray (keV) and intensity (%)
$^{27}Al(n,\alpha)^{24}Na$	100	15.02 h	1368.5 (100)
$^{27}Al(n,p)^{27}Mg$	100	9.46 m	843.8 (73.0)
$^{42}Ca(n,p)^{42}K$	0.647	12.36 h	1524.6 (18.8)
$^{43}Ca(n,p)^{43}K$	0.135	22.3 h	617.8 (80)
$^{46}Ti(n,p)^{46}Sc$	8.2	83.8 d	889.3 (100)
$^{47}Ti(n,p)^{47}Sc$	7.4	3.42 d	159.4 (68.5)
$^{48}Ti(n,p)^{48}Sc$	73.7	43.7 h	983.5 (100)
$^{54}Fe(n,p)^{54}Mn$	5.8	312 d	834.8 (100)
$^{56}Fe(n,p)^{56}Mn$	91.8	2.579 h	846.8 (98.87)
$^{59}Co(n,p)^{59}Fe$	100	44.6 h	1099.2 (56.5)
$^{58}Ni(n,p)^{58}Co$	68.3	70.8 d	810.8 (99.4)
$^{60}Ni(n,p)^{60}Co$	26.1	5.271 y	1173.2 (100)
$^{61}Ni(n,p)^{61}Co$	1.13	1.65 h	67.4 (86)
$^{64}Zn(n,p)^{64}Cu$	48.6	12.70 h	1345.6 (0.6)
$^{67}Zn(n,p)^{67}Cu$	4.10	61.9 h	184.5 (47)
$^{84}Sr(n,p)^{84}Rb$	0.56	32.9 d	881.6 (74.1)
$^{86}Sr(n,p)^{86}Rb$	9.8	18.8 d	1076.6 (8.79)
$^{92}Mo(n,p)^{92}Nb$	14.8	10.15 d	934.7 (99.2)
$^{95}Mo(n,p)^{95}Nb$	15.9	35.0 d	765.2 (99.82)
$^{96}Mo(n,p)^{96}Nb$	16.7	23.4 h	1091.3 (49.4)
$^{103}Rh(n,p)^{103}Ru$	100	39.4 d	497.1 (86.4)
$^{115}In(n,p)^{115}Cd$	95.7	53.58 h	527.7 (28.5)*
$^{115}In(n,p)^{115m}Cd$	95.7	44.8 d	933.6 (2.0)
$^{140}Ce(n,p)^{140}La$	88.5	40.3 h	1596.5 (95.5)
$^{45}Sc(n,\alpha)^{42}K$	100	12.36 h	1524.6 (18.8)
$^{50}Ti(n,\alpha)^{47}Ca$	5.2	4.536 d	1297.1 (77)
$^{54}Fe(n,\alpha)^{51}Cr$	5.8	27.70 d	320.1 (10.2)
$^{59}Co(n,\alpha)^{56}Mn$	100	2.579 h	846.8 (98.87)
$^{68}Zn(n,\alpha)^{65}Ni$	18.8	2.52 h	1481.8 (23.5)
$^{103}Rh(n,n')^{103m}Rh$	100	51.6 m	20.2 (5.8)
$^{113}In(n,n')^{113m}In$	4.3	1.658 h	391.7 (64)
$^{115}In(n,n')^{115m}In$	95.7	4.49 h	336.2 (45.9)
$^{59}Co(n,2n)^{58}Co$	100	70.8 d	810.8 (99.4)

These data were quoted from "Table of Isotopes" 7-th edition other than *.

cross sections, thus large errors resulted from the errors which have been estimated for the measured photo peak areas to be usually larger than 30 and 20%, respectively. However, the large error for $^{64}Zn(n,p)$ reaction cross section is mainly due to a large uncertainty of a transition intensity of 1345.6 keV decay gamma of ^{64}Cu, that is, $(0.6\pm0.2)\%$.

In the calculation of the $^{115}In(n,p)$ cross section, we temporarily used 32.5% for the intensity of 527.7 keV decay gamma of ^{115}Cd, though 50.1% is given in Isotopes of Table (7-th ed.). This is because, a beta feed to the upper level of 527.7 keV gamma transition is 33% and no gamma deexcite to the level exists.

Products of the $^{61}Ni(n,p)$ and $^{62}Ni(n,n'p)$ are identical, so that our cross section of the former may contain that of the later. The contribution of the later, however, seems to be negligible, because the former cross is about 100 mb and the later, about 4 mb at energy of

TABLE 3(a).   FINAL RESULTS OF THE MEASURED CROSS SECTIONS.

No.	Reaction	Cross section (mb)	Uncertainty ±(mb)	(%)
1	^{27}Al(n,α)^{24}Na	0.705	0.044	6.20
2	^{24}Mg(n,p)^{24}Na	1.38	0.09	6.78
3	^{46}Ti(n,p)^{46}Sc	11.6	0.8	6.68
4	^{47}Ti(n,p)^{47}Sc	20.2	1.4	7.10
5	^{48}Ti(n,p)^{48}Sc	0.305	0.020	6.65
6	^{54}Fe(n,p)^{54}Mn	81.7	5.2	6.35
7	^{56}Fe(n,p)^{56}Mn	1.13	0.07	6.36
8	^{58}Ni(n,p)^{58}Co	106	7	6.72
9	^{60}Ni(n,p)^{60}Co	2.19	0.17	7.87
10	^{61}Ni(n,p)^{61}Co	1.33	0.10	7.69
11	^{64}Zn(n,p)^{64}Cu	29.4	7.5	25.6
12	^{67}Zn(n,p)^{67}Cu	1.01	0.09	9.04
13	^{103}Rh(n,p)^{103}Ru	0.119	0.013	11.2
14	^{140}Ce(n,p)^{140}La	0.00415	0.00029	7.07
15	^{50}Ti(n,α)^{47}Ca	0.0210	0.0021	10.2
16	^{54}Fe(n,α)^{51}Cr	0.860	0.079	9.18
17	^{68}Zn(n,α)^{65}Ni	0.0771	0.0238	30.9
18	^{103}Rh(n,n')^{103m}Rh	955	101	10.6
19	^{59}Co(n,p)^{59}Fe	1.39	0.10	7.05
20	^{115}In(n,p)^{115}Cd	0.00938	0.00104	11.1
21	^{115}In(n,p)^{115m}Cd	0.0486	0.0080	16.4
22	^{59}Co(n,α)^{56}Mn	0.170	0.012	6.82
23	^{113}In(n,n')^{113m}In	172	11	6.42
24	^{115}In(n.n')^{115m}In	198	12	6.19
25	^{59}Co(n,2n)^{58}Co	0.303	0.021	7.06
26	^{27}Al(n,p)^{27}Mg	4.09	0.26	6.45
27	^{42}Ca(n,p)^{42}K	2.92	0.22	7.68
28	^{43}Ca(n,p)^{43}K	2.58	0.19	7.39
29	^{84}Sr(n,p)^{84}Rb	5.36	0.45	8.31
30	^{86}Sr(n,p)^{86}Rb	0.664	0.067	10.1
31	^{92}Mo(n,p)^{92m}Nb	6.78	0.42	6.12
32	^{95}Mo(n,p)^{95}Nb	0.142	0.011	7.50
33	^{96}Mo(n,p)^{96}Nb	0.0256	0.0025	9.70
34	^{45}Sc(n,α)^{42}K	0.254	0.019	7.34

TABLE 3(b).   CORRELATION MATRIX OF THE RESULTS IN TABLE 3(a).

CORRELATION MATRIX   (PRINTED VALUE HAS BEEN MULTIPLIED BY 100.)

ROW/COL	1	2	3	4	5	6	7	8	9	10	11	12	13	14	15	16	17	18	19	20	21	22	23	24	25	26	27	28	29	30	31	32	33	34
1	100																																	
2	96	100																																
3	99	96	100																															
4	94	91	95	100																														
5	99	96	99	95	100																													
6	99	96	99	95	99	100																												
7	99	96	99	96	99	99	100																											
8	99	96	99	96	100	99	100	100																										
9	88	85	88	84	88	88	88	88	100																									
10	89	87	70	88	90	90	90	91	79	100																								
11	26	25	26	25	26	26	26	26	23	23	100																							
12	70	68	71	69	71	71	71	72	63	66	18	100																						
13	54	52	55	53	55	55	55	55	48	51	15	39	100																					
14	83	80	82	78	83	82	82	83	74	74	22	59	45	100																				
15	71	69	71	68	71	71	71	71	63	64	19	51	39	60	100																			
16	69	68	70	68	70	70	70	70	62	64	18	51	39	57	50	100																		
17	21	21	21	20	21	21	21	21	18	19	6	15	12	17	15	14	100																	
18	60	59	60	58	60	60	60	60	53	55	16	43	33	50	43	42	13	100																
19	87	85	87	84	88	87	88	88	78	79	23	63	48	73	63	62	18	53	100															
20	52	51	53	51	53	53	53	53	47	49	14	38	30	44	38	36	11	32	47	100														
21	38	37	38	37	38	38	38	38	34	35	10	27	21	31	27	27	8	23	34	20	100													
22	94	91	95	91	95	95	95	95	84	85	25	63	52	79	66	67	20	57	84	51	36	100												
23	95	92	96	93	96	96	96	96	85	88	25	70	53	79	68	68	20	58	84	52	37	92	100											
24	97	95	98	96	99	97	99	99	87	91	25	72	56	81	70	70	20	60	87	53	38	95	97	100										
25	87	85	88	85	88	88	88	88	78	80	23	63	49	73	63	62	18	53	75	47	34	84	85	88	100									
26	95	92	95	91	95	95	95	95	84	87	25	68	53	79	68	67	20	58	84	51	36	91	92	95	88	100								
27	81	78	80	76	81	80	81	81	72	72	21	57	44	63	58	56	17	48	71	43	31	77	77	79	71	77	100							
28	92	89	92	89	93	93	93	93	82	84	24	67	52	77	66	66	19	56	82	50	35	88	90	92	82	59	75	100						
29	75	73	75	72	75	75	75	75	67	65	19	54	42	62	54	53	16	45	66	40	29	72	73	75	67	72	61	70	100					
30	60	58	60	58	60	60	60	61	54	55	16	43	33	50	43	43	13	36	53	32	23	58	58	60	53	58	49	56	46	100				
31	99	96	99	95	99	99	99	100	88	90	26	71	55	82	71	70	21	60	85	53	38	95	96	99	88	95	81	93	75	60	100			
32	77	75	77	75	77	77	78	78	69	71	20	56	43	64	55	55	16	47	68	42	30	74	75	77	69	74	63	72	59	47	77	100		
33	66	64	66	63	66	66	66	66	59	60	17	47	36	55	47	47	14	40	58	35	25	63	64	65	59	63	54	62	50	40	66	52	100	
34	82	79	81	77	81	81	81	81	72	73	21	53	44	68	59	57	17	49	72	43	31	77	78	80	72	76	69	76	62	50	81	63	54	100

TABLE 4. COMPARISON OF OUR AND OTHER MEASURED VALUES.

Reaction	Cross section (mb)				
	Horibe	Fabry[1]	Mannhart[2]	Kobayashi[3]	
^{27}Al(n, α)	(0.705±0.044)	0.705±0.040	0.706±0.028	(0.644)	(0.705)
^{27}Al(n, p)	4.09±0.26	3.86±0.25	3.95±0.20	3.64±0.17	3.98
^{54}Fe(n, p)	81.7±5.2	79.7±4.9	80.5±2.3		
^{56}Fe(n, p)	1.13±0.07	1.0350±0.075	1.09±0.041		
^{58}Ni(n, p)	106±7.0		103.5±5%	(102)	112
^{59}Co(n, α)	0.170±0.012	0.143±0.010	0.161±0.007	0.131±0.0061	0.143
^{59}Co(n, 2n)	0.303±0.021		0.202±0.006		
^{24}Mg(n, p)	1.38±0.09	1.48±0.082	1.50±0.06	1.36±0.065	1.49
^{115}In(n, n')^m	198±12	189±8	190.3±7.3	(177)	193.8
^{46}Ti(n, p)	11.6±0.80	11.8±0.75	11.6±0.4	10.9±0.59	11.9
^{47}Ti(n, p)	20.2±1.4	19.0±1.4	17.7±0.6	18.9±0.87	20.7
^{48}Ti(n, p)	0.305±0.020	3.00±0.018	0.302±0.010	0.256±0.013	0.280
^{103}Rh(n, n')^m	955±101	733±5.2%			
^{64}Zn(n, p)	29.4±7.5			30.9±2.1	33.8
^{92}Mo(n, p)^m	6.78±0.42			6.11±0.29	6.69

[1]. W. L. Zijp. ECN-90 (1979).

[2]. W. Mannhart. 5th ASTM-Euratom Symp. on Reactor Dosimetry (1984).

[3]. K. Kobayashi et al.. J. Nucl. Sci. Tech. 13. No.10 (1976).

14 MeV neutron (JENDL-2 data). While abundance ratios are 1.13 and 3.59, respectively, and moreover the threshold energy of the former is lower than that of the later.

Table 4 shows the comparison of our data and other data. Our results agree well with data by Fabry and Mannhart, except for those of ^{59}Co(n,2n), ^{24}Mg(n,p) and ^{103}Rh(n,n') as seen in the table.

We can not compare directly with Kobayashi's data, because their values had been normalized with the cross sections in parentheses, which differ from the other values, correspondingly. Then we renormalize their values with 0.705 mb for ^{27}Al(n,α) instead of 0.644 mb. Thus normalized values are also given in this table. Comparison of our values with these values are useful, because a renormalization factor for the ^{27}Al(n,α) cross section is 1.09. While those for their two other reference cross sections are ranging from 1.04 to 1.12 using our and Mannhart's values as new reference ones. Agreement of these renormalization factors seems to be well with one another considering the experimental errors. Thus renormalized values agree with ours within the errors, except for ^{59}Co(n,α).

Our value of ^{59}Co(n,2n) is larger than that by Mannhart by 1.5 times, however it is consistent with the recommended value by Calamand. The threshold energy of this reaction is high as 10.64 MeV. Measurements for those cross sections of which effective threshold energies are higher than about 10 MeV are usually difficult to obtain reliable values. The matter is the same as is seen in the next comparison with calculated ones accordingly.

Our value of ^{103}Rh(n,n') cross section was consistent with that obtained from our another measurement with 40 keV gamma. On the other hand, it is larger than that by Fabry by 1.3 times. Many other data so far reported are ranging form 403 to 716 mb,[10,11,12] except for an early data of 1093 mb by Beckurts.[13] Most of them are however calculated ones and are lower than the Fabry's data. Causes for the discrepancy should be clarified in future.

For comparison with recommended values by Calamand[9], we recalculated our cross sections using 0.725 mb for the ^{27}Al(n,α) cross section as reference, because he had used the same reference values to renormalize many experimental data in his evaluation. Thus obtained our values agree with his values within the errors, except for ^{45}Sc(n,α), ^{50}Ti(n,α), ^{59}Co(n,2n) and ^{103}Rh(n,n') cross sections.

(2) Comparison with Calculated Data

For comparison of our results with calculated values, we cited results of the recent work done by Ohsawa (to be published in JAERI-M) for verification of the U-235 fission neutron spectrum. Table 5 shows our results and his calculated ones. For ease of comparison, ratios of the calculated to our values are shown in Fig. 2 as C/E. Agreement of ours with those calculated using ENDF/B-V data file and shapes of Maxwellian, Madland and Watt spectra for both ^{47}Ti(n,p) and ^{27}Al(n,p) cross sectons are excellent. On the other hand, C/E for Mannhart's data is 1.2 to 1.28, and 0.5 to 1.0 for these reactions, respectively. On the whole, distribution of the plotted points around the unit ratio is similar with those for

928

TABLE 5. COMPARISON OF OUR MEASURED AND OHSAWA'S CALCULATED
DATA.

Spectrum	Exp'tal data (Horibe)	JENDL-2 ENDF/B-IV (Maxwell)		JENDL-3T (Madland)		ENDF/B-V (Watt)	
Cross Section		ENDF/B-V	JENDL-2	ENDF/B-V	JENDL-2	ENDF/B-V	JENDL-2
$^{27}Al(n,p)^{27}Mg$	4.09±0.26	4.264	3.772	4.160	3.689	4.271	3.785
$^{27}Al(n,a)^{27}Na$	0.705±0.044	0.8189	0.8310	0.6794	0.6929	0.7267	0.7402
$^{46}Ti(n,p)^{46}Sc$	11.6±0.8	11.16		10.90		11.20	
$^{47}Ti(n,p)^{47}Sc$	20.2±1.4	21.67		22.52		22.48	
$^{48}Ti(n,p)^{48}Sc$	0.305±0.020	0.3180		0.2670		0.2846	
$^{55}Mn(n,2n)^{54}Mn$		0.3270	0.3335	0.1881	0.1920	0.2148	0.2192
$^{54}Fe(n,p)^{54}Mn$	81.7±5.2	78.53	71.93	81.37	73.85	81.57	74.39
$^{56}Fe(n,p)^{56}Mn$	1.13±0.10	1.119	1.162	0.9937	1.031	1.047	1.087
$^{58}Ni(n,p)^{58}Co$	106.±7	102.6	99.70	106.33	103.39	106.46	103.52
$^{58}Ni(n,2n)^{57}Ni$		0.00532	0.0052	0.00256	0.00251	0.00296	0.0029
$^{59}Co(n,a)^{56}Mn$	0.170±0.012	0.1711	0.1836	0.1450	0.1567	0.1543	0.1665
$^{59}Co(n,2n)^{58}Co$	0.303±0.021	0.2977	0.2764	0.1684	0.1575	0.1926	0.1800
$^{63}Cu(n,a)^{60}Co$		0.6087	0.5852	0.5422	0.5264	0.5703	0.5526
$^{65}Cu(n,2n)^{64}Cu$		0.4809	0.4794	0.2853	0.2829	0.3246	0.3222
$^{115}In(n,n')^{115}In$	198.±12	173.2		181.5		179.3	
$^{127}I(n,2n)^{126}I$		1.730		1.129		1.270	
$^{19}F(n,2n)^{18}F$			0.0147		0.00792		0.0090
$^{63}Cu(n,2n)^{62}Cu$			0.1499		0.0781		0.0900

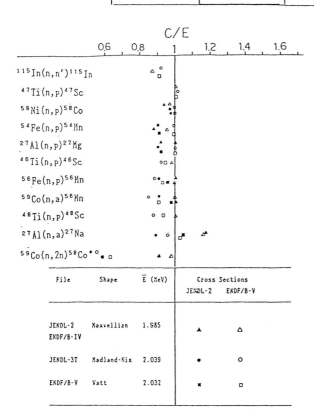

FIGURE 2. RATIO OF CALCULATED TO MEASURED DATA. INPUT DATA
FOR THE CALCULATIONS AND SYMBOLS ARE AS SHOWN IN
THE LOWER PART.

Mannhat's data, except for $^{47}Ti(n,p)$ reaction.
However, in both cases for the cross sections
whose effective threshold energies are larger
than about 10 MeV, the values of C/E deviate
largely from unit.

In our measurements of the $^{58}Ni(n,2n)$
cross section, the most dominant gamma peaks at
1378 keV were interfered with natural backround
peaks and moreover we could not confirm traces
of the 1919keV peaks of the product, so that it
is difficult to estimate reliably their peak
areas and hence we omitted the result. We also
omitted the $^{55}Mn(n,2n)$ cross section, because
the photo peak at 834.8 keV were interfered
with a background peak. We would report these
two cross sections as well as the cross section
of the $^{58}Ni(n,n'p)$ reaction, after precise
estimations of these photo peak areas.

ACKNOWLEDGEMENT

This work was done under the joint
research program of Research Reactor Institute,
Kyoto University. We are indebted to Dr. Maria
Petilli of CNEN , Italy for our data processing
done successfully by using her code BOLIK. We
would like to thank Professor I. Kimura of
Kyoto University for his encouragement throughout the work. We would like to thank Dr. K.
Kobayashi, Resarch Reactor Institute, Kyoto
University for his kind guidance in data
processing.

REFERENCES

1.   D. E. CULLEN, N. P. KOCHEROV, and P. M. McLAUGHLIN, Nucl. Sci. Eng., 83, 497 (1983).

2.   K. KANDA, K. KOBAYASHI, H. CHATANI, and T. SHIBATA, KURRI-TR-96, Research Reactor Institute, Kyoto University (1972).

3.   K. KOBAYASHI, I. KIMURA, and W. MANNHART, J. Nucl. Sci. Technol. 19, 341 (1982).

4.   M. PETILLI, CNEN-RT/FI(80)-18 (1980).

5.   O. HORIBE, Proceedings of the International Conf. Santa Fe, New Mexico, 1, 517 (1985).

6.   T. KOBAYASHI, T. KOZUKA, H. CHATANI and T. SHIBATA, Ann. Rep. Research Reactor Institute, Kyoto University, 18, 133 (1985).

7.   International Tables of X-ray Crystal Graphy, 3, (1968).

8.   J. B. DRAGT, J. W. M. DECKKER, H. GRUPPENLLAA, and A. J. JANSSEN, Nucl. Sci. Eng., 62, 117 (1977).

9.   A. CALAMAND, Handbook on Nuclear Activation Cross-sections, IAEA, Vienna, (1974) p237.

10.   I. KIMURA, K. KOBAYASHI, and T. SHIBATA, J. Nucl. Sci. and Technol., 6, 455 (1969).

11.   J. P. BUTLER, and D. C. STANRY, "The Neutron Inelestic Cross Section for the Production of ^{103}Rh. Proc. of Conf. on Neutron Cross Sections and Technology, NBS Special Publication, 299, 2, 803 (1968).

12.   W. KEOLER and K. KNOPF, Nukleonik. 10, 181 (1967).

13.   A. BECKURTS and K. WIRTZ, Neutron Physics. Springer-Verglage,   Berlin,   (1964).

CALCULATED MEDIUM ENERGY FISSION CROSS SECTIONS

E. D. Arthur
T-DO M S B210
Los Alamos National Labratory
Los Alamos, New Mexico 87545
(505) 665-1708

P. G. Young
T-2 M S B243
Los Alamos National Laboratory
Los Alamos, New Mexico 87545
(505) 667-7670

ABSTRACT

An analysis has been made of medium-energy nucleon induced fission of ^{238}U and ^{237}Np using detailed models of fission, based upon the Bohr-Wheeler formalism. Two principal motivations were associated with these calculations. The first was determination of barrier parameters for proton-rich uranium and neptunium isotopes normally not accessible in lower energy reactions. The second was examination of the consistency between (p,f) experimental data versus new (n,f) data that has recently become available. Additionally, preliminary investigations were also made concerning the effect of fission dynamics on calculated fission cross sections at higher energies where neutron emission times may be significantly less than those associated with fission.

INTRODUCTION

A variety of techniques are available for calculation of fission cross sections induced by medium energy nucleon reactions. Many of these, especially those appearing in intranuclear cascade codes such as NMTC and HETC, are based upon systematics or simple theoretical parameterizations[1] of (Γ_n / Γ_f) where the Γ's refer to the neutron and fission width respectively. Such models parameterize the behavior of these ratios as a function of mass, charge, and sometimes excitation energy. The calculations to be discussed here employ a more detailed treatment of the fission channel based upon the Bohr-Wheeler formalism[2] including both fission penetrabilities as well as explicit calculation of fission transition state spectra and densities occurring at the fission saddle point. Although in the present calculations we determined the barrier parameters empirically, we were interested in the systematics of barrier parameters asociated with more proton-rich compound systems compound systems are reached at higher energies. Additionally once we had determined a set of barrier parameters that reproduced one type of nucleon-induced fission data (either proton or neutron induced), we were interested in observing the consistency of predicted data for the other projectile type. Recent experimental data for neutron-induced reactions measured at Los Alamos[3] over large energy ranges (few MeV to several hundred MeV) offer tantalizing possibilities for such comparisons as well as in the determination of barrier parameters mentioned pre-

viously. Finally we have begun a preliminary investigation of fission dynamics for fission occurring at high excitation energies in a given compound system. From recent heavy-ion experimental[4] and theoretical work[5], one expects that the time scale involved in reaching the scission point is significantly longer than that for neutron emission at high excitation energies. Thus instances may occur where the assumption of statistical equilibrium is not valid, and particle emission can occur before the fissioning system can reach the scission point. We have approximated these effects and have investigated their impact on total calculated fission cross sections as well as on cross sections associated with specific multichance fission components.

CALCULATIONAL MODELS AND METHODS

For the fission cross section calculations described here the GNASH[6] pre-equilibrium-statistical model code was used. This code uses either the Hauser Feshbach statistical model or the Weisskopf Ewing evaporation model to describe equilibrium reaction processes. It also includes a pre-equilibrium model based upon the exciton formalism of Kalbach[7] to describe nonequilibrium particle emission processes that are expected to occur in the initial stages of the reaction sequence for incident energies of interest here. The model framework treats explicitly the population and subsequent depopulation (through particle, gamma-ray emission and fission) of up to 60 compound systems to determine reaction cross sections and emission spectra (particle and γ ray) at a given incident energy. Particle and gamma ray emission probabilities are calculated using penetrabilities determined from optical model calculations (for particle emission) or through a gamma ray strength model such as that of Brink Axel.[8] The product of such penetrabilities with the density of nuclear levels determined using the Gilbert-Cameron nuclear level density model[9] produce partial and total particle and gamma-ray emission widths needed to determine cross sections. Fission cross sections are calculated in a similar fashion using Hill-Wheeler penetrabilities and state density expressions that will be described next.

Fission cross sections are calculated for each compound system where fission is energetically possible by use of the Hill-Wheeler penetrability expression given by

$$P_f = \left[1 + \exp\left(2\pi/\hbar\,\omega\,(E_b - E)\right) \right]^{-1} \qquad (1)$$

where E_b is the barrier height and $\hbar\omega$ is the curvature. Contributions from discrete transition states are obtained by a sum over such penetrabilities, while the contribution from the continuum of such states (which is generally the most important case except near thresholds) is given by

$$\Gamma_f(U) = \int_{E_l}^{E_c} d\varepsilon\, \rho(U - E_b + E_c - \varepsilon)\, P_f(\varepsilon) \qquad (2)$$

where E_c is the excitation energy at which the continuum of fission transition states begins, and ρ is the transition state density which is given also by the Gilbert-Cameron expression used in other parts of the calculation. However because of symmetry conditions (or lack thereof) that exist at the fission barrier relative to the ground state configuration, the normal Gilbert-Cameron expression is multiplied by the following enhancement factor

$$\rho^{TS}(U) = f_0\,(1 + U^{0.25})\,\rho^{GC}(U) \qquad (3)$$

where f_0 is (for these calculations) an externally provided factor used to help match calculated results to data. This factor can also be computed based on knowledge of the symmetries expected at the fission barrier for a given compound system. Since one expects from microscopic density calculations[10] that such enhancements die out at higher excitation energies, we allowed the enhancement to saturate around excitation energies of 10 MeV and then to linearly decrease to a factor of one over the excitation energy range between 10 and 20 MeV.

Since particle transmission coefficients (or penetrabilities) are an important factor influencing both the calculation of particle emission widths as well as compound nucleus reaction cross sections, we determined such data through coupled-channel optical model calculations performed using the ECIS[11] code. Comparisons were made to neutron total, elastic, inelastic cross sections as well as elastic proton scattering data to confirm optical model parameters. Transmission coefficients for both neutrons and protons were determined in this fashion.

CALCULATED RESULTS AND DISCUSSION

Comparisons will be made first with fission cross sections induced by proton reactions on ^{238}U for incident energies below 100 MeV. For these calculations we included contributions from (p,xn) and (p,pxn) reactions chains which means that neptunium and uranium compound systems were explicitly treated in the calculations. We did not include other proton or charged-particle reaction channels because of the low probability for emission due to Coulomb barrier effects. Under these assumptions we included a total

of 29 compound systems ranging from mass numbers 225 to 239 for neptunium isotopes and 225 to 238 for uranium compound systems. With so many compound systems and with numerous barrier parameters per system, unique parameters cannot be obtained by use of p + ^{238}U data alone. In our fission parameter determinations we also used (n,f) data on $^{235,238}U$ and ^{237}Np. From our analysis of the p + ^{238}U data we found that the major contributions (> 90%) came from portions of the (p,xn) reaction sequence producing compound systems ranging from ^{239}Np to ^{229}Np. Thus the p + ^{238}U system is very equivalent to n + ^{237}Np because of the dominance of neptunium compound systems that are populated.

Figure 1 compares our calculated results with data available for p + ^{238}U reactions dating mainly from the 1950's. Reasonable agreement is obtained. We then used the same barrier parameters for n + ^{237}Np calculations to compare with new data from the Los Alamos WNR facility recently measured by Lisowski (reported at this meeting) that cover the energy range from a few MeV to 400-500 MeV. These comparisons are shown in Fig. 2 where the Np^{237} experimental data originate from ratios to ^{235}U results which have been translated into cross sections using new absolute ^{235}U (n,f) data also measured by Lisowski. The agreement at low energies (< 20 MeV) is reasonable considering that the proton data on ^{238}U is not sensitive to neptunium compound system fission because of the general shape of the reaction cross section which is dominated by Coulomb effects in this energy region. Even up to 30-35 MeV the agreement remains good, although structure appearing in the measurements is not reproduced. Of more concern is the systematic overprediction of these neutron data for neutron energies above 40 MeV even though for the p + ^{238}U comparison there was good agreement in this energy region.

We then made similar calculations for n + ^{238}U fission data to compare with these measurements. Here we used uranium compound system parameters resulting from the p + ^{238}U analysis (even though there is reduced sensitivity to their determination for the reasons described earlier). We also analyzed n + ^{235}U data for energies below 30 MeV to determine barrier parameters for ^{233}U through ^{239}U compound systems. Our calculations based on these analysis steps are shown in Fig. 3 and compared with the new Los Alamos data. Again there is good agreement up to about 30 MeV but the theoretical results overpredict the experimental data at higher energies. Attempts to determine parameters that fit these new n + ^{237}Np and n + ^{238}U data resulted in p + ^{238}U calculated results that underpredicted the data illustrated in Fig. 1. Thus confusion exists as to whether there are calculational difficulties or whether there is a basic inconsistency between the older proton-induced fission data and the newer neutron data.

We now return to the n + ^{237}Np fission results to discuss in more detail certain features of the calculation. We also illustrate preliminary results from our approximation of effects due to differing time scales associated with fission and particle emission that occur at higher energies. Figure 4 illustrates the calculated multichance fission components that

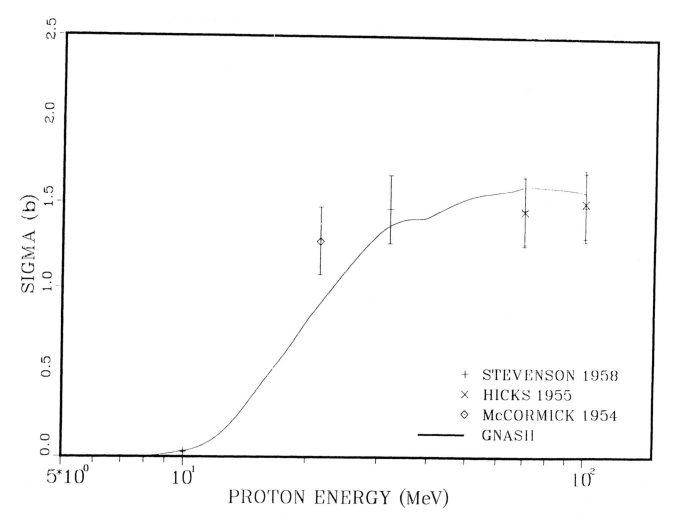

Fig. 1 A comparison of the present calculations with data for p + ^{238}U fission in the energy range up to 100 MeV.

produced the total fission cross section shown earlier in Fig. 2. In this figure we compare contributions from neptunium compound systems ranging in mass number from 237 to 230. We have not included contributions from the ^{238}Np compound nucleus fission since at energies above forty or so MeV pre-equilibrium particle emission dominates so there is little or no strength left for fission of this system. In this context differing time scales for particle emission versus fission occur, except here one is dealing with a pre-equilibrium emission phenomena that completely depletes available compound system population before fission can occur.

Other features of note include the fact that at higher energies (> 40 MeV), the total fission cross section is made up of almost equal contributions from several fissioning neptunium systems. Thus by 80-100 MeV seven systems contribute to the total fission cross section in roughly equal proportions (~ 0.2 barns each). In this calculation ^{236}Np continues to dominate at high energies, probably due in part to its odd-odd nature and the subsequent effect on calculated transition state and nuclear level densities. Referring again to Fig. 2, in order to reproduce the neutron data shown would require decreases in the calculated fission cross

section of these eight compound systems by almost a factor of two. To do this would require utilization of abnormally high barrier heights for several compound systems in the mass range from 230-236. An alternative method for reducing the calculated total fission cross section at high energies would involve changes in the transition state enhancement factor (Eq. 3). It is doubtful that such changes would have significant effects except on the most proton-rich systems occurring here. For systems that have their largest contribution at lower energies, the effect is minimized since the enhancement factor shape described earlier produces enhancements of order one at these higher incident energies.

As stated above increased barrier heights could bring the calculated results into better agreement with the data at these higher energies. However Fig. 5 illustrates why such actions would be undesirable and unphysical. Fig. 5 compares the neutron separation energies for neptunium systems occurring in the n + ^{237}Np and p + ^{238}U calculations with our deduced barrier heights. The trend established in these calculations is that barrier heights, commensurate in magnitude with the neutron binding energy for a given compound system, are needed to produce reasonable fission results. For the more proton-rich systems

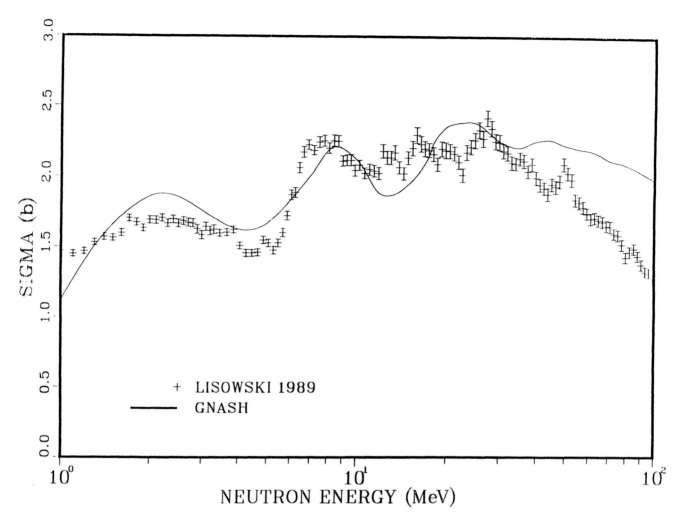

Fig. 2   A comparison of present calculations of n + ^{237}Np fission using fission parameters determined from proton reaction analyses to new Los Alamos data.

(lighter neptunium isotopes) the neutron binding energy follows a trend towards larger values (reaching near 7.5 MeV for some cases).   In these cases the barrier heights were increased to prevent the situation where the barriers might lie several MeV below the neutron separation energy. In such instances fission would dominate, thereby producing an even greater tendency to overpredict the total fission cross section at higher energies. Increasing barrier heights in this manner is, however, counter to results obtained from liquid drop barrier calculations (with ground state mass corrections)[12] shown in the figure as well as with certain trends obtained from barrier determinations using charged-particle fission probability data. Again to force agreement with the (n,f) data by the significant barrier height increase required would further exacerbate this difference.

A final area in which we have begun investigation of fission phenomena at high incident (and excitation) energies involves the influence of fission dynamics on predicted fission cross sections. This area has been of recent interest for heavy-ion reaction induced fission and has been investigated through Foker-Plank diffusion calculations performed by Nix, Hoffman, Weidenmuller and others (see Ref 5). Such calculations have examined characteristic

diffusion rates and times to reach either fission saddle or scission points in various over or under-damped fissioning systems. At high excitation energies (around 100 MeV) such calculations indicate significant departures from results obtained using standard Bohr-Wheeler widths which assume the existence of statistical equilibrium in a fissioning system. The most immediate modification of the Bohr-Wheeler calculated width is due to Kramers[13] which involves a multiplicative factor that includes a viscosity coefficient β associated with the fission process. In the present work we have not replaced our Bohr-Wheeler fission widths since the factors occurring in the Kramers expressions would uniformly reduce the fission widths for most compound systems occurring in our calculations. In order to reproduce available experimental data we would then have to readjust barrier heights and state density enhancement factors so that the resulting fission cross section would probably not change significantly. Instead we have approximated master equation calculations performed by Hassani et al[14] which explicitly include fission rates calculated via diffusion methods. For fissioning systems having temperatures of approximately 2 MeV (appropriate for excitation energies of interest here) characteristic times for fission are on the order

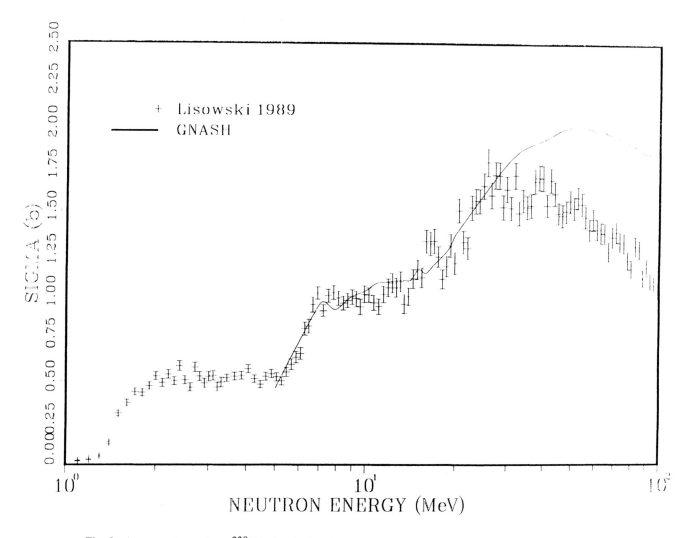

Fig. 3   A comparison of our ^{238}U(n,f) calculated cross sections with new Los Alamos measurements.

of 50-100 $\times 10^{-22}$ seconds.[15]   We can compute also an equivalent neutron emission characteristic time from $\tau = \hbar / \Gamma_n$ where the neutron width is determined by

$$\Gamma_n(U) = \frac{1}{\pi \rho(U)} \int_0^U d\varepsilon \sum (2\ell + 1) \, T_\ell \, \rho(U - \varepsilon) \quad (4)$$

where T and ρ refer respectively to optical model transmission coefficients and level density data. Characteristic neutron emission times computed at an excitation energy U are then compared with the characteristic fission time range given above. At high excitation energies neutron emission times were found to be significantly less than these times. In such cases we bypassed our normal calculation of the fission width in the equilibrium portion of the GNASH code and allowed only particle and gamma ray emission.

As an indication of the effects of this approximation, Fig. 6 illustrates the change in fission contributions occurring from several fissioning systems involve n + ^{237}Np fission in the incident energy range from 60-100 MeV. The systems shown there are the same as shown

earlier in Fig. 4 where the magnitudes of various contributions to the total fission cross section were presented. Several trends are apparent from the results shown in Fig. 6. First the contribution from fission of the ^{237}Np compound system decreases significantly. This occurs because ^{237}Np exists at the highest excitation energy of the set considered here and neutron emission thus occurs on the shortest time scale. This means that population strength occurring in this system is available for neutron emission which then populates compound systems occurring later in the reaction chain. This increased population is then followed by fission of these systems. Note that the fission probability of these later compound systems is not significantly affected by our fission dynamics approximation since they exist at lower excitation energies where characteristic neutron emission times are large. Because of this increased initial population, their overall fission contribution increases relative to the case where no fission dynamics effects were included. This trend continues up to higher incident energies where neutron emission times of systems such as ^{235,236}Np become short because of the higher excitation energies that are reached. These systems then exhibit a decline in their fission contribution relative to the non-fission dynamics case.

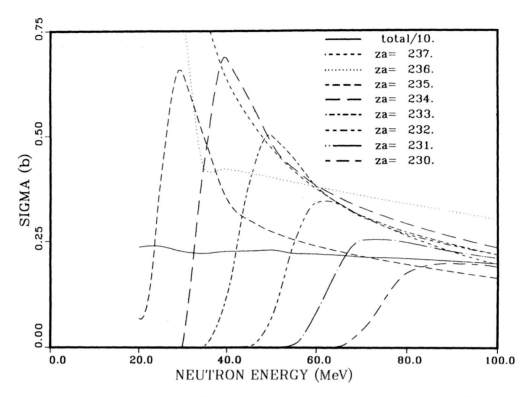

Fig. 4 Calculated multi chance fission components of the total fission cross section for n + ^{237}Np in the incident energy range from 20-100 MeV.

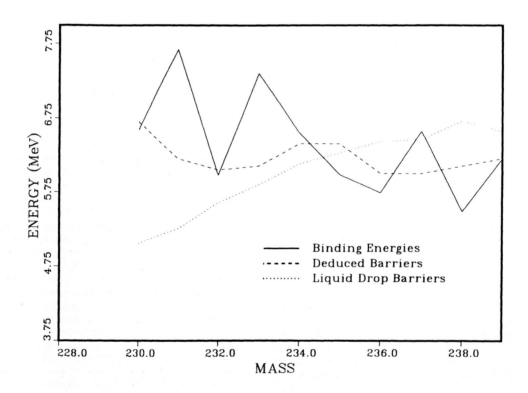

Fig. 5 A comparison is made of the deduced barrier heights for the neptunium compound systems occurring in our calculation of n + ^{237}Np and p + ^{238}U fission to neutron separation energies for these nuclei. Also shown are trends predicted from liquid drop calculation of barrier heights as described in the text.

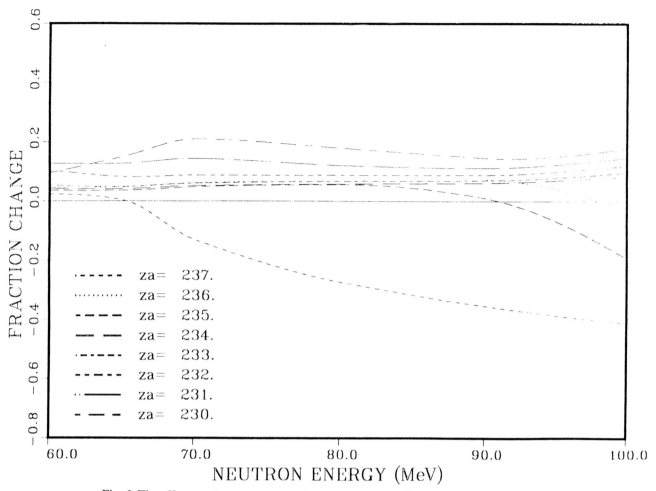

Fig. 6 The effect on the components of the calculated n + ^{237}Np fission cross section due to approximation of fission dynamics is illustrated for reactions occurring in the energy range from 60 to 100 MeV.

The overall effect of this crude approximation to fission diffusion on the total fission cross section is small. This occurs because of the off setting of reduced fission probabilities for specific compound systems with increased neutron population of later stages of the reaction chain as discussed above. We thus see little effect upon our calculations at high energies using this approximation but caution that these investigations are still in a preliminary form.

CONCLUSION

To summarize the conclusions discussed thus far in this paper, we find good agreement between our calculations of p + ^{238}U fission cross sections and data using reasonable fission parameters. When translated to the case of n + ^{237}Np fission and compared with new Los Alamos results, the agreement is not good at energies above 40 MeV. This situation is also observed for the case of ^{238}U(n,f). We also examined calculated contributions to the total fission cross section for n + ^{237}Np and found at higher energies that several compound systems contribute in approximately equal fashions. Since most of these are very proton rich systems, we would have to increase further the barrier heights used in

the calculations by significant amounts to produce agreement with the data. Finally we examined an approximation to fission dynamic effects and found that it had little influence on the total calculated fission cross section.

In summary we believe that the new neutron data covering wide energy ranges that is now becoming available will have an important effect on the determination of parameters applicable to (p,f) data analyses as well as in the determination of the fission properties of proton rich compound systems. However the discrepancy between either proton and neutron-induced experimental data or between theoretical calculations and the neutron data must be resolved before such benefits can be realized.

References

1. R. Vandenbosch and J. Huizenga, Nuclear Fission (Academic Press, New York, 1973)

2. N. Bohr and J. A. Wheeler, Phys. Rev. 56, 426 (1939)

3. P. W. Lisowski, personal communication, Los Alamos National Laboratory (1989).

4. A. Gavron et al., Phys. Rev. C35, 579 (1987).

5. P. Grange et al., Phys. Rev. C34, 209 (1986); J. R. Nix et al., Nucl. Phys. A424, 239 (1984)

6. P. G. Young and E. D. Arthur, Los Alamos Report LA-6947(1977); E. D. Arthur, Los Alamos Report LA-UR-88-382 (1988).

7. C. Kalbach, Zeit fur Physik, A283, 401(1977).

8. D. M. Brink, thesis, Oxford University (1955); P. Axel, Phys. Rev. 125, 671 (1962).

9. A. Gilbert and A. G. W. Cameron, Can J. Phys. 43 , 1446 (1965).

10. A. Jensen, "Recent Developments in the Theory of Nuclear Level Densities", Proceeding Int. Conf on Neutron Physics and Nuclear Data, Harwell, p378 (1978).

11. J. Raynal, "Optical Model and Coupled-Channel Calculations in Nuclear Physics", International Atomic Energy Agency Report IAEA SMR-9/8 (1970).

12. D. G. Madland, personal communication, Los Alamos National Laboratory, 1988 and Applied Nuclear Science Group Informal Report T2-IR-8-2 (1988).

13. H. A. Kramers, Physica (The Hague) 7, 284 (1940).

14. S. Hasani and P. Grange, Phys. Lett. 137B, 281 (1984).

15. Yi-Zhong and Xi-Zhen Wu, "Recent Progress in Fission Theory Based on Diffusion Models", Nuclear Data for Science and Technology, Mito, Japan, p667 (1988).

ANALYSIS OF THE ^{235}U NEUTRON CROSS SECTIONS IN THE RESOLVED RESONANCE RANGE

L. C. Leal, G. de Saussure, and R. B. Perez
Oak Ridge National Laboratory
Engineering Physics and Mathematics Division
P. O. Box 2008
Oak Ridge, Tennessee 37831-6356
and
The University of Tennessee
Nuclear Engineering Department
315 Pasqua Building
Knoxville, TN 37996-2300
(615) 574-6114, 574-6125

ABSTRACT

Using recent high-resolution measurements of the neutron transmission of ^{235}U and the spin-separated fission cross-section data of Moore et al., a multilevel analysis of the ^{235}U neutron cross sections was performed up to 300 eV. The Dyson Metha Δ_3 statistics were used to help locate small levels above 100 eV where resonances are not clearly resolved even in the best resolution measurements available. The statistical properties of the resonance parameters are discussed.

INTRODUCTION

An accurate resonance analysis of the ^{235}U neutron cross sections was recently completed for ENDF/B-VI.[1,2] In this analysis, the resolved resonance formalism is used up to 2250 eV. However, since the level spacing in ^{235}U is approximately 0.5 eV the resonances cannot be truly resolved over that range, and at the higher energies the goal of the analysis was mainly to provide pseudo-parameters that represented well the observed structures of the cross sections. Such a representation is expected to yield a better estimate of resonance self-shielding than the often-used unresolved formalism.[3,4]

As part of this analysis, an attempt was made to determine as accurately as possible the resonance energies up to 300 eV. Even at this lower energy it is not possible to resolve unambiguously all the levels. However, the availability of spin-separated fission cross-section data[5] and of high-resolution measurements done on samples cooled to the liquid nitrogen temperature[6,7] to reduce Doppler broadening of the resonances, allows resolving levels up to 300 eV with reasonable confidence. The Dyson Metha Δ_3 statistics[8] introduce strong correlations in the expected level spacings and help determine the energies of small resonances that cannot be unambiguously resolved.

METHOD OF ANALYSIS

The resonance parameter analysis code SAMMY[9] was used to perform a consistent R-matrix multilevel analysis of selected neutron cross section and transmission measurements. The computer code SAMMY uses the Reich-Moore formalism and a fitting procedure based on the Bayes' method which allows the successive incorporation of new data in a consistent manner. The code allows for searching not only resonance parameters but also experimental parameters such as sample thickness, residual backgrounds, local renormalization, effective temperature and the parameters of the resolution function, all consistent with predetermined uncertainty limits. A special feature of SAMMY, programmed for this analysis, allows the fitting of separated spin contributions to the fission cross section.

UTILIZATION OF THE Δ_3 STATISTICS

The Δ_3 statistics of Dyson and Metha[8] are particularly sensitive to long-range correlations within a set of levels. The mean-square deviation Δ_3 is defined by a sequence of n consecutive resonance energies in the range $(-L, +L)$ by:

$$\Delta_3 = \min_{A, B} \left\{ \left(\frac{1}{2L} \right) \int_{-L}^{+L} [N(E) - AE - B]^2 dE \right\} ,$$

where $N(E)$ is the cumulative number of levels versus neutron energy, and $AE + B$ is the line fitted to the histogram. The expected value of Δ_3 is $\frac{1}{\pi^2}(\ln n - 0.0686)$ with a variance of 0.012 where n is the total number of levels. Using the results of the high-resolution low Doppler-broadening transmission and fission measurements and the spin-separated fission cross-section data, essentially all the resonances can be resolved up to 60 eV. The Δ_3 statistics can then be used to determine precise values of the level spacings for each spin levels.

Above 60 eV, the Δ_3 statistics which constrain the number of levels per unit energy are used again to determine the probable spin of a level where the spin-separated fission cross-section data have large uncertainties or to decide where to place additional levels where the resolutions of the measurements do not permit an unambiguous interpretation of the resonance structure.

RESULTS OF THE ANALYSIS

The results of the Δ_3 statistical test and the average values of the resonance parameters for each spin state are summarized in Table 1. Figure 1 shows histograms of the cumulative number of observed levels versus energy for each spin state as well as the lines fitted to these histograms. Figures 2 and 3 show the distributions of the reduced neutron widths for each spin state compared to an expected Porter-Thomas distribution.[10] In Figs. 4 and 5 the nearest neighbor level spacing distributions observed for each spin state are compared to theoretical Wigner distributions.[10] Finally, in Figs. 6 to 8 the transmission ratios and fission cross sections computed with our resonance parameters are compared to results of measurements. These figures illustrate how accurately the resonance parameters represent the experimental measurements. However, there are significant differences between observed and expected distributions of the spin 4 levels. These differences are under investigation. More extensive comparisons between cross sections computed with the resonance parameters and results of measurements are given in Refs. 1 and 2.

CONCLUSIONS

Recent high-resolution measurements and the spin-separated fission cross-section data permit resolving essentially all the levels in ^{235}U up to 60 eV. The use of the Δ_3 statistical test allows the extension of a multilevel analysis up to 300 eV. The resonance parameters obtained represent the available experimental data accurately. The observed distributions of the resonance parameters are consistent with the distribution predicted by R-matrix theory. Of course, the partial fission width is not unique since rotations and other transformations of the fission vectors leave the fission cross section invariant.[11,12] A discussion of the fission vectors orientations has been presented elsewhere.[13]

ACKNOWLEDGEMENTS

This research was sponsored by the Office of Energy Research, Nuclear Physics, U.S. Department of Energy, under contract DE-AC05-84OR21400 with Martin Marietta Energy Systems, Inc., and under contract DOE-DE-F605-85ER-40188 with the University of Tennessee.

REFERENCES

1. L. C. LEAL, G. DE SAUSSURE, and R. B. PEREZ, "R-Matrix Analysis of the ^{235}U Neutron Cross Sections," *TANSAO* **56**, 587 (1988).

2. G. DE SAUSSURE, et al., "A New Resonance Region Evaluation of Neutron Cross Sections for ^{235}U," p. 293 in *Proc. International Reactor Physics Conference, Jackson Hole, Wyoming, Sept. 18-22, 1988*, Vol. 1. Also to be published in *Nucl. Sci. and Eng.*.

3. G. DE SAUSSURE and R. B. PEREZ, *Ann. Nucl. Energy* **9**, 79 (1982).

4. R. B. PEREZ et al., "On the Unresolved Resonance Region Representation of Neutron Induced Cross Sections," p. 183 in *Proc. International Reactor Physics Conference, Jackson Hole, Wyoming, Sept. 18-22, 1988*, Vol. 3.

5. M. S. MOORE et al., *Phys. Rev.* **C18**, 1328 (1978).

6. J. BLONS, *Nucl. Sci. Eng.* **51**, 130 (1973).

7. J. A. HARVEY et al., "High-Resolution Neutron Transmission Measurements on ^{235}U, ^{238}U, and ^{239}Pu," p. 115 in *Nuclear Data for Science and Technology, Proc. of International Conference, Mito, Japan, May 30 – June 3, 1988*, S. Igarasi, Ed.

8. P. G. DYSON and M. L. METHA, *J. Math. Phys* **4**, 701 (1963).

9. N. M. LARSON and F. G. PEREY, "Resonance Parameter Analysis with SAMMY," p. 573 in *Nuclear Data for Science and Technology, Proc. of International Conference, Mito, Japan, May 30 – June 3, 1988*, S. Igarasi, Ed.

10. C. F. PORTER and R. G. THOMAS, *Phys. Rev.* **104**, 483 (1956).

11. G. F. AUCHAMPAUGH, *Nucl. Phys.* **A175**, 65 (1971).

12. D. B. ADLER and F. T. ADLER, *Phys. Rev.* **C6**, 985 (1972).

13. M. S. MOORE et al. "Resonance Structure in the Fission of (^{235}U + n)," paper presented at the International Conference "Fifty Years Research in Nuclear Fission," Berlin, Germany, April 3–7, 1989.

Table 1. Average value of observed ^{235}U resonance parameters up to 300 eV

	$J = 3$	$J = 4$
Level spacing (eV)	1.39 ± 0.09	0.90 ± 0.04
Reduced neutron width (meV$^{1/2}$)	0.12 ± 0.09	0.09 ± 0.08
s-wave strength function $\times 10^4$	0.89 ± 0.09	1.01 ± 0.08
Fission width (meV)	239	189
Capture width (meV)	38 ± 7	35 ± 3
Observed Δ_3	0.57	0.53
Expected Δ_3	0.54 ± 0.11	0.58 ± 0.11

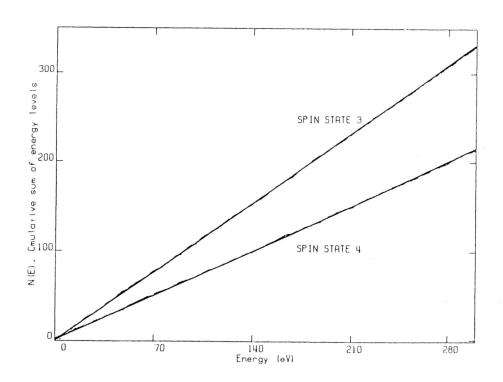

FIG. 1. CUMULATIVE SUM OF OBSERVED LEVELS

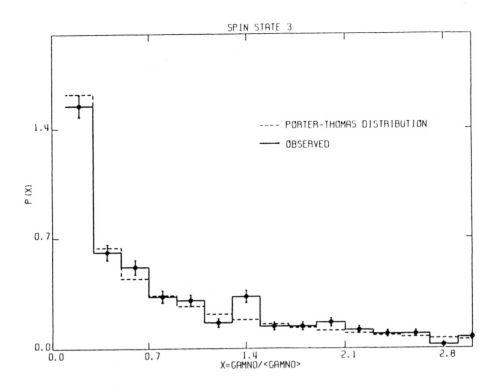

FIG. 2. DISTRIBUTION OF THE REDUCED NEUTRON WIDTH (SPIN STATE 3)

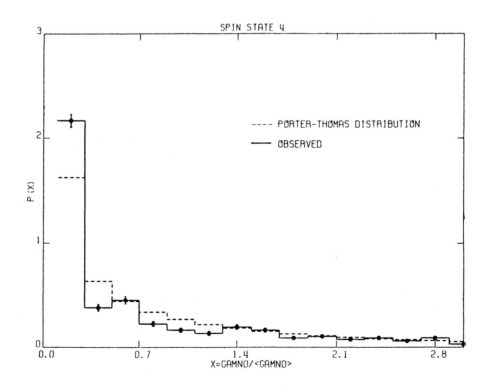

FIG. 3. DISTRIBUTION OF THE REDUCED NEUTRON WIDTH (SPIN STATE 4)

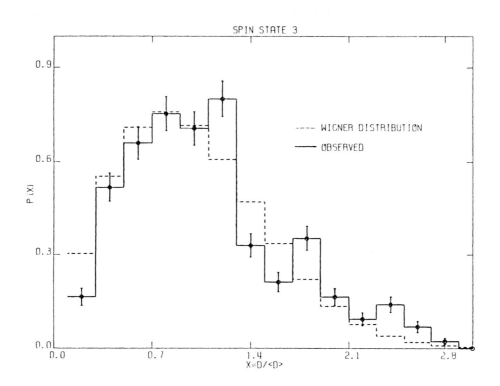

FIG. 4. LEVEL SPACING DISTRIBUTION (SPIN STATE 3)

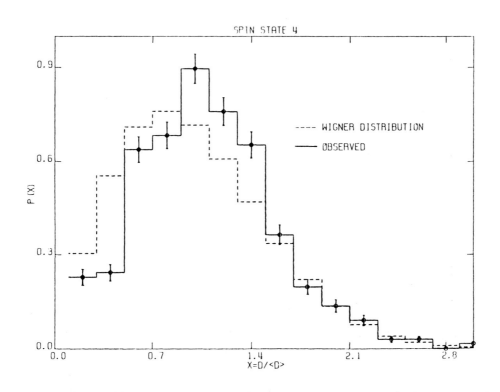

FIG. 5. LEVEL SPACING DISTRIBUTION (SPIN STATE 4)

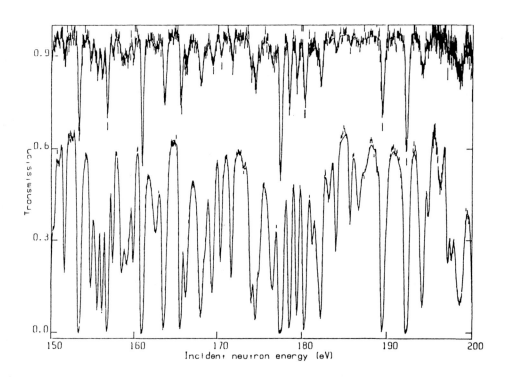

FIG. 6. COMPARISON OF COMPUTED AND MEASURED TRANSMISSION RATIOS.
(0.00234 atm/b, 0.03269 atm/b)

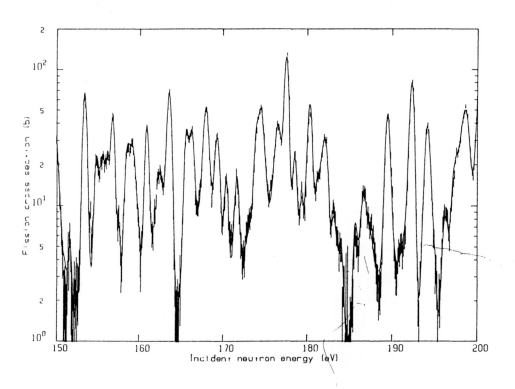

FIG. 7. COMPARISON OF COMPUTED AND MEASURED FISSION CROSS SECTIONS

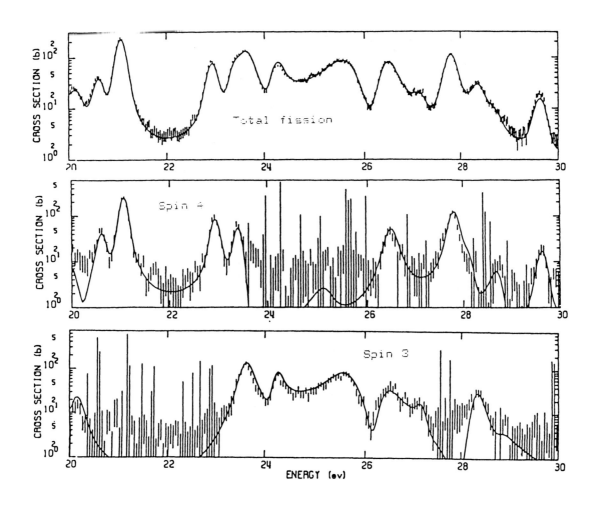

FIG. 8. TOTAL AND SPIN SEPARATED FISSION CROSS SECTION

945

A WARNING ON FISSION RESONANCE INTEGRALS - *CAVEAT UTOR* !

Norman E. Holden
National Nuclear Data Center
Brookhaven National Laboratory
Upton, New York 11973
(516) 282-5204

ABSTRACT

A common error is made in defining the resonance integral in most tabulations and handbooks. Although it has a minor effect on the capture resonance integral and on the fission resonance integral for the fissile nuclides, it leads to gross errors in the fission resonance integral for the fertile nuclides. The errors in the fission resonance integral for fertile nuclides of the elements from thorium through curium in the ENDF/B-V library will be presented.
Let the user beware.

INTRODUCTION

Experimenters utilize tables of nuclear data to provide a preliminary estimate of what they might anticipate as the result of a given experiment. If the tabulation indicates a nuclide's value where none exists or it grossly overestimates the value, the experimenter will be misled and an experiment may be performed uselessly. Such a problem exists for calculated resonance integrals of fission reactions in the fertile actinide nuclides, for which fission is a threshold reaction. The integration of the pointwise cross section with a $1/E$ neutron spectrum leads to significantly different results, depending upon the upper energy limit chosen for the resonance integral. The problem will be examined in this paper.

FORMULATION OF THE PROBLEM

In reactor design, a usual practice has been to analyse the reaction rate by separating the neutron flux into two components. One component is a thermalized neutron flux with an assumed Maxwellian energy distribution and the other is an epithermal or resonance neutron flux, whose energy distribution is assumed to be inversely proportional to the neutron energy, E.

Consider a dimensionless variable, the lethargy u, which can be introduced in place of the energy, E, and defined as

$$du = - d(\ln E) = - dE/E$$

and

$$u = \ln (E_o/E), \text{ or } E = E_o e^{-u},$$

where the negative sign indicates that u decreases as E increases, and E_o, the constant of integration, is a fixed energy usually taken to be 10 Mev, because few neutrons produced in the fission process have energies above this value.

The neutron flux density, Φ, can be expressed as a function of lethargy. If $\Phi(u)$ is the flux per unit lethargy interval, the flux in an infinitesmal range, du, is $\Phi(u) \, du$. This must be equal to the flux expressed as a function of energy, $\Phi(E) \, dE$, i.e.

$$\Phi(u) \, du = - \Phi(E) \, dE,$$

where the negative sign again indicates that u decreases when E increases. We have

$$\Phi(u) \, du = \Phi(u) \, (-dE/E) = - \Phi(E) \, dE.$$

This implies that

$$\Phi(u)/E = \Phi(E).$$

In a region where the neutron flux density varies as $1/E$, the flux per unit lethargy is seen to be a constant from the above equation. Marshak[1] showed that for neutrons slowing down in a moderating medium without absorption, but which have not yet reached thermal equilibrium, the neutron flux density varies inversely with energy.

REACTION RATE

For a small amount of a material, so-called infinite dilution, the total rate for a neutron reaction in that material is given by the equation

$$R = \Phi_{th} \, \sigma_{th} + \Phi_r \, RI,$$

where Φ_{th} is the thermal neutron flux density, Φ_r is the epithermal (resonance) neutron flux density per unit lethargy, σ_{th} is the thermal neutron cross section for the reaction and RI is the infinitely dilute resonance integral for the reaction. The problems of resonance self–shielding and flux depression are avoided by the infinite dilution assumption.

In the epi–thermal energy region, the above reaction rate for reaction X which has a reaction probability (cross section) $\sigma_X(E)$ becomes

$$\int_{E_L}^{E_U} \sigma_X(E) \ \Phi(E) \ dE$$

$$= \int_{E_L}^{E_U} \sigma_X(E) \ \Phi(u)/E \ dE$$

$$= \int_{E_L}^{E_U} \Phi(u) \ \sigma_X(E) \ dE/E.$$

In this region of constant flux per unit lethargy, the reaction rate becomes

$$\int_{E_L}^{E_U} \Phi(u) \ \sigma_X(E) \ dE/E =$$

$$\Phi(u) \int_{E_L}^{E_U} \sigma_X(E) \ dE/E = \Phi(u) \ RI_X,$$

where the last integral gives the form of this so–called Resonance Integral for reaction X. Since the reaction rate in this epi–thermal region is the product of the resonance integral and the flux per unit lethargy in the sample location, and since the flux per unit lethargy is approximately a constant in this region, if we know the constant flux value for a particular reactor, we can determine the epi–thermal reaction rate using the resonance integral.

The integration in the resonance integral is performed over the entire 1/E flux region, from the lower limit, E_L, to the upper limit, E_U. There are several advantages to the concept of the resonance integral. It is independent of the temperature and the reactor system. It only requires that the neutron energy spectrum vary as 1/E in the defined energy interval from E_L to E_U. Also, a resonance integral can be directly estimated experimentally with the use of a high pass filter, such as a cadmium cover.

The usefulness of the resonance integral concept to determine reaction rates is limited to those cases where the neutron flux density is characterized by a 1/E distribution (or constant lethargy). Although the intermediate energy range varies for different reactors, the lethargy is reasonably constant from an energy of a few tenths of an eV up to approximately a tenth of an MeV for a light–water–moderated reactor. As you extend the energy above the upper energy limit of the epi–thermal region into the fast neutron region, the neutron flux density is characterized by a fission spectrum energy distribution. In this fast neutron region, the flux per unit lethargy is no longer a constant and the integral becomes reactor dependent. Rowlands[2] shows the flux per unit lethargy for a carbon moderator.

INTEGRATION LIMITS

The integration limits of the resonance integral are important. Goldstein[3] has recommended a definition for a resonance integral which included a lower energy limit, E_L, of 0.55 eV and an upper energy limit, E_U, of 2.0 MeV. The lower bound, E_L, has been taken by various authors to be from 0.4 eV to 0.625 eV, where the thickness and the geometry of the cadmium cover leads to the various choices. In the USA, the most common lower limit is 0.5 eV. Unless there is a resonance in the reaction near this lower bound, the final choice is not critical. It is the upper boundary that is of interest here.

Goldstein's 2.0 MeV upper energy limit appears to be high when one considers that 2/3 of the fission spectrum source lies below this cutoff. Rowlands[2] indicates that the 1/E flux dependence holds below about 0.1 MeV. Many of the reactor codes use the twentieth MUFT group lower boundary at 67 keV as the breakpoint for the 1/E and the fast spectrum matching of the neutron flux.

As mentioned earlier, the region of constant lethargy extends upward in energy to about a tenth of an MeV. The upper limit on the resonance integral should then be in the range from 50 keV to about 200 keV. In the case of exoergic nuclear reactions, such as neutron capture, the major contribution to the integral comes from the region of the lower limit. Since the background cross section (in the absence of resonances) will vary as $E^{-\frac{1}{2}}$ and the flux as E^{-1}, the contribution in the tenths of an eV energy range will be about three orders of magnitude larger than the contribution in the tenths of an MeV range. The effects of resonances at low energies will greatly enhance this ratio. As a result, whether the upper limit, E_U, is 100 keV, 10 MeV, or ∞, any difference would be well within the experimental uncertainty of a measurement. Many standard tabulations of these resonance integrals, such as those found in BNL–325[4], the IAEA Handbook[5], and the ENDF/B–V guidebook[6] make the substitution of ∞ for this upper limit. This substitution is an implicit assumption that the 1/E neutron flux distribution extends to ∞, or at least to the current ENDF/B upper limit of 20 MeV, which is, of course, in contradiction to the facts. However, it is of no consequence for these exoergic reactions.

PROBLEM WITH THRESHOLD REACTIONS

For an endoergic reaction, such as neutron fission in a fertile nuclide, the threshold for the reaction is often at an energy which is higher than the constant lethargy region. Thus the resonance integral concept is not valid. In such a case, the indiscriminate integration of the cross section with a 1/E flux to the upper limit of available data, i.e., 20 MeV, results in a calculated resonance integral when, in fact, none exists. This error is due to the unthinking extrapolation of the upper limit of the resonance integral for threshold reactions.

Even when the energy threshold of the reaction does not exceed the integral's upper limit, the calculated value of the resonance integral is still much larger than it should be, since the energy range of the integration to 20 MeV is 200 times larger than it should be. Once again, the user could be misled into thinking that there is some small cross section in the eV and the low keV energy range.

RESULTS

Table I compares the resonance integrals as reported in BNL-325[4], in the IAEA handbook[5], and in the ENDF/B-V guidebook[6] with the values calculated using the proper upper limit of 100 keV. It demonstrates that large differences exist, depending upon the upper limit, E_U, used. In searching tabulations, the user should carefully check the textual material to insure that the data presented is the data required. The compilers of resonance integral tabulations should likewise be careful that, whenever calculated values from resonance parameters and point-wise cross sections are included, the upper limit utilized in the calculation is appropriate for the reaction. Values used for any threshold reactions should always be carefully scrutinized for the upper energy limit.

ACKNOWLEDGEMENT

I thank Joe Halperin (ORNL) for bringing this problem to my attention and also Frances Scheffel (BNL) for assistance in the calculations.

REFERENCES

1. R. E. MARSHAK, "Theory of the Slowing Down of Neutrons by Elastic Collision with Atomic Nuclei," Rev. Mod. Phys. 19, 185 (1947).

2. G. ROWLANDS, "The Slowing Down of Fission Neutrons in an Infinite Homogeneous Medium," J. Nucl. Energy 11, 150 (1960).

3. J. A. HARVEY, H. GOLDSTEIN, J. S. STORY, C. H. WESTCOTT, "Recommended Definitions for Epithermal Integrals Cross-Sections" EANDC-12 (1961).

4. S. F. MUGHABGHAB, Neutron Cross Sections, Volume 1, Neutron Resonance Parameters and Thermal Cross Sections part B, Z = 61-100. Academic Press, Inc. (1984).

5. E. GRYNTAKIS, D. E. CULLEN, G. MUNDY, "Thermal Neutron Cross-Sections and Infinite Dilution Resonance Integrals" in IAEA Technical Report Series No. 273 page 199, IAEA, Vienna (1987).

6. B. A. MAGURNO, R. R. KINSEY, F. M. SCHEFFEL, "Guidebook for the ENDF/B-V Nuclear Data Files" EPRI-NP-2510 (1982).

*This work was performed under the auspices of the US Department of Energy (contract DE-AC02-76CH0016).

Table I. Fission Resonance Integral Comparison

Nuclide	BNL-325 Value[4] (barns)	IAEA Value[5] (barns)	ENDF/B-V Value[6] (barns)	E_U = 100 kev Value (barns)
^{232}Th	no value quoted	0.0746 ± 0.0016	0.6185	0.0
^{233}Pa	3.0	no value quoted	2.947	0.0
^{236}U	7.8 ± 1.6	2.	7.768	4.38
^{238}U	0.00154 ± 0.00015	0.0013 ± 0.0002	2.0324	0.00153
^{237}Np	6.9 ± 1.0	6.5 ± 1.2	6.870	0.317
^{240}Pu	8.8	5.	8.830	2.41
^{242}Pu	no value quoted	5.	5.568	0.23
^{243}Am	6.151	13. ± 2.5	6.151	0.056
^{244}Cm	12.5 ± 2.5	13.4 ± 1.5	18.697	10.8

DECAY DATA OF ^{161}Tb

CHANG YONGFU, YAN CHUNGUANG, DING YUZHEN
Northwest Institute of Nuclear Technology
P.O.Box 69
Xian, P.R.China

ABSTRACT

The gamma-ray emission probabilities per decay of ^{161}Tb were obtained by ratio of the gamma-ray emission rates and the activity. The gamma-ray emission rates were determined by means of the calibrated planar HPGe detector. The activity was measured by $4\pi\beta-\gamma$ coincidence absorption method. The gamma-ray emission probability of 74.6kev was determined as (10.3 ± 0.3)%. The half-live of ^{161}Tb decay was measured by following the decay of ^{161}Tb sources for over 7 half-lives with the planar HPGe detector. The half-life value was found to be 6.954 ± 0.005 d.

INTRODUCTION

In fast neutron induced fission of the mixed ^{235}U and ^{239}Pu, the fission numbers of ^{235}U and ^{239}Pu are given by

$$\frac{N_i^{5+9}}{Y_i^9} = N_f^9 + N_f^5 \frac{Y_i^5}{Y_i^9} \qquad (1)$$

where N_f^5 and N_f^9 are the fission numbers of ^{235}U and ^{239}Pu, respectively; Y_i^5 and Y_i^9 are, respectively, the fission yields of fission product i; N_i^{5+9} is total number of fission product i. Y_i^5/Y_i^9 data for some fission products are follows as: $0.04(^{161}$Tb), $0.14(^{156}$Eu), $0.26(^{155}$Eu), $1.1(^{147}$Nd), $1.4(^{95}$Zr),etc. The intercept(N_f^9) and slope(N_f^5) were obtained from eq.(1) by the least-squares analysis. This method required for accurate fission yields and decay data of fission products. The aim of our work is to measure the half-life and gamma-ray emission probabilityies of ^{161}Tb decay more accurately.

The half-life of ^{161}Tb dcay was measured by following the decay of ^{161}Tb sources for over 7 half-lives with the planar HPGe detector. The half-live value was found to be 6.954 ± 0.005d (the 1σ level). The gamma-ray emission probabilities per decay of ^{161}Tb were obtained by ratio of the gamma-ray emission rates and the activity. The gamma-ray emission rates were determined by means of the calibrated planar HPGe detector. The activity was measured by $4\pi\beta-\gamma$ coincidence absorption method. The gamma-ray emission probability of 74.6 Kev was determind as (10.3 ± 0.3)%.

EXPERIMENT AND RESULT

The natural Gd_2O_3 were irradiated in a thermal reactor and then ^{161}Tb solution was purified by the radiochemical procedure. The different amount of pure ^{161}Tb solution was measured with a precision balance by means of pycnometer method and the sources were prepared.

The gamma-ray spectrometer was composed a Canberra 2000mm^2×16mm planar HPGe detector, a spectroscopy amplifier, a multi-channel analyzer with a 8192 channel 450 MHz ADC and minicomputer PDP-11/34. The detector was shielded by 10cm lead blocks. The energy resolutions of the detector is 740ev for 122Kev of ^{57}Co. The detector efficiencies were determined with ^{57}Co, ^{75}Se, ^{109}Cd, ^{133}Ba, ^{152}Eu, ^{169}Yb, ^{182}Ta and ^{241}Am. The distance between the source and the detector case was 14cm. The total numbers of calibration measurements were more than 300. We examined various kinds of efficiency curve function. The best fitted curve was $\ln\varepsilon = \sum A_i E^i$, where A_i ($i=1,0,-1,-2,-3$) were parametrs. The efficiency curves were determined with errors of 0.5-3.5%. After the efficiency measurements, twenty sources of ^{161}Tb were measured. There measurments were repeated under the same conditions as the efficiency calibration. The total numbers of ^{161}Tb measurement were more than 200. The intergrated peak counts of 74.6Kev gamma-ray for every measurement were more than 6×10^4. The emission rates of gamma-ray emitted in decay of ^{161}Tb were obtained from the integrated peak counts,efficiencies and sum corrections. The error of the emission rate for 74.6kev gamma-ray were less then 2%.

The radioactivity concentration of the solution was determined by means of $4\pi\beta$-γ coincidence absorption method. Thirty samples were made from three diluted solution. The radioactivity concntration of the original solution was obtained from the weighted average of three diluted solutions. The total error of the concentration was less than 0.5%.

The gamma-ray emission probabilities per decay of ^{161}Tb were obtained by ratio of the gamma-ray emission rates and the activity. The mean results,obtained for the measurements on all the sources, were given in Table 1. The given uncertainties correspond to a 1σ confidence level. They were given by the root-square sum of uncertainties of the gamma-ray emission rates and the activity.

The half-life of ^{161}Tb decay was measured by following the decay of ^{161}Tb sources for over 7 half-lives with the planar HPGe spectrometer. Sixty spctra were acquired,each for 1000-10000s (live time) followed by a 1 day wait period. the areas of each peaks were determined by adding the counts in the peaks after subtracting background and sum corrections were applied to the peak areas. These data were fit by a weighted nonlinear least-squares fitting program with a function $Y=Y_0 e^{-\lambda t}$. From this fit, the half-life value was found to be 6.954±0.005 d (the 1σ level).

Our results were compared those of other authors in Table 1.

Table 1   Decay   Data   of ^{161}Tb

$E\gamma$ (kev)	γ-ray emission probabilities $P\gamma$ (%)		half-life (day)	
	this work	ref.1	this work	ref.2
25.7	21.2±0.9	22.9	6.955±0.006	
48.9	16.1±0.6	16.7	6.953±0.005	
74.6	10.3±0.3	10.7±1.2	6.954±0.005	
mean value			6.954±0.005	6.90±0.02

REFERENCES
1. R. G. Helmer, Nucl. Data Sheets, 43 (1984) 1.
2. S. Baba el al, J. Inoyg. Nucl. Chem., 33 (1971) 589.

950

TEST FOR THE CORRECTIONS IN THE MEASUREMENT OF ^{252}Cf SPONTANEOUS FISSION PROMPT NEUTRON SPECTRUM IN LOW PORTION

S.L. BAO, G.Y. TANG, J.H FAN, W.T. CAO
Institute of Heavy Ion Physics
Peking University
Beijing, China, 100871
281166

ABSTRACT

The prompt neutron spectrum from the spontaneous fission of ^{252}Cf has been measured in low energy portion with a NE912 lithium detector as the neutron detector and a mini-ion chamber as a fragment detector. Some corrections have been measured or calculated. After the corrections the result from above 150 keV has been improved.

INTRODUCTION

The prompt neutron spectrum from the spontaneous fission of ^{252}Cf has been defined as a standard neutron spectrum[1,2]. The determination of the neutron spectrum at high precision is required. The californium source are widely used for neutron detector calibration and for other applications. We have measured the neutron spectrum in low energy with a NE912 lithium glass (45mm in diameter and 9.5mm in thickness) as the neutron detector and a mini-chamber as the fragment detector. The primary result was presented in Mito Conference[3]. From the result one sees that the result was systematically higher compared with Maxwell distribution at T=1.42 MeV in the energy range of below 200 keV. We thought that the possible reason was in two sides. One of them was that the neutron detector efficiency was not experimentally determined at high accuracy. The other was that the corrections were not been carefully considered. For the first reason we need to calibrate the neutron detector efficiency, which will be done as a cooperation program with Geel Establishment, Belgium in near future. For the corrections we have tested, calculated and presented here.

DESCRIPTION OF THE EXPERIMENT

The detail description of the experiment can be found somewhere else[3]. Only the concerning content is introduced here. Our experiment was performed in a neutron hall, which was 20 meter long, 12 meter width and 8 meter high. The neutron hall has never been used before and almost empty during our experiment performance. The neutron and the fragment detectors were hung up in the middle of the hall with a thin wall steel pipe that was 30 mm in diameter and the pipe was one meter high above the detectors.

The intensity of the ^{252}Cf source was $3.8*10^3$ fissions per second, which was made by means of transfusion in vacuum on a polished stainless steel disk that was 0.1 mm thick. The impurity of the source was less than $4*10^{-4}$ in atomic purity. The fragment detector was a mini-ion chamber. The total weight was 1.6g. The detector efficiency of the chamber was 99.4% and 99.41% for fast and slow threshold in the TOF measuring system respectively. We have checked the event los for small angle emission fragments by measuring the counts of the fragments in 5° and 90° respect to the source plane. The result was consist well and showed that the event of the fragment didn't loss obviously.

The neutron detector was a NE912 lithium glass, which was 45.5 mm in diameter and 9.55 mm in thickness. The detector was matching with a RCA 8850 PM tube. The cover of the detector was a thin Al shell. In the front of the detector there was only a few mg/cm^2 aluminum film existed.

THE DETERMINATION OF THE NEUTRON DETECTOR EFFICIENCY

The detector efficiency was calculated using a Monte Carlo code[4]. The neutron multiple scattering in the relative thick detector was considered through the prompt neutron detector efficiency. Usually the neutron detector efficiency was defined as the ratio of the number of the measured neutrons to the number of the total neutrons, which was called integration detection efficiency(IDE). In the TOF measurement and the case of using a thick lithium glass one has to consider the time delay effect caused by multiple scattering neutrons in the detector, which was not easily to be measured, but can be calculated with Monte Carlo method. The neutron detector efficiency that has considered the time delay effect is called the prompt neutron detector efficiency(PNDE) which was got from the Monte Carlo code. Using the calculated PNDE we got the IDE with following formula:

$$\eta(E) = \int_0^{t_{max}} \eta(E,t)\,dt \qquad (1)$$

where t_{max} was the maximum time for a certain energy neutron lasted in the detector caused by the multiple scattering, which was got by adding the paths of the neutron during its scattering in the detector, $\eta(E)$ was the IDE for a certain energy neutron. The calculated IDE was compared with A. Lajtai's relatively measured data[5] (for same size same type lithium glass). The result showed that except the three points in the resonance peak of the $^6Li(n,alpha)T$ reaction and some system deviation in the very lower energy portion the consistent was well. Further check need to be done by a separated experiment.

SOME CORRECTIONS IN THE MEASUREMENT

The main corrections in the measurement considered as following:

1. THE SCATTERING AT THE PRE-AMPLIFIER

The pre-amplifier was used to match the fragment detector was ORTEC142A. The scattering in the pre-amplifier caused a increase of the events in low energy portion. In order to estimate the effect, we measured the TOF spectra with the different length of the connecting lines between the detector and the pre-amplifier, which was hung up at the same line with the two detectors in outside direction of the fragment detector. The result showed that the difference was clear when the line length was 15, 30 and 60 cm. In order to remove the scattering events, we measured the spectrum in the case that the 142A was hung up under the ion chamber during the data acquisition and the scattering was estimated using copper bar for the background measurement.

2. THE SCATTERING AT THE AIR COLUMN BETWEEN THE TWO DETECTORS

The effect was not possible to be measured with a copper bar and instead of a Monte Carlo simulation. The result showed that the maximum correction was 0.91%, which was located in the energy range of oxygen resonance around 450 keV. In other energy range the correction was less than 0.5 %.

3. THE SCATTERING ON THE BACKING OF THE ^{252}Cf SOURCE

In order to estimate the effect, we have measured the data by adding the different thickness stainless steel disks to the source. We also calculated the effect using the intensity decay method for different energy neutron over the 0.1 mm backing material. The results were consistent each other and the maximum value was less than 1%.

4. THE SCATTERING IN THE ENVIRONMENT OF THE MEASUREMENT

The scattering was measured by the copper bar between the two detectors. The copper bar was 20 cm long and 3 cm in diameter. The TOF spectra that included the spectrum measured with the copper bar (marked with number 2 in the Fig.1) was shown in Fig.1.

THE CORRECTIONS FOR DELAYED GAMMA-RAY

The lithium glass detector is also sensitive to gamma-ray. Usually people measured it with a pair of NE 913 ^{7}Li glass[5]. From Fig.1 one sees that the prompt gamma-ray was well separated from neutron events. But for events from the delayed gamma-ray it was difficult to be took out from TOF spectrum because the half life for this gamma-ray varied from a few ns to one hundred ns. But in our case only the delayed gamma-rays which half life were more than 30 ns were interested (for neutron energy was less than 2 MeV). For these gamma-rays that their half life from 30 ns to 100 ns were calculated using formula (2):

$$C=[\varepsilon_r N_r(E)]/[\varepsilon_n N_n(E)]$$

$$=K[(\varepsilon_r/\varepsilon_n)]*E^{-2}\exp(E/T-aE^{-1/2}) \quad (2)$$

where C is the ratio factor of detected neutrons for a certain energy neutron $\varepsilon_n N_n(E)$ to the detected corresponding delayed gamma-ray $\varepsilon_r N_r(E)$, and

$$K=[n_0 \lambda(522.9\pi)^{1/2}T^{3/2}L]/4\widetilde{\nu}$$

$$a=[0.693*(522.7)^{1/2}L]/t_{\frac{1}{2}}$$

n_0 -number of delayed gamma-ray per fission

λ -average decay constant of delayed gamma-ray

$\widetilde{\nu}$ -average neutron number per fission

ε_r -delayed gamma-ray detector efficiency

ε_n -neutron detector efficiency

$t_{\frac{1}{2}}$ -half life of the delayed gamma-ray(ns)

L - The flight path (cm)

In our measurement, the threshold was set up to 0.9 MeV electron equivalent energy. The gamma-ray efficiency of the NE912 detector was determined with 60Co, 22Na gamma-ray sources and it was 0.02. Using our measured TOF spectrum by a pair of NE913 ^{7}Li at 10 cm flight path we got the ratio between the delayed and the prompt gamma-ray and the ratio was not beyond 10%, which was same with the reference [6]. From the recent published data[7] we got the absolute value of the delayed gamma-ray was 1.2 per fission. Using above data and took T=1.42MeV, L=30 cm, we got k=3.59*10^4, and If we took t =100 ns[6], then a=4.75. Using this data set we have treated the data with formula (2).

RESULT ANALYSIS

For a measured TOF spectrum, we subtracted the random coincident background, which mainly caused by accidental coincidence of unrelated start-stop events. This correction is determined by the counts averaged over 100 channels beyond the prompt gamma-ray peak. Then we drew the correction of TOF-Channel-dependent background due to non-correlated Stop signal[8], the correction for i'th channel was given by:

$$Nacc(i)=\sum_{k>i}\exp(-N_f*t)[1-\exp(-N_f*\Delta t)*N(i)] \quad (3)$$

where N_f was the count rate of TAC for the fragments, t was the time of the neutron flight counted in i'th channel and Δt was the channel width. In our case the correction for the low energy neutrons was not more than 1%.

Then the environment scattering background was also been subtracted.

After all the treatments mentioned above the result of the neutron energy spectrum compared with Maxwell distribution at T=1.42 MeV was shown in table 1 and Fig. 2.

The uncertainties of the result listed on table 1 were following:

1. THE STATISTICAL UNCERTAINTY

For treating the initial data of the time spectrum, the three channel data were added and the maximum statistical uncertainty was not more than 4% at very low energy portion.

2. THE UNCERTAINTY FROM THE NEUTRON DETECTOR EFFICIENCY CALCULATION

Because we did not have the absolute measured neutron detector efficiency, so that we took the uncertainty 6%, which got referenced from A. Lajtai's measured data 5.6% (the uncertainty in our Monte Carlo calculation was mainly determined by the input data of the uncertainty from the reaction ^{6}Li(n, alpha), which was much smaller compared with 5.6%, but the multiple scattering effect in the detector was not so surely determined in our calculation, therefore we took the uncertainty 6%).

3. THE UNCERTAINTY OF ENERGY SCALAR IN THE MEASUREMENT

The uncertainty was mainly caused by the uncertainties of the flight length and the calibration of the time scalar in the measurement system, which was:

$$\delta^2 E_i = 4(\delta^2 L + \delta^2 t_i) \qquad (4)$$

where δE_i was the relative derivation of energy scalar at the channel i, δt_i was the relative derivation of time scalar at channel i and δL was the relative derivation from the measurement of flight path.

In our measurement, the relative derivation from the measurement of flight length is ±1mm.

The measurement derivation of time calibration was mainly caused by the time channel width, TAC linear and the time zero position. We used standard delay line box and ORTEC462 time calibrator to determine the linear and channel width of TAC separately. The two results were well consistent and was determined to be 0.66%. The stability of the measuring system in our measurement was monitored and was found to be very well. The peak of the prompt gamma-ray was never been shifted more than half channel during the measurement (0.193ns).

From above statement the relative uncertainty of the measuring neutron energy spectrum (suppose it could be fitted by Maxwell distribution) was given by:

$$\delta^2 N(E) = a^2 \delta^2 E_i$$

were $a = [1/2 - E/T + (E/\varepsilon)(\partial \varepsilon / \partial E)]$

and ε was the neutron detector efficiency corresponding to the neutron energy E, $\partial \varepsilon / \partial E$ was the change rate of neutron detector efficiency at the neutron energy E.

4. THE CORRECTION FROM THE DELAYED GAMMA-RAY CORRECTION

The uncertainty was mainly caused by the gamma-ray detector efficiency determination and the data for the half life of the delayed gamma-ray, which was determined to be 2% in our case.

All the derivations mentioned above were listed in Table 1.

CONCLUSION

In our measurement of ^{252}Cf prompt neutron spectrum we have considered some corrections, but further effects needed to be done both at higher accuracy and more lower energy.

ACKNOWLEDGMENT

Our work has been financially aided by the Headquarters of China Nuclear Industry Company. The early work was cooperated with J. Meng[3] of The Institute of Atomic Energy, Beijing.

REFERENCES

1. Proc. IAEA Panel on Neutron Standard Reference Data, 20-40 Nov. 1972, CONF 721127, p.362, IAEA, Vienna (1974).
2. Proc. IAEA consultants' Meeting on Prompt Fission Neutron Spectra, Aug. 1971, p.169, IAEA, Vienna (1972).
3. G.Y. TANG, S.L. BAO, J. WANG, W.G. ZHONG, Y.L. LI, Z.M. SHI, F.Z. HUANG, J.X. CHEN, Ins. of Heavy Ion Physics, Peking University, and J.C. MENG, A.L. LI, Z.Y. BAO, S.W. HUANG, Ins. of Atomic Energy, P. O. Box 275, Nuclear Data for Science and Technology (1988 MITO), P755-757.
4. G.Y. TANG, S.L. BAO, Y.L. LI, W.G. ZHONG, Institute of Heavy Ion Physics, and C.S. JI, Nuclear Instrument Company, Beijing, Report of China Nuclear Science & Technology CNIC, to be published.
5. P. P. DYACHENKO, E. A. SEREGINA, L. C. KUTSAEVA, A. LAJTAI, INDC(CCP)-293/L, p5-17.
6. J. W. MEASOWS, Physics Review 157(1967)1076

7. H.B. DING, N. WANG, "Physics of Neutron Source", Scientific Publish Company, P. R. China, P122.
8. H. MARTEN, D. RICHTER, D. SEELINGER, INDC(GDR)-201, Technical University, Dresden 8027 Dresden, Mommsenstrabe 13, GDR.

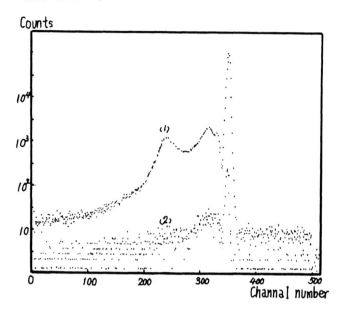

Fig. 1. THE TOF SPECTRUM OF ^{252}Cf
1: MEASURED IN NORMAL CONDITION
2: MEASURE WITH COPPER BAR

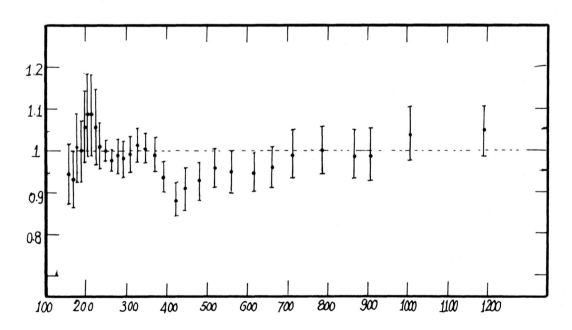

Fig. 2. THE RATIO OF THE EXPERIMENT DATA AND
MAXWELL DISTRIBUTION AT T=1.42 MeV

TABLE 1. THE RESULT AFTER SOME CORRECTIONS FOR

THE ^{252}CF PROMPT FISSION NEUTRON SPECTRUM AT LOW ENERGY PORTION

En(kev)	R	Eff (%)	δEff (%)	δNst (%)	δN(E) (%)	δN (%)
148.70	0.88	1.72	6.0	3.46	5.39	8.78
154.89	0.95	1.86	6.0	3.14	6.24	9.21
161.47	0.93	2.05	6.0	3.03	6.82	9.58
168.48	0.96	2.29	6.0	2.75	7.15	9.72
175.96	1.02	2.57	6.0	2.44	7.38	9.82
183.95	0.99	2.92	6.0	2.30	7.56	9.93
192.49	1.06	3.34	6.0	2.02	8.11	10.29
201.65	1.09	3.90	6.0	1.80	8.32	10.42
211.47	1.09	4.55	6.0	1.61	8.44	10.49
222.03	1.06	5.33	6.0	1.46	8.36	9.70
233.40	1.01	5.90	6.0	1.37	4.97	7.91
245.67	1.00	6.01	6.0	1.31	2.29	6.43
258.93	0.97	5.53	6.0	1.32	1.69	6.37
273.29	0.99	4.69	6.0	1.35	2.61	7.00
288.88	0.98	3.85	6.0	1.42	3.75	7.21
305.85	0.99	3.13	6.0	1.48	3.73	7.22
324.35	1.02	2.54	6.0	1.52	3.43	7.07
344.59	1.00	2.10	6.0	1.60	2.68	6.76
366.78	0.99	1.78	6.0	1.65	1.68	6.45
391.19	0.94	1.56	6.0	1.72	1.24	6.37
418.11	0.88	1.35	6.0	1.79	2.21	6.64
447.92	0.91	1.10	6.0	1.85	3.00	6.96
481.03	0.93	0.91	6.0	1.87	2.00	6.60
517.95	0.96	0.78	6.0	1.87	0.99	6.37
559.29	0.95	0.71	6.0	1.85	1.10	6.39
605.78	0.95	0.65	6.0	1.81	1.48	6.39
658.33	0.96	0.60	6.0	1.77	1.48	6.43
718.02	0.99	0.57	6.0	1.69	1.80	6.49
786.20	1.00	0.53	6.0	1.62	1.96	6.52
864.59	0.99	0.52	6.0	1.56	2.23	6.59
955.31	0.99	0.49	6.0	1.50	1.60	6.39
1061.09	1.04	0.46	6.0	1.42	1.73	6.41
1185.47	1.06	0.44	6.0	1.35	2.91	6.49

Note: Eff:prompt neutron detector efficiency
    δEff:uncertainty of Eff
    δNst:statistical uncertainty
    δN(E):the uncertainty caused by the efficiency
        curve shape factor
    δN:total uncertainty

HIGH RESOLUTION FISSION CROSS SECTION MEASUREMENTS AT ORELA

L. W. Weston and J. H. Todd
Oak Ridge National Laboratory
Building 6010, MS 6354
P. O. Box 2008
Oak Ridge, Tennessee 37831-6354
615 574-6129

ABSTRACT

Multilevel fitting of the transmission, fission, and capture cross sections have dramatically indicated the need for higher resolution and lower background fission cross section measurements of the fissile nuclides. High resolution is needed for extending the resolved resonance region to higher neutron energies, investigation of theoretical phenomena and background determination.

New measurements of the neutron fission cross sections of ^{235}U and ^{239}Pu have been carried out with the white neutron source of ORELA at a flight path of 85 meters. Fission chambers with fast current amplifiers and a parallel plate ^{10}B ionization chamber were used as detectors. These measurements have resolution more nearly comparable with recent transmission measurements and will aid in multilevel fits to higher neutron energies than previously feasible.

INTRODUCTION

High resolution fission cross section measurements of ^{235}U and ^{239}Pu were undertaken because simultaneous Reich-Moore multilevel fits of new transmission and previous fission and capture cross section measurements strongly indicated a need for better resolution in the resolved resonance region. The multilevel fits by H. Derrien, R. B. Perez, G. de Saussure, L. Leal, N. M. Larson and M. S. Moore[1,2] using the code SAMMY[3] were needed to extend the resolved resonance region for the ENDF/B-VI evaluation and to investigate theoretical phenomena. The resolved resonance region of the ENDF evaluation will be extended so that self-shielding effects in reactors can be properly calculated. The multi-level fits of ^{235}U, ^{239}Pu, and ^{241}Pu indicated that the highest resolution fission cross section measurements previously reported by Blons[4] in the resonance region had an uncorrected, neutron energy-dependant background which limited their usefulness. This is an interesting case

where a multilevel fit has indicated a specific problem with previous data and a need for a new measurement which can have a significant impact on the evaluation of these fission cross sections in the resolved resonance region.

The fission cross section measurements used ORELA (Oak Ridge Electron Linear Accelerator) as a white source of neutrons. A series of high resolution, low background, accurate fission cross section measurements have been produced at ORELA. ORELA has proven to be uniquely suited for such measurements since it operates primarily in the stored energy mode so as to produce pulses of time-width which are optimized for keV neutron energies and the neutron flight tubes are well collimated and underground. Also, pioneer work has been carried out at ORELA on fission chambers, amplifiers, and flux monitors suitable for such measurements.

EXPERIMENTAL TECHNIQUE

In the presently reported measurement, neutron energies were determined by time-of-flight over a flight path of 85 meters following a 14-ns burst from ORELA. A burst repetition rate of 400 pps and a ^{10}B filter to prevent burst-to-burst overlap were used. Fission events were detected in two parallel plate ionization chambers each using 10 fast-current amplifiers which were capable of 3-ns time resolution. Both the ^{235}U and ^{239}Pu fission chamber contained 20 plates of 5.08-cm diameter and 100 micrograms per square centimeter thickness on an 12.7-micron Al backing. There was a 3.6 mm spacing between back-to-back coated plates and the 25.4-micron thick collector plates which separated them. The Al was just thick enough to stop the alpha particles so that neutron scattering effects would be minimized. Since 10 amplifiers per chamber were used to minimize alpha-particle pile up, corrections could be made for the different flight paths to the pairs of coated plates. The fission chambers were in tandem in the same 5.08 cm neutron beam. The shape of the neutron flux was measured with a parallel plate ^{10}B chamber which was placed in front of the fission chambers and had a coating 5.08 cm in diameter and 28 micrograms per square centimeter in thickness. A slower amplifier with an integrating time of 1 microsecond was necessary for this chamber because of the much lower energy available from the ^{10}B(n,α) reaction than from fission. The time resolution from this detector was 35 ns which was acceptable because the flux shape varied slowly with time as compared to the fission rate. Data were collected simultaneously from the three detectors which were at room temperature.

The instrumental resolution of the measurement was dominated by time spreading produced in the thickness of the ORELA target moderator (3.18 cm) below 20 keV neutron energy and by the burst width of ORELA (14 ns or 0.16 ns/m) at higher neutron energies. The experimental resolution was appreciably less than the Doppler width of the resonances up to a neutron energy of about 4 keV.

RESULTS

Figure 1 is a comparison of the present ^{235}U fission cross section data with ENDF/B-V in the neutron energy region from 70 to 100 eV. The resolved resonance region for ENDF/B-V only extended to 82 eV. Figure 2 is a comparison of the present data with the data of

Blons[4] which is the highest resolution data previously available. In this neutron energy range, the Doppler width of the resonances is dominant in the present data and the two sets of data appear to have equivalent resolution. In Figs. 3 and 4 at higher neutron energies (500 to 600 eV and 1000 to 1200 eV) the present data clearly have superior resolution as compared to the previous data of Blons.[4]

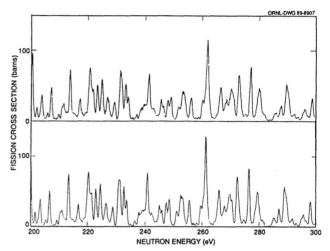

Fig. 2. Comparison of the present ^{235}U fission cross section data (bottom curve) with the data of Blons[4] in the neutron energy range from 200 to 300 eV where the Doppler width dominates resolution.

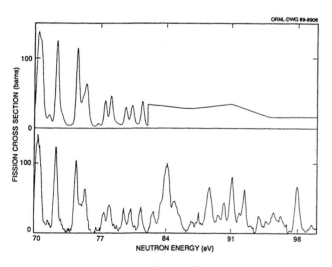

Fig. 1. Comparison of the present ^{235}U fission cross section data (bottom curve) with ENDF/B-V in the neutron energy region from 70 to 100 eV.

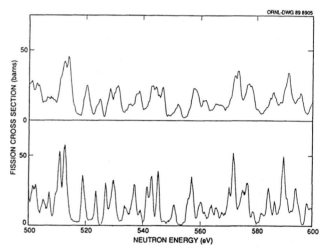

Fig. 3. Comparison of the present ^{235}U data (bottom curve) with the data of Blons[4] in the neutron energy range from 500 to 600 eV. The high resolution of the present data is clearly illustrated.

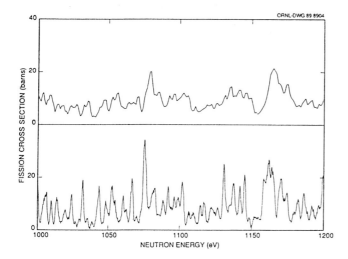

Fig. 4. The present ^{235}U data (bottom curve) and the data of Blons[4] in the neutron energy range from 1000 to 1200 eV. The large resonances and clumps of resonances are much better resolved than previously.

The presently reported fission cross section measurements enable a more unique multilevel fit of the resolved resonance region of ^{235}U and ^{239}Pu. These measurements are the highest resolution reported in the resonance region of neutron energy region above 300 eV. The multilevel fit will be useful in an evaluation for applied purposes and for theoretical study. This measurement is the latest in a long series of high resolution, differential, fission cross section measurements at ORELA and previously RPI/ORNL which have spanned a period of 25 years; half the period since the discovery of fission.

REFERENCES

1. G. de SAUSSURE, L. LEAL, R. B. PEREZ, N. M. LARSON and M. S. MOORE, "A New Resonance-Region Evaluation of Neutron Cross Sections for U-235," Proc. Intern. Reactor Physics Conf., I-293, Jackson Hole, Wyoming, September 18-22, 1988.

2. H. DERRIEN and G. de SAUSSURE, "Current Plutonium Cross Section Evaluations in the Resolved Resonance Region," Proc. Intern. Reactor Physics Conference, S-65, Jackson Hole, Wyoming, September 18-22, 1988.

3. N. M. LARSON and F. G. PEREY, "Resonance Parameter Analysis with SAMMY," Proc. Intern. Conf. Nuclear Data for Science and Tech, May 30-June 3, Mito, Japan, 1988, pp. 573-576.

4. J. BLONS, Nucl. Sci. Eng. 51, 130 (1973).

APPENDIX A

PHOTOGRAPHS FROM FIFTY YEARS WITH NUCLEAR FISSION

Why was this 50th anniversary conference, acknowledging a German discovery, held in Washington, D.C.? How did the American Nuclear Society (ANS), the National Academy of Sciences (NAS), and the National Institute of Standards and Technology (NIST) become involved?

The desire to hold the conference originated while I was attending the 50th anniversary of the discovery of the neutron in Cambridge, England, in 1982. I felt that nuclear fission should receive a similar celebration. Actual work to gather individuals and organizations began in 1986. During this same year, the Germans announced that they planned to hold a similar conference in West Berlin. It was agreed to make the two conferences complementary. The German conference would take place in early April 1989 and would emphasize the fundamental side of fission, whereas the U.S. conference would emphasize the applied side later that same month. The ANS was encouraged to become the major sponsor for the U.S. conference, and NIST to host the event. The NAS was asked to join the effort and provide the setting for the plenary sessions on the history of fission, and the conference was scheduled so that the plenaries could be part of NAS's traditional technical day following its annual meeting. After three years of hard work, the planning became a reality on April 25–28, 1989.

The history of nuclear fission contains relevant events making the Washington, D.C., area the logical place for the conference. News of the German discovery of fission was carried to the United States by Niels Bohr, who officially announced the discovery on January 26, 1939, at the Fifth Washington Conference on Theoretical Physics sponsored by the Carnegie Institution of Washington's Department of Ter-restrial Magnetism and George Washington University. A letter of concern was drafted by Leo Szilard, with input from Albert Einstein, Edward Teller, Eugene Wigner, and Alexander Sachs. This letter, signed by Einstein, was delivered to President Franklin Roosevelt, who appointed the Advisory Committee on Uranium to consider the merits of the letter. Committee members advised the President that Einstein's letter raised valid concerns about the potential applications of nuclear fission. The U.S. Army agreed to provide $6000 of funding for further study of the fission process. The Advisory Committee on Uranium was the forerunner of Vannevar Bush's National Defense Research Council and Office of Science Research and Development, Leslie Groves' Manhattan Project, the postwar Atomic Energy Commission, and today's Department of Energy and Nuclear Regulatory Commission.

During the conference, many photographs were taken, some of which are assembled here. Among the 400 registered attendees were many who have made major contributions to the field of nuclear fission science and technology. Some are shown here at various sessions, as are several past ANS presidents. We are indebted to Octave Du Temple, ANS executive director, and John Hubbell, NIST, for making the effort to photograph what became a truly historic event. The conference was well attended and enjoyed by all.

James W. Behrens
Joint Staff/J-5
International Negotiations
The Pentagon
Washington, D.C.

Darleane C. Hoffman (LBL), V. Strutinsky (INR–USSR), and Leslie G. Cook (ERE–retired).

Walter H. Zinn (GNEC–retired).

Walter H. Zinn (GNEC–retired) and Gail de Planque (ANS President/DOE).

Bertrand Goldschmidt (CEA Paris–France).

Walter H. Zinn (GNEC–retired), Rudolf E. Peierls (Nuclear Physics Laboratory–England), Bertrand Goldschmidt (CEA Paris–France), James W. Behrens (NIST), Pavle Savić (Serbian Academy of Sciences and Arts–Yugoslavia), and Edoardo Amaldi (Univ of Rome–Italy).

Leslie G. Cook (ERE–retired), Paul Kuroda (EPA/Univ of Nevada), and Georgy N. Flerov (Joint Inst for Nuclear Research–USSR).

John A. Wheeler (Princeton Univ/Univ of Texas–Austin), Glenn T. Seaborg (LBL), and Alvin M. Weinberg (IEA).

Bertram Wolfe (General Electric), Gail de Planque (ANS president/DOE), and E. Linn Draper (Gulf States Utilities).

Glenn T. Seaborg (LBL) and Walker L. Cisler (Overseas Advisory Assoc).

E. Linn Draper (Gulf States Utilities), Gail de Planque (ANS president/DOE), and Octave J. Du Temple (ANS executive director).

Rémy Carle (EdF–France), John W. Simpson (IEA), Bertram Wolfe (General Electric), and Chauncey Starr (EPRI).

National Academy of Sciences.

Glenn T. Seaborg (LBL), Lando W. Zech (NRC), Edoardo Amaldi (Univ of Rome-Italy), and Bertrand Goldschmidt (CEA Paris-France).

Yigal Ronen (Ben-Gurion Univ-Israel) and Sakae Shimizu (Univ of Kyoto-Japan).

Milton Shaw (consultant) and John W. Landis (Stone and Webster).

John Hubbell (NIST) and Sakae Shimizu (Univ of Kyoto-Japan).

APPENDIX B

LIST OF ATTENDEES

Irshad Ahmad
Lawrence K. Akers
Tunc Aldemir
Charles W. Alexander
Carol T. Alonso
Edoardo Amaldi
Kevin Anderson
D. G. Andrews
Alan Angelman
George A. Anzelon
Jose M. Aragones
Edward D. Arthur
George Auchampaugh

Birger B. Back
Joseph F. Bader
Erich Bagge
Patricia A. Baisden
Russell M. Ball
Sergio Barabaschi
Henry H. Barschall
Fred Becchetti
James W. Behrens
Gary L. Bennett
David W. Bensen
Jean Francois Berger
John A. Bernard, Jr.
John E. Bigelow
Carleton D. Bingham
Jean Blachot
Robert C. Block
Steven M. Blush
Kartl H. Bockhoff
Donald Bogart
Eugene T. Booth
Daniel Boutet
Charles D. Bowman
Michael Bozoian
Alan Brailsford
Howard E. Braun
Manuel M. Bretscher
Sarita Brewer
R. A. Brightsen
Robert M. Brugger
John L. Burnett

David C. Camp
N. Carjan
Rémy Louis Carle

Allan Carlson
B. Stephen Carpenter
Robert E. Carter
Wayne A. Cassatt
Randall S. Caswell
Daniel Chavardes
R. E. Chrien
Chien Chung
Walker L. Cisler
David Clark
Mary E. Clark
John C. Clayton
Alain L. Colomb
Henri Condé
Michael J. Connor
L. G. Cook
Gus P. Couchell
F. Morgan Cox
John K. Crum
James R. Curtiss

Michael D. D'Agostino
Dirk A. Dahlgren
Joseph C. Danko
Michael Danos
Prarab Dastidar
Jay C. Davis
Deslonde deBoisblanc
Samuel J. Dechter
T. De Mazancourt
Harold R. Denton
Gail de Planque
Alexander De Volpi
Denis Dewez
J. K. Dickens
Tom DiFrancisco
Ben C. Diven
Harold L. Dodds, Jr.
Rodney J. Dougan
E. Linn Draper, Jr.
Stamatina Dritsa
Romney B. Duffey
Raymond W. Durante
Octave J. Du Temple
Kenneth C. Duvall
Maria Dworzecka

Milton C. Edlund
Chester S. Ehrman

Geoffrey Eichholz
Charles M. Eisenhauer
Herbert S. Eleuterio
Takashi Emoto
Talmadge R. England
Cetin Ertek
S. Y. Ettinger
Albert E. Evans, Jr.
Ersel A. Evans

W. Edwin Farley
Robert Faron
George W. Farwell
T. Michael Flanders
G. N. Flerov
Richard A. Forman
John D. Fox
Charles B. Franklin
William A. Frederick
Everett G. Fuller

Otto O. Gamba
Arthur E. Gasparian
Robert J. Gehrke
John F. Gibbons
David M. Gilliam
Luc P. Gillon
Carl V. Gogolak
Bertrand Goldschmidt
I. N. Golovin
Friedrich Gönnenwein
S. William Gouse
J. Nelson Grace
James J. Griffin
Marshall Grotenhuis
James A. Grundl
Jules Gueron
Jacob Gut

Mahmaud H. Haghighi
Joseph Halperin
Malcolm Harvey
William W. Havens, Jr.
Robert B. Hayman
Evans Hayward
Peter Heeg
Philip B. Hemmig
Guenter Herrmann
Erwin N. Hiebert

David L. Hill
Robert C. Hochel
Stephen Hoefp
Darleane C. Hoffman
Marvin Hoffman
Norman E. Holden
Jack Hollander
Osamu Horibe
Neil M. Howard
William M. Howard
H. Hsu
John Howard Hubbell
John R. Huizenga
E. Kenneth Hulet
Ken Hull
Robert Hunter, Jr.
Homer B. Hupf
Earl K. Hyde

Hiroshi Ikezoe
John Illige
Kenneth G. W. Inn

Etienne Jacobs
J. P. Jacobus
Jacek Jedruch
Peter Jelinek
William A. Jester
C. Martin Johnson, Jr.
Thomas M. Jordan
Sheri Juergens
Clyde P. Jupiter
Pat Jupiter
Raymond J. Juzaitis

Peter B. Kahn
George Kao
Seymour Katcoff
G. Robert Keepin
J. R. Kiely
William E. Kiker
W. Frank Kinard
Glenn F. Knoll
William J. Knox
Arnold Kramish
Myron B. Kratzer
Paul Kuroda
Chris E. Kuyatt

Albert Lajtai
George T. Lalos
Luiz Leal
R. Eric Leber
R. J. A. Levesque
Bruce Libby
Robert Liimatainen
Michael J. Lineberry
Paul Lisowski
Gerhard K. Locke
M. A. K. Lodhi
Walter B. Loewenstein
Edward J. Lofgren
M. Aslam Lone
Stewart W. Long
Ronald W. Lougheed
Walter Loveland
J. E. Lynn

David MacArthur
Ronald D. Macfarlane
Houria Madani
David G. Madland
B. Maglich
F. B. Malik
Wilfred Mann
Paul Mantica
Alfredo Marchetti
Gail H. Marcus
Predrag Marinkovic
Samuel S. Markowitz
Antoinette Massey
Philip J. Mattson
Leonard C. Maximon
Mike Mc Cormack
Victor McCree
E. D. McGarry
David J. Mc Goff
Victoria McLane
Michael A. McMurphy
James W. Meadows, Jr.
Bradley Meyer
R. A. Meyer
Andre F. Michaudon
Alice C. Mignerey
G. H. Miley
Robert W. Mills
John Miskel
Peter Möller
Kenton J. Moody
Michael S. Moore
Stefano Moretti
Luciano G. Moretto
Bruce Morrison
E. D. Mshelia
Ragnwald Muller
Ernest H. Mund
Wanda Munn
Jan Murray
Peter Murray
William A. Myers

Yoshihiro Nakagome
V. Narayanamurti
Giovanni Naschi
J. W. Negele
Donald J. Nelson
David R. Nethaway
Dale Newbury
J. Rayford Nix
MaryAnn Novak

Richard G. Oehl
Yu. Ts. Oganessian
Tsutomu Ohtsuki
Koji Onishi

Hsiang L. Pai
Dipti Pal
Manoj Kuma Pal
George L. Pappas
Daniel Paya
William Pearce
J. M. Pearson
Robert W. Peelle
Rudolf E. Peierls

Rafael B. Perez
Lars Persson
Milan Pešić
Herzel H. E. Plaine
Marleen Plessens
Wolfgang P. Poenitz
Carl H. Poppe
Cynthia Poston
Hans G. Priesmeyer
Caroline B. Purdy

V. S. Ramammurthy
David A. Rapaport
John E. Rasmussen
Andree Reed
Shane L. Regdos
Krish Rengan
Anna R. Reolon Cora
Robert W. Richards
Thomas M. Roberts
J. W. Rogers
Kenneth C. Rogers
Yigal Ronen
A. David Rossin
Zoltan R. Rosztoczy
Eli B. Roth
Etienne Roth
J. Michael Rowe
Frank H. Rowsome III
Gosta Rudstam
Clifford R. Rudy
Ben C. Rusche

Kenneth Sale
Stephen N. Salomon
Jagdish K. Saluja
Carlo Salvetti
Scott L. Samuelson
Natividad C. Santamaria
Louis J. Sas
Pavle Savić
Jack C. Scarborough
Robert E. Schenter
Josef J. Schmidt
Roald A. Schrack
Robert B. Schwartz
Glenn T. Seaborg
Dieter Seeliger
Farhang Sefidvash
Thomas Semkow
Shivaji S. Seth
Joseph Shapiro
Milton Shaw
Sakae Shimizu
Frederick J. Shon
Pekka Silvennoinen
Joseph Silverman
Massoud T. Simnad
John W. Simpson
James H. Sinclair
Mats Skalberg
Gunnar Skarnemark
John Small
Alan B. Smith
J. Richard Smith
David L. Solorio
L. Patrick Somerville

Esther B. Sparberg
Mary H. Sparks
William Spindel
M. R. Srinivasan
Brijesh K. Srivastava
John M. Stamos
Chauncey Starr
Meyer Steinberg
Leona Stewart
Ronald C. Stinson
Craig Stone
Philip M. Stone
Lee E. Strawbridge
V. M. Strutinsky
David S. Stuart
T. T. Sugihara
Osamu Suto
John A. Swartout
W. J. Swiatecki
Timothy Symons

W. L. Talbert, Jr.
John J. Taylor
Edward Teller
Georges M. Temmer
James Terrell
J. Theobald
Friedrich-K. Thielemann
Barbara H. Thomas
Ronald H. Thompson

Gunnar Thornton
Charles E. Till
Cornelius A. Tobias
Hans Toffer
F. Tomzcyk
Clyde R. Toole
James R. Tourtellotte
Jean Trochon
Frank Turvey

Robert Vandenbosch
Jacobus Van Geel
Guillermo Velarde
R. Vijuk
Vic Viola
George Virtes
Peter von Der Hardt
Carl F. von Weiszacker
Susan S. Voss

William J. Wachter
Arthur C. Wahl
Earl Wahlquist
R. L. Walsh
W. B. Walters
Mary E. Ward
Oren A. Wasson
James D. Watkins
Albert Wattenberg
D. R. Weaver

Hermann Weigmann
Alvin M. Weinberg
Thomas A. Werner
Lawrence W. Weston
John A. Wheeler
Stanley L. Whetstone
Peter White
Roger M. White
William L. Whittemore
Sherrill Whyte
Carl O. Widell
E. P. Wigner
John F. Wild
Lawrence Wilets
J. Ernest Wilkins
Bertram Wolfe
Bill V. Wright

Zhong Yun Xiao

Leo Yaffe
Charles D. Young
Phillip G. Young, Jr.

Jiahua Zhang
Delin Zhou
W. H. Zinn
Alexander Zucker
Atsushi Zukeran
Lloyd R. Zumwalt

APPENDIX C

NEUTRON DATA REFERENCES

Element	Quantity	Energy (eV) Min	Max	Type	Documentation Ref	Page	Date	Lab	Comments
^{24}Mg	$\sigma_{n,p}$	FISS		Expt	89WASH	2 923	Apr89	KNK	Horibe+ TBLS CFD EXPT, EVAL.
^{27}Al	$\sigma_{n,p}$	FISS		Expt	89WASH	2 923	Apr89	KNK	Horibe+ TBLS CFD EXPT, EVAL.
^{27}Al	$\sigma_{n,\alpha}$	FISS		Expt	89WASH	2 923	Apr89	KNK	Horibe+ TBLS CFD EXPT, EVAL.
^{42}Ca	$\sigma_{n,p}$	FISS		Expt	89WASH	2 923	Apr89	KNK	Horibe+ TBLS CFD EXPT, EVAL.
^{43}Ca	$\sigma_{n,p}$	FISS		Expt	89WASH	2 923	Apr89	KNK	Horibe+ TBLS CFD EXPT, EVAL.
^{45}Sc	$\sigma_{n,\alpha}$	FISS		Expt	89WASH	2 923	Apr89	KNK	Horibe+ TBLS CFD EXPT, EVAL.
^{46}Ti	$\sigma_{n,p}$	FISS		Expt	89WASH	2 923	Apr89	KNK	Horibe+ TBLS CFD EXPT, EVAL.
^{47}Ti	$\sigma_{n,p}$	FISS		Expt	89WASH	2 923	Apr89	KNK	Horibe+ TBLS CFD EXPT, EVAL.
^{48}Ti	$\sigma_{n,p}$	FISS		Expt	89WASH	2 923	Apr89	KNK	Horibe+ TBLS CFD EXPT, EVAL.
^{50}Ti	$\sigma_{n,\alpha}$	FISS		Expt	89WASH	2 923	Apr89	KNK	Horibe+ TBLS CFD EXPT, EVAL.
^{54}Fe	$\sigma_{n,p}$	FISS		Expt	89WASH	2 923	Apr89	KNK	Horibe+ TBLS CFD EXPT, EVAL.
^{54}Fe	$\sigma_{n,\alpha}$	FISS		Expt	89WASH	2 923	Apr89	KNK	Horibe+ TBLS CFD EXPT, EVAL.
^{56}Fe	$\sigma_{n,p}$	FISS		Expt	89WASH	2 923	Apr89	KNK	Horibe+ TBLS CFD EXPT, EVAL.
^{59}Co	$\sigma_{n,2n}$	FISS		Expt	89WASH	2 923	Apr89	KNK	Horibe+ TBLS CFD EXPT, EVAL.
^{59}Co	$\sigma_{n,p}$	FISS		Expt	89WASH	2 923	Apr89	KNK	Horibe+ TBLS CFD EXPT, EVAL.
^{59}Co	$\sigma_{n,\alpha}$	FISS		Expt	89WASH	2 923	Apr89	KNK	Horibe+ TBLS CFD EXPT, EVAL.
^{58}Ni	$\sigma_{n,p}$	FISS		Expt	89WASH	2 923	Apr89	KNK	Horibe+ TBLS CFD EXPT, EVAL.
^{60}Ni	$\sigma_{n,p}$	FISS		Expt	89WASH	2 923	Apr89	KNK	Horibe+ TBLS CFD EXPT, EVAL.
^{61}Ni	$\sigma_{n,p}$	FISS		Expt	89WASH	2 923	Apr89	KNK	Horibe+ TBLS CFD EXPT, EVAL.
^{64}Zn	$\sigma_{n,p}$	FISS		Expt	89WASH	2 923	Apr89	KNK	Horibe+ TBLS CFD EXPT, EVAL.
^{67}Zn	$\sigma_{n,p}$	FISS		Expt	89WASH	2 923	Apr89	KNK	Horibe- TBLS CFD EXPT, EVAL.
^{68}Zn	$\sigma_{n,\alpha}$	FISS		Expt	89WASH	2 923	Apr89	KNK	Horibe+ TBLS CFD EXPT, EVAL.
^{84}Sr	$\sigma_{n,p}$	FISS		Expt	89WASH	2 923	Apr89	KNK	Horibe+ TBLS CFD EXPT, EVAL.
^{86}Sr	$\sigma_{n,p}$	FISS		Expt	89WASH	2 923	Apr89	KNK	Horibe+ TBLS CFD EXPT, EVAL.
^{92}Mo	$\sigma_{n,p}$	FISS		Expt	89WASH	2 923	Apr89	KNK	Horibe+ TBLS CFD EXPT, EVAL.
^{95}Mo	$\sigma_{n,p}$	FISS		Expt	89WASH	2 923	Apr89	KNK	Horibe+ TBLS CFD EXPT, EVAL.
^{96}Mo	$\sigma_{n,p}$	FISS		Expt	89WASH	2 923	Apr89	KNK	Horibe+ TBLS CFD EXPT, EVAL.
^{103}Rh	$\sigma_{dif.inl}$	FISS		Expt	89WASH	2 923	Apr89	KNK	Horibe+ TBLS CFD EXPT, EVAL.
^{103}Rh	$\sigma_{n,p}$	FISS		Expt	89WASH	2 923	Apr89	KNK	Horibe+ TBLS CFD EXPT, EVAL.
^{113}In	$\sigma_{dif.inl}$	FISS		Expt	89WASH	2 923	Apr89	KNK	Horibe+ TBLS CFD EXPT, EVAL.
^{115}In	$\sigma_{dif.inl}$	FISS		Expt	89WASH	2 923	Apr89	KNK	Horibe+ TBLS CFD EXPT, EVAL.
^{115}In	$\sigma_{n,p}$	FISS		Expt	89WASH	2 923	Apr89	KNK	Horibe+ TBLS CFD EXPT, EVAL.
^{140}Ce	$\sigma_{n,p}$	FISS		Expt	89WASH	2 923	Apr89	KNK	Horibe+ TBLS CFD EXPT, EVAL.

Element	Quantity	Energy (eV) Min	Max	Type	Documentation Ref	Page	Date	Lab	Comments
^{229}Th	ν_p	2.5-2		Revw	89WASH	1 83	Apr89	BRK	Hoffman. GRPH. NU CFD OTHER NUCLIDES
^{229}Th	Spect.fiss n	2.5-2		Theo	89WASH	1 429	Apr89	LAS	Madland. GRPH CFD 239PU, 249CF.
^{229}Th	Fiss.Yield	2.5-2		Eval	89WASH	1 471	Apr89	BIR	Mills+ TBL FITTED PARAMETERS.
^{230}Th	$\sigma_{n,f}$	6.8+5	7.6+5	Revw	89WASH	1 168	Apr89	GEL	Weigmann. GRPH. EXPT CFD CALC.
^{230}Th	$\sigma_{n,f}$	6.8+5	5.9+6	Theo	89WASH	1 319	Apr89	SAC	Paya+ GRPH. CALC CFD EXPT.
^{230}Th	$\sigma_{n,f}$	6.9+5	7.5+5	Revw	89WASH	1 418	Apr89	ANL	Lynn. GRPH. CALC SIG CFD EXPT.
^{230}Th	Frag Spectra	6.9+5	7.4+5	Revw	89WASH	1 418	Apr89	ANL	Lynn. GRPH. FP YLD. 20 CFD 70 DEGS.
^{232}Th	$\sigma_{n,f}$	6.3+6	6.4+6	Theo	89WASH	1 319	Apr89	SAC	Paya+ GRPH. CALC CFD EXPT.
^{232}Th	$\sigma_{n,f}$	1.0+0	2.0+4	Expt	89WASH	1 354	Apr89	RPI	Block+ GRPH.
^{232}Th	$\sigma_{n,f}$	1.0+5	1.1+6	Revw	89WASH	1 368	Apr89	ORL	Perez+ GRPH. EXPT CFD CALCS.
^{232}Th	$\sigma_{n,f}$	1.0+6	4.0+8	Expt	89WASH	1 443	Apr89	LAS	Lisowski+ GRPHS.REL 235U;CFD ENDF/B5.
^{232}Th	Res.Int.Fiss	5.0-1	1.0+5	Eval	89WASH	1 946	Apr89	BNL	Holden. TBL. CORRECTED FISS.INT.CFD.
^{232}Th	ν_p	SPON		Revw	89WASH	1 83	Apr89	BRK	Hoffman. GRPH. NU CFD OTHER NUCLIDES.
^{232}Th	Fiss.Yield	1.4+7		Eval	89WASH	1 471	Apr89	BIR	Mills+ TBL FITTED PARAMETERS.
^{232}Th	Fiss.Yield	FAST		Eval	89WASH	1 471	Apr89	BIR	Mills+ TBL FITTED PARAMETERS.
^{232}Th	Fiss.Yield	FAST		Theo	89WASH	2 525	Apr89	WAS	Wahl. TBL. MODEL PARAMETERS.
^{232}Th	Frag Spectra	2.5-2	6.0+6	Theo	89WASH	2 743	Apr89	TUD	Maerten+GRPH KE(FRAG)CFD 235U,239PU.
^{232}Th	Frag.Chg.	FAST		Theo	89WASH	2 525	Apr89	WAS	Wahl. TBL. MODEL PARAMETERS.
^{232}Th	Photo-fissn	7.0+6	1.4+7	Expt	89WASH	2 673	Apr89	GHT	Piessens+ GRPHS, MASS, ENERGY DIST.
^{233}Pa	Res.Int.Fiss	5.0-1	1.0+5	Eval	89WASH	1 946	Apr89	BNL	Holden. TBL. CORRECTED FISS.INT.CFD.
^{232}U	ν_p	2.5-2		Revw	89WASH	1 83	Apr89	BRK	Hoffman. GRPH. NU CFD OTHER NUCLIDES.
^{233}U	ν_p	2.5-2		Revw	89WASH	1 83	Apr89	BRK	Hoffman. GRPH. NU CFD OTHER NUCLIDES.
^{233}U	ν_{frag}	2.5-2		Expt	89WASH	1 360	Apr89	KTO	Nakagome+ TBL,GRPH NU CFD FRAG.MASS.
^{233}U	Fiss.Yield	2.5-2		Expt	89WASH	1 313	Apr89	BRC	Trochon+ GRPHS.SIMULT.MASS,E,CHARGE.
^{233}U	Fiss.Yield	1.4+7		Eval	89WASH	1 471	Apr89	BIR	Mills+ TBL FITTED PARAMETERS.
^{233}U	Fiss.Yield	2.5-2		Eval	89WASH	1 471	Apr89	BIR	Mills+ TBL FITTED PARAMETERS.
^{233}U	Frag Spectra	2.5-2		Expt	89WASH	1 313	Apr89	BRC	Trochon+ GRPHS.SIMULT.MASS,E,CHARGE.
^{233}U	Frag Spectra	2.5-2		Expt	89WASH	1 360	Apr89	KTO	Nakagome+GRPH KE DIST CFD FRAG.MASS.
^{233}U	Frag Spectra	2.5-2		Theo	89WASH	2 515	Apr89	TUE	Goennenwein+ COLD FISSION ANALYSIS.
^{233}U	Frag.Chg.	2.5-2		Expt	89WASH	1 313	Apr89	BRC	Trochon+ GRPHS.SIMULT.MASS,E,CHARGE.
^{233}U	Frag.Chg.	2.5-2		Theo	89WASH	2 515	Apr89	TUE	Goennenwein+ COLD FISSION ANALYSIS.
^{235}U	σ_{tot}		3.0+2	Eval	89WASH	2 939	Apr89	ORL	Leal+ GRPH CFD EXPT.
^{235}U	$\sigma_{n,f}$	1.0+0	2.0+4	Expt	89WASH	1 354	Apr89	RPI	Block+ GRPH.

NEUTRON DATA REFERENCES

Element	Quantity	Energy (eV) Min	Max	Type	Documentation Ref	Page	Date	Lab	Comments
^{235}U	$\sigma_{n,f}$	FISS		Eval	89WASH	1 408	Apr89	ANL	Poenitz. TBL EXPT CFD EVALS.
^{235}U	$\sigma_{n,f}$	4.0+4	1.4+7	Expt	89WASH	1 436	Apr89	ALD	White. UNCERTAINTIES RE-EXAMINED.
^{235}U	$\sigma_{n,f}$	1.0+6	4.0+8	Expt	89WASH	1 443	Apr89	LAS	Lisowski+ GRPHS. CFD ENDF/B-V.
^{235}U	$\sigma_{n,f}$		3.0+2	Eval	89WASH	2 939	Apr89	ORL	Leal+ GRPHS CFD EXPT.
^{235}U	$\sigma_{n,f}$	7.0+1	1.2+3	Expt	89WASH	2 957	Apr89	ORL	Weston+ GRPHS CFD ENDF/B-V, EXPT.
^{235}U	ν_p	2.5-2		Revw	89WASH	1 83	Apr89	BRK	Hoffman. GRPH. NU CFD OTHER NUCLIDES.
^{235}U	ν_p	2.5-2	6.0+6	Theo	89WASH	1 429	Apr89	LAS	Madland. GRPH CALC NUBAR VS EXPT.
^{235}U	ν_d	2.5-2		Expt	89WASH	1 449	Apr89	LTI	Couchell+ GRPHS. 6 GP SPECTRA CFD.
^{235}U	ν_{frag}	2.5-2		Expt	89WASH	1 360	Apr89	KTO	Nakagome+ TBL,GRPH NU CFD FRAG.MASS.
^{235}U	ν_{frag}	2.5-2	6.0+6	Theo	89WASH	2 743	Apr89	TUD	Maerten+ GRPH. CFD INCIDENT E(NEUT).
^{235}U	Spect.fiss n	2.5-2	1.4+7	Theo	89WASH	1 429	Apr89	LAS	Madland. GRPHS CALC CFD MAXW,OTHERS.
^{235}U	Spect.fiss n	2.0+6		Theo	89WASH	2 624	Apr89	LAS	Bozoian+ GRAPH CFD ENDF/B-V.
^{235}U	Spect.Fis γ	1.0+0	3.6+1	Expt	89WASH	2 727	Apr89	DUB	Bogdzel+ GRPHS,TBL,GAM.YLD FISS.FRAG.
^{235}U	Fiss.Yield	2.5-2		Revw	89WASH	1 168	Apr89	GEL	Weigmann. GRPH.EXPT CFD 3 FISS MODE.
^{235}U	Fiss.Yield	2.5-2		Expt	89WASH	1 313	Apr89	BRC	Trochon+ GRPHS.SIMULT.MASS,E,CHARGE.
^{235}U	Fiss.Yield	2.5-2		Expt	89WASH	1 457	Apr89	SWR	Rudstam+ GRPH IND, CUM, ISOM. YLDS.
^{235}U	Fiss.Yield	2.5-2		Eval	89WASH	1 471	Apr89	BIR	Mills+ TBL FITTED PARAMETERS.
^{235}U	Fiss.Yield	1.4+7		Eval	89WASH	1 471	Apr89	BIR	Mills+ TBL FITTED PARAMETERS.
^{235}U	Fiss.Yield	FAST		Eval	89WASH	1 471	Apr89	BIR	Mills+ TBL FITTED PARAMETERS.
^{235}U	Fiss.Yield	2.5-2		Theo	89WASH	2 525	Apr89	WAS	Wahl. GRPHS. IND. YLDS.
^{235}U	Fiss.Yield	NDG		Theo	89WASH	2 643	Apr89	PUC	Gupta+ GRPH. CALC CFD EXPT.
^{235}U	Fiss.Yield	1.6+7		Theo	89WASH	2 650	Apr89	LMS	Compani-Tabrizi+ GRPH CALC CFD EXPT.
^{235}U	Frag Spectra	2.5-2		Expt	89WASH	1 313	Apr89	BRC	Trochon+ GRPHS.SIMULT.MASS,E,CHARGE.
^{235}U	Frag Spectra	2.5-2		Expt	89WASH	1 360	Apr89	KTO	Nakagome+GRPH KE DIST CFD FRAG.MASS.
^{235}U	Frag Spectra	2.5-2		Theo	89WASH	2 515	Apr89	TUE	Goennenwein+ COLD FISSION ANALYSIS.
^{235}U	Frag Spectra	1.6+7		Theo	89WASH	2 650	Apr89	LMS	Compani-Tabrizi+ GRPH CALC CFD EXPT.
^{235}U	Frag Spectra	2.5-2	6.0+6	Theo	89WASH	2 743	Apr89	TUD	Maerten+GRPH KE(FRAG)CFD 232TH,239PU.
^{235}U	Frag.Chg.	2.5-2		Expt	89WASH	1 313	Apr89	BRC	Trochon+ GRPHS.SIMULT.MASS,E,CHARGE.
^{235}U	Frag.Chg.	2.5-2		Theo	89WASH	2 515	Apr89	TUE	Goennenwein+ COLD FISSION ANALYSIS.
^{235}U	Res.Params.		3.0+2	Eval	89WASH	2 939	Apr89	ORL	Leal+ TBL. AVG PARAMETERS.
^{236}U	Res.Int.Fiss	5.0-1	1.0+5	Eval	89WASH	1 946	Apr89	BNL	Holden. TBL. CORRECTED FISS.INT.CFD.
^{236}U	ν_p	SPON		Revw	89WASH	1 83	Apr89	BRK	Hoffman. GRPH. NU CFD OTHER NUCLIDES.
^{238}U	$\sigma_{n,\gamma}$	6.0+2	9.0+2	Revw	89WASH	1 368	Apr89	ORL	Perez+ GRPH. (N,G)CFD(N,F)MEAS.SIG.

Element	Quantity	Energy (eV) Min	Max	Type	Documentation Ref	Page	Date	Lab	Comments
^{238}U	$\sigma_{n,\gamma}$	3.0+4		Theo	89WASH	2 592	Apr89	HRV	Thielemann+ TBL. CALC SIG (30 KEV).
^{238}U	$\sigma_{n,f}$	1.4+0	1.0+5	Expt	89WASH	1 354	Apr89	RPI	Block+ GRPH.
^{238}U	$\sigma_{n,f}$	5.0+0	3.5+6	Revw	89WASH	1 368	Apr89	ORL	Perez+ GRPHS EXPT'L SIG.
^{238}U	$\sigma_{n,f}$	FISS		Eval	89WASH	1 408	Apr89	ANL	Poenitz. TBL EXPT CFD EVALS.
^{238}U	$\sigma_{n,f}$		1.8+6	Revw	89WASH	1 418	Apr89	ANL	Lynn. GRPH. AVG SIG MDC CALC.
^{238}U	$\sigma_{n,f}$	1.0+6	4.0+8	Expt	89WASH	1 443	Apr89	LAS	Lisowski+ GRPHS.REL 235U;CFD ENDF/B5.
^{238}U	$\sigma_{n,f}$	3.0+4		Theo	89WASH	2 592	Apr89	HRV	Thielemann+ TBL. CALC SIG (30 KEV).
^{238}U	$\sigma_{n,f}$	1.0+6	1.0+8	Theo	89WASH	2 931	Apr89	LAS	Arthur+ GRPH CFD EXPT.
^{238}U	Res.Int.Fiss	5.0-1	1.0+5	Eval	89WASH	1 946	Apr89	BNL	Holden. TBL. CORRECTED FISS.INT.CFD.
^{238}U	ν_p	SPON		Revw	89WASH	1 83	Apr89	BRK	Hoffman. GRPH. NU CFD OTHER NUCLIDES.
^{238}U	ν_d	FAST		Expt	89WASH	1 449	Apr89	LTI	Couchell+ GRPHS. 6 GP SPECTRA CFD.
^{238}U	ν_{frag}	1.5+7		Theo	89WASH	2 624	Apr89	LAS	Bozoian+ GRAPH CFD EXPT.
^{238}U	Spect.fiss n	5.0+6	1.5+7	Theo	89WASH	2 624	Apr89	LAS	Bozoian+ GRAPH CFD ENDF/B-V.
^{238}U	Fiss.Yield	FAST		Eval	89WASH	1 471	Apr89	BIR	Mills+ TBL FITTED PARAMETERS.
^{238}U	Fiss.Yield	1.4+7		Eval	89WASH	1 471	Apr89	BIR	Mills+ TBL FITTED PARAMETERS.
^{238}U	Fiss.Yield	FAST		Theo	89WASH	2 525	Apr89	WAS	Wahl. TBL. MODEL PARAMETERS.
^{238}U	Fiss.Yield	1.4+7		Theo	89WASH	2 525	Apr89	WAS	Wahl. TBL. MODEL PARAMETERS.
^{238}U	Fiss.Yield	3.6+6	4.1+6	Expt	89WASH	2 705	Apr89	BIR	Randle+ LONG RANGE ALFA, TRITON.
^{238}U	Frag Spectra	1.5+7		Theo	89WASH	2 624	Apr89	LAS	Bozoian+ GRAPH CFD EXPT.
^{238}U	Frag Spectra	3.6+6	4.1+6	Expt	89WASH	2 705	Apr89	BIR	Randle+ LONG RANGE ALFA, TRITON.
^{238}U	Frag.Chg.	2.5-2		Theo	89WASH	2 525	Apr89	WAS	Wahl. TBL. MODEL PARAMETERS.
^{238}U	Frag.Chg.	FAST		Theo	89WASH	2 525	Apr89	WAS	Wahl. TBL. MODEL PARAMETERS.
^{239}U	$\sigma_{n,\gamma}$	3.0+4		Theo	89WASH	2 592	Apr89	HRV	Thielemann+ TBL. CALC SIG (30 KEV).
^{239}U	$\sigma_{n,f}$	3.0+4		Theo	89WASH	2 592	Apr89	HRV	Thielemann+ TBL. CALC SIG (30 KEV).
^{240}U	$\sigma_{n,\gamma}$	3.0+4		Theo	89WASH	2 592	Apr89	HRV	Thielemann+ TBL. CALC SIG (30 KEV).
^{240}U	$\sigma_{n,f}$	3.0+4		Theo	89WASH	2 592	Apr89	HRV	Thielemann+ TBL. CALC SIG (30 KEV).
^{241}U	$\sigma_{n,\gamma}$	3.0+4		Theo	89WASH	2 592	Apr89	HRV	Thielemann+ TBL. CALC SIG (30 KEV).
^{241}U	$\sigma_{n,f}$	3.0+4		Theo	89WASH	2 592	Apr89	HRV	Thielemann+ TBL. CALC SIG (30 KEV).
^{242}U	$\sigma_{n,\gamma}$	3.0+4		Theo	89WASH	2 592	Apr89	HRV	Thielemann+ TBL. CALC SIG (30 KEV).
^{242}U	$\sigma_{n,f}$	3.0+4		Theo	89WASH	2 592	Apr89	HRV	Thielemann+ TBL. CALC SIG (30 KEV).
^{243}U	$\sigma_{n,\gamma}$	3.0+4		Theo	89WASH	2 592	Apr89	HRV	Thielemann+ TBL. CALC SIG (30 KEV).
^{243}U	$\sigma_{n,f}$	3.0+4		Theo	89WASH	2 592	Apr89	HRV	Thielemann+ TBL. CALC SIG (30 KEV).
^{244}U	$\sigma_{n,\gamma}$	3.0+4		Theo	89WASH	2 592	Apr89	HRV	Thielemann+ TBL. CALC SIG (30 KEV).

Element	Quantity	Energy (eV) Min	Max	Type	Documentation Ref	Page	Date	Lab	Comments
^{244}U	$\sigma_{n,f}$	3.0+4		Theo	89WASH	2 592	Apr89	HRV	Thielemann+ TBL. CALC SIG (30 KEV).
^{245}U	$\sigma_{n,\gamma}$	3.0+4		Theo	89WASH	2 592	Apr89	HRV	Thielemann+ TBL. CALC SIG (30 KEV).
^{245}U	$\sigma_{n,f}$	3.0+4		Theo	89WASH	2 592	Apr89	HRV	Thielemann+ TBL. CALC SIG (30 KEV).
^{246}U	$\sigma_{n,\gamma}$	3.0+4		Theo	89WASH	2 592	Apr89	HRV	Thielemann+ TBL. CALC SIG (30 KEV).
^{246}U	$\sigma_{n,f}$	3.0+4		Theo	89WASH	2 592	Apr89	HRV	Thielemann+ TBL. CALC SIG (30 KEV).
^{247}U	$\sigma_{n,\gamma}$	3.0+4		Theo	89WASH	2 592	Apr89	HRV	Thielemann+ TBL. CALC SIG (30 KEV).
^{247}U	$\sigma_{n,f}$	3.0+4		Theo	89WASH	2 592	Apr89	HRV	Thielemann+ TBL. CALC SIG (30 KEV).
^{248}U	$\sigma_{n,\gamma}$	3.0+4		Theo	89WASH	2 592	Apr89	HRV	Thielemann+ TBL. CALC SIG (30 KEV).
^{248}U	$\sigma_{n,f}$	3.0+4		Theo	89WASH	2 592	Apr89	HRV	Thielemann+ TBL. CALC SIG (30 KEV).
^{249}U	$\sigma_{n,\gamma}$	3.0+4		Theo	89WASH	2 592	Apr89	HRV	Thielemann+ TBL. CALC SIG (30 KEV).
^{249}U	$\sigma_{n,f}$	3.0+4		Theo	89WASH	2 592	Apr89	HRV	Thielemann+ TBL. CALC SIG (30 KEV).
^{250}U	$\sigma_{n,\gamma}$	3.0+4		Theo	89WASH	2 592	Apr89	HRV	Thielemann+ TBL. CALC SIG (30 KEV).
^{250}U	$\sigma_{n,f}$	3.0+4		Theo	89WASH	2 592	Apr89	HRV	Thielemann+ TBL. CALC SIG (30 KEV).
^{251}U	$\sigma_{n,\gamma}$	3.0+4		Theo	89WASH	2 592	Apr89	HRV	Thielemann+ TBL. CALC SIG (30 KEV).
^{251}U	$\sigma_{n,f}$	3.0+4		Theo	89WASH	2 592	Apr89	HRV	Thielemann+ TBL. CALC SIG (30 KEV).
^{252}U	$\sigma_{n,\gamma}$	3.0+4		Theo	89WASH	2 592	Apr89	HRV	Thielemann+ TBL. CALC SIG (30 KEV).
^{252}U	$\sigma_{n,f}$	3.0+4		Theo	89WASH	2 592	Apr89	HRV	Thielemann+ TBL. CALC SIG (30 KEV).
^{253}U	$\sigma_{n,\gamma}$	3.0+4		Theo	89WASH	2 592	Apr89	HRV	Thielemann+ TBL. CALC SIG (30 KEV).
^{253}U	$\sigma_{n,f}$	3.0+4		Theo	89WASH	2 592	Apr89	HRV	Thielemann+ TBL. CALC SIG (30 KEV).
^{254}U	$\sigma_{n,\gamma}$	3.0+4		Theo	89WASH	2 592	Apr89	HRV	Thielemann+ TBL. CALC SIG (30 KEV).
^{254}U	$\sigma_{n,f}$	3.0+4		Theo	89WASH	2 592	Apr89	HRV	Thielemann+ TBL. CALC SIG (30 KEV).
^{255}U	$\sigma_{n,\gamma}$	3.0+4		Theo	89WASH	2 592	Apr89	HRV	Thielemann+ TBL. CALC SIG (30 KEV).
^{255}U	$\sigma_{n,f}$	3.0+4		Theo	89WASH	2 592	Apr89	HRV	Thielemann+ TBL. CALC SIG (30 KEV).
^{256}U	$\sigma_{n,\gamma}$	3.0+4		Theo	89WASH	2 592	Apr89	HRV	Thielemann+ TBL. CALC SIG (30 KEV).
^{256}U	$\sigma_{n,f}$	3.0+4		Theo	89WASH	2 592	Apr89	HRV	Thielemann+ TBL. CALC SIG (30 KEV).
^{257}U	$\sigma_{n,\gamma}$	3.0+4		Theo	89WASH	2 592	Apr89	HRV	Thielemann+ TBL. CALC SIG (30 KEV).
^{257}U	$\sigma_{n,f}$	3.0+4		Theo	89WASH	2 592	Apr89	HRV	Thielemann+ TBL. CALC SIG (30 KEV).
^{237}Np	$\sigma_{n,f}$	2.5+1	5.5+1	Revw	89WASH	1 168	Apr89	GEL	Weigmann. GRPH.PARALLEL VS ANTI-SPIN.
^{237}Np	$\sigma_{n,f}$	1.0+6	4.0+8	Expt	89WASH	1 443	Apr89	LAS	Lisowski+ GRPHS.REL 235U;CFD ENDF/B5.
^{237}Np	$\sigma_{n,f}$	1.0+6	1.0+8	Theo	89WASH	2 931	Apr89	LAS	Arthur+ GRPH CFD EXPT.
^{237}Np	Res.Int.Fiss	5.0-1	1.0+5	Eval	89WASH	1 946	Apr89	BNL	Holden. TBL. CORRECTED FISS.INT.CFD.
^{236}Pu	ν_p	SPON		Revw	89WASH	1 83	Apr89	BRK	Hoffman. GRPH. NU CFD OTHER NUCLIDES.
^{238}Pu	ν_p	SPON		Revw	89WASH	1 83	Apr89	BRK	Hoffman. GRPH. NU CFD OTHER NUCLIDES.

Element	Quantity	Energy (eV) Min	Max	Type	Documentation Ref	Page	Date	Lab	Comments
^{238}Pu	ν_p	2.5-2		Revw	89WASH	1 83	Apr89	BRK	Hoffman. GRPH. NU CFD OTHER NUCLIDES.
^{238}Pu	Spect.fiss n	SPON		Theo	89WASH	1 274	Apr89	AUA	Walsh+ GRPH, CFD MAXW. SPECTRUM.
^{239}Pu	$\sigma_{n,f}$	5.0+1	1.0+2	Revw	89WASH	1 168	Apr89	GEL	Weigmann. GRPH. ORELA MEAS.
^{239}Pu	$\sigma_{n,f}$	FISS		Eval	89WASH	1 408	Apr89	ANL	Poenitz. TBL EXPT CFD EVALS.
^{239}Pu	$\sigma_{n,f}$	1.0+6	4.0+8	Expt	89WASH	1 443	Apr89	LAS	Lisowski+ GRPHS.REL 235U;CFD ENDF/B5.
^{239}Pu	$\sigma_{n,f}$	NDG		Expt	89WASH	2 957	Apr89	ORL	Weston+ NDG.
^{239}Pu	ν_p	2.5-2		Revw	89WASH	1 83	Apr89	BRK	Hoffman. GRPH. NU CFD OTHER NUCLIDES.
^{239}Pu	ν_d	2.5-2		Expt	89WASH	1 449	Apr89	LTI	Couchell+ GRPHS. 6 GP SPECTRA CFD.
^{239}Pu	Spect.fiss n	2.5-2		Theo	89WASH	1 429	Apr89	LAS	Madland. GRPH CFD 249CF, 229TH.
^{239}Pu	Fiss.Yield	2.5-2		Expt	89WASH	1 313	Apr89	BRC	Trochon+ GRPHS.SIMULT.MASS,E,CHARGE.
^{239}Pu	Fiss.Yield	2.5-2		Eval	89WASH	1 471	Apr89	BIR	Mills+ TBL FITTED PARAMETERS.
^{239}Pu	Fiss.Yield	5.5+6	2.2+7	Theo	89WASH	2 650	Apr89	LMS	Compani-Tabrizi+ GRPH CALC CFD EXPT.
^{239}Pu	Frag Spectra	2.5-2		Expt	89WASH	1 313	Apr89	BRC	Trochon+ GRPHS.SIMULT.MASS,E,CHARGE.
^{239}Pu	Frag Spectra	2.5-2		Theo	89WASH	2 515	Apr89	TUE	Goennenwein+ COLD FISSION ANALYSIS.
^{239}Pu	Frag Spectra	5.5+6	2.2+7	Theo	89WASH	2 650	Apr89	LMS	Compani-Tabrizi+ GRPH CALC CFD EXPT.
^{239}Pu	Frag Spectra	2.5-2	6.0+6	Theo	89WASH	2 743	Apr89	TUD	Maerten+GRPH KE(FRAG)CFD 235TH,239PU.
^{239}Pu	Frag.Chg.	2.5-2		Expt	89WASH	1 313	Apr89	BRC	Trochon+ GRPHS.SIMULT.MASS,E,CHARGE.
^{239}Pu	Frag.Chg.	2.5-2		Theo	89WASH	2 515	Apr89	TUE	Goennenwein+ COLD FISSION ANALYSIS.
^{240}Pu	σ_{tot}	5.0+2	3.0+3	Revw	89WASH	1 168	Apr89	GEL	Weigmann. GRPH. CFD SUBBARRIER FISS.
^{240}Pu	$\sigma_{n,p}$	5.0+2	3.0+3	Revw	89WASH	1 168	Apr89	GEL	Weigmann. GRPH. CFD TOTAL SIG.
^{240}Pu	$\sigma_{n,f}$	2.0+1	2.0+5	Revw	89WASH	1 368	Apr89	ORL	Perez+ GRPH. EXPT'L SIG.
^{240}Pu	Res.Int.Fiss	5.0-1	1.0+5	Eval	89WASH	1 946	Apr89	BNL	Holden. TBL. CORRECTED FISS.INT.CFD.
^{240}Pu	ν_p	SPON		Revw	89WASH	1 83	Apr89	BRK	Hoffman. GRPH. NU CFD OTHER NUCLIDES.
^{240}Pu	Spect.fiss n	SPON		Theo	89WASH	1 274	Apr89	AUA	Walsh+ GRPHS,CFD MAXW.,WATT SPECTRUM.
^{241}Pu	ν_p	2.5-2		Revw	89WASH	1 83	Apr89	BRK	Hoffman. GRPH. NU CFD OTHER NUCLIDES.
^{241}Pu	Fiss.Yield	2.5-2		Eval	89WASH	1 471	Apr89	BIR	Mills+ TBL FITTED PARAMETERS.
^{241}Pu	Fiss.Yield	2.5-2		Theo	89WASH	2 525	Apr89	WAS	Wahl. TBL. MODEL PARAMETERS.
^{241}Pu	Frag.Chg.	2.5-2		Theo	89WASH	2 525	Apr89	WAS	Wahl. TBL. MODEL PARAMETERS.
^{242}Pu	Res.Int.Fiss	5.0-1	1.0+5	Eval	89WASH	1 946	Apr89	BNL	Holden. TBL. CORRECTED FISS.INT.CFD.
^{242}Pu	ν_p	SPON		Revw	89WASH	1 83	Apr89	BRK	Hoffman. GRPH. NU CFD OTHER NUCLIDES.
^{242}Pu	Spect.fiss n	SPON		Theo	89WASH	1 274	Apr89	AUA	Walsh+ GRPH, CFD MAXW. SPECTRUM.
^{244}Pu	$\sigma_{n,f}$	4.0+5	8.0+6	Revw	89WASH	1 418	Apr89	ANL	Lynn. GRPH. CALC SIG CFD EXPT.
^{244}Pu	ν_p	SPON		Revw	89WASH	1 83	Apr89	BRK	Hoffman. GRPH. NU CFD OTHER NUCLIDES.

NEUTRON DATA REFERENCES

Element	Quantity	Energy (eV) Min	Max	Type	Documentation Ref	Page	Date	Lab	Comments
^{241}Am	ν_p	2.5-2		Revw	89WASH	1 83	Apr89	BRK	Hoffman. GRPH. NU CFD OTHER NUCLIDES.
^{242}Am	ν_p	2.5-2		Revw	89WASH	1 83	Apr89	BRK	Hoffman. GRPH. NU CFD OTHER NUCLIDES.
^{243}Am	Res.Int.Fiss	5.0-1	1.0+5	Eval	89WASH	1 946	Apr89	BNL	Holden. TBL. CORRECTED FISS.INT.CFD.
^{242}Cm	$\sigma_{n,f}$	1.0-1	1.0+5	Expt	89WASH	1 354	Apr89	RPI	Block+ GRPH.
^{242}Cm	ν_p	SPON		Revw	89WASH	1 83	Apr89	BRK	Hoffman. GRPH. NU CFD OTHER NUCLIDES.
^{243}Cm	ν_p	2.5-2		Revw	89WASH	1 83	Apr89	BRK	Hoffman. GRPH. NU CFD OTHER NUCLIDES.
^{244}Cm	$\sigma_{n,f}$	1.0-1	1.0+5	Expt	89WASH	1 354	Apr89	RPI	Block+ GRPH.
^{244}Cm	Res.Int.Fiss	5.0-1	1.0+5	Eval	89WASH	1 946	Apr89	BNL	Holden. TBL. CORRECTED FISS.INT.CFD.
^{244}Cm	ν_p	SPON		Revw	89WASH	1 83	Apr89	BRK	Hoffman. GRPH. NU CFD OTHER NUCLIDES.
^{245}Cm	$\sigma_{n,f}$	1.0+0	1.0+5	Expt	89WASH	1 354	Apr89	RPI	Block+ GRPH.
^{245}Cm	ν_p	2.5-2		Revw	89WASH	1 83	Apr89	BRK	Hoffman. GRPH. NU CFD OTHER NUCLIDES.
^{246}Cm	$\sigma_{n,f}$	1.0-1	1.0+5	Expt	89WASH	1 354	Apr89	RPI	Block+ GRPH.
^{246}Cm	ν_p	SPON		Revw	89WASH	1 83	Apr89	BRK	Hoffman. GRPH. NU CFD OTHER NUCLIDES.
^{247}Cm	$\sigma_{n,f}$	NDG		Expt	89WASH	1 354	Apr89	RPI	Block+ NDG. TBD.
^{248}Cm	$\sigma_{n,f}$	1.0-1	1.0+5	Expt	89WASH	1 354	Apr89	RPI	Block+ GRPH.
^{248}Cm	ν_p	SPON		Revw	89WASH	1 83	Apr89	BRK	Hoffman. GRPH. NU CFD OTHER NUCLIDES.
^{250}Cm	ν_p	SPON		Revw	89WASH	1 83	Apr89	BRK	Hoffman. GRPH. NU CFD OTHER NUCLIDES.
^{249}Bk	ν_p	SPON		Revw	89WASH	1 83	Apr89	BRK	Hoffman. GRPH. NU CFD OTHER NUCLIDES.
^{246}Cf	ν_p	SPON		Revw	89WASH	1 83	Apr89	BRK	Hoffman. GRPH. NU CFD OTHER NUCLIDES.
^{249}Cf	ν_p	SPON		Revw	89WASH	1 83	Apr89	BRK	Hoffman. GRPH. NU CFD OTHER NUCLIDES.
^{249}Cf	Spect.fiss n	2.5-2		Theo	89WASH	1 429	Apr89	LAS	Madland. GRPH CFD 239PU, 229TH.
^{250}Cf	$\sigma_{n,f}$	NDG		Expt	89WASH	1 354	Apr89	RPI	Block+ NDG. TBD.
^{250}Cf	ν_p	SPON		Revw	89WASH	1 83	Apr89	BRK	Hoffman. GRPH. NU CFD OTHER NUCLIDES.
^{250}Cf	Fiss.Yield	SPON		Revw	89WASH	1 83	Apr89	BRK	Hoffman. GRPH. CFD OTHER SF NUCLIDES.
^{252}Cf	ν_p	SPON		Revw	89WASH	1 83	Apr89	BRK	Hoffman. GRPH. NU CFD OTHER NUCLIDES.
^{252}Cf	ν_p	SPON		Expt	89WASH	1 299	Apr89	THD	Heeg+ GRPH. TERNARY FISS.
^{252}Cf	ν_p	SPON		Expt	89WASH	2 684	Apr89	AEP	Han+ NU VS LRA OR TRITON.
^{252}Cf	Spect.fiss n	SPON		Theo	89WASH	1 429	Apr89	LAS	Madland. GRPHS CALC CFD EXPT.
^{252}Cf	Spect.fiss n	SPON		Theo	89WASH	2 632	Apr89	AUA	Walsh+ GRPHS,CALC CFD EVAL.
^{252}Cf	Spect.fiss n	SPON		Theo	89WASH	2 743	Apr89	TUD	Maerten+ GRPHS CFD MAXW, OTHER EVAL.
^{252}Cf	Spect.fiss n	SPON		Expt	89WASH	2 951	Apr89	BJG	Bao+ TBL. GRPH. LOW EN CFD MAXW.
^{252}Cf	Fiss.Prod γ	SPON		Expt	89WASH	2 684	Apr89	AEP	Han+ G-YLD OF LRA, TRITON.
^{252}Cf	Fiss.Yield	SPON		Revw	89WASH	1 83	Apr89	BRK	Hoffman. GRPH. CFD OTHER SF NUCLIDES.

Element	Quantity	Energy (eV) Min	Max	Type	Documentation Ref	Page	Date	Lab	Comments
^{252}Cf	Fiss.Yield	SPON		Expt	89WASH	1 299	Apr89	THD	Heeg+ GRPHS. TERNARY FISS.
^{252}Cf	Fiss.Yield	SPON		Expt	89WASH	1 313	Apr89	BRC	Trochon+ GRPHS.SIMULT.MASS,E,CHARGE.
^{252}Cf	Fiss.Yield	SPON		Eval	89WASH	1 471	Apr89	BIR	Mills+ TBL FITTED PARAMETERS.
^{252}Cf	Fiss.Yield	SPON		Revw	89WASH	2 833	Apr89	INL	Gehrke+ GRPH CFD 235U, 239PU YIELDS.
^{252}Cf	Frag Spectra	SPON		Expt	89WASH	1 313	Apr89	BRC	Trochon+ GRPHS.SIMULT.MASS,E,CHARGE.
^{252}Cf	Frag Spectra	SPON		Theo	89WASH	2 643	Apr89	PUC	Gupta+ GRPH. CALC CFD EXPT.
^{252}Cf	Frag Spectra	SPON		Expt	89WASH	2 684	Apr89	AEP	Han+ LONG RANGE ALFA, TRITON.
^{252}Cf	Frag Spectra	SPON		Expt	89WASH	2 881	Apr89	TRM	Rao+ GRPH KE VS CHG, ODD-EVEN.
^{252}Cf	Frag.Chg.	SPON		Expt	89WASH	1 313	Apr89	BRC	Trochon+ GRPHS.SIMULT.MASS,E,CHARGE.
^{252}Cf	Frag.Chg.	SPON		Expt	89WASH	2 881	Apr89	TRM	Rao+ GRPH LIGHT YLD, ODD-EVEN.
^{254}Cf	ν_p	SPON		Revw	89WASH	1 83	Apr89	BRK	Hoffman. GRPH. NU CFD OTHER NUCLIDES.
^{254}Cf	Fiss.Yield	SPON		Revw	89WASH	1 83	Apr89	BRK	Hoffman. GRPH. CFD OTHER SF NUCLIDES.
^{256}Cf	Fiss.Yield	SPON		Revw	89WASH	1 83	Apr89	BRK	Hoffman. GRPH. CFD OTHER SF NUCLIDES.
^{253}Es	Fiss.Yield	SPON		Revw	89WASH	1 83	Apr89	BRK	Hoffman. GRPH. CFD OTHER SF NUCLIDES.
^{254}Es	$\sigma_{n,f}$	NDG		Expt	89WASH	1 354	Apr89	RPI	Block+ NDG. TBD.
^{255}Es	Fiss.Yield	SPON		Revw	89WASH	1 83	Apr89	BRK	Hoffman. GRPH. CFD OTHER SF NUCLIDES.
^{246}Fm	Fiss.Yield	SPON		Revw	89WASH	1 83	Apr89	BRK	Hoffman. GRPH. CFD OTHER SF NUCLIDES.
^{248}Fm	Fiss.Yield	SPON		Revw	89WASH	1 83	Apr89	BRK	Hoffman. GRPH. CFD OTHER SF NUCLIDES.
^{254}Fm	ν_p	SPON		Revw	89WASH	1 83	Apr89	BRK	Hoffman. GRPH. NU CFD OTHER NUCLIDES.
^{254}Fm	Fiss.Yield	SPON		Revw	89WASH	1 83	Apr89	BRK	Hoffman. GRPH. CFD OTHER SF NUCLIDES.
^{256}Fm	ν_p	SPON		Revw	89WASH	1 83	Apr89	BRK	Hoffman. GRPH. NU CFD OTHER NUCLIDES.
^{256}Fm	Fiss.Yield	SPON		Revw	89WASH	1 83	Apr89	BRK	Hoffman. GRPH. CFD OTHER SF NUCLIDES.
^{257}Fm	ν_p	SPON		Revw	89WASH	1 83	Apr89	BRK	Hoffman. GRPH. NU CFD OTHER NUCLIDES.
^{257}Fm	Fiss.Yield	SPON		Revw	89WASH	1 83	Apr89	BRK	Hoffman. GRPH. CFD OTHER SF NUCLIDES.
^{258}Fm	Fiss.Yield	SPON		Revw	89WASH	1 83	Apr89	BRK	Hoffman. GRPH. CFD OTHER SF NUCLIDES.
^{258}Fm	Fiss.Yield	SPON		Expt	89WASH	2 533	Apr89	LRL	Hulet. BIMODAL FISS. GRAPH MASS DIST.
^{258}Fm	Frag Spectra	SPON		Expt	89WASH	2 533	Apr89	LRL	Hulet. BIMODAL FISS. GRAPH KE DIST.
^{259}Fm	Fiss.Yield	SPON		Revw	89WASH	1 83	Apr89	BRK	Hoffman. GRPH. CFD OTHER SF NUCLIDES.
^{252}No	ν_p	SPON		Revw	89WASH	1 83	Apr89	BRK	Hoffman. GRPH. NU CFD OTHER NUCLIDES.
^{252}No	Fiss.Yield	SPON		Revw	89WASH	1 83	Apr89	BRK	Hoffman. GRPH. CFD OTHER SF NUCLIDES.
^{256}No	Fiss.Yield	SPON		Revw	89WASH	1 83	Apr89	BRK	Hoffman. GRPH. CFD OTHER SF NUCLIDES.
^{258}No	Fiss.Yield	SPON		Revw	89WASH	1 83	Apr89	BRK	Hoffman. GRPH. CFD OTHER SF NUCLIDES.
^{258}No	Fiss.Yield	SPON		Expt	89WASH	2 533	Apr89	LRL	Hulet. BIMODAL FISS. GRAPH MASS DIST.

Element	Quantity	Energy (eV) Min	Max	Type	Documentation Ref	Page	Date	Lab	Comments
^{258}No	Frag Spectra	SPON		Expt	89WASH	2 533	Apr89	LRL	Hulet. BIMODAL FISS. GRAPH KE DIST.
^{262}No	Fiss.Yield	SPON		Revw	89WASH	1 83	Apr89	BRK	Hoffman. GRPH. CFD OTHER SF NUCLIDES.
^{262}No	Fiss.Yield	SPON		Expt	89WASH	2 533	Apr89	LRL	Hulet. BIMODAL FISS. GRAPH MASS DIST.
^{262}No	Frag Spectra	SPON		Expt	89WASH	2 533	Apr89	LRL	Hulet. BIMODAL FISS. GRAPH KE DIST.
^{259}Md	Fiss.Yield	SPON		Revw	89WASH	1 83	Apr89	BRK	Hoffman. GRPH. CFD OTHER SF NUCLIDES.
^{259}Md	Fiss.Yield	SPON		Expt	89WASH	2 533	Apr89	LRL	Hulet. BIMODAL FISS. GRAPH MASS DIST.
^{259}Md	Frag Spectra	SPON		Expt	89WASH	2 533	Apr89	LRL	Hulet. BIMODAL FISS. GRAPH KE DIST.
^{260}Md	ν_p	SPON		Revw	89WASH	1 83	Apr89	BRK	Hoffman. GRPH. NU CFD OTHER NUCLIDES.
^{260}Md	ν_p	SPON		Expt	89WASH	2 681	Apr89	LRL	Wild+ GRPH. NUBAR=2.58+/-0.11.
^{260}Md	ν_{frag}	SPON		Expt	89WASH	2 681	Apr89	LRL	Wild+ GRPH. NU VS FRAG. MASS.
^{260}Md	Fiss.Yield	SPON		Revw	89WASH	1 83	Apr89	BRK	Hoffman. GRPH. CFD OTHER SF NUCLIDES.
^{260}Md	Fiss.Yield	SPON		Expt	89WASH	2 533	Apr89	LRL	Hulet. BIMODAL FISS. GRAPH MASS DIST.
^{260}Md	Frag Spectra	SPON		Expt	89WASH	2 533	Apr89	LRL	Hulet. BIMODAL FISS. GRAPH KE DIST.
^{260}Md	Frag Spectra	SPON		Expt	89WASH	2 681	Apr89	LRL	Wild+ GRPH. KE DISTRIBUTION.
^{260}Rf	Fiss.Yield	SPON		Revw	89WASH	1 83	Apr89	BRK	Hoffman. GRPH. CFD OTHER SF NUCLIDES.
^{260}Rf	Fiss.Yield	SPON		Expt	89WASH	2 533	Apr89	LRL	Hulet. BIMODAL FISS. GRAPH MASS DIST.
^{260}Rf	Frag Spectra	SPON		Expt	89WASH	2 533	Apr89	LRL	Hulet. BIMODAL FISS. GRAPH KE DIST.
^{262}Ha	Fiss.Yield	SPON		Revw	89WASH	1 83	Apr89	BRK	Hoffman. GRPH. CFD OTHER SF NUCLIDES.

AUTHOR INDEX

977